Course	Business Decision Models
	ADM2302
Course Number	**Telfer School of Management**
	University of Ottawa

http://create.mcgraw-hill.com

ISBN-10: 1259091783   ISBN-13: 9781259091780

Contents

Credits

Preface

We have long been concerned that traditional management science textbooks have not taken the best approach in introducing business students to this exciting field. Our goal when initially developing this book during the late 1990s was to break out of the old mold and present new and innovative ways of teaching management science more effectively. We have been gratified by the favorable response to our efforts. Many reviewers and other users of the first four editions of the book have expressed appreciation for its various distinctive features, as well as for its clear presentation at just the right level for their business students.

Our goal for this fifth edition has been to build on the strengths of the first four editions. Co-author Mark Hillier has won several schoolwide teaching awards for his spreadsheet modeling and management science courses at the University of Washington while using the first four editions, and this experience has led to many improvements in the current edition. We also incorporated many user comments and suggestions. Throughout this process, we took painstaking care to enhance the quality of the preceding edition while maintaining the distinctive orientation of the book.

This distinctive orientation is one that closely follows the recommendations in the 1996 report of the operating subcommittee of the INFORMS Business School Education Task Force, including the following extract.

> There is clear evidence that there must be a major change in the character of the (introductory management science) course in this environment. There is little patience with courses centered on algorithms. Instead, the demand is for courses that focus on business situations, include prominent non-mathematical issues, use spreadsheets, and involve model formulation and assessment more than model structuring. Such a course requires new teaching materials.

This book is designed to provide the teaching materials for such a course.

In line with the recommendations of this task force, we believe that a modern introductory management science textbook should have three key elements. As summarized in the subtitle of this book, these elements are a *modeling* and *case studies* approach with *spreadsheets*.

SPREADSHEETS

The modern approach to the teaching of management science clearly is to use *spreadsheets* as a primary medium of instruction. Both business students and managers now live with spreadsheets, so they provide a comfortable and enjoyable learning environment. Modern spreadsheet software, including Microsoft Excel used in this book, now can be used to do real management science. For student-scale models (which include many practical real-world models), spreadsheets are a much better way of implementing management science models than traditional algebraic solvers. This means that the algebraic curtain that was so prevalent in traditional management science courses and textbooks now can be lifted.

However, with the new enthusiasm for spreadsheets, there is a danger of going overboard. Spreadsheets are not the only useful tool for performing management science analyses. Occasional modest use of algebraic and graphical analyses still have their place and we would be doing a disservice to the students by not developing their skills in these areas when appropriate. Furthermore, the book should not be mainly a spreadsheet cookbook that focuses largely on spreadsheet mechanics. Spreadsheets are a means to an end, not an end in themselves.

A MODELING APPROACH

This brings us to the second key feature of the book, a *modeling approach*. Model formulation lies at the heart of management science methodology. Therefore, we heavily emphasize the art of model formulation, the role of a model, and the analysis of model results. We primarily (but not exclusively) use a spreadsheet format rather than algebra for formulating and presenting a model.

Some instructors have many years of experience in teaching modeling in terms of for-mulating algebraic models (or what the INFORMS Task Force called "model structuring"). Some of these instructors feel that students should do their modeling in this way and then transfer the model to a spreadsheet simply to use the Excel Solver to solve the model. We dis-agree with this approach. Our experience (and the experience reported by many others) is that most business students find it more natural and comfortable to do their modeling directly in a spreadsheet. Furthermore, by using the best spreadsheet modeling techniques (as presented in this edition), formulating a spreadsheet model tends to be considerably more efficient and transparent than formulating an algebraic model. Another benefit is that the spreadsheet model includes all the relationships that can be expressed in an algebraic form and we often will summarize the model in this format as well.

Another break from tradition in this book (and several contemporary textbooks) is to virtually ignore the algorithms that are used to solve the models. We feel that there is no good reason why typical business students should learn the details of algorithms executed by computers. Within the time constraints of a one-term management science course, there are far more important lessons to be learned. Therefore, the focus in this book is on what we believe are these far more important lessons. High on this list is the art of modeling managerial problems on a spreadsheet.

Formulating a spreadsheet model of a real problem typically involves much more than designing the spreadsheet and entering the data. Therefore, we work through the process step by step: understand the unstructured problem, verbally develop some structure for the problem, gather the data, express the relationships in quantitative terms, and then lay out the spreadsheet model. The structured approach highlights the typical components of the model (the data, the decisions to be made, the constraints, and the measure of performance) and the different types of spreadsheet cells used for each. Consequently, the emphasis is on the mod-eling rather than spreadsheet mechanics.

A CASE STUDIES APPROACH

However, all this still would be quite sterile if we simply presented a long series of brief examples with their spreadsheet formulations. This leads to the third key feature of this book—a *case studies* approach. In addition to examples, nearly every chapter includes one or two case studies patterned after actual applications to convey the whole process of applying management science. In a few instances, the entire chapter revolves around a case study. By drawing the student into the story, we have designed each case study to bring that chapter's technique to life in a context that vividly illustrates the relevance of the technique for aiding managerial decision making. This storytelling, case-centered approach should make the mate-rial more enjoyable and stimulating while also conveying the practical considerations that are key factors in applying management science.

We have been pleased to have several reviewers of the first four editions express particular appreciation for our case study approach. Even though this approach has received little use in other management science textbooks, we feel that it is a real key to preparing students for the practical application of management science in all its aspects. Some of the reviewers have highlighted the effectiveness of the dialogue/scenario enactment approach used in some of the case studies. Although unconventional, this approach provides a way of demonstrating the process of managerial decision making with the help of management science. It also enables previewing some key concepts in the language of management.

Every chapter also contains full-fledged cases following the problems at the end of the chapter. These cases usually continue to employ a stimulating storytelling approach, so they can be assigned as interesting and challenging projects. Most of these cases were developed jointly by two talented case writers, Karl Schmedders (a faculty member at the University of Zurich in Switzerland) and Molly Stephens (formerly a management science consultant with Andersen Consulting). The authors also have added some cases, including several shorter ones. In addition, the University of Western Ontario Ivey School of Business (the second-largest producer of teaching cases in the world) has specially selected cases from their case collection that match the chapters in this textbook. These cases are available on the Ivey website, **cases.ivey.uwo.ca/cases**, in the segment of the CaseMate area designated for this book. This website address is provided at the end of each chapter as well.

We are, of course, not the first to incorporate any of these key features into a management science textbook. However, we believe that the book currently is unique in the way that it fully incorporates all three key features together.

OTHER SPECIAL FEATURES

We also should mention some additional special features of the book that are continued from the fourth edition.

- Diverse examples, problems, and cases convey the pervasive relevance of management science.
- A strong managerial perspective.
- Learning objectives at the beginning of each chapter.
- Numerous margin notes that clarify and highlight key points.
- Excel tips interspersed among the margin notes.
- Review questions at the end of each section.
- A glossary at the end of each chapter.
- Partial answers to selected problems in the back of the book.
- Supplementary text material on the CD-ROM (as identified in the table of contents).
- An Excel-based software package (MS Courseware) on the CD-ROM and website that includes many add-ins, templates, and files (described below).
- Other helpful supplements on the CD-ROM and website (described later).

A NEW SOFTWARE PACKAGE

This edition continues to integrate Excel 2010 and its Solver (a product of Frontline Systems) throughout the book. However, we are excited to also add to this edition an impressive more recent product of Frontline Systems called **Risk Solver Platform for Education** (or **RSPE** for short). RSPE also is an Excel add-in and its Solver shares some of the features of the Excel Solver. However, in addition to providing all the key capabilities of the Excel Solver, RSPE adds some major new functionalities as outlined below:

- A more interactive user interface, with the model parameters always visible alongside the main spreadsheet, rather than only in the Solver dialog box.
- Parameter analysis reports that provide an easy way to see the effect of varying data in a model in a systematic way.
- A model analysis tool that reveals the characteristics of a model (e.g., whether it is linear or nonlinear, smooth or nonsmooth).
- Tools to build and solve decision trees within a spreadsheet.
- The ability to build and run sophisticated Monte Carlo simulation models.
- An interactive simulation mode that allows simulation results to be shown instantly whenever a change is made to a simulation model.
- The RSPE Solver can be used in combination with computer simulation to perform simulation optimization.

A CONTINUING FOCUS ON EXCEL AND ITS SOLVER

As with all the preceding editions, this edition continues to focus on spreadsheet modeling in an Excel format. Although it lacks some of the functionalities of RSPE, the Excel Solver continues to provide a completely satisfactory way of solving most of the spreadsheet models encountered in this book. This edition continues to feature this use of the Excel Solver whenever either it or the RSPE Solver could be used.

Many instructors prefer this focus because it avoids introducing other complications that might confuse their students. We agree.

However, the key advantage of introducing RSPE in this edition is that it provides an all-in-one complement to the Excel Solver. There are some important topics in the book (including decision analysis and computer simulation) where the Excel Solver lacks the functionalities needed to deal with these kinds of problems. Multiple Excel add-ins—Solver Table, Tree-Plan, SensIt, RiskSim, Crystal Ball, and OptQuest (a module of Crystal Ball)—were introduced in previous editions to provide the needed functionalities. RSPE alone now replaces all of these add-ins.

OTHER SOFTWARE

Each edition of this book has provided a comprehensive Excel-based software package called *MS Courseware* on the CD-ROM and website. RSPE replaces various Excel add-ins in this package. Otherwise, the remainder of this package is being provided again with the current edition.

This package includes Excel files that provide the live spreadsheets for all the various examples and case studies throughout the book. In addition to further investigating the examples and case studies, these spreadsheets can be used by either the student or instructor as templates to formulate and solve similar problems. The package also includes dozens of Excel templates for solving various models in the book.

MS Courseware includes additional software as well.

- **Interactive Management Science Modules** for interactively exploring certain management science techniques in depth (including techniques presented in Chapters 1, 2, 5, 10, 11, 12, and 18).
- **Queueing Simulator** for performing computer simulations of queueing systems (used in Chapter 12).

NEW FEATURES IN THIS EDITION

We have made some important enhancements to the fifth edition.

- **A Substantial Revision of Chapter 1.** In addition to some updates and a new end-of-chapter case, the example at the heart of the chapter has been modernized to better attract the interest of the students. The example now deals with iWatches instead of grandfather clocks.
- **A New Section Introduces Risk Solver Platform for Education (RSPE).** Section 2.6 presents the basics of how to use RSPE. It is placed near the end of Chapter 2 to avoid disrupting the flow of the chapter, including the introduction of the Excel Solver.
- **Parameter Analysis Reports Are Introduced and Widely Used.** Parameter analysis reports are introduced in Chapter 5 for performing sensitivity analysis systematically. This key tool of RSPE also receives important use in Chapters 7, 8, and 13.
- **Chapter 8 Is Revised to Better Identify the Available Solving Methods for Nonlinear Programming.** The Excel Solver and the RSPE Solver share some solving methods for nonlinear programming and then the RSPE Solver adds another one. These solving methods and when each one should be used are better identified now.
- **A New Section on Using RSPE to Analyze a Model and Choose a Solving Method.** A new Section 8.6 describes a key tool of RSPE for analyzing a model and choosing the best solving method.
- **A Substantial Revision of Chapter 9 (Decision Analysis).** RSPE has outstanding functionality for constructing and analyzing decision trees. This functionality is thoroughly exploited in the revised Chapter 9.
- **A Key Revision of the First Computer Simulation Chapter.** Computer simulation commonly is used to analyze complicated queueing systems, so it is natural for Chapter 12 (Computer Simulation: Basic Concepts) to refer back to Chapter 11 (Queueing Models) occasionally. However, some instructors cover Chapter 12 but skip over Chapter 11. Therefore, we have revised Chapter 12 to make it as independent of Chapter 11 as possible while still covering this important kind of application of computer simulation.

- **A Major Revision of the Second Computer Simulation Chapter.** Although the examples remain the same, the old Chapter 13 (Computer Simulation with Crystal Ball) has been thoroughly revised to replace Crystal Ball by Risk Solver Platform for Education (RSPE). Most students already will be familiar with RSPE from preceding chapters, which should provide a gentler entry into this chapter. More importantly, this impressive, relatively new software package has some significant advantages over Crystal Ball for performing and analyzing computer simulations. However, an updated version of the old Chapter 13 still will be available on the CD-ROM (now Chapter 20) for instructors who wish to stick with Crystal Ball for the time being.

- **A New Section on Decision Making with Computer Simulations.** A key tool of RSPE is its use of multiple simulation runs to generate parameter analysis reports and trend charts that can provide an important guide to managerial decision making. Section 13.8 describes this approach to decision making.

- **A New Section on Optimizing with Computer Simulations.** Another key tool of RSPE is that its Solver can use multiple simulation runs to automatically search for an optimal solution for simulation models with any number of decision variables. Section 13.9 describes this approach.

- **Additional Links to Articles that Describe Dramatic Real Applications.** The fourth edition includes 23 application vignettes that describe in a few paragraphs how an actual application of management science had a powerful effect on a company or organization by using techniques like those being studied in that portion of the book. The current edition adds seven more vignettes based on recent applications (while deleting two old ones). We also continue the practice of adding a link to the journal articles that fully describe these applications, through a special arrangement with the Institute for Operations Research and the Management Sciences (INFORMS®). Thus, the instructor now can motivate his or her lectures by having the students delve into real applications that dramatically demonstrate the relevance of the material being covered in the lectures. The end-of-chapter problems also include an assignment after reading each of these articles.

  We continue to be excited about this partnership with INFORMS, our field's preeminent professional society, to provide a link to these 28 articles describing spectacular applications of management science. INFORMS is a learned professional society for students, academics, and practitioners in quantitative and analytical fields. Information about INFORMS journals, meetings, job bank, scholarships, awards, and teaching materials is available at **www.informs.org**.

- **Refinements in Each Chapter.** Each chapter in the fourth edition has been carefully examined and revised as needed to update and clarify the material after also taking into account the input provided by reviewers and others.

OTHER SUPPLEMENTS

The Instructor's Edition of this book's Online Learning Center, **www.mhhe.com/hillier5e**, is password-protected and a convenient place for instructors to access course supplements. Resources for professors include the complete solutions to all problems and cases, a test bank with hundreds of multiple-choice and true-false questions, and PowerPoint Presentation. The PowerPoint slides include both lecture materials for nearly every chapter and nearly all the figures (including all the spreadsheets) in the book.

The student's CD-ROM bundled with the book provides most of the MS Courseware package. It also includes a tutorial with sample test questions (different from those in the instructor's test bank) for self-testing quizzes on the various chapters.

The materials on the student CD-ROM can also be accessed on the Student's Edition of the Online Learning Center, **www.mhhe.com/hillier5e**. The website also provides the remainder of the MS Courseware package, as well as access to the INFORMS articles cited in the application vignettes and updates about the book, including errata. In addition, the publisher's operations management supersite at **www.mhhe.com/pom/** links to many resources on the Internet that you might find pertinent to this book.

We invite your comments, suggestions, and errata. You can contact either one of us at the e-mail addresses given below. While giving these addresses, let us also assure instructors that *we will continue our policy of not providing solutions to problems and cases in the book to anyone* (including your students) who contacts us. We hope that you enjoy the book.

Frederick S. Hillier
Stanford University (fhillier@stanford.edu)

Mark S. Hillier
University of Washington (mhillier@uw.edu)

June 2012

Chapter **One**

Introduction

Learning Objectives

After completing this chapter, you should be able to

1. Define the term *management science.*
2. Describe the nature of management science.
3. Explain what a mathematical model is.
4. Use a mathematical model to perform break-even analysis.
5. Use a spreadsheet model to perform break-even analysis.
6. Identify the levels of annual savings that management science sometimes can provide to organizations.
7. Identify some special features of this book.

Welcome to the field of *management science!* We think that it is a particularly exciting and interesting field. Exciting because management science is having a dramatic impact on the profitability of numerous business firms around the world. Interesting because the methods used to do this are so ingenious. We are looking forward to giving you a guided tour to introduce you to the special features of the field.

Some students approach a course (and textbook) about management science with a certain amount of anxiety and skepticism. The main source of the anxiety is the reputation of the field as being highly mathematical. This reputation then generates skepticism that such a theoretical approach can have much relevance for dealing with practical managerial problems. Most traditional courses (and textbooks) about management science have only reinforced these perceptions by emphasizing the mathematics of the field rather than its practical application.

Rest easy. This is not a traditional management science textbook. We realize that most readers of this book are aspiring to become managers, not mathematicians. Therefore, the emphasis throughout is on conveying what a future manager needs to know about management science. Yes, this means including a little mathematics here and there, because it is a major language of the field. The mathematics you do see will be at the level of high school algebra plus (in the later chapters) basic concepts of elementary probability theory. We think you will be pleasantly surprised by the new appreciation you gain for how useful and intuitive mathematics at this level can be. However, managers do not need to know any of the heavy mathematical theory that underlies the various techniques of management science. Therefore, the use of mathematics plays only a strictly secondary role in the book.

One reason we can deemphasize mathematics is that powerful *spreadsheet software* now is available for applying management science. Spreadsheets provide a comfortable and familiar environment for formulating and analyzing managerial problems. The spreadsheet takes care of applying the necessary mathematics automatically in the background with only a minimum of guidance by the user. This has begun to revolutionize the use of management science. In the past, technically trained management scientists were needed to carry out significant management science studies for management. Now spreadsheets are bringing many of the tools and concepts of management science within the reach of managers for conducting their own analyses. Although busy managers will continue to call upon management science teams to conduct major studies for them, they are increasingly becoming direct users themselves through the medium of spreadsheet software. Therefore, since this book is aimed at future managers (and management consultants), we will emphasize the use of spreadsheets for applying management science.

What does an enlightened future manager need to learn from a management science course?

1. Gain an appreciation for the relevance and power of management science. (Therefore, we include many *application vignettes* throughout the book that give examples of *actual applications* of management science and the *impact* they had on the organizations involved.)

2. Learn to recognize when management science can (and cannot) be fruitfully applied. (Therefore, we will emphasize the *kinds of problems* to which the various management science techniques can be applied.)

3. Learn how to apply the major techniques of management science to analyze a variety of managerial problems. (Therefore, we will focus largely on how spreadsheets enable many such applications with no more background in management science than provided by this book.)

4. Develop an understanding of how to interpret the results of a management science study. (Therefore, we will present many *case studies* that illustrate management science studies and how their results depend on the assumptions and data that were used.)

The objectives just described are the key teaching goals of this book.

We begin this process in the next two sections by introducing the nature of management science and the impact that it is having on many organizations. (These themes will continue throughout the remaining chapters as well.) Section 1.4 then points out some of the special features of this book that you can look forward to seeing in the subsequent chapters.

1.1 THE NATURE OF MANAGEMENT SCIENCE

What is the name *management science* (sometimes abbreviated MS) supposed to convey? It does involve *management* and *science* or, more precisely, *the science of management,* but this still is too vague. Here is a more suggestive definition.

> Management science is a *discipline* that attempts to *aid managerial decision making* by applying a *scientific approach* to managerial problems that involve *quantitative factors.*

Now let us see how elaborating upon each of the italicized terms in this definition conveys much more about the nature of management science.

Management Science Is a Discipline

As a discipline, management science is a whole body of knowledge and techniques that are based on a scientific foundation. For example, it is analogous in some ways to the medical field. A medical doctor has been trained in a whole body of knowledge and techniques that are based on the scientific foundations of the medical field. After receiving this training and entering practice, the doctor must diagnose a patient's illness and then choose the appropriate medical procedures to apply to the illness. The patient then makes the final decision on which medical procedures to accept. For less serious cases, the patient may choose not to consult a doctor and instead use his own basic knowledge of medical principles to treat himself. Similarly, a management scientist must receive substantial training (albeit considerably less than for a medical doctor). This training also is in a whole body of knowledge and techniques that are based on the scientific foundations of the discipline. After entering practice, the management scientist must diagnose a managerial problem and then choose the appropriate management science techniques to apply in analyzing the problem. The cognizant manager then makes the final decision as to which conclusions from this analysis to accept. For less extensive managerial problems where management science can be helpful, the manager may choose not to consult a management scientist and instead use his or her own basic knowledge of management science principles to analyze the problem.

Although it has considerably longer roots, the rapid development of the discipline began in the 1940s and 1950s. The initial impetus came early in World War II, when large numbers of scientists were called upon to apply a scientific approach to the management of the war effort for the allies. Another landmark event was the discovery in 1947 by George Dantzig of the *simplex method* for solving linear programming problems. (Linear programming is the subject of several early chapters.) Another factor that gave great impetus to the growth of the discipline was the onslaught of the computer revolution.

The traditional name given to the discipline (and the one that still is widely used today outside of business schools) is **operations research.** This name was applied because the teams of scientists in World War II were doing *research* on how to manage military *operations.* The abbreviation OR also is widely used. This abbreviation often is combined with the one for management science (MS), thereby referring to the discipline as OR/MS. According to projections from the U.S. Bureau of Labor Statistics for the year 2013, there are approximately 65,000 individuals working as operations research analysts in the United States with an average annual salary of about $79,000.

operations research
Management science began its rapid development during World War II with the name *operations research.*

Another discipline that is closely related to management science is **business analytics.** Like management science, business analytics attempts to aid managerial decision making but with particular emphasis on three types of analysis: (1) *descriptive analytics*—the use of data (sometimes massive amounts of data) to analyze trends, (2) *predictive analytics*—the use of data to predict what will happen in the future (perhaps by using the forecasting techniques described in Chapter 10), and (3) *prescriptive analytics*—the use of data to prescribe the best course of action (frequently by using the optimization techniques described throughout this book). Broadly speaking, the techniques of the management science discipline provide the firepower for prescriptive analytics and, to a lesser extent, for predictive analytics, but not so much for descriptive analytics.

One major international professional society for the management science discipline (as well as for business analytics) is the *Institute for Operations Research and the Management Sciences* (INFORMS). Headquartered in the United States, with over 10,000 members, this society holds major conferences in the United States each year (including an annual Conference for Business Analytics and Operations Research) plus occasional conferences elsewhere. It also publishes several prominent journals, including *Management Science, Operations Research, Analytics,* and *Interfaces.* (Articles describing actual applications of management science are featured in *Interfaces,* so you will see many references and links to this journal throughout the book.) In addition, a few dozen countries around the world have their own national operations research societies. (More about this in Section 1.3.)

Thus, operations research/management science (OR/MS) is a truly international discipline. (We hereafter will just use the name *management science* or the abbreviation MS.)

Management Science Aids Managerial Decision Making

The key word here is that management science *aids* managerial decision making. Management scientists don't make managerial decisions. Managers do. A management science study only provides an analysis and recommendations, based on the quantitative factors involved in the problem, as input to the cognizant managers. Managers must also take into account various intangible considerations that are outside the realm of management science and then use their best judgment to make the decision. Sometimes managers find that qualitative factors are as important as quantitative factors in making a decision.

A small informal management science study might be conducted by just a single individual, who may be the cognizant manager. However, management science *teams* normally are used for larger studies. (We often will use the term *team* to cover both cases throughout the book.) Such a team often includes some members who are not management scientists but who provide other types of expertise needed for the study. Although a management science team often is entirely *in-house* (employees of the company), part or all of the team may instead be *consultants* who have been hired for just the one study. Consulting firms that partially or entirely specialize in management science currently are a growing industry.

Management Science Uses a Scientific Approach

Management science is based strongly on some scientific fields, including mathematics and computer science. It also draws on the social sciences, especially economics. Since the field is concerned with the practical management of organizations, a management scientist should have solid training in business administration, including its various functional areas, as well.

To a considerable extent, a management science team will attempt to use the *scientific method* in conducting its study. This means that the team will emphasize conducting a *systematic investigation* that includes careful data gathering, developing and testing hypotheses about the problem (typically in the form of a mathematical model), and then applying sound logic in the subsequent analysis.

When conducting this systematic investigation, the management science team typically will follow the (overlapping) steps outlined and described below.

Step 1: Define the problem and gather data. In this step, the team consults with management to clearly identify the problem of concern and ascertain the appropriate objectives for the study. The team then typically spends a surprisingly large amount of time gathering relevant data about the problem with the assistance of other key individuals in the organization. A common frustration is that some key data are either very rough or completely unavailable. This may necessitate installing a new computer-based management information system.

Another increasingly common problem is that there may be *too much* data available to be easily analyzed. Dramatic advances in computerized data capture, processing power, data transmission, and storage capabilities are enabling organizations to integrate their various databases into massive *data warehouses*. This has led to the development of *data-mining software* for extracting hidden predictive information, correlations, and patterns from large databases.

Fortunately, the rapid development of the *information technology (IT)* field in recent years is leading to a dramatic improvement in the quantity and quality of data that may be available to the management science (MS) team. Corporate IT now is often able to provide the computational resources and databases, as well as any helpful data mining, that are needed by the MS team. Thus, the MS team often will collaborate closely with the IT group.

Step 2: Formulate a model (typically a mathematical model) to represent the problem. Models, or approximate representations, are an integral part of everyday life. Common examples include model airplanes, portraits, globes, and so on. Similarly, models play an important role in science and business, as illustrated by models of the atom, models of genetic structure, mathematical equations describing physical laws of motion or chemical reactions, graphs, organization charts, and industrial accounting systems. Such models are invaluable for abstracting the essence of the subject of inquiry, showing interrelationships, and facilitating analysis.

Mathematical models are also approximate representations, but they are expressed in terms of mathematical symbols and expressions. Such laws of physics as $F = ma$ and $E = mc^2$ are familiar examples. Similarly, the mathematical model of a business problem is the system of equations and related mathematical expressions that describes the essence of the problem.

With the emergence of powerful spreadsheet technology, **spreadsheet models** now are widely used to analyze managerial problems. A spreadsheet model lays out the relevant data, measures of performance, interrelationships, and so forth, on a spreadsheet in an organized way that facilitates fruitful analysis of the problem. It also frequently incorporates an underlying mathematical model to assist in the analysis, but the mathematics is kept in the background so the user can concentrate on the analysis.

The *modeling process* is a creative one. When dealing with real managerial problems (as opposed to some cut-and-dried textbook problems), there normally is no single "correct" model but rather a number of alternative ways to approach the problem. The modeling process also is typically an evolutionary process that begins with a simple "verbal model" to define the essence of the problem and then gradually evolves into increasingly more complete mathematical models (perhaps in a spreadsheet format).

We further describe and illustrate such mathematical models in the next section.

Step 3: Develop a computer-based procedure for deriving solutions to the problem from the model. The beauty of a well-designed mathematical model is that it enables the use of mathematical procedures to find good solutions to the problem. These procedures usually are run on a computer because the calculations are too extensive to be done by hand. In some cases, the management science team will need to develop the procedure. In others, a standard software package already will be available for solving the model. When the mathematical model is incorporated into a spreadsheet, the spreadsheet software normally includes a Solver that usually will solve the model.

Step 4: Test the model and refine it as needed. Now that the model can be solved, the team needs to thoroughly check and test the model to make sure that it provides a sufficiently accurate representation of the real problem. A number of questions should be addressed, perhaps with the help of others who are particularly familiar with the problem. Have all the relevant factors and interrelationships in the problem been accurately incorporated into the model? Does the model seem to provide reasonable solutions? When it is applied to a past situation, does the solution improve upon what was actually done? When assumptions about costs and revenues are changed, do the solutions change in a plausible manner?

Step 5: Apply the model to analyze the problem and develop recommendations for management. The management science team now is ready to solve the model, perhaps under a variety of assumptions, in order to analyze the problem. The resulting recommendations then are presented to the managers who must make the decisions about how to deal with the problem.

If the model is to be applied repeatedly to help guide decisions on an ongoing basis, the team might also develop a **decision support system.** This is an interactive computer-based system that aids managerial decision making. The system draws current data from *databases* or *management information systems* and then solves the various versions of the model specified by the manager.

Step 6: Help to implement the team's recommendations that are adopted by management. Once management makes its decisions, the management science team normally is asked to help oversee the implementation of the new procedures. This includes providing some information to the operating management and personnel involved on the rationale for the changes that are being made. The team also makes sure that the new operating system is consistent with its recommendations as they have been modified and approved by management. If successful, the new system may be used for years to come. With this in mind, the team monitors the initial experience with the system and seeks to identify any modifications that should be made in the future.

Management Science Considers Quantitative Factors

Many managerial problems revolve around such quantitative factors as production quantities, revenues, costs, the amounts available of needed resources, and so on. By incorporating these quantitative factors into a *mathematical model* and then applying mathematical procedures to solve the model, management science provides a uniquely powerful way of analyzing such managerial problems. Although management science is concerned with the practical management of organizations, including taking into account relevant qualitative factors, its special contribution lies in this unique ability to deal with the quantitative factors.

The Special Products Company example discussed below will illustrate how management science considers quantitative factors.

Review
Questions

1. When did the rapid development of the management science discipline begin?
2. What is the traditional name given to this discipline that still is widely used outside of business schools?
3. What does a management science study provide to managers to aid their decision making?
4. Upon which scientific fields and social sciences is management science especially based?
5. What is a *decision support system?*
6. What are some common quantitative factors around which many managerial problems revolve?

6   Chapter One   *Introduction*

1.2   AN ILLUSTRATION OF THE MANAGEMENT SCIENCE APPROACH: BREAK-EVEN ANALYSIS

The **Special Products Company** produces expensive and unusual gifts to be sold in stores that cater to affluent customers who already have everything. The latest new-product proposal to management from the company's Research Department is a first-of-its-kind iWatch. This iWatch would combine the features of a top-of-the-line atomic wristwatch and a next-generation smartphone, including the ability to respond to voice commands or questions with voice responses. It also would connect to the Internet wirelessly to provide weather, sports scores, stock quotes, and more. An extensive research-and-development project would be needed to develop the iWatch. The proposal is to provide a generous budget of $10 million for this project in order to provide as many desirable features as possible within this budget. It is clear that the production costs for the iWatch would be very large because of the extreme miniaturization that would be required, so the selling price would need to be far beyond the reach of middle-class customers. Therefore, the marketing of the iWatch would be aimed at wealthy customers who want the most advanced products regardless of cost.

Management needs to decide whether to develop and market this new product and, if so, how many of these watches to produce. Before making these decisions, a sales forecast will be obtained to estimate how many watches can be sold. Since most of these sales would occur quickly during the relatively brief time before the "next big thing" arrives to take over the market, there would be only one production run for the iWatch and the number produced would be set equal to the sales forecast. Following the production run, the iWatch would be marketed as aggressively as needed to sell this entire inventory if possible. Management now needs a management science study to be conducted to determine how large this sales potential needs to be to make the iWatch profitable after considering all the prospective revenues and costs, so let's next look at the estimates of these financial figures.

A cost that remains the same regardless of the production volume is referred to as a *fixed cost,* whereas a cost that varies with the production volume is called a *variable cost.*

If the company goes ahead with this product, the research-and-development cost of $10 million is referred to as a *fixed cost* because it remains the same regardless of how many watches are produced and sold. (However, note that this cost would *not* be incurred if management decides not to introduce the product since the research-and-development project then would not be undertaken.)

In addition to this fixed cost, there is a production cost that varies with the number of watches produced. This *variable cost* is $1,000 per watch produced, which adds up to $1,000 *times* the number of watches produced. (The cost for each additional unit produced, $1,000, is referred to as the *marginal cost.*) Each watch sold would generate a unit revenue of $2,000 for the company.

Spreadsheet Modeling of the Problem

You will see throughout this book that spreadsheets provide a very convenient way of using a management science approach for modeling and analyzing a wide variety of managerial problems. This certainly is true for the Special Products Company problem as well, as we now will demonstrate.

Figure 1.1 shows a spreadsheet formulation of this problem after obtaining a sales forecast that indicates 30,000 watches can be sold. The data have been entered into cells C4 to C7. Cell C9 is used to record a trial value for the decision as to how many watches to produce. As one of the many possibilities that eventually might be tried, Figure 1.1 shows the specific trial value of 20,000.

Cells F4 to F7 give the resulting total revenue, total costs, and profit (loss) by using the Excel equations shown under the spreadsheet in Figure 1.1. The Excel equations could have been written using cell references (e.g., F6 = C6*C9). However, the spreadsheet model is made clearer by giving "range names" to key cells or blocks of cells. (A **range name** is a descriptive name given to a cell or range of cells that immediately identifies what is there. Appendix A provides details about how to incorporate range names into a spreadsheet model.) To define a name for a selected cell (or range of cells), click on the name box (on the left of the formula bar above the spreadsheet) and type a name. These cell names then can be used in other formulas to create an equation that is easy to decipher (e.g., TotalVariable-Cost = MarginalCost*ProductionQuantity rather than the more cryptic F6 = C6*C9). Note

Excel Tip: To update formulas throughout the spreadsheet to incorporate a newly defined range name, choose Apply Names from the Define Name menu on the Formulas tab

FIGURE 1.1

A spreadsheet formulation of the Special Products Company problem.

	A	B	C	D	E	F
1		**Special Products Co. Break-Even Analysis**				
2						
3			**Data**			**Results**
4		Unit Revenue	$2,000		Total Revenue	$40,000,000
5		Fixed Cost	$10,000,000		Total Fixed Cost	$10,000,000
6		Marginal Cost	$1,000		Total Variable Cost	$20,000,000
7		Sales Forecast	30,000		Profit (Loss)	$10,000,000
8						
9		Production Quantity	20,000			

Range Name	Cell
FixedCost	C5
MarginalCost	C6
ProductionQuantity	C9
Profit	F7
SalesForecast	C7
TotalFixedCost	F5
TotalRevenue	F4
TotalVariableCost	F6
UnitRevenue	C4

	E	F
3		**Results**
4	Total Revenue	=UnitRevenue * MIN(SalesForecast, ProductionQuantity)
5	Total Fixed Cost	=IF(ProductionQuantity > 0, FixedCost, 0)
6	Total Variable Cost	=MarginalCost * ProductionQuantity
7	Profit (Loss)	=TotalRevenue − (TotalFixedCost + TotalVariableCost)

that spaces are not allowed in range names. When a range name has more than one word, we have used capital letters to distinguish the start of each new word (e.g., ProductionQuantity).

The lower left-hand corner of Figure 1.1 lists the names of the quantities in the spreadsheet in alphabetical order and then gives cell references where the quantities are found. Although this isn't particularly necessary for such a small spreadsheet, you should find it helpful for the larger spreadsheets found later in the book.

This same spreadsheet is provided for you live in your MS Courseware on the CD-ROM. (All the spreadsheets in the book are included in your MS Courseware.) As you can see for yourself by bringing up and playing with the spreadsheet, it provides a straightforward way of performing *what-if analysis* on the problem. What-if analysis involves addressing such questions as what happens if the sales forecast should have been considerably lower? What happens if some of the cost and revenue estimates are wrong? Simply enter a variety of new values for these quantities in the spreadsheet and see what happens to the profit shown in cell F7.

The lower right-hand corner of Figure 1.1 introduces two useful Excel functions, the MIN(a, b) function and the IF(a, b, c) function. The equation for cell F4 uses the MIN(a, b) function, which gives the minimum of a and b. In this case, the estimated number of watches that will be sold is the minimum of the sales forecast and the production quantity, so

$$F4 = UnitRevenue*MIN(SalesForecast, ProductionQuantity)$$

enters the unit revenue (from cell C4) times the minimum of the sales forecast (from C7) and the production quantity (from C9) into cell F4.

Also note that the equation for cell F5 uses the IF(a, b, c) function, which does the following: If statement a is true, it uses b; otherwise, it uses c. Therefore,

$$F5 = IF(ProductionQuantity > 0, FixedCost, 0)$$

says to enter the fixed cost (C5) into cell F5 if the production quantity (C9) is greater than zero, but otherwise enter 0 (the fixed cost is avoided if production is not initiated).

The spreadsheet in Figure 1.1, along with its equations for the results in column F, constitutes a *spreadsheet model* for the Special Products Company problem. You will see many examples of such spreadsheet models throughout the book.

Excel Tip: A list of all the defined names and their corresponding cell references can be pasted into a spreadsheet by choosing Paste Names from the Use in Formula menu on the Formulas tab, and then clicking on Paste List.

A spreadsheet is a convenient tool for performing what-if analysis.

The Excel function MIN (a, b) gives the minimum of the numbers in the cells whose addresses are a and b.

The Excel function IF (a, b, c) tests if a is true. If so, it uses b; otherwise it uses c.

This particular spreadsheet model is based on an underlying *mathematical model* that uses algebra to spell out the equations in cells F4:F7 and then to derive some additional useful information. Let us take a look at this mathematical model next.

Expressing the Problem Mathematically

The issue facing management is to make the following decision.

> Decision to be made: Number of watches to produce (if any).

Since this number is not yet known, we introduce an algebraic variable Q to represent this quantity. Thus,

$$Q = \text{Number of watches to produce},$$

where Q is referred to as a **decision variable.** Naturally, the value chosen for Q should not exceed the sales forecast for the number of watches that can be sold. Choosing a value of 0 for Q would correspond to deciding not to introduce the product, in which case none of the costs or revenues described in the preceding paragraph would be incurred.

The objective is to choose the value of Q that maximizes the company's profit from this new product. The management science approach is to formulate a mathematical model to represent this problem by developing an equation that expresses the profit in terms of the decision variable Q. To get there, it is necessary first to develop equations in terms of Q for the total cost and revenue generated by the watches.

If $Q = 0$, no cost is incurred. However, if $Q > 0$, there is both a fixed cost and a variable cost.

$$\text{Fixed cost} = \$10 \text{ million (if } Q > 0)$$
$$\text{Variable cost} = \$1{,}000\,Q$$

Therefore, the total cost would be

$$\text{Total cost} = \begin{cases} 0 & \text{if } Q = 0 \\ \$10 \text{ million } + \$1{,}000Q & \text{if } Q > 0 \end{cases}$$

Since each watch sold would generate a revenue of \$2,000 for the company, the total revenue from selling Q watches would be

$$\text{Total revenue} = \$2{,}000Q$$

Consequently, the profit from producing and selling Q watches would be

$$\text{Profit} = \text{Total revenue} - \text{Total cost}$$
$$= \begin{cases} 0 & \text{if } Q = 0 \\ \$2{,}000Q - (\$10 \text{ million } + \$1{,}000Q) & \text{if } Q > 0 \end{cases}$$

Thus, since $\$2{,}000Q - \$1{,}000Q = \$1{,}000Q$

$$\text{Profit} = -\$10 \text{ million } + \$1{,}000Q \qquad \text{if } Q > 0$$

Analysis of the Problem

This last equation shows that the attractiveness of the proposed new product depends greatly on the value of Q, that is, on the number of watches that can be produced and sold. A small value of Q means a loss (negative profit) for the company, whereas a sufficiently large value would generate a positive profit for the company. For example, look at the difference between $Q = 2{,}000$ and $Q = 20{,}000$.

$$\text{Profit} = -\$10 \text{ million } + \$1{,}000 \,(2{,}000) = -\$8 \text{ million} \qquad \text{if } Q = 20$$
$$\text{Profit} = -\$10 \text{ million } + \$1{,}000 \,(20{,}000) = \$10 \text{ million} \qquad \text{if } Q = 200$$

Figure 1.2 plots both the company's total cost and total revenue for the various values of Q. Note that the cost line and the revenue line intersect at $Q = 10{,}000$. For any value of $Q < 10{,}000$, cost exceeds revenue, so the gap between the two lines represents the *loss* to the company. For any $Q > 10{,}000$, revenue exceeds cost, so the gap between the two lines now

FIGURE 1.2

Break-even analysis for the Special Products Company shows that the cost line and revenue line intersect at $Q = 10,000$ watches, so this is the break-even point for the proposed new product.

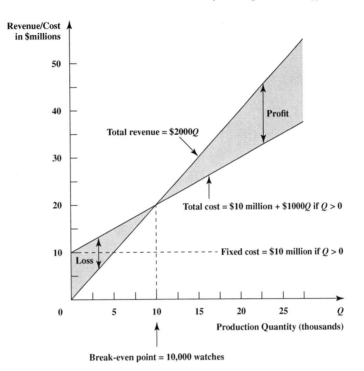

Break-even point = 10,000 watches

shows positive profit. At $Q = 10,000$, the profit is 0. Since 10,000 units is the production and sales volume at which the company would break even on the proposed new product, this volume is referred to as the **break-even point.** This is the point that must be exceeded to make it worthwhile to introduce the product. Therefore, the crucial question is whether the sales forecast for how many watches can be sold is above or below the break-even point.

Figure 1.2 illustrates the *graphical procedure* for finding the break-even point. Another alternative is to use an *algebraic procedure* to solve for the point. Because the profit is 0 at this point, the procedure consists of solving the following equation for the unknown Q.

$$\text{Profit} = -\$10 \text{ million} + \$1,000Q = 0$$

Thus,

$$\$1,000Q = \$10 \text{ million}$$
$$Q = \frac{\$10 \text{ million}}{\$1,000}$$
$$Q = 10,000$$

A Complete Mathematical Model for the Problem

The preceding analysis of the problem made use of a basic mathematical model that consisted of the equation for profit expressed in terms of Q. However, implicit in this analysis were some additional factors that can be incorporated into a complete mathematical model for the problem.

Two of these factors concern restrictions on the values of Q that can be considered. One of these is that the number of watches produced cannot be less than 0. Therefore,

$$Q \geq 0$$

constraints

A *constraint* in a mathematical model is an inequality or equation that expresses some restrictions on the values that can be assigned to the decision variables.

is one of the **constraints** for the complete mathematical model. Another restriction on the value of Q is that it should not exceed the number of watches that can be sold. A sales forecast has not yet been obtained, so let the symbol s represent this currently unknown value.

s = Sales forecast (not yet available) of the number of watches that can be sold

Consequently,

10   Chapter One   *Introduction*

$$Q \leq s$$

parameter
The constants in a mathematical model are referred to as the *parameters* of the model.

is another constraint, where s is a **parameter** of the model whose value has not yet been chosen.

The final factor that should be made explicit in the model is the fact that management's objective is to make the decision that maximizes the company's profit from this new product. Therefore, the complete mathematical model for this problem is to find the value of the decision variable Q so as to

$$\text{Maximize profit} = \begin{cases} 0 & \text{if } Q = 0 \\ -\$10 \text{ million} + \$1{,}000Q & \text{if } Q > 0 \end{cases}$$

subject to

$$Q \leq s$$
$$Q \geq 0$$

objective function
The *objective function* for a mathematical model is a mathematical expression that gives the measure of performance for the problem in terms of the decision variables.

where the algebraic expression given for Profit is called the **objective function** for the model. The value of Q that solves this model depends on the value that will be assigned to the parameter s (the future forecast of the number of units that can be sold). Because the break-even point is 10,000 here is how the solution for Q depends on s.

Solution for Mathematical Model

$$\text{Break-even point} = \frac{\text{Fixed cost}}{\text{Unit revenue} - \text{Marginal cost}} = \frac{\$10 \text{ million}}{\$2{,}000 - \$1{,}000} = 10{,}000$$

If $s \leq 10{,}000$, then set $Q = 0$
If $s > 10{,}000$, then set $Q = s$

Therefore, the company should introduce the product and produce the number of units that can be sold *only* if this production and sales volume exceeds the break-even point.

What-if Analysis of the Mathematical Model

A mathematical model is intended to be only an approximate representation of the problem. For example, some of the numbers in the model inevitably are only estimates of quantities that cannot be determined precisely at this time.

The above mathematical model is based on four numbers that are only estimates—the fixed cost of $10 million, the marginal cost of $1,000, the unit revenue of $2,000, and the sales forecast (after it is obtained). A management science study usually devotes considerable time to investigating what happens to the recommendations of the model if any of the estimates turn out to considerably miss their targets. This is referred to as **what-if analysis.**

what-if analysis
Since estimates can be wrong, *what-if analysis* is used to check the effect on the recommendations of a model if the estimates turn out to be wrong.

To assist you in performing what-if analysis on this kind of model in a straightforward and enjoyable way, we have provided a *Break-Even Analysis* module in the *Interactive Management Science Modules* at **www.mhhe.com/hillier5e.** (All of the modules in this software package also are included on your CD-ROM.) By following the simple directions given there, you can drag either the cost line or the revenue line to change the fixed cost, the marginal cost, or the unit revenue. This immediately enables you to see the effect on the break-even point if any of these cost or revenue numbers should turn out to have values that are somewhat different than their estimates in the model.

Incorporating the Break-Even Point into the Spreadsheet Model

A key finding of the above mathematical model is its formula for the break-even point,

$$\text{Break-even point} = \frac{\text{Fixed cost}}{\text{Unit revenue} - \text{Marginal cost}}$$

Therefore, once both the quantities in this formula and the sales forecast have been carefully estimated, the solution for the mathematical model specifies what the production quantity should be.

By contrast, although the spreadsheet in Figure 1.1 enables trying a variety of trial values for the production quantity, it does not directly indicate what the production quantity should be. Figure 1.3 shows how this spreadsheet can be expanded to provide this additional guidance.

FIGURE 1.3

An expansion of the spreadsheet in Figure 1.1 that uses the solution for the mathematical model to calculate the break-even point.

	A	B	C	D	E	F
1		**Special Products Co. Break-Even Analysis**				
2						
3			**Data**			**Results**
4		Unit Revenue	$2,000		Total Revenue	$60,000,000
5		Fixed Cost	$10,000,000		Total Fixed Cost	$10,000,000
6		Marginal Cost	$1,000		Total Variable Cost	$30,000,000
7		Sales Forecast	30,000		Profit (Loss)	$20,000,000
8						
9		Production Quantity	30,000		Break-Even Point	10,000

Range Name	Cell
BreakEvenPoint	F9
FixedCost	C5
MarginalCost	C6
ProductionQuantity	C9
Profit	F7
SalesForecast	C7
TotalFixedCost	F5
TotalRevenue	F4
TotalVariableCost	F6
UnitRevenue	C4

	E	F
3		**Results**
4	Total Revenue	=UnitRevenue * MIN(SalesForecast, ProductionQuantity)
5	Total Fixed Cost	=IF(ProductionQuantity > 0, FixedCost, 0)
6	Total Variable Cost	=MarginalCost * ProductionQuantity
7	Profit (Loss)	=TotalRevenue – (TotalFixedCost + TotalVariableCost)
8		
9	Break-Even Point	=FixedCost/(UnitRevenue – MarginalCost)

Suppose that a sales forecast of 30,000 has been obtained, as shown in cell C7. As indicated by its equation at the bottom of the figure, cell F9 calculates the break-even point by dividing the fixed cost ($10 million) by the net profit per watch sold ($1,000), where this net profit is the unit revenue ($2,000) *minus* the marginal cost ($1,000). Since the sales forecast of 30,000 exceeds the break-even point of 10,000 this forecast has been entered into cell C9.

If desired, the complete mathematical model for break-even analysis can be *fully* incorporated into the spreadsheet by requiring that the model solution for the production quantity be entered into cell C9. This would be done by using the equation

$$C9 = IF(SalesForecast > BreakEvenPoint, SalesForecast, 0)$$

However, the disadvantage of introducing this equation is that it would eliminate the possibility of trying other production quantities that might still be of interest. For example, if management does not have much confidence in the sales forecast and wants to minimize the danger of producing more watches than can be sold, consideration would be given to production quantities smaller than the forecast. For example, the trial value shown in cell C9 of Figure 1.1 might be chosen instead. As in any application of management science, a mathematical model can provide useful guidance but management needs to make the final decision after considering factors that may not be included in the model.

Review Questions

1. How do the production and sales volume of a new product need to compare to its break-even point to make it worthwhile to introduce the product?
2. What are the factors included in the complete mathematical model for the Special Products Company problem, in addition to an equation for profit?
3. What is the purpose of what-if analysis?
4. How can a spreadsheet be used to perform what-if analysis?
5. What does the MIN(*a, b*) Excel function do?
6. What does the IF(*a, b, c*) Excel function do?

An Application Vignette

Federal Express (FedEx) is the world's largest express transportation company. Every working day, it delivers more than 6.5 million documents, packages, and other items throughout the United States and more than 220 countries and territories around the world. In some cases, these shipments can be guaranteed overnight delivery by 10:30 AM the next morning.

The logistical challenges involved in providing this service are staggering. These millions of daily shipments must be individually sorted and routed to the correct general location (usually by aircraft) and then delivered to the exact destination (usually by motorized vehicle) in an amazingly short period of time. How is this possible?

Management science (which usually is referred to as operations research within FedEx) is the technological engine that drives this company. Ever since the company's founding in 1973, management science (MS) has helped make its major business decisions, including equipment investment,

route structure, scheduling, finances, and location of facilities. After MS was credited with literally saving the company during its early years, it became the custom to have MS represented at the weekly senior management meetings and, indeed, several of the senior corporate vice presidents have come up from the outstanding FedEx MS group.

FedEx has come to be acknowledged as a world-class company. It routinely ranks among the top companies on *Fortune* magazine's annual listing of the "World's Most Admired Companies." It also was the first winner (in 1991) of the prestigious prize now known as the INFORMS Prize, which is awarded annually for the effective and repeated integration of management science into organizational decision making in pioneering, varied, novel, and lasting ways.

Source: R. O. Mason, J. L. McKenney, W. Carlson, and D. Copeland, "Absolutely, Positively Operations Research: The Federal Express Story," *Interfaces* 27, no. 2 (March–April 1997), pp. 17–36. (A link to this article is provided on our Website, **www.mhhe.com/hillier5e.**)

1.3 THE IMPACT OF MANAGEMENT SCIENCE

Management science (or *operations research* as it is commonly called by practitioners) has had an impressive impact on improving the efficiency of numerous organizations around the world. In the process, management science has made a significant contribution to increasing the productivity of the economies of various countries. There now are a few dozen member countries in the International Federation of Operational Research Societies (IFORS), with each country having a national operations research society. Both Europe and Asia have federations of such societies to coordinate holding international conferences and publishing international journals in those continents. In addition, we described in Section 1.1 how the Institute for Operations Research and the Management Sciences (INFORMS) is a particularly prominent international society in this area. Among its various journals is one called *Interfaces* that regularly publishes articles describing major management science studies and the impact they had on their organizations.

The most important applications of management science in business and industry have resulted in annual savings in the hundreds of millions of dollars.

Management science (MS) has had numerous applications of various types in business and industry, sometimes resulting in annual savings of millions, or even hundreds of millions, of dollars. As an example, many hundreds of management scientists work on such airline problems as how to most effectively assign airplanes and crews to flights and how to develop fare structures that maximize revenue. For decades, financial services firms have used portfolio selection techniques that were developed by management scientists who won the Nobel Prize in Economics for their work. Management science models have become a core component of the marketing discipline. Multinational corporations rely on MS for guiding the management of their supply chains. There are numerous other examples of MS applications that are having a dramatic impact on the companies involved.

Management science also has had a major impact in the health care area, in guiding key governmental policies, and in military applications.

Management science also is widely used outside business and industry. For example, it is having an increasing impact in the health care area, with applications involving improved management of health care delivery and operations, disease modeling, clinical diagnosis and decision making, radiation therapy, and so on. Applications of MS also abound at various levels of government, ranging from dealing with national security issues at the federal level to managing the delivery of emergency services at the municipal level. Other key governmental applications involve the use of MS modeling to help guide energy, environmental, and global warming policies. Some of the earliest MS applications were military applications, including logistical planning and war gaming, and these continue today.

These are just a sampling of the numerous applications of management science that are having a major impact on the organizations involved. The list goes on and on.

To give you a better notion of the wide applicability of management science, we list some actual applications in Table 1.1. Note the diversity of organizations and applications in the first two columns. The third column identifies the section where an "application vignette" devotes several paragraphs to describing the application and also references an article that provides full details. (You can see the first of these application vignettes in this section.) The last column indicates that these applications typically resulted in annual savings in the many millions of dollars. Furthermore, additional benefits not recorded in the table (e.g., improved service to customers and better managerial control) sometimes were considered to be even more important than these financial benefits. (You will have an opportunity to investigate these less tangible benefits further in Problems 1.9 and 1.10.)

A link to the articles in *Interfaces* that describes these applications in detail is included on our Website, **www.mhhe.com/hillier5e**. We are grateful to INFORMS for our special partnership to make these articles available to you through this link. We think you will find these articles interesting and enlightening in illustrating the dramatic impact that management science sometimes can have on the success of a variety of organizations.

You also will see a great variety of applications of management science throughout the book in the form of case studies, examples, and end-of-chapter cases. Some of the applications are similar to ones described in application vignettes, but many others are quite different. However, they all generally fall into one of three broad categories, namely, applications

TABLE 1.1 Applications of Management Science to Be Described in Application Vignettes

Organization	Area of Application	Section	Annual Savings
Federal Express	Logistical planning of shipments	1.3	Not estimated
Swift & Company	Improve sales and manufacturing performance	2.1	$12 million
Samsung Electronics	Reduce manufacturing times and inventory levels	2.6	$200 million more revenue
INDEVAL	Settle all securities transactions in Mexico	3.2	$150 million
United Airlines	Plan employee work schedules at airports and reservations offices	3.3	$6 million
Procter & Gamble	Redesign the production and distribution system	3.5	$200 million
Welch's	Optimize use and movement of raw materials	4.3	$150,000
Pacific Lumber Company	Long-term forest ecosystem management	5.4	$398 million NPV
Hewlett-Packard	Product portfolio management	6.1	$180 million
Norwegian companies	Maximize flow of natural gas through offshore pipeline network	6.3	$140 million
Canadian Pacific Railway	Plan routing of rail freight	6.4	$100 million
Waste Management	Develop a route-management system for trash collection and disposal	7.1	$100 million
MISO	Administer the transmission of electricity in 13 states	7.2	$700 million
Netherlands Railways	Optimize operation of a railway network	7.4	$105 million
Continental Airlines	Reassign crews to flights when schedule disruptions occur	7.5	$40 million
Bank Hapoalim Group	Develop a decision-support system for investment advisors	8.2	$31 million more revenue
DHL	Optimize the use of marketing resources	8.4	$22 million
Workers' Compensation Board	Manage high-risk disability claims and rehabilitation	9.3	$4 million
Westinghouse	Evaluate research and development projects	9.7	Not estimated
Conoco-Phillips	Evaluate petroleum exploration projects	9.9	Not estimated
L. L. Bean	Forecast staffing needs at call centers	10.2	$300,000
Taco Bell	Forecast the level of business throughout the day	10.3	$13 million
CSAV	Optimize global shipping	10.6	$81 million
General Motors	Improve the throughput of its production lines	11.5	$200 million
KeyCorp	Improve efficiency of bank teller service	11.6	$20 million
Federal Aviation Administration	Manage air traffic flows in severe weather	12.2	$200 million
Sasol	Improve the efficiency of its production processes	12.4	$23 million
Merrill Lynch	Pricing analysis for providing financial services	13.5	$50 million more revenue

14 Chapter One *Introduction*

TABLE 1.2
Case Studies and
Examples in the Area of
Operations Management

Location	Type of Application
Sec. 2.1 onward	A case study: What is the most profitable mix of products?
Case 2-1	Which mix of car models should be produced?
Case 2-2	Which mix of ingredients should go into the casserole in a university cafeteria?
Case 2-3	Which mix of customer–service agents should be hired to staff a call center?
Sec. 3.3	Personnel scheduling of customer–service agents
Sec. 3.5	Minimize the cost of shipping a product from factories to customers
Sec. 3.7	Optimize the assignment of personnel to tasks
Case 3-1	How should a product be shipped to market?
Case 3-3	Which mix of women's clothing should be produced for next season?
Cases 3-5, 5-4, 7-3	Develop a plan for assigning students to schools so as to minimize busing costs
Case 3-6	Which mixes of solid waste materials should be amalgamated into different grades of a salable product?
Case 3-7	How should qualified managers be assigned to new R&D projects?
Case 5-2	Develop and analyze a steel company's plan for pollution abatement
Case 5-3	Plan the mix of livestock and crops on a farm with unpredictable weather
Sec. 6.1	Minimize the cost of operating a distribution network
Secs. 6.2, 6.3	A case study: Maximize the flow of goods through a distribution network
Sec. 6.4	Find the shortest path from an origin to a destination
Case 6-1	Logistical planning for a military campaign
Case 6-3	Develop the most profitable flight schedules for an airline
Cases 6-4, 7-4	Operate and expand a private computer network
Sec. 7.2	Choose the best combination of R&D projects to pursue
Sec. 7.3	Select the best sites for emergency services facilities
Sec. 7.4	Airline crew scheduling
Sec. 7.5	Production planning when setup costs are involved
Case 7-2	Make inventory decisions for a retailer's warehouse
Sec. 8.3	Production planning when overtime is needed
Sec. 8.5	Find the shortest route to visit all the American League ballparks
Sec. 11.2	Many examples of commercial service systems, internal service systems, and transportation service systems that can be analyzed with queueing models
Sec. 11.4 onward	A case study: An analysis of competing proposals for more quickly providing maintenance services to customers
Cases 11-2, 12-2	Analysis of proposals for reducing in-process inventory
Sec. 12.1	Comparison of whether corrective maintenance or preventive maintenance is better
Secs. 12.2, 12.3	A case study: Would it be profitable for the owner of a small business to add an associate?
Case 12-1	Analysis of proposals for relieving a production bottleneck
Sec. 13.1	A case study: How much of a perishable product should be added to a retailer's inventory?
Sec. 13.3	Plan a complex project to ensure a strong likelihood of meeting the project deadline

in the areas of operations management, finance, and marketing. Tables 1.2, 1.3, and 1.4 list these applications in these three respective areas, where the first column identifies where the application is described. In the second column of each table, note the many different ways in which management science can have a real impact in helping improve managerial decisions.

Even these long lists of applications in Tables 1.1 to 1.4 are just a sample of the numerous important ways in which management science is applied in organizations around the world. We do not have enough space to provide a more comprehensive compilation of the important applications. (Other applications are included in the supplementary chapters on the CD-ROM.) A hallmark of management science is its great flexibility in dealing with new managerial problems as they arise.

1.4   SOME SPECIAL FEATURES OF THIS BOOK

The focus of this book is on teaching what an enlightened future manager needs to learn from a management science course. It is not on trying to train technical analysts. This focus has led us to include a number of special features that we hope you enjoy.

TABLE 1.3

Case Studies and Examples in the Area of Finance

Location	Type of Application
Sec. 1.2	Break-even analysis
Case 1-1	Break-even analysis and what-if analysis
Sec. 3.2	An airline choosing which airplanes to purchase
Sec. 3.2	Capital budgeting of real-estate development projects
Case 3-2	Develop a schedule for investing in a company's computer equipment
Sec. 4.1 onward	A case study: Develop a financial plan for meeting future cash flow needs
Case 4-1	Develop an investment and cash flow plan for a pension fund
Sec. 6.4	Minimize the cost of car ownership
Case 6-2	Find the most cost-effective method of converting various foreign currencies into dollars
Sec. 7.1	A case study: Determine the most profitable combination of investments
Case 7-1	Develop an investment plan for purchasing art
Sec. 8.2	Portfolio selection that balances expected return and risk
Sec. 8.5	Select a portfolio to beat the market as frequently as possible
Case 8-2	Determine an optimal investment portfolio of stocks
Case 8-3	Develop a long-range plan to purchase and sell international bonds
Sec. 9.1 onward	A case study: Choose whether to drill for oil or sell the land instead
Case 9-1	Choose a strategy for the game show, "Who Wants to Be a Millionaire?"
Sec. 12.1	Analysis of a new gambling game
Sec. 13.2	Choose the bid to submit in a competitive bidding process
Sec. 13.4	Develop a financial plan when future cash flows are somewhat unpredictable
Sec. 13.5	Risk analysis when assessing financial investments
Sec. 13.6	How much overbooking should be done in the travel industry?
Case 13-1	Analysis of how a company's cash flows might evolve over the next year
Case 13-2	Calculate the value of a European call option

TABLE 1.4

Case Studies and Examples in the Area of Marketing

Location	Type of Application
Secs. 2.6, 3.3	Determine the best mix of advertising media
Case 2-1	Evaluate whether an advertising campaign would be worthwhile
Secs. 3.1, 3.4	A case study: Which advertising plan best achieves managerial goals?
Case 3-4	Develop a representative marketing survey
Case 5-1	Analysis of the trade-off between advertising costs and the resulting increase in sales of several products
Sec. 6.4	Balance the speed of bringing a new product to market and the associated costs
Sec. 8.3	Deal with nonlinear marketing costs
Case 8-1	Refine the advertising plan developed in the case study presented in Sections 3.1 and 3.4
Case 9-2	Should a company immediately launch a new product or test-market it first?
Case 9-3	Should a company buy additional marketing research before deciding whether to launch a new product?
Case 9-4	Plan a sequence of decisions for a possible new product
Sec. 10.2 onward	A case study: Manage a call center for marketing goods over the telephone
Case 10-1	Improve forecasts of demand for a call center
Case 11-1	Estimate customer waiting times for calling into a call center

One special feature is that the entire book revolves around *modeling* as an aid to managerial decision making. This is what is particularly relevant to a manager. Although they may not use this term, all managers often engage in at least informal modeling (abstracting the essence of a problem to better analyze it), so learning more about the art of modeling is important. Since managers instigate larger management science studies done by others, they also need to be able to recognize the kinds of managerial problems where such a study might be helpful. Thus, a future manager should acquire the ability both to recognize when a management science model might be applicable and to properly interpret the results from analyzing the model. Therefore, rather than spending substantial time in this book on mathematical theory, the mechanics of solution procedures, or the manipulation of spreadsheets, the focus is on the art of model formulation, the role of a model, and the analysis of model results. A wide range of model types is considered.

Another special feature is a heavy emphasis on *case studies* to better convey these ideas in an interesting way in the context of applications. Every subsequent chapter includes at least one case study that introduces and illustrates the application of that chapter's techniques in a realistic setting. In a few instances, the entire chapter revolves around a case study. Although considerably smaller and simpler than most real studies (to maintain clarity), these case studies are patterned after actual applications requiring a major management science study. Consequently, they convey the whole process of such a study, some of the pitfalls involved, and the complementary roles of the management science team and the manager responsible for the decisions to be made.

To complement these case studies, every chapter also includes major cases at the end. These realistic cases can be used for individual assignments, team projects, or case studies in class. In addition, the University of Western Ontario Ivey School of Business (the second largest producer of teaching cases in the world) also has specially selected cases from its case collection that match the chapters in this textbook. These cases are available on the Ivey Website, **www.cases.ivey.uwo.ca/cases**, in the segment of the CaseMate area designated for this book.

The book also places heavy emphasis on conveying the impressive impact that management science is having on improving the efficiency of numerous organizations around the world. Therefore, you will see many examples of actual applications throughout the book in the form of boxed *application vignettes,* such as the one already shown in Section 1.3. You then will have the opportunity to learn more about these actual applications by reading the articles fully describing them that are accessed by a link on our Website. As indicated in Table 1.1, these applications sometimes resulted in annual savings of millions, tens of millions, or even hundreds of millions of dollars.

In addition, we try to provide you with a broad perspective about the nature of the real world of management science in practice. It is easy to lose sight of this world when cranking through textbook exercises to master the mechanics of a series of techniques. Therefore, we shift some emphasis from mastering these mechanics to seeing the big picture. The case studies, cases, and descriptions of actual applications are part of this effort.

Another feature is the inclusion of one or more *solved problems* for each chapter to help you get started on your homework for that chapter. The statement of each solved problem is given just above the Problems section of the chapter, and then the complete solution is given on both the CD-ROM and the Website for the book.

The last, but certainly not the least, of the special features of this book is the accompanying software. We will describe and illustrate how to use today's premier spreadsheet package, Microsoft Excel, to formulate many management science models in a spreadsheet format. Excel 2007 implemented a significant overhaul of the user interface. Excel 2010 brought other significant changes and improvements. Many of the models considered in this book can be solved using standard Excel. Some Excel add-ins also are available to solve other models. Appendix A provides a primer on the use of Excel.

Included with the book is an extensive collection of software that we collectively refer to as **MS Courseware.** This collection includes spreadsheet files, Frontline Systems' Risk Solver Platform for Education, and a package of Interactive Management Science Modules. Each of these is briefly described below.

MS Courseware includes numerous spreadsheet files for every chapter in this book. Each time a spreadsheet example is presented in the book, a live spreadsheet that shows the formulation and solution for the example also is available in MS Courseware. This provides a convenient reference, or even useful templates, when you set up spreadsheets to solve similar problems. Also, for many models in the book, template spreadsheet files are provided that already include all the equations necessary to solve the model. You simply enter the data for the model and the solution is immediately calculated.

Included with standard Excel is an add-in, called Solver, which is used to solve most of the optimization models considered in the first half of this book. Solver is a product of Frontline Systems, Inc. New with this edition of the textbook is a very powerful software package from Frontline Systems, Inc., called Risk Solver Platform for Education (RSPE). Some special features of RSPE are a significantly enhanced version of the basic Solver included with Excel, the ability to build decision trees within Excel, as covered in Chapter 9, and tools to build computer simulation models within Excel, as covered in Chapter 13.

As mentioned in Section 1.2, another learning aid accompanying the book is the package of Interactive Management Science Modules provided at **www.mhhe.com/hillier5e**. This innovative tool includes several modules that enable you to interactively explore several management science techniques in depth. For your convenience, an offline version of this package also is included in your MS Courseware on the CD-ROM.

Most of the software used in this book is compatible with both Excel for Windows PCs and Excel for Macintosh computers (Macs). Some software (e.g., Risk Solver Platform for Education) is not directly compatible with Macs, although it works well on any recent (Intel) Mac with Boot Camp or virtualization software. For the most up-to-date information on software compatibility and relevant differences between Windows PC versions and Mac versions, please refer to the Software Compatibility link at **www.mhhe.com/hillier5e**.

We should point out that Excel is not designed for dealing with the really large management science models that occasionally arise in practice. More powerful software packages that are not based on spreadsheets generally are used to solve such models instead. However, management science teams, not managers, primarily use these sophisticated packages (including using *modeling languages* to help input the large models). Since this book is aimed mainly at future managers rather than future management scientists, we will not have you use these packages.

To alert you to relevant material in MS Courseware, the end of each chapter has a list entitled "Learning Aids for This Chapter in Your MS Courseware."

1.5 Summary

Management science is a discipline area that attempts to aid managerial decision making by applying a scientific approach to managerial problems that involve quantitative factors. The rapid development of this discipline began in the 1940s and 1950s. The onslaught of the computer revolution has since continued to give great impetus to its growth. Further impetus now is being provided by the widespread use of spreadsheet software, which greatly facilitates the application of management science by managers and others.

A major management science study involves conducting a systematic investigation that includes careful data gathering, developing and testing hypotheses about the problem (typically in the form of a mathematical model), and applying sound logic in the subsequent analysis. The management science team then presents its recommendations to the managers who must make the decisions about how to resolve the problem. Smaller studies might be done by managers themselves with the aid of spreadsheets.

A major part of a typical management science study involves incorporating the quantitative factors into a mathematical model (perhaps incorporated into a spreadsheet) and then applying mathematical procedures to solve the model. Such a model uses *decision variables* to represent the quantifiable decisions to be made. An *objective function* expresses the appropriate measure of performance in terms of these decision variables. The *constraints* of the model express the restrictions on the values that can be assigned to the decision variables. The *parameters* of the model are the constants that appear in the objective function and the constraints. An example involving *break-even analysis* was used to illustrate a mathematical model.

Management science has had an impressive impact on improving the efficiency of numerous organizations around the world. In fact, many award-winning applications have resulted in annual savings in the millions, tens of millions, or even hundreds of millions of dollars.

The focus of this book is on emphasizing what an enlightened future manager needs to learn from a management science course. Therefore, the book revolves around modeling as an aid to managerial decision making. Many case studies (within the chapters) and cases (at the end of chapters) are used to better convey these ideas.

Glossary

break-even point The production and sales volume for a product that must be exceeded to achieve a profit. (Section 1.2), 9

business analytics A discipline closely related to management science that makes extensive use of data to analyze trends, make forecasts, and apply optimization techniques. (Section 1.1), 3

constraint An inequality or equation in a mathematical model that expresses some restrictions on the values that can be assigned to the decision variables. (Section 1.2), 9

decision support system An interactive computer-based system that aids managerial decision making. (Section 1.1), 5

decision variable   An algebraic variable that represents a quantifiable decision to be made. (Section 1.2), 8

mathematical model   An approximate representation of, for example, a business problem that is expressed in terms of mathematical symbols and expressions. (Section 1.1), 4

model   An approximate representation of something. (Section 1.1), 4

MS Courseware   The name of the software package that is shrinkwrapped with the book or is on its Website. (Section 1.4), 16

objective function   A mathematical expression in a model that gives the measure of performance for a problem in terms of the decision variables. (Section 1.2), 10

operations research   The traditional name for management science that still is widely used outside of business schools. (Section 1.1), 3

parameter   One of the constants in a mathematical model. (Section 1.2), 10

range name   A descriptive name given to a cell or range of cells that immediately identifies what is there. (Section 1.2), 6

spreadsheet model   An approximate representation of, for example, a business problem that is laid out on a spreadsheet in a way that facilitates analysis of the problem. (Section 1.1), 4

what-if analysis   Analysis of how the recommendations of a model might change if any of the estimates providing the numbers in the model eventually need to be corrected. (Section 1.2), 10

Learning Aids for This Chapter in Your MS Courseware

Chapter 1 Excel Files:

Special Products Co. Example

Interactive Management Science Modules:

Module for Break-Even Analysis

Solved Problem (See the CD-ROM or Website for the Solution)

1.S1. Make or Buy?

Power Notebooks, Inc., plans to manufacture a new line of notebook computers. Management is trying to decide whether to purchase the LCD screens for the computers from an outside supplier or to manufacture the screens in-house. The screens cost $100 each from the outside supplier. To set up the assembly process required to produce the screens in-house would cost $100,000. The company could then produce each screen for $75. The number of notebooks that eventually will be produced (Q) is unknown at this point.

a. Set up a spreadsheet that will display the total cost of both options for any value of Q. Use trial and error with the spreadsheet to determine the range of production volumes for which each alternative is best.

b. Use a graphical procedure to determine the break-even point for Q (i.e., the quantity at which both options yield the same cost).

c. Use an algebraic procedure to determine the break-even point for Q.

Problems

1.1.   The manager of a small firm is considering whether to produce a new product that would require leasing some special equipment at a cost of $20,000 per month. In addition to this leasing cost, a production cost of $10 would be incurred for each unit of the product produced. Each unit sold would generate $20 in revenue.

Develop a mathematical expression for the monthly profit that would be generated by this product in terms of the number of units produced and sold per month. Then determine how large this number needs to be each month to make it profitable to produce the product.

1.2.   Refer to Problem 1.1. A sales forecast has been obtained that indicates that 4,000 units of the new product could be sold. This forecast is considered to be quite reliable, but there is considerable uncertainty about the accuracy of the estimates given for the leasing cost, the marginal production cost, and the unit revenue.

Use the Break-Even Analysis module in the Interactive Management Science Modules to perform what-if analysis on these estimates.

a. How large can the leasing cost be before this new product ceases to be profitable?

b. How large can the marginal production cost be before this new product ceases to be profitable?

c. How small can the unit revenue be before this new product ceases to be profitable?

1.3.   Management of the Toys R4U Company needs to decide whether to introduce a certain new novelty toy for the upcoming Christmas season, after which it would be discontinued. The total cost required to produce and market this toy would be $500,000 plus $15 per toy produced. The company would receive revenue of $35 for each toy sold.

a. Assuming that every unit of this toy that is produced is sold, write an expression for the profit in terms of the number produced and sold. Then find the break-even point that this number must exceed to make it worthwhile to introduce this toy.

b. Now assume that the number that can be sold might be less than the number produced. Write an expression for the profit in terms of these two numbers.

c. Formulate a spreadsheet that will give the profit in part *b* for any values of the two numbers.

d. Write a mathematical expression for the constraint that the number produced should not exceed the number that can be sold.

1.4. A reliable sales forecast has been obtained indicating that the Special Products Company (see Section 1.2) would be able to sell 30,000 iWatches, which appears to be enough to justify introducing this new product. However, management is concerned that this conclusion might change if more accurate estimates were available for the research-and-development cost, the marginal production cost, and the unit revenue. Therefore, before a final decision is made, management wants what-if analysis done on these estimates.

Use the spreadsheet from Figure 1.3 (see this chapter's Excel files) and trial-and-error to perform what-if analysis by *independently* investigating each of the following questions.

a. How large can the research-and-development cost be before the watches cease to be profitable?

b. How large can the marginal production cost be before the watches cease to be profitable?

c. How small can the unit revenue be before the watches cease to be profitable?

1.5. Reconsider the problem facing the management of the Special Products Company as presented in Section 1.2.

A more detailed investigation now has provided better estimates of the data for the problem. The research-and-development cost still is estimated to be $10 million, but the new estimate of the marginal production cost is $1,300. The revenue from each watch sold now is estimated to be $1,700.

a. Use a graphical procedure to find the new break-even point.

b. Use an algebraic procedure to find the new break-even point.

c. State the mathematical model for this problem with the new data.

d. Incorporate this mathematical model into a spreadsheet with a sales forecast of 30,000. Use this spreadsheet model to find the new break-even point, and then determine the production quantity and the estimated total profit indicated by the model.

e. Suppose that management fears that the sales forecast may be overly optimistic and so does not want to consider producing more than 20,000 watches. Use the spreadsheet from part *d* to determine what the production quantity should be and the estimated total profit that would result.

1.6. The Best-for-Less Corp. supplies its two retail outlets from its two plants. Plant A will be supplying 30 shipments next month. Plant B has not yet set its production schedule for next month but has the capacity to produce and ship any amount up to a maximum of 50 shipments. Retail outlet 1 has submitted its order for 40 shipments for next month. Retail outlet 2 needs a minimum of 25 shipments next month but would be happy to receive more. The production costs are the same at the two plants but the shipping costs differ. The shipping cost per shipment from each plant to each retail outlet is given below, along with a summary of the other data.

The distribution manager, Jennifer Lopez, now needs to develop a plan for how many shipments to send from each plant to each of the retail outlets next month. Her objective is to minimize the total shipping cost.

	Unit Shipping Cost		
	Retail Outlet 1	Retail Outlet 2	Supply
Plant A	$700	$400	= 30 shipments
Plant B	$800	$600	≤ 50 shipments
Needed = 40 shipments		≥ 25 shipments	

a. Identify the individual decisions that Jennifer needs to make. For each of these decisions, define a decision variable to represent the decision.

b. Write a mathematical expression for the total shipping cost in terms of the decision variables.

c. Write a mathematical expression for each of the constraints on what the values of the decision variables can be.

d. State a complete mathematical model for Jennifer's problem.

e. What do you think Jennifer's shipping plan should be? Explain your reasoning. Then express your shipping plan in terms of the decision variables.

1.7. The Water Sports Company soon will be producing and marketing a new model line of motor boats. The production manager, Michael Jensen, now is facing a *make-or-buy decision* regarding the outboard motor to be installed on each of these boats. Based on the total cost involved, should the motors be produced internally or purchased from a vendor? Producing them internally would require an investment of $1 million in new facilities as well as a production cost of $1,600 for each motor produced. If purchased from a vendor instead, the price would be $2,000 per motor.

Michael has obtained a preliminary forecast from the company's marketing division that 3,000 boats in this model line will be sold.

a. Use spreadsheets to display and analyze Michael's two options. Which option should be chosen?

b. Michael realizes from past experience that preliminary sales forecasts are quite unreliable, so he wants to check on whether his decision might change if a more careful forecast differed significantly from the preliminary forecast. Determine a *break-even point* for the production and sales volume below which the buy option is better and above which the make option is better.

1.8. Reconsider the Special Products Company problem presented in Section 1.2.

Although the company is well qualified to do most of the work in producing the iWatch, it currently lacks much expertise in one key area, namely, developing and producing a miniature camera to be embedded into the iWatch. Therefore, management now is considering contracting out this part of the job to another company that has this expertise. If this were done, the Special Products Company would reduce its research-and-development cost to $5 million, as well as reduce its marginal production cost to $750. However, the Special Products Company also would pay this other company $500 for each miniature camera and so would incur a total marginal cost of $1,250 (including its payment to the other company) while still obtaining revenue of $2,000 for each watch produced and sold. However, if the company does all the production itself, all the data presented in Section 1.2 still apply. After obtaining an analysis of the sales potential, management believes that 30,000 watches can be sold.

Management now wants to determine whether the *make option* (do all the development and production internally) or the *buy option* (contract out the development and production of the miniature cameras) is better.

   a. Use a spreadsheet to display and analyze the buy option. Show the relevant data and financial output, including the total profit that would be obtained by producing and selling 30,000 watches.

   b. Figure 1.3 shows the analysis for the make option. Compare these results with those from part *a* to determine which option (make or buy) appears to be better.

   c. Another way to compare these two options is to find a *break-even point* for the production and sales volume, below which the buy option is better and above which the make option is better. Begin this process by developing an expression for the *difference* in profit between the make and buy options in terms of the number of grandfather clocks to produce for sale. Thus, this expression should give the *incremental profit* from choosing the make option rather than the buy option, where this incremental profit is 0 if 0 watches are produced but otherwise

is negative below the break-even point and positive above the break-even point. Using this expression as the objective function, state the overall mathematical model (including constraints) for the problem of determining whether to choose the make option and, if so, how many units of the LCD display (one per watch) to produce.

   d. Use a graphical procedure to find the break-even point described in part *c*.

   e. Use an algebraic procedure to find the break-even point described in part *c*.

   f. Use a spreadsheet model to find the break-even point described in part *c*. What is the conclusion about what the company should do?

1.9. Select one of the applications of management science listed in Table 1.1. Read the article that is referenced in the application vignette presented in the section shown in the third column. (A link to all these articles is provided on our Website, **www.mhhe.com/hillier5e**.) Write a two-page summary of the application and the benefits (including nonfinancial benefits) it provided.

1.10. Select three of the applications of management science listed in Table 1.1. For each one, read the article that is referenced in the application vignette presented in the section shown in the third column. (A link to all these articles is provided on our Website, **www.mhhe.com/hillier5e**.) For each one, write a one-page summary of the application and the benefits (including nonfinancial benefits) it provided.

1.11. Read the referenced article that fully describes the management science study summarized in the application vignette presented in Section 1.3. Summarize the five major reasons given for why operations research/management science (OR/MS) was so successful.

Case 1-1

Keeping Time

Founded nearly 50 years ago by Alfred Lester-Smith, **Beautiful Clocks** specializes in developing and marketing a diverse line of large ornamental clocks for the finest homes. Tastes have changed over the years, but the company has prospered by continually updating its product line to satisfy its affluent clientele. The Lester-Smith family continues to own a majority share of the company and the grandchildren of Alfred Lester-Smith now hold several of the top managerial positions. One of these grandchildren is Meredith Lester-Smith, the new CEO of the company.

Meredith feels a great responsibility to maintain the family heritage with the company. She realizes that the company needs to continue to develop and market exciting new products. Since the 50th anniversary of the founding of the company is rapidly approaching, she has decided to select a particularly special new product to launch with great fanfare on this anniversary. But what should it be? As she ponders this crucial decision, Meredith's thoughts go back to the magnificent grandfather clock that her grandparents had in their home many years ago. She had admired the majesty of that clock as a child. How about launching a modern version of this clock?

This is a difficult decision. Meredith realizes that grandfather clocks now are largely out of style. However, if she is so nostalgic about the memory of the grandfather clock in her grandparents' home, wouldn't there be a considerable number of other relatively wealthy couples with similar memories who would welcome the prestige of adding the grandeur of a beautifully designed limited-edition grandfather clock in their home? Maybe. This also would highlight the heritage and continuity of the company. It all depends on whether there would be enough sales potential to make this a profitable product.

Meredith had an excellent management science course as part of her MBA program in college, so she realizes that break-even analysis is needed to help make this decision. With this in mind, she instructs several staff members to investigate this prospective product further, including developing estimates of the related costs and revenues as well as forecasting the potential sales.

One month later, the preliminary estimates of the relevant financial figures come back. The cost of designing the grandfather clock and then setting up the production facilities to produce this product would be approximately $250,000. There would be only one production run for this limited-edition grandfather clock. The additional cost for each clock produced would be roughly $2,000. The marketing department estimates that their price for selling the clocks can be successfully set at about $4,500 apiece, but a firm forecast of how many clocks can be sold at this price has not yet been obtained. However, it is believed that the sales likely would reach into three digits.

Meredith wants all these numbers pinned down considerably further. However, she feels that some analysis can be done now to draw preliminary conclusions.

a. Assuming that all clocks produced are sold, develop a spreadsheet model for estimating the profit or loss from producing any particular number of clocks.

b. Use this spreadsheet to find the break-even point by trial and error.

c. Develop the corresponding mathematical expression for the estimated profit in terms of the number of clocks produced.

d. Use a graphical procedure to find the break-even point.

e. Use the algebraic procedure to find the break-even point.

A fairly reliable forecast now has been obtained indicating that the company would be able to sell 300 of the limited-edition grandfather clocks, which appears to be enough to justify introducing this new product. However, Meredith is concerned that this conclusion might change if more accurate estimates were available for the various costs and revenues. Therefore, she wants sensitivity analysis done on these estimates. Use the Break-Even Analysis module in the Interactive Management Science Modules to perform sensitivity analysis by *independently* investigating each of the following questions.

f. How large can the cost of designing this product and setting up the production facilities be before the grandfather clocks cease to be profitable?

g. How large can the production cost for each additional clock be before the grandfather clocks cease to be profitable?

h. If both of the costs identified in parts *f* and *g* were 50% larger than their initial estimates, would producing and selling the grandfather clocks still be profitable?

i. How small can the price for selling each clock be before the grandfather clocks cease to be profitable?

Now suppose that 300 grandfather clocks are produced but only 200 are sold.

j. Would it still be profitable to produce and sell the grandfather clocks under this circumstance?

Additional Case

An additional case for this chapter is also available at the University of Western Ontario Ivey School of Business Website, **cases.ivey.uwo.ca/cases**, in the segment of the CaseMate area designated for this book.

Chapter **Two**

Linear Programming: Basic Concepts

Learning Objectives

After completing this chapter, you should be able to

1. Explain what linear programming is.
2. Identify the three key questions to be addressed in formulating any spreadsheet model.
3. Name and identify the purpose of the four kinds of cells used in linear programming spreadsheet models.
4. Formulate a basic linear programming model in a spreadsheet from a description of the problem.
5. Present the algebraic form of a linear programming model from its formulation on a spreadsheet.
6. Apply the graphical method to solve a two-variable linear programming problem.
7. Use Excel to solve a linear programming spreadsheet model.

The management of any organization regularly must make decisions about how to allocate its resources to various activities to best meet organizational objectives. Linear programming is a powerful problem-solving tool that aids management in making such decisions. It is applicable to both profit-making and not-for-profit organizations, as well as governmental agencies. The resources being allocated to activities can be, for example, money, different kinds of personnel, and different kinds of machinery and equipment. In many cases, a wide variety of resources must be allocated simultaneously. The activities needing these resources might be various production activities (e.g., producing different products), marketing activities (e.g., advertising in different media), financial activities (e.g., making capital investments), or some other activities. Some problems might even involve activities of *all* these types (and perhaps others), because they are competing for the same resources.

You will see as we progress that even this description of the scope of linear programming is not sufficiently broad. Some of its applications go beyond the allocation of resources. However, activities always are involved. Thus, a recurring theme in linear programming is the need to find the *best mix* of activities—which ones to pursue and at what levels.

Like the other management science techniques, linear programming uses a *mathematical model* to represent the problem being studied. The word *linear* in the name refers to the form of the mathematical expressions in this model. *Programming* does not refer to computer programming; rather, it is essentially a synonym for planning. Thus, linear programming means the *planning of activities* represented by a *linear* mathematical model.

Because it comprises a major part of management science, linear programming takes up several chapters of this book. Furthermore, many of the lessons learned about how to apply linear programming also will carry over to the application of other management science techniques.

This chapter focuses on the basic concepts of linear programming.

2.1   A CASE STUDY: THE WYNDOR GLASS CO. PRODUCT-MIX PROBLEM

Jim Baker has had an excellent track record during his seven years as manager of new product development for the Wyndor Glass Company. Although the company is a small one, it has been experiencing considerable growth largely because of the innovative new products developed by Jim's group. Wyndor's president, John Hill, has often acknowledged publicly the key role that Jim has played in the recent success of the company.

Therefore, John felt considerable confidence six months ago in asking Jim's group to develop the following new products:

- An 8-foot glass door with aluminum framing.
- A 4-foot × 6-foot double-hung, wood-framed window.

Although several other companies already had products meeting these specifications, John felt that Jim would be able to work his usual magic in introducing exciting new features that would establish new industry standards.

Background

The **Wyndor Glass Co.** produces high-quality glass products, including windows and glass doors that feature handcrafting and the finest workmanship. Although the products are expensive, they fill a market niche by providing the highest quality available in the industry for the most discriminating buyers. The company has three plants that simultaneously produce the components of its products.

Plant 1 produces aluminum frames and hardware.

Plant 2 produces wood frames.

Plant 3 produces the glass and assembles the windows and doors.

Because of declining sales for certain products, top management has decided to revamp the company's product line. Unprofitable products are being discontinued, releasing production capacity to launch the two new products developed by Jim Baker's group if management approves their release.

The 8-foot glass door requires some of the production capacity in Plants 1 and 3, but not Plant 2. The 4-foot × 6-foot double-hung window needs only Plants 2 and 3.

Management now needs to address two issues:

1. Should the company go ahead with launching these two new products?
2. If so, what should be the *product mix*—the number of units of each produced per week—for the two new products?

Management's Discussion of the Issues

Having received Jim Baker's memorandum describing the two new products, John Hill now has called a meeting to discuss the current issues. In addition to John and Jim, the meeting includes Bill Tasto, vice president for manufacturing, and Ann Lester, vice president for marketing.

Let's eavesdrop on the meeting.

John Hill (president):   Bill, we will want to rev up to start production of these products as soon as we can. About how much production output do you think we can achieve?

Bill Tasto (vice president for manufacturing):   We do have a little available production capacity, because of the products we are discontinuing, but not a lot. We should be able to achieve a production rate of a few units per week for each of these two products.

John: Is that all?

Bill: Yes. These are complicated products requiring careful crafting. And, as I said, we don't have much production capacity available.

John: Ann, will we be able to sell several of each per week?

Ann Lester (vice president for marketing):   Easily.

An Application Vignette

Swift & Company is a diversified protein-producing business based in Greeley, Colorado. With annual sales of over $8 billion, beef and related products are by far the largest portion of the company's business.

To improve the company's sales and manufacturing performance, upper management concluded that it needed to achieve three major objectives. One was to enable the company's customer service representatives to talk to their more than 8,000 customers with accurate information about the availability of current and future inventory while considering requested delivery dates and maximum product age upon delivery. A second was to produce an efficient shift-level schedule for each plant over a 28-day horizon. A third was to accurately determine whether a plant can ship a requested order-line-item quantity on the requested date

and time given the availability of cattle and constraints on the plant's capacity.

To meet these three challenges, a management science team developed an *integrated system of 45 linear programming models* based on three model formulations to dynamically schedule its beef-fabrication operations at five plants in real time as it receives orders. *The total audited benefits realized in the first year* of operation of this system were **$12.74 million,** including $12 million due to *optimizing the product mix.* Other benefits include a reduction in orders lost, a reduction in price discounting, and better on-time delivery.

Source: A. Bixby, B. Downs, and M. Self, "A Scheduling and Capable-to-Promise Application for Swift & Company, *Interfaces* 36, no. 1 (January–February 2006), pp. 69–86. (A link to this article is provided on our website, **www.mhhe.com/hillier5e.**)

John: Good. Now there's one more issue to resolve. With this limited production capacity, we need to decide how to split it between the two products. Do we want to produce the same number of both products? Or mostly one of them? Or even just produce as much as we can of one and postpone launching the other one for a little while?

Jim Baker (manager of new product development): It would be dangerous to hold one of the products back and give our competition a chance to scoop us.

Ann: I agree. Furthermore, launching them together has some advantages from a marketing standpoint. Since they share a lot of the same special features, we can combine the advertising for the two products. This is going to make a big splash.

The issue is to find the most profitable mix of the two new products.

John: OK. But which mixture of the two products is going to be most profitable for the company?

Bill: I have a suggestion.

John: What's that?

Bill: A couple times in the past, our Management Science Group has helped us with these same kinds of product-mix decisions, and they've done a good job. They ferret out all the relevant data and then dig into some detailed analysis of the issue. I've found their input very helpful. And this is right down their alley.

John: Yes, you're right. That's a good idea. Let's get our Management Science Group working on this issue. Bill, will you coordinate with them?

The meeting ends.

The Management Science Group Begins Its Work

At the outset, the Management Science Group spends considerable time with Bill Tasto to clarify the general problem and specific issues that management wants addressed. A particular concern is to ascertain the appropriate objective for the problem from management's viewpoint. Bill points out that John Hill posed the issue as determining which mixture of the two products is going to be most profitable for the company.

Therefore, with Bill's concurrence, the group defines the key issue to be addressed as follows.

Question: Which combination of *production rates* (the number of units produced per week) for the two new products would *maximize the total profit* from both of them?

The group also concludes that it should consider *all* possible combinations of production rates of both new products permitted by the available production capacities in the three plants. For example, one alternative (despite Jim Baker's and Ann Lester's objections) is to forgo producing one of the products for now (thereby setting its production rate equal to zero) in order

TABLE 2.1
Data for the Wyndor
Glass Co. Product-Mix
Problem

Plant	Production Time Used for Each Unit Produced		Available per Week
	Doors	**Windows**	
1	1 hour	0	4 hours
2	0	2 hours	12 hours
3	3 hours	2 hours	18 hours
Unit profit	$300	$500	

to produce as much as possible of the other product. (We must not neglect the possibility that maximum profit from both products might be attained by producing none of one and as much as possible of the other.)

The Management Science Group next identifies the information it needs to gather to conduct this study:

1. Available production capacity in each of the plants.
2. How much of the production capacity in each plant would be needed by each product.
3. Profitability of each product.

Concrete data are not available for any of these quantities, so estimates have to be made. Estimating these quantities requires enlisting the help of key personnel in other units of the company.

Bill Tasto's staff develops the estimates that involve production capacities. Specifically, the staff estimates that the production facilities in Plant 1 needed for the new kind of doors will be available approximately four hours per week. (The rest of the time Plant 1 will continue with current products.) The production facilities in Plant 2 will be available for the new kind of windows about 12 hours per week. The facilities needed for both products in Plant 3 will be available approximately 18 hours per week.

The amount of each plant's production capacity actually used by each product depends on its production rate. It is estimated that each door will require one hour of production time in Plant 1 and three hours in Plant 3. For each window, about two hours will be needed in Plant 2 and two hours in Plant 3.

By analyzing the cost data and the pricing decision, the Accounting Department estimates the profit from the two products. The projection is that the profit per unit will be $300 for the doors and $500 for the windows.

Table 2.1 summarizes the data now gathered.

The Management Science Group recognizes this as being a classic **product-mix problem.** Therefore, the next step is to develop a *mathematical model*—that is, a *linear programming model*—to represent the problem so that it can be solved mathematically. The next four sections focus on how to develop this model and then how to solve it to find the most profitable mix between the two products, assuming the estimates in Table 2.1 are accurate.

Review
Questions

1. What were the two issues addressed by management?
2. The Management Science Group was asked to help analyze which of these issues?
3. How did this group define the key issue to be addressed?
4. What information did the group need to gather to conduct its study?

2.2   FORMULATING THE WYNDOR PROBLEM ON A SPREADSHEET

Spreadsheets provide a powerful and intuitive tool for displaying and analyzing many management problems. We now will focus on how to do this for the Wyndor problem with the popular spreadsheet package Microsoft Excel.[1]

---

[1] Other spreadsheet packages with similar capabilities also are available, and the basic ideas presented here are still applicable.

Formulating a Spreadsheet Model for the Wyndor Problem

Figure 2.1 displays the Wyndor problem by transferring the data in Table 2.1 onto a spreadsheet. (Columns E and F are being reserved for later entries described below.) We will refer to the cells showing the data as **data cells.** To distinguish the data cells from other cells in the spreadsheet, they are shaded light blue. (In the textbook figures, the light blue shading appears as light gray.) The spreadsheet is made easier to interpret by using *range names*. (As mentioned in Section 1.2, a **range name** is simply a descriptive name given to a cell or range of cells that immediately identifies what is there. Excel allows you to use range names instead of the corresponding cell addresses in Excel equations, since this usually makes the equations much easier to interpret at a glance.) The data cells in the Wyndor Glass Co. problem are given the range names UnitProfit (C4:D4), HoursUsedPerUnitProduced (C7:D9), and Hours Available (G7:G9). To enter a range name, first select the range of cells, then click in the name box on the left of the formula bar above the spreadsheet and type a name. (See Appendix A for further details about defining and using range names.)

Three questions need to be answered to begin the process of using the spreadsheet to formulate a mathematical model (in this case, a **linear programming model**) for the problem.

Excel Tip: Cell shading and borders can be added by using the borders button and the fill color button in the Font Group of the Home tab.

Excel Tip: See the margin notes in Section 1.2 for tips on adding range names.

These are the three key questions to be addressed in formulating any spreadsheet model.

1. What are the *decisions* to be made?
2. What are the *constraints* on these decisions?
3. What is the overall *measure of performance* for these decisions?

The preceding section described how Wyndor's Management Science Group spent considerable time with Bill Tasto, vice president for manufacturing, to clarify management's view of their problem. These discussions provided the following answers to these questions.

Some students find it helpful to organize their thoughts by answering these three key questions before beginning to formulate the spreadsheet model.

1. The decisions to be made are the *production rates* (number of units produced per week) for the two new products.
2. The constraints on these decisions are that the number of hours of production time used per week by the two products in the respective plants cannot exceed the number of hours available.
3. The overall measure of performance for these decisions is the *total profit* per week from the two products.

Figure 2.2 shows how these answers can be incorporated into the spreadsheet. Based on the first answer, the *production rates* of the two products are placed in cells C12 and D12 to locate them in the columns for these products just under the data cells. Since we don't know yet what these production rates should be, they are just entered as zeroes in Figure 2.2. (Actually, any trial solution can be entered, although *negative* production rates should be excluded since they are impossible.) Later, these numbers will be changed while seeking the best mix of production rates. Therefore, these cells containing the decisions to be made are called **changing cells.** To highlight the changing cells, they are shaded bright yellow with a light border. (In the textbook figures, the bright yellow appears as gray.) The changing cells are given the range name UnitsProduced (C12:D12).

The changing cells contain the decisions to be made.

FIGURE 2.1
The initial spreadsheet for the Wyndor problem after transferring the data in Table 2.1 into data cells.

	A	B	C	D	E	F	G
1		**Wyndor Glass Co. Product-Mix Problem**					
2							
3			**Doors**	**Windows**			
4		Unit Profit	$300	$500			
5							Hours
6			Hours Used per Unit Produced				Available
7		Plant 1	1	0			4
8		Plant 2	0	2			12
9		Plant 3	3	2			18

FIGURE 2.2

The complete spreadsheet for the wyndor problem with an initial trial solution (both production rates equal to zero) entered into the changing cells (C12 and D12).

	A	B	C	D	E	F	G
1		**Wyndor Glass Co. Product-Mix Problem**					
2							
3			**Doors**	**Windows**			
4		Unit Profit	$300	$500			
5					Hours		Hours
6			Hours Used per Unit Produced		Used		Available
7		Plant 1	1	0	0	≤	4
8		Plant 2	0	2	0	≤	12
9		Plant 3	3	2	0	≤	18
10							
11			**Doors**	**Windows**			**Total Profit**
12		Units Produced	0	0			$0

Using the second answer, the total number of hours of production time used per week by the two products in the respective plants is entered in cells E7, E8, and E9, just to the right of the corresponding data cells. The total number of production hours depends on the production rates of the two products, so this total is zero when the production rates are zero. With positive production rates, the total number of production hours used per week in a plant is the sum of the production hours used per week by the respective products. The production hours used by a product is the number of hours needed for *each* unit of the product *times* the number of units being produced. Therefore, when positive numbers are entered in cells C12 and D12 for the number of doors and windows to produce per week, the data in cells C7:D9 are used to calculate the total production hours per week as follows:

The colon in C7:D9 is Excel shorthand for the *range from* C7 to D9; that is, the entire block of cells in column C or D and in row 7, 8, or 9.

Production hours in Plant 1 = 1(# of doors) + 0(# of windows)

Production hours in Plant 2 = 0(# of doors) + 2(# of windows)

Production hours in Plant 3 = 3(# of doors) + 2(# of windows)

Consequently, the Excel equations for the three cells in column E are

E7 = C7*C12 + D7*D12

E8 = C8*C12 + D8*D12

E9 = C9*C12 + D9*D12

Output cells show quantities that are calculated from the changing cells.

where each asterisk denotes multiplication. Since each of these cells provides output that depends on the changing cells (C12 and D12), they are called **output cells.**

Notice that each of the equations for the output cells involves the sum of two products. There is a function in Excel called SUMPRODUCT that will sum up the product of each of the individual terms in two different ranges of cells when the two ranges have the same number of rows and the same number of columns. Each product being summed is the product of a term in the first range and the term in the corresponding location in the second range. For example, consider the two ranges, C7:D7 and C12:D12, so that each range has one row and two columns. In this case, SUMPRODUCT (C7:D7, C12:D12) takes each of the individual terms in the range C7:D7, multiplies them by the corresponding term in the range C12:D12, and then sums up these individual products, just as shown in the first equation above. Applying the range name for UnitsProduced (C12:D12), the formula becomes SUMPRODUCT(C7:D7, UnitsProduced). Although optional with such short equations, this function is especially handy as a shortcut for entering longer equations.

The SUMPRODUCT function is used extensively in linear programming spreadsheet models.

The formulas in the output cells E7:E9 are very similar. Rather than typing each of these formulas separately into the three cells, it is quicker (and less prone to typos) to type the formula just once in E7 and then copy the formula down into cells E8 and E9. To do this, first enter the formula =SUMPRODUCT(C7:D7, UnitsProduced) in cell E7. Then select cell

E7 and drag the fill handle (the small box on the lower right corner of the cell cursor) down through cells E8 and E9.

When copying formulas, it is important to understand the difference between relative and absolute references. In the formula in cell E7, the reference to cells C7:D7 is based upon the relative position to the cell containing the formula. In this case, this means the two cells in the same row and immediately to the left. This is known as a **relative reference.** When this formula is copied to new cells using the fill handle, the reference is automatically adjusted to refer to the new cell(s) at the same relative location (the two cells in the same row and immediately to the left). The formula in E8 becomes =SUMPRODUCT(C8:D8, UnitsProduced) and the formula in E9 becomes =SUMPRODUCT(C9:D9, UnitsProduced). This is exactly what we want, since we always want the hours used at a given plant to be based upon the hours used per unit produced at that same plant (the two cells in the same row and immediately to the left).

In contrast, the reference to the UnitsProduced in E7 is called an **absolute reference.** These references do not change when they are filled into other cells but instead always refer to the same absolute cell locations.

You can make the column absolute and the row relative (or vice versa) by putting a $ sign in front of only the letter (or number) of the cell reference.

To make a relative reference, simply enter the cell address (e.g., C7:D7). References referred to by a range name are treated as absolute references. Another way to make an absolute reference to a range of cells is to put $ signs in front of the letter and number of the cell reference (e.g., $C$12:$D$12). See Appendix A for more details about relative and absolute referencing and copying formulas.

Excel Tip: *After entering a cell reference, repeatedly pressing the F4 key (or command-T on a Mac) will rotate among the four possibilities of relative and absolute references (e.g., C12, $C$12, C$12, $C12).*

Next, ≤ signs are entered in cells F7, F8, and F9 to indicate that each total value to their left cannot be allowed to exceed the corresponding number in column G. (On the computer ≤ (or ≥) is often represented as <= (or >=), since there is no ≤ (or ≥) key on the keyboard.) The spreadsheet still will allow you to enter trial solutions that violate the ≤ signs. However, these ≤ signs serve as a reminder that such trial solutions need to be rejected if no changes are made in the numbers in column G.

Finally, since the answer to the third question is that the overall measure of performance is the total profit from the two products, this profit (per week) is entered in cell G12. Much like the numbers in column E, it is the sum of products. Since cells C4 and D4 give the profit from *each* door and window produced, the total profit per week from these products is

$$\text{Profit} = \$300(\text{\# of doors}) + \$500(\text{\# of windows})$$

One easy way to enter a ≤ (or ≥) in a spreadsheet is to type < (or >) with underlining turned on.

Hence, the equation for cell G12 is

$$\text{G12} = \text{SUMPRODUCT(C4:D4, C12:D12)}$$

Utilizing range names of TotalProfit (G12), UnitProfit (C4:D4), and UnitsProduced (C12:D12), this equation becomes

$$\text{TotalProfit} = \text{SUMPRODUCT(UnitProfit, UnitsProduced)}$$

This is a good example of the benefit of using range names for making the resulting equation easier to interpret.

TotalProfit (G12) is a special kind of output cell. It is our objective to make this cell as large as possible when making decisions regarding production rates. Therefore, TotalProfit

The objective cell contains the overall measure of performance for the decisions in the changing cells.

(G12) is referred to as the **objective cell.** This cell is shaded orange with a heavy border. (In the textbook figures, the orange appears as gray and is distinguished from the changing cells by its darker shading and heavy border.)

The bottom of Figure 2.3 summarizes all the formulas that need to be entered in the Hours Used column and in the Total Profit cell. Also shown is a summary of the range names (in alphabetical order) and the corresponding cell addresses.

This completes the formulation of the spreadsheet model for the Wyndor problem.

With this formulation, it becomes easy to analyze any trial solution for the production rates. Each time production rates are entered in cells C12 and D12, Excel immediately calculates the output cells for hours used and total profit. For example, Figure 2.4 shows the spreadsheet when the production rates are set at four doors per week and three windows per week. Cell G12 shows that this yields a total profit of $2,700 per week. Also note that E7 = G7, E8 < G8, and E9 = G9, so the ≤ signs in column F are all satisfied. Thus, this

FIGURE 2.3

The spreadsheet model for the Wyndor problem, including the formulas for the objective cell Total-Profit (G12) and the other output cells in column E, where the goal is to maximize the objective cell.

	A	B	C	D	E	F	G
1		**Wyndor Glass Co. Product-Mix Problem**					
2							
3			**Doors**	**Windows**			
4		Unit Profit	$300	$500			
5					Hours		Hours
6			Hours Used per Unit Produced		Used		Available
7		Plant 1	1	0	0	≤	4
8		Plant 2	0	2	0	≤	12
9		Plant 3	3	2	0	≤	18
10							
11			**Doors**	**Windows**			**Total Profit**
12		Units Produced	0	0			$0

Range Name	Cell
HoursAvailable	G7:G9
HoursUsed	E7:E9
HoursUsedPerUnitProduced	C7:D9
TotalProfit	G12
UnitProfit	C4:D4
UnitsProduced	C12:D12

	E
5	Hours
6	Used
7	=SUMPRODUCT(C7:D7, UnitsProduced)
8	=SUMPRODUCT(C8:D8, UnitsProduced)
9	=SUMPRODUCT(C9:D9, UnitsProduced)

	G
11	Total Profit
12	=SUMPRODUCT(UnitProfit, UnitsProduced)

FIGURE 2.4

The spreadsheet for the Wyndor problem with a new trial solution entered into the changing cells, UnitsProduced (C12:D12).

	A	B	C	D	E	F	G
1		**Wyndor Glass Co. Product-Mix Problem**					
2							
3			**Doors**	**Windows**			
4		Unit Profit	$300	$500			
5					Hours		Hours
6			Hours Used per Unit Produced		Used		Available
7		Plant 1	1	0	4	≤	4
8		Plant 2	0	2	6	≤	12
9		Plant 3	3	2	18	≤	18
10							
11			**Doors**	**Windows**			**Total Profit**
12		Units Produced	4	3			$2,700

trial solution is *feasible*. However, it would *not* be feasible to further increase both production rates, since this would cause E7 > G7 and E9 > G9.

Does this trial solution provide the best mix of production rates? Not necessarily. It might be possible to further increase the total profit by simultaneously increasing one production rate and decreasing the other. However, it is not necessary to continue using trial and error to explore such possibilities. We shall describe in Section 2.5 how the Excel Solver can be used to quickly find the best (optimal) solution.

This Spreadsheet Model Is a Linear Programming Model

The spreadsheet model displayed in Figure 2.3 is an example of a *linear programming* model. The reason is that it possesses all the following characteristics.

Characteristics of a Linear Programming Model on a Spreadsheet

1. Decisions need to be made on the levels of a number of activities, so *changing cells* are used to display these levels. (The two activities for the Wyndor problem are the production of the two new products, so the changing cells display the number of units produced per week for each of these products.)

2. These activity levels can have any value (including fractional values) that satisfy a number of constraints. (The production rates for Wyndor's new products are restricted only by the constraints on the number of hours of production time available in the three plants.)

3. Each **constraint** describes a restriction on the feasible values for the levels of the activities, where a constraint commonly is displayed by having an output cell on the left, a mathematical sign ($\leq$, $\geq$, or $=$) in the middle, and a data cell on the right. (Wyndor's three constraints involving hours available in the plants are displayed in Figures 2.2–2.4 by having output cells in column E, $\leq$ signs in column F, and data cells in column G.)

4. The decisions on activity levels are to be based on an overall measure of performance, which is entered in the *objective cell*. The goal is to either *maximize* the objective cell or *minimize* the objective cell, depending on the nature of the measure of performance. (Wyndor's overall measure of performance is the total profit per week from the two new products, so this measure has been entered in the objective cell G12, where the goal is to maximize this objective cell.)

5. The Excel equation for each *output cell* (including the objective cell) can be expressed as a SUMPRODUCT function,[2] where each term in the sum is the product of a *data cell* and a *changing cell*. (The bottom of Figure 2.3 shows how a SUMPRODUCT function is used for each output cell for the Wyndor problem.)

Linear programming models are not the only models that can have characteristics 1, 3, and 4. However, characteristics 2 and 5 are *key assumptions* of linear programming. Therefore, these are the two key characteristics that together differentiate a linear programming model from other kinds of mathematical models that can be formulated on a spreadsheet.

Characteristic 2 rules out situations where the activity levels need to have *integer* values. For example, such a situation would arise in the Wyndor problem if the decisions to be made were the *total* numbers of doors and windows to produce (which must be integers) rather than the numbers per week (which can have fractional values since a door or window can be started in one week and completed in the next week). When the activity levels do need to have integer values, a similar kind of model (called an *integer programming* model) is used instead by making a small adjustment on the spreadsheet, as will be illustrated in Section 3.2.

Characteristic 5 describes the so-called *proportionality assumption* of linear programming, which states that each term in an output cell must be proportional to a particular changing cell. This prohibits those cases where the Excel equation for an output cell cannot be expressed as a SUMPRODUCT function. To illustrate such a case, suppose that the weekly profit from producing Wyndor's new windows can be *more* than doubled by doubling the production rate because of economies in marketing larger amounts. This would mean that this weekly profit is *not* simply proportional to this production rate, so the Excel equation for the objective cell would need to be more complicated than a SUMPRODUCT function. Consideration of how to formulate such models will be deferred to Chapter 8.

Summary of the Formulation Procedure

The procedure used to formulate a linear programming model on a spreadsheet for the Wyndor problem can be adapted to many other problems as well. Here is a summary of the steps involved in the procedure.

1. Gather the data for the problem (such as summarized in Table 2.1 for the Wyndor problem).

2. Enter the data into *data cells* on a spreadsheet.

3. Identify the decisions to be made on the levels of activities and designate *changing cells* for displaying these decisions.

---

[2] There also are some special situations where a SUM function can be used instead because all the numbers that would have gone into the corresponding data cells are 1's.

4. Identify the constraints on these decisions and introduce *output cells* as needed to specify these constraints.
5. Choose the overall measure of performance to be entered into the *objective cell.*
6. Use a SUMPRODUCT function to enter the appropriate value into each output cell (including the objective cell).

This procedure does not spell out the details of how to set up the spreadsheet. There generally are alternative ways of doing this rather than a single "right" way. One of the great strengths of spreadsheets is their flexibility for dealing with a wide variety of problems.

Review
Questions

1. What are the three questions that need to be answered to begin the process of formulating a linear programming model on a spreadsheet?
2. What are the roles for the data cells, the changing cells, the output cells, and the objective cell when formulating such a model?
3. What is the form of the Excel equation for each output cell (including the objective cell) when formulating such a model?

2.3   THE MATHEMATICAL MODEL IN THE SPREADSHEET

A linear programming model can be formulated either as a spreadsheet model or as an algebraic model.

There are two widely used methods for formulating a linear programming model. One is to formulate it directly on a spreadsheet, as described in the preceding section. The other is to use algebra to present the model. The two versions of the model are equivalent. The only difference is whether the language of spreadsheets or the language of algebra is used to describe the model. Both versions have their advantages, and it can be helpful to be bilingual. For example, the two versions lead to different, but complementary, ways of analyzing problems like the Wyndor problem (as discussed in the next two sections). Since this book emphasizes the spreadsheet approach, we will only briefly describe the algebraic approach.

Formulating the Wyndor Model Algebraically

The reasoning for the algebraic approach is similar to that for the spreadsheet approach. In fact, except for making entries on a spreadsheet, the initial steps are just as described in the preceding section for the Wyndor problem.

1. Gather the relevant data (Table 2.1 in Section 2.1).
2. Identify the decisions to be made (the production rates for the two new products).
3. Identify the constraints on these decisions (the production time used in the respective plants cannot exceed the amount available).
4. Identify the overall measure of performance for these decisions (the total profit from the two products).
5. Convert the verbal description of the constraints and measure of performance into quantitative expressions in terms of the data and decisions (see below).

To start performing step 5, note that Table 2.1 indicates that the number of hours of production time available per week for the two new products in the respective plants are 4, 12, and 18. Using the data in this table for the number of hours used per door or window produced then leads to the following quantitative expressions for the constraints:

Plant 1:   (# of doors) $\leq$ 4
Plant 2:   2(# of windows) $\leq$ 12
Plant 3:   3(# of doors) + 2(# of windows) $\leq$ 18

In addition, negative production rates are impossible, so two other constraints on the decisions are

(# of doors) $\geq$ 0   (# of windows) $\geq$ 0

The overall measure of performance has been identified as the total profit from the two products. Since Table 2.1 gives the unit profits for doors and windows as $300 and $500, respectively, the expression obtained in the preceding section for the total profit per week from these products is

$$\text{Profit} = \$300(\text{\# of doors}) + \$500(\text{\# of windows})$$

The goal is to make the decisions (number of doors and number of windows) so as to maximize this profit, subject to satisfying all the constraints identified above.

To state this objective in a compact algebraic model, we introduce algebraic symbols to represent the measure of performance and the decisions. Let

P = Profit (total profit per week from the two products, in dollars)

D = # of doors (number of the special new doors to be produced per week)

W = # of windows (number of the special new windows to be produced per week)

Substituting these symbols into the above expressions for the constraints and the measure of performance (and dropping the dollar signs in the latter expression), the linear programming model for the Wyndor problem now can be written in algebraic form as shown below.

Algebraic Model

Choose the values of D and W so as to maximize

$$P = 300D + 500W$$

subject to satisfying all the following constraints:

$$D \leq 4$$
$$2W \leq 12$$
$$3D + 2W \leq 18$$

and

$$D \geq 0 \qquad W \geq 0$$

Terminology for Linear Programming Models

Much of the terminology of algebraic models also is sometimes used with spreadsheet models. Here are the key terms for both kinds of models in the context of the Wyndor problem.

1. D and W (or C12 and D12 in Figure 2.3) are the **decision variables.**
2. $300D + 500W$ [or SUMPRODUCT (UnitProfit, UnitsProduced)] is the **objective function.**
3. P (or G12) is the *value of the objective function* (or *objective value* for short).
4. $D \geq 0$ and $W \geq 0$ (or C12 ≥ 0 and D12 ≥ 0) are called the **nonnegativity constraints** (or *nonnegativity conditions*).
5. The other constraints are referred to as **functional constraints** (or *structural constraints*).
6. The **parameters** of the model are the constants in the algebraic model (the numbers in the data cells).
7. *Any* choice of values for the decision variables (regardless of how desirable or undesirable the choice) is called a **solution** for the model.
8. A **feasible solution** is one that satisfies all the constraints, whereas an **infeasible solution** violates at least one constraint.
9. The *best* feasible solution, the one that maximizes P (or G12), is called the **optimal solution.** (It is possible to have a *tie* for the best feasible solution, in which case all the tied solutions are called optimal solutions.)

Comparisons

Management scientists often use algebraic models, but managers generally prefer spreadsheet models.

So what are the relative advantages of algebraic models and spreadsheet models? An algebraic model provides a very concise and explicit statement of the problem. Sophisticated software packages that can solve huge problems generally are based on algebraic models because of both their compactness and their ease of use in rescaling the size of a problem.

Management science practitioners with an extensive mathematical background find algebraic models very useful. For others, however, spreadsheet models are far more intuitive. Both managers and business students training to be managers generally live with spreadsheets, not algebraic models. Therefore, the emphasis throughout this book is on spreadsheet models.

Review Questions

1. When formulating a linear programming model, what are the initial steps that are the same with either a spreadsheet formulation or an algebraic formulation?
2. When formulating a linear programming model algebraically, algebraic symbols need to be introduced to represent which kinds of quantities in the model?
3. What are decision variables for a linear programming model? The objective function? Non-negativity constraints? Functional constraints?
4. What is meant by a feasible solution for the model? An optimal solution?

2.4   THE GRAPHICAL METHOD FOR SOLVING TWO-VARIABLE PROBLEMS

graphical method
The graphical method provides helpful intuition about linear programming.

Linear programming problems having only two decision variables, like the Wyndor problem, can be solved by a **graphical method.**

Although this method cannot be used to solve problems with more than two decision variables (and most linear programming problems have far more than two), it still is well worth learning. The procedure provides geometric intuition about linear programming and what it is trying to achieve. This intuition is helpful in analyzing larger problems that cannot be solved directly by the graphical method.

It is more convenient to apply the graphical method to the *algebraic version* of the linear programming model rather than the spreadsheet version. We shall briefly illustrate the method by using the algebraic model obtained for the Wyndor problem in the preceding section. (A far more detailed description of the graphical method, including its application to the Wyndor problem, is provided in the supplement to this chapter on the CD-ROM.) For this purpose, keep in mind that

D = Production rate for the special new doors (the number in changing cell C12 of the spreadsheet)

W = Production rate for the special new windows (the number in changing cell D12 of the spreadsheet)

The key to the graphical method is the fact that possible solutions can be displayed as points on a two-dimensional graph that has a horizontal axis giving the value of D and a vertical axis giving the value of W. Figure 2.5 shows some sample points.

Notation: Either $(D, W) = (2, 3)$ or just $(2, 3)$ refers to the solution where $D = 2$ and $W = 3$, as well as to the corresponding point in the graph. Similarly, $(D, W) = (4, 6)$ means $D = 4$ and $W = 6$, whereas the origin $(0, 0)$ means $D = 0$ and $W = 0$.

To find the optimal solution (the best feasible solution), we first need to display graphically where the feasible solutions are. To do this, we must consider each constraint, identify the solutions graphically that are permitted by that constraint, and then combine this information to identify the solutions permitted by all the constraints. The solutions permitted by all the constraints are the feasible solutions and the portion of the two-dimensional graph where the feasible solutions lie is referred to as the **feasible region.**

feasible region
The points in the feasible region are those that satisfy *every* constraint.

The shaded region in Figure 2.6 shows the feasible region for the Wyndor problem. We now will outline how this feasible region was identified by considering the five constraints one at a time.

To begin, the constraint $D \geq 0$ implies that consideration must be limited to points that lie on or to the right of the W axis. Similarly, the constraint $W \geq 0$ restricts consideration to the points on or above the D axis.

Next, consider the first functional constraint, $D \leq 4$, which limits the usage of Plant 1 for producing the special new doors to a maximum of four hours per week. The solutions permitted by this constraint are those that lie on, or to the left of, the vertical line that intercepts the D axis at $D = 4$, as indicated by the arrows pointing to the left from this line in Figure 2.6.

34 Chapter Two *Linear Programming: Basic Concepts*

FIGURE 2.5

Graph showing the points
$(D, W) = (2, 3)$ and
$(D, W) = (4, 6)$ for the
Wyndor Glass Co.
product-mix problem.

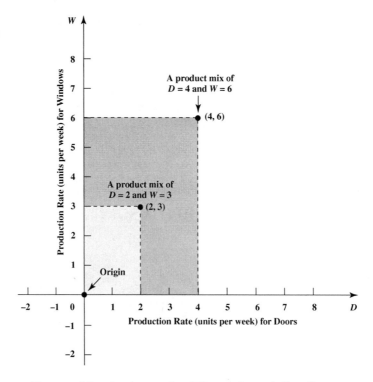

The second functional constraint, $2W \leq 12$, has a similar effect, except now the boundary of its permissible region is given by a *horizontal* line with the equation, $2W = 12$ (or $W = 6$), as indicated by the arrows pointing downward from this line in Figure 2.6. The line forming the boundary of what is permitted by a constraint is sometimes referred to as

FIGURE 2.6

Graph showing how the
feasible region is formed
by the constraint boundary lines, where the
arrows indicate which
side of each line is permitted by the corresponding
constraint.

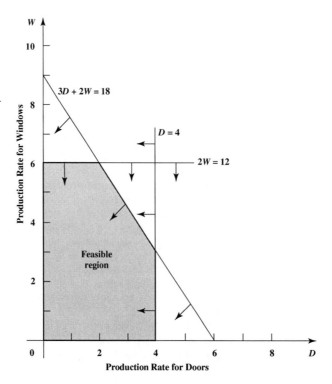

For any constraint with an inequality sign, its constraint boundary equation is obtained by replacing the inequality sign by an equality sign.

a **constraint boundary line,** and its equation may be called a **constraint boundary equation.** Frequently, a *constraint boundary line* is identified by its equation.

For each of the first two functional constraints, $D \leq 4$ and $2W \leq 12$, note that the equation for the constraint boundary line ($D = 4$ and $2W = 12$, respectively) is obtained by replacing the inequality sign with an equality sign. For *any* constraint with an inequality sign (whether a functional constraint or a nonnegativity constraint), the general rule for obtaining its constraint boundary equation is to substitute an equality sign for the inequality sign.

We now need to consider one more functional constraint, $3D + 2W \leq 18$. Its constraint boundary equation

$$3D + 2W = 18$$

includes both variables, so the boundary line it represents is neither a vertical line nor a horizontal line. Therefore, the boundary line must intercept (cross through) both axes somewhere. But where?

> When a constraint boundary line is neither a vertical line nor a horizontal line, the line *intercepts* the D axis at the point on the line where $W = 0$. Similarly, the line *intercepts* the W axis at the point on the line where $D = 0$.

Hence, the constraint boundary line $3D + 2W = 18$ intercepts the D axis at the point where $W = 0$.

When $W = 0$, $3D + 2W = 18$ becomes $3D = 18$
so the intercept with the D axis is at $D = 6$

The location of a slanting constraint boundary line is found by identifying where it intercepts each of the two axes.

Similarly, the line intercepts the W axis where $D = 0$.

When $D = 0$, $3D + 2W = 18$ becomes $2W = 18$
so the intercept with the D axis is at $W = 9$

Consequently, the constraint boundary line is the line that passes through these two intercept points, as shown in Figure 2.6.

Checking whether (0, 0) satisfies a constraint indicates which side of the constraint boundary line satisfies the constraint.

As indicated by the arrows emanating from this line in Figure 2.6, the solutions permitted by the constraint $3D + 2W \leq 18$ are those that lie on the *origin* side of the constraint boundary line $3D + 2W = 18$. The easiest way to verify this is to check whether the origin itself, $(D, W) = (0, 0)$, satisfies the constraint.[3] If it does, then the permissible region lies on the side of the constraint boundary line where the origin is. Otherwise, it lies on the other side. In this case,

$$3(0) + 2(0) = 0$$

so $(D, W) = (0, 0)$ satisfies

$$3D + 2W \leq 18$$

(In fact, the origin satisfies *any* constraint with a $\leq$ sign and a positive right-hand side.)

A feasible solution for a linear programming problem must satisfy *all* the constraints *simultaneously.* The arrows in Figure 2.6 indicate that the nonnegative solutions permitted by each of these constraints lie on the side of the constraint boundary line where the origin is (or on the line itself). Therefore, the *feasible solutions* are those that lie nearer to the origin than *all three* constraint boundary lines (or on the line nearest the origin).

Having identified the feasible region, the final step is to find which of these feasible solutions is the best one—the *optimal solution.* For the Wyndor problem, the objective happens to be to *maximize* the total profit per week from the two products (denoted by P). Therefore, we want to find the feasible solution (D, W) that makes the value of the objective function

$$P = 300D + 500W$$

as large as possible.

To accomplish this, we need to be able to locate all the points (D, W) on the graph that give a specified value of the objective function. For example, consider a value of $P = 1,500$ for the objective function. Which points (D, W) give $300D + 500W = 1,500$?

---

[3] The one case where using the origin to help determine the permissible region does *not* work is if the constraint boundary line passes through the origin. In this case, any other point *not* lying on this line can be used just like the origin.

36 Chapter Two   *Linear Programming: Basic Concepts*

This equation is the equation of a *line*. Just as when plotting constraint boundary lines, the location of this line is found by identifying its intercepts with the two axes. When $W = 0$, this equation yields $D = 5$, and similarly, $W = 3$ when $D = 0$, so these are the two intercepts, as shown by the bottom slanting line passing through the feasible region in Figure 2.7.

$P = 1,500$ is just one sample value of the objective function. For any other specified value of P, the points (D, W) that give this value of P also lie on a line called an *objective function line*.

An **objective function line** is a line whose points all have the same value of the objective function.

For the bottom objective function line in Figure 2.7, the points on this line that lie in the feasible region provide alternate ways of achieving an objective function value of $P = 1,500$. Can we do better? Let us try doubling the value of P to $P = 3,000$. The corresponding objective function line

$$300D + 500W = 3,000$$

is shown as the middle line in Figure 2.7. (Ignore the top line for the moment.) Once again, this line includes points in the feasible region, so $P = 3,000$ is achievable.

Let us pause to note two interesting features of these objective function lines for $P = 1,500$ and $P = 3,000$. First, these lines are *parallel*. Second, *doubling* the value of P from 1,500 to 3,000 also *doubles* the value of W at which the line intercepts the W axis from $W = 3$ to $W = 6$. These features are no coincidence, as indicated by the following properties.

Key Properties of Objective Function Lines: All objective function lines for the same problem are *parallel*. Furthermore, the value of W at which an objective function line intercepts the W axis is *proportional* to the value of P.

These key properties of objective function lines suggest the strategy to follow to find the optimal solution. We already have tried $P = 1,500$ and $P = 3,000$ in Figure 2.7 and found that their objective function lines include points in the feasible region. Increasing P again will generate another parallel objective function line farther from the origin. The objective function line of special interest is the one farthest from the origin that still includes a point in the feasible region. This is the third objective function line in Figure 2.7. The point on this line

FIGURE 2.7

Graph showing three objective function lines for the Wyndor Glass Co. product-mix problem, where the top one passes through the optimal solution.

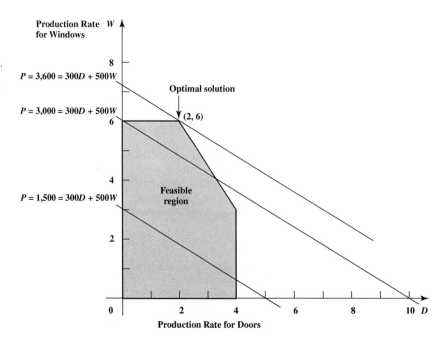

that is in the feasible region, $(D, W) = (2, 6)$, is the optimal solution since no other feasible solution has a larger value of P.

Optimal Solution

> $D = 2$ (Produce 2 special new doors per week)
>
> $W = 6$ (Produce 6 special new windows per week)

These values of D and W can be substituted into the objective function to find the value of P.

$$P = 300D + 500W = 300(2) + 500(6) = 3,600$$

This has been a fairly quick description of the graphical method. You can go to the supplement to this chapter on the CD-ROM if you would like to see a fuller description of how to use the graphical method to solve the Wyndor problem.

Check out this module in the Interactive Management Science Modules to learn more about the graphical method.

The Interactive Management Science Modules (available at **www.mhhe.com/hillier5e** or in your CD-ROM) also includes a module that is designed to help increase your understanding of the graphical method. This module, called *Graphical Linear Programming and Sensitivity Analysis,* enables you to immediately see the constraint boundary lines and objective function lines that result from any linear programming model with two decision variables. You also can see how the objective function lines lead you to the optimal solution. Another key feature of the module is the ease with which you can use the graphical method to perform *what-if analysis* to see *what* happens *if* any changes occur in the data for the problem. (We will focus on what-if analysis for linear programming, including the role of the graphical method for this kind of analysis, in Chapter 5.)

This module also can be used to check out how unusual situations can arise when solving linear programming problems. For example, it is possible for a problem to have *multiple* solutions that tie for being an optimal solution. (*Hint*: See what happens if the unit profit for the windows in the Wyndor problem were reduced to $200.) It is possible for a problem to have *no* optimal solutions because it has no feasible solutions. (*Hint*: See what happens if the Wyndor management decides to require that the total number of doors and windows produced per week must be at least 10 to justify introducing these new products.) Still another remote possibility is that a linear programming model has no optimal solution because the constraints do not prevent increasing (when maximizing) the objective function value indefinitely. (*Hint*: See what happens when the functional constraints for Plants 2 and 3 in the Wyndor problem are inadvertently left out of the model.) Try it. (See Problem 2.17.)

Summary of the Graphical Method

The graphical method can be used to solve any linear programming problem having only two decision variables. The method uses the following steps:

1. Draw the constraint boundary line for each functional constraint. Use the origin (or any point not on the line) to determine which side of the line is permitted by the constraint.
2. Find the feasible region by determining where all constraints are satisfied simultaneously.
3. Determine the slope of one objective function line. All other objective function lines will have the same slope.
4. Move a straight edge with this slope through the feasible region in the direction of improving values of the objective function. Stop at the last instant that the straight edge still passes through a point in the feasible region. This line given by the straight edge is the optimal objective function line.
5. A feasible point on the optimal objective function line is an optimal solution.

Review
Questions

1. The graphical method can be used to solve linear programming problems with how many decision variables?
2. What do the axes represent when applying the graphical method to the Wyndor problem?
3. What is a constraint boundary line? A constraint boundary equation?
4. What is the easiest way of determining which side of a constraint boundary line is permitted by the constraint?

2.5   USING EXCEL'S SOLVER TO SOLVE LINEAR PROGRAMMING PROBLEMS

Excel Tip: If you select cells by clicking on them, they will first appear in the dialog box with their cell addresses and with dollar signs (e.g., *C9:D9*). You can ignore the dollar signs. Solver eventually will replace both the cell addresses and the dollar signs with the corresponding range name (if a range name has been defined for the given cell addresses), but only after either adding a constraint or closing and reopening the Solver dialog box.

Solver Tip: To select changing cells, click and drag across the range of cells. If the changing cells are not contiguous, you can type a comma and then select another range of cells. Up to 200 changing cells can be selected with the basic version of Solver that comes with Excel.

The Add Constraint dialog box is used to specify all the functional constraints.

When solving a linear programming problem, be sure to specify that nonnegativity constraints are needed and that the model is linear by choosing Simplex LP.

Solver Tip: The message "Solver could not find a feasible solution" means that there are no solutions that satisfy all the constraints. The message "The Objective Cell values do not converge" means that Solver could not find a best solution, because better solutions always are available (e.g., if the constraints do not prevent infinite profit). The message "The linearity conditions required by this LP Solver are not satisfied" means Simplex LP was chosen as the Solving Method, but the model is not linear.

The graphical method is very useful for gaining geometric intuition about linear programming, but its practical use is severely limited by only being able to solve tiny problems with two decision variables. Another procedure that will solve linear programming problems of any reasonable size is needed. Fortunately, Excel includes a tool called **Solver** that will do this once the spreadsheet model has been formulated as described in Section 2.2. (Section 2.6 will show how Risk Solver Platform, which includes a more advanced version of Solver, can be used to solve this same problem.) To access Solver the first time, you need to install it. Click the Office Button, choose Excel Options, then click on Add-Ins on the left side of the window, select Manage Excel Add-Ins at the bottom of the window, and then press the Go button. Make sure Solver is selected in the Add-Ins dialog box, and then it should appear on the Data tab. For Excel 2011 (for the Mac), go to **www.solver.com/mac** to download and install the Solver application.

Figure 2.3 in Section 2.2 shows the spreadsheet model for the Wyndor problem. The values of the decision variables (the production rates for the two products) are in the *changing cells,* UnitsProduced (C12:D12), and the value of the objective function (the total profit per week from the two products) is in the *objective cell* TotalProfit (G12). To get started, an arbitrary trial solution has been entered by placing zeroes in the changing cells. Solver will then change these to the optimal values after solving the problem.

This procedure is started by choosing Solver on the Data tab (for Excel 2007 or 2010 on a PC), or choosing Solver in the Tools menu (for Excel 2011 on a Mac). Figure 2.8 shows the Solver dialog box that is used to tell Solver where each component of the model is located on the spreadsheet.

You have the choice of typing the range names, typing the cell addresses, or clicking on the cells in the spreadsheet. Figure 2.8 shows the result of using the first choice, so TotalProfit (rather than G12) has been entered for the objective cell. Since the goal is to maximize the objective cell, Max also has been selected. The next entry in the Solver dialog box identifies the *changing cells,* which are UnitsProduced (C12:D12) for the Wyndor problem.

Next, the cells containing the functional constraints need to be specified. This is done by clicking on the Add button on the Solver dialog box. This brings up the Add Constraint dialog box shown in Figure 2.9. The ≤ signs in cells F7, F8, and F9 of Figure 2.3 are a reminder that the cells in HoursUsed (E7:E9) all need to be less than or equal to the corresponding cells in HoursAvailable (G7:G9). These constraints are specified for Solver by entering HoursUsed (or E7:E9) on the left-hand side of the Add Constraint dialog box and HoursAvailable (or G7:G9) on the right-hand side. For the sign between these two sides, there is a menu to choose between <=, =, or >=, so <= has been chosen. This choice is needed even though ≤ signs were previously entered in column F of the spreadsheet because the Solver only uses the constraints that are specified with the Add Constraint dialog box.

If there were more functional constraints to add, you would click on Add to bring up a new Add Constraint dialog box. However, since there are no more in this example, the next step is to click on OK to go back to the Solver dialog box.

Before asking Solver to solve the model, two more steps need to be taken. We need to tell Solver that nonnegativity constraints are needed for the changing cells to reject negative production rates. We also need to specify that this is a *linear* programming problem so the simplex method (the standard method used by Solver to solve linear programming problems) can be used. This is demonstrated in Figure 2.10, where the *Make Unconstrained Variables Non-Negative* option has been checked and the *Solving Method* chosen is *Simplex LP* (rather than *GRG Nonlinear* or *Evolutionary,* which are used for solving nonlinear problems). The Solver dialog box shown in this figure now summarizes the complete model.

Now you are ready to click on Solve in the Solver dialog box, which will start the solving of the problem in the background. After a few seconds (for a small problem), Solver will then indicate the results. Typically, it will indicate that it has found an optimal solution, as specified in the Solver Results dialog box shown in Figure 2.11. If the model has no feasible solutions or no optimal solution, the dialog box will indicate that instead by stating that

FIGURE 2.8

The Solver dialog box after specifying the first components of the model for the Wyndor problem. TotalProfit (G12) is being maximized by changing UnitsProduced (C12:D12). Figure 2.9 will demonstrate the addition of constraints and then Figure 2.10 will demonstrate the changes needed to specify that the problem being considered is a linear programming problem. (The default *Solving Method* shown here—*GRG Nonlinear*—is not applicable to linear programming problems.)

The Incomplete Solver Dialog Box

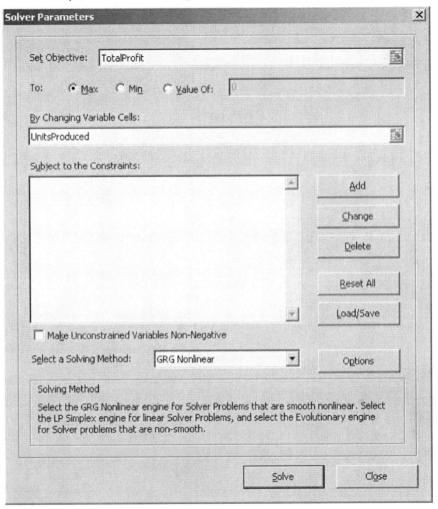

"Solver could not find a feasible solution" or that "The Objective Cell values do not converge." (Section 14.1 will describe how these possibilities can occur.) The dialog box also presents the option of generating various reports. One of these (the Sensitivity Report) will be discussed in detail in Chapter 5.

FIGURE 2.9

The Add Constraint dialog box after specifying that cells E7, E8, and E9 in Figure 2.3 are required to be less than or equal to cells G7, G8, and G9, respectively.

40   Chapter Two   *Linear Programming: Basic Concepts*

FIGURE 2.10
The completed Solver dialog box after specifying the entire model in terms of the spreadsheet.

The Completed Solver Dialog Box

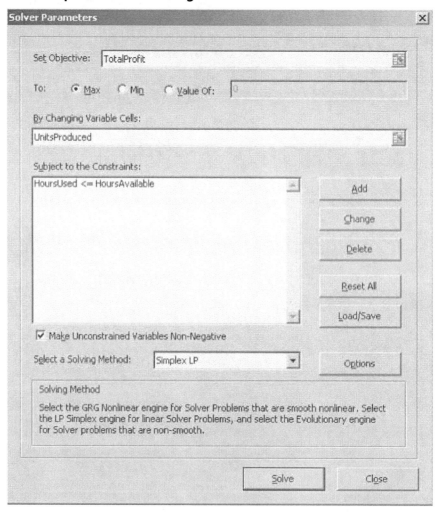

After solving the model and clicking OK in the Solver Results dialog box, Solver replaces the original numbers in the changing cells with the optimal numbers, as shown in Figure 2.12. Thus, the optimal solution is to produce two doors per week and six windows per week, just as was found by the graphical method in the preceding section. The spreadsheet also indicates the corresponding number in the objective cell (a total profit of $3,600 per week), as well as the numbers in the output cells HoursUsed (E7:E9).

The entries needed for the Solver dialog box are summarized in the *Solver Parameters* box shown on the bottom left of Figure 2.12. This more compact summary of the Solver Parameters will be shown for all of the many models that involve the Solver throughout the book.

At this point, you might want to check what would happen to the optimal solution if any of the numbers in the data cells were to be changed to other possible values. This is easy to do because Solver saves all the addresses for the objective cell, changing cells, constraints, and so on when you save the file. All you need to do is make the changes you want in the data cells and then click on Solve in the Solver dialog box again. (Chapter 5 will focus on this kind of *what-if analysis,* including how to use the Solver's Sensitivity Report to expedite the analysis.)

FIGURE 2.11

The Solver Results dialog box that indicates that an optimal solution has been found.

Solver Results ☒

Solver found a solution. All Constraints and optimality conditions are satisfied.

Reports
Answer
Sensitivity
Limits

⦿ Keep Solver Solution
◯ Restore Original Values

☐ Return to Solver Parameters Dialog   ☐ Outline Reports

OK   Cancel   Save Scenario...

Solver found a solution. All Constraints and optimality conditions are satisfied.

When the GRG engine is used, Solver has found at least a local optimal solution. When Simplex LP is used, this means Solver has found a global optimal solution.

FIGURE 2.12

The spreadsheet obtained after solving the Wyndor problem.

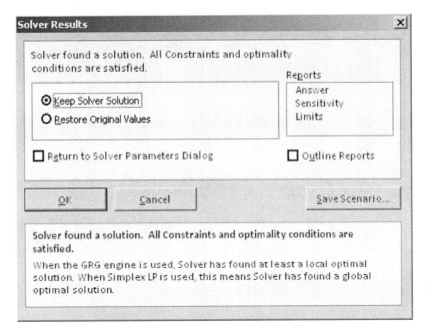

	A	B	C	D	E	F	G
1		**Wyndor Glass Co. Product-Mix Problem**					
2							
3			**Doors**	**Windows**			
4		Unit Profit	$300	$500			
5					Hours		Hours
6			Hours Used per Unit Produced		Used		Available
7		Plant 1	1	0	2	≤	4
8		Plant 2	0	2	12	≤	12
9		Plant 3	3	2	18	≤	18
10							
11			**Doors**	**Windows**			**Total Profit**
12		Units Produced	2	6			$3,600

Solver Parameters

Set Objective Cell: Total Profit
To: Max
By Changing Variable Cells:
  UnitsProduced
Subject to the Constraints:
  HoursUsed <= HoursAvailable

Solver Options:
  Make Variables Nonnegative
  Solving Method: Simplex LP

	E
5	Hours
6	Used
7	=SUMPRODUCT(C7:D7, UnitsProduced)
8	=SUMPRODUCT(C8:D8, UnitsProduced)
9	=SUMPRODUCT(C9:D9, UnitsProduced)

	G
11	Total Profit
12	=SUMPRODUCT(UnitProfit, UnitsProduced)

Range Name	Cell
HoursAvailable	G7:G9
HoursUsed	E7:E9
HoursUsedPerUnitProduced	C7:D9
TotalProfit	G12
UnitProfit	C4:D4
UnitsProduced	C12:D12

To assist you with experimenting with these kinds of changes, your MS Courseware includes Excel files for this chapter (as for others) that provide a complete formulation and solution of the examples here (the Wyndor problem and the one in Section 2.7) in a spreadsheet format. We encourage you to "play" with these examples to see what happens with different data, different solutions, and so forth. You might also find these spreadsheets useful as templates for homework problems.

Review
Questions

1. Which dialog box is used to enter the addresses for the objective cell and the changing cells?
2. Which dialog box is used to specify the functional constraints for the model?
3. Which options normally need to be chosen to solve a linear programming model?

2.6   RISK SOLVER PLATFORM FOR EDUCATION (RSPE)

Frontline Systems, the original developer of the standard Solver included with Excel (hereafter referred to as Excel's Solver), also has developed Premium versions of Solver that provide greatly enhanced functionality. The company now features a particularly powerful Premium Solver called *Risk Solver Platform*. New with this edition, we are excited to provide access to the Excel add-in, Risk Solver Platform for Education (RSPE) from Frontline Systems. Instructions for installing this software are on a supplementary insert included with the book and also on the book's website, **www.mhhe.com/hillier5e**.

While Excel's Solver is sufficient for most of the problems considered in this book, RSPE includes a number of important features not available with Excel's Solver. Where either Excel's Solver or RSPE can be used, the book will often use the term Solver generically to mean either Excel's Solver or RSPE. Where there are differences, the book will include instructions for both Excel's Solver and RSPE. The enhanced features of RSPE will be highlighted as they come up throughout the book. However, if you and your instructor prefer to focus on only using Excel's Solver, you will find that there is plenty of material to cover in the book that does not require the use of RSPE.

When RSPE is installed, a new tab is available on the Excel ribbon called Risk Solver Platform. Choosing this tab will reveal the ribbon shown in Figure 2.13. The buttons on this ribbon will be used to interact with RSPE. This same figure also reveals a nice feature of RSPE—the Solver Options and Model Specifications pane (showing the objective cell, changing cells, constraints, etc.)—that can be seen alongside your main spreadsheet, with both visible simultaneously. This pane can be toggled on (to see the model) or off (to hide the model and leave more room for the spreadsheet) by clicking on the Model button on the far left of the Risk Solver Platform ribbon. Also, since the model was already set up with Excel's Solver in Section 2.5, it is already set up in the RSPE Model pane, with the objective specified as TotalProfit (G12) with changing cells UnitsProduced (C12:D12) and the constraints HoursUsed (E7:E9) <= HoursAvailable (G7:G9). The data for Excel's Solver and RSPE are compatible with each other. Making a change with one makes the same change in the other. Thus, you can work with either Excel's Solver or RSPE, and then go back and forth, without losing any Solver data.

If the model had not been previously set up with Excel's Solver, the steps for doing so with RSPE are analogous to the steps used with Excel's Solver as covered in Section 2.5. In both cases, we need to specify the location of the objective cell, the changing cells, and the functional constraints, and then click to solve the model. However, the user interface is somewhat different. RSPE uses the buttons on the Risk Solver Platform ribbon instead of the Solver dialog box. We will now walk you through the steps to set up the Wyndor problem in RSPE.

To specify TotalProfit (G12) as the objective cell, select the cell in the spreadsheet and then click on the Objective button on the Risk Solver Platform ribbon. As shown in Figure 2.14, this will drop down a menu where you can choose to minimize (Min) or maximize (Max) the objective cell. Within the options of Min or Max are further options (Normal, Expected, VaR, etc.). For now, we will always choose the Normal option.

FIGURE 2.13

The screenshot for the Wyndor problem that shows both the ribbon and the *Solver Options and Model Specifications pane* that are revealed after choosing the tab called Risk Solver Platform on the Excel ribbon.

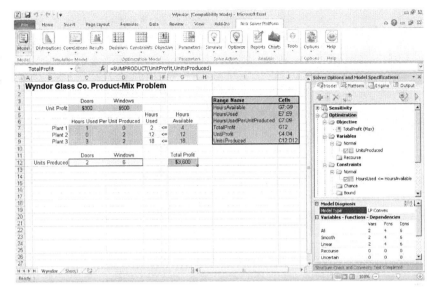

FIGURE 2.14

The screenshot for the Wyndor problem that shows the drop-down menu generated by clicking on the Objective button on the Risk Solver Platform ribbon after choosing TotalProfit (G12) as the objective cell.

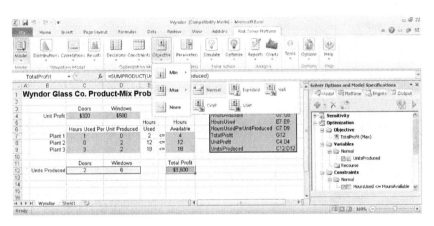

RSPE Tip: Another way to add an objective, changing cells, or constraints using RSPE is to click on the big green plus (+) on the Mode pane and choose Add Objective, Add Variable, or Add Constraint, respectively.

To specify UnitsProduced (C12:D12) as the changing cells, select these cells in the spreadsheet and then click on the Decisions button on the Risk Solver Platform ribbon. As shown in Figure 2.15, this will drop down a menu where you can choose various options (Plot, Normal, Recourse). For linear programming, we will always choose the Normal option.

Next the functional constraints need to be specified. For the Wyndor problem, the functional constraints are HoursUsed (E7:E9) <= HoursAvailable (G7:G9). To enter these constraints in RSPE, select the cells representing the left-hand side of these constraints (HoursUsed, or E7:E9) and click the Constraints button on the Risk Solver Platform ribbon. As shown in Figure 2.16, this drops down a menu for various kinds of constraints. For linear programming functional constraints, choose Normal Constraint and then the type of constraint desired (either <=, =, or >=). For the Wyndor problem, choosing <= would then bring up the Add Constraint dialog box shown in Figure 2.17. This is much like the Add Constraint dialog box for Excel's Solver (see Figure 2.9). HoursUsed and <= already are filled in when the Add Constraint dialog box is brought up (because the HoursUsed cells were selected and <= was chosen under the Constraints button menu). The Add Constraint dialog box then can be used to fill in the remaining right-hand side of the constraint—HoursAvailable (G7:G9)—by clicking in the box labeled Constraint and choosing these cells on the spreadsheet. Figure 2.17 shows the dialog box after this has been done.

44   Chapter Two   *Linear Programming: Basic Concepts*

FIGURE 2.15

The screenshot for the Wyndor problem that shows the drop-down menu generated by clicking on the Decision button on the Risk Solver Platform ribbon after choosing UnitsProduced (C12:D12) as the changing variable cells.

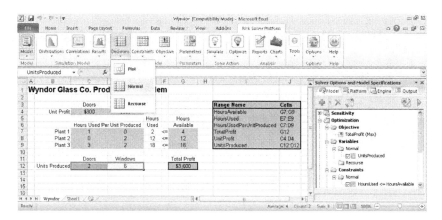

FIGURE 2.16

The screenshot of the Wyndor problem that shows the drop-down menu generated by clicking on the Constraints button on the Risk Solver Platform ribbon after choosing HoursUsed (E7:E9) as the left-hand side of the functional constraints.

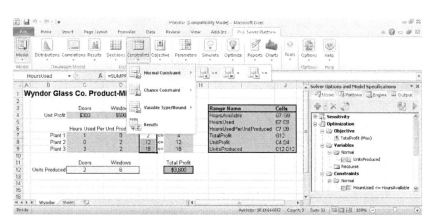

FIGURE 2.17

The Add Constraint dialog box that is brought up after choosing <= in Figure 2.16. This dialog box also shows HoursAvailable (G7:G9) as the right-hand side of the functional constraints after clicking in the Constraint box and choosing these cells on the spreadsheet.

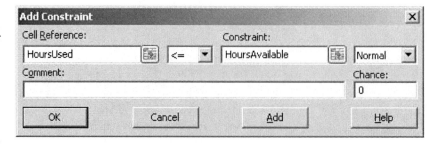

RSPE Tip: Double-clicking on any element of the model (e.g., the objective, any of the changing cells, or any of the constraints) will bring up a dialog box allowing you to make changes to that part of the model.

Changes to the model can easily be made within the Model pane shown in Figure 2.13. For example, to delete an element of the model (e.g., the objective, changing cells, or constraints), select that part of the model and then click on the red X near the top of the Model pane. To change an element of the model, click on that element in the Model pane. The bottom of the Model pane will then show information about that element. For example, clicking on the HoursUsed <= HoursAvailable constraint in the Model pane will then show the information seen in Figure 2.18. Clicking on any piece of the information will allow you to change it (e.g., you can change <= to >=, or you can change the cell references for either side of the constraint).

Selecting the Engine tab at the top of the Model pane will show information about the algorithm that will be used to solve the problem as well as a variety of options for that algorithm.

FIGURE 2.18
This figure shows the result of clicking on the HoursUsed <= Hours Available constraint in the Model pane prior to considering possible changes in the constraint.

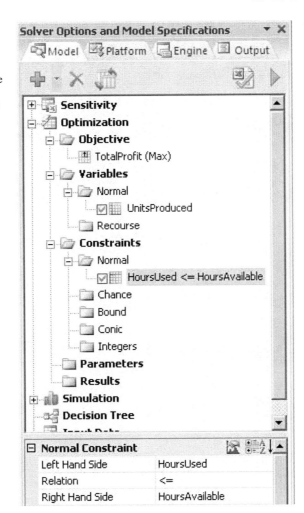

The drop-down menu at the top will allow you to choose the algorithm. For a linear programming model (such as the Wyndor problem), you will want to choose the Standard LP/ Quadratic Engine. This is equivalent to the Simplex LP option in Excel's Solver. To make unconstrained variables nonnegative (as we did in Figure 2.10 with Excel's Solver), be sure that the Assume Nonnegative option is set to true. Figure 2.19 shows the model pane after making these selections.

Once the model is all set up in RSPE, the model would be solved by clicking on the Optimize button on the Risk Solver Platform ribbon. Just like Excel's Solver, this will then display the results of solving the model on the spreadsheet, as shown in Figure 2.20. As seen in this figure, the Output tab of the Model pane also will show a summary of the solution process, including the message (similar to Figure 2.11) that "Solver found a solution. All constraints and optimality conditions are satisfied."

Review
Questions

1. Which button on the Risk Solver Platform ribbon should be pressed to specify the objective cell?
2. Which button on the Risk Solver Platform ribbon should be pressed to specify the changing cells?
3. Which button on the Risk Solver Platform ribbon should be pressed to enter the constraints?
4. Which button on the Risk Solver Platform ribbon should be pressed to solve the model?

46   Chapter Two   *Linear Programming: Basic Concepts*

FIGURE 2.19

The model pane after selecting the Standard LP/Quadratic Engine and setting the Assume Non-negative option to True.

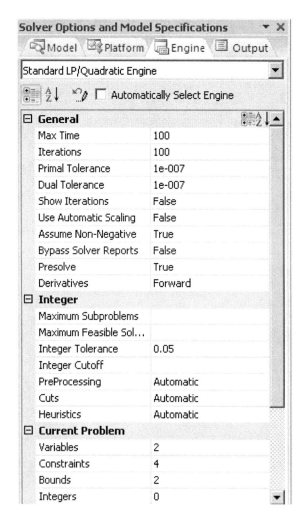

FIGURE 2.20

A screen shot showing the final solution of the Wyndor problem and the Output tab of the model pane showing a summary of the solution process.

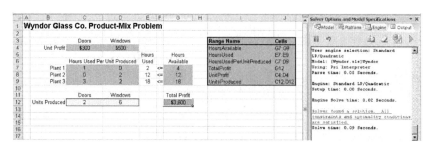

2.7   A MINIMIZATION EXAMPLE—THE PROFIT & GAMBIT CO. ADVERTISING-MIX PROBLEM

The analysis of the Wyndor Glass Co. case study in Sections 2.2, 2.5, and 2.6 illustrated how to formulate and solve one type of linear programming model on a spreadsheet. The same general approach can be applied to many other problems as well. The great flexibility of linear programming and spreadsheets provides a variety of options for how to adapt the formulation of the spreadsheet model to fit each new problem. Our next example illustrates some options not used for the Wyndor problem.

Planning an Advertising Campaign

The **Profit & Gambit Co.** produces cleaning products for home use. This is a highly competitive market, and the company continually struggles to increase its small market share. Management has decided to undertake a major new advertising campaign that will focus on the following three key products:

- A spray prewash stain remover.
- A liquid laundry detergent.
- A powder laundry detergent.

This campaign will use both television and the print media. A commercial has been developed to run on national television that will feature the liquid detergent. The advertisement for the print media will promote all three products and will include cents-off coupons that consumers can use to purchase the products at reduced prices. The general goal is to increase the sales of each of these products (but especially the liquid detergent) over the next year by a significant percentage over the past year. Specifically, management has set the following goals for the campaign:

- Sales of the stain remover should increase by at least 3 percent.
- Sales of the liquid detergent should increase by at least 18 percent.
- Sales of the powder detergent should increase by at least 4 percent.

Table 2.2 shows the estimated increase in sales for each *unit* of advertising in the respective outlets.[4] (A *unit* is a standard block of advertising that Profit & Gambit commonly purchases, but other amounts also are allowed.) The reason for -1 percent for the powder detergent in the Television column is that the TV commercial featuring the new liquid detergent will take away some sales from the powder detergent. The bottom row of the table shows the cost per unit of advertising for each of the two outlets.

Management's objective is to determine how much to advertise in each medium to meet the sales goals at a minimum total cost.

Formulating a Spreadsheet Model for This Problem

The procedure summarized at the end of Section 2.2 can be used to formulate the spreadsheet model for this problem. Each step of the procedure is repeated below, followed by a description of how it is performed here.

1. Gather the data for the problem. This has been done as presented in Table 2.2.
2. Enter the data into *data cells* on a spreadsheet. The top half of Figure 2.21 shows this spreadsheet. The data cells are in columns C and D (rows 4 and 8 to 10), as well as in cells

TABLE 2.2
Data for the Profit & Gambit Co. Advertising-Mix Problem

Product	Increase in Sales per Unit of Advertising		Minimum Required Increase
	Television	Print Media	
Stain remover	0%	1%	3%
Liquid detergent	3	2	18
Powder detergent	−1	4	4
Unit cost	$1 million	$2 million	

[4] A simplifying assumption is being made that each additional unit of advertising in a particular outlet will yield the same increase in sales regardless of how much advertising already is being done. This becomes a poor assumption when the levels of advertising under consideration can reach a saturation level (as in Case 8.1), but is a reasonable approximation for the small levels of advertising being considered in this problem.

48   Chapter Two   *Linear Programming: Basic Concepts*

FIGURE 2.21

The spreadsheet model for the Profit & Gambit problem, including the formulas for the objective cell TotalCost (G14) and the other output cells in column E, as well as the specifications needed to set up Solver. The changing cells, AdvertisingUnits (C14:D14), show the optimal solution obtained by Solver.

	A	B	C	D	E	F	G
1		**Profit & Gambit Co. Advertising-Mix Problem**					
2							
3			**Television**	**Print Media**			
4		Unit Cost ($millions)	1	2			
5							
6					Increased		Minimum
7			Increase in Sales per Unit of Advertising		Sales		Increase
8		Stain Remover	0%	1%	3%	≥	3%
9		Liquid Detergent	3%	2%	18%	≥	18%
10		Powder Detergent	-1%	4%	8%	≥	4%
11							
12							**Total Cost**
13			**Television**	**Print Media**			**($millions)**
14		Advertising Units	4	3			10

Solver Parameters
Set Objective Cell: TotalCost
To: Min
By Changing (Variable) Cells:
AdvertisingUnits
Subject to the Constraints:
IncreasedSales >= MinimumIncrease
Solver Options:
Make Variables Nonnegative
Solving Method: Simplex LP

	E
6	Increased
7	Sales
8	=SUMPRODUCT(C8:D8, AdvertisingUnits)
9	=SUMPRODUCT(C9:D9, AdvertisingUnits)
10	=SUMPRODUCT(C10:D10, AdvertisingUnits)

	G
12	Total Cost
13	($millions)
14	=SUMPRODUCT(UnitCost, AdvertisingUnits)

Range Name	Cells
AdvertisingUnits	C14: D14
IncreasedSales	E8: E10
IncreasedSalesPerUnitAdvertising	C8: D10
MinimumIncrease	G8: G10
TotalCost	G14
UnitCost	C4: D4

G8:G10. Note how this particular formatting of the spreadsheet has facilitated a direct transfer of the data from Table 2.2.

3. Identify the decisions to be made on the levels of activities and designate *changing cells* for making these decisions. In this case, the activities of concern are *advertising on television* and *advertising in the print media,* so the *levels* of these activities refer to the *amount* of advertising in these media. Therefore, the decisions to be made are

Decision 1: TV = Number of units of advertising on television

Decision 2: PM = Number of units of advertising in the print media

The two gray cells with light borders in Figure 2.21—C14 and D14—have been designated as the changing cells to hold these numbers:

TV → cell C14   PM → cell D14

with AdvertisingUnits as the range name for these cells. (See the bottom of Figure 2.21 for a list of all the range names.) These are natural locations for the changing cells, since each one is in the column for the corresponding advertising medium. To get started, an arbitrary trial solution (such as all zeroes) is entered into these cells. (Figure 2.21 shows the optimal solution after having already applied Solver.)

4. Identify the constraints on these decisions and introduce *output cells* as needed to specify these constraints. The three constraints imposed by management are the goals for the increased sales for the respective products, as shown in the rightmost column of Table 2.2. These constraints are

> *Unlike the Wyndor problem, we need to use ≥ signs for these constraints.*

Stain remover:	Total increase in sales ≥ 3%
Liquid detergent:	Total increase in sales ≥ 18%
Powder detergent:	Total increase in sales ≥ 4%

The second and third columns of Table 2.2 indicate that the *total* increases in sales from both forms of advertising are

Total for stain remover	= 1% of PM
Total for liquid detergent	= 3% of TV + 2% of PM
Total for powder detergent	= −1% of TV + 4% of PM

Consequently, since rows 8, 9, and 10 in the spreadsheet are being used to provide information about the three products, cells E8, E9, and E10 are introduced as output cells to show the total increase in sales for the respective products. In addition, ≥ signs have been entered in column F to remind us that the increased sales need to be at least as large as the numbers in column G. (The use of ≥ signs here rather than ≤ signs is one key difference from the spreadsheet model for the Wyndor problem in Figure 2.3.)

> *Unlike the Wyndor problem, the objective now is to minimize the objective cell.*

5. Choose the overall measure of performance to be entered into the *objective cell.* Management's stated objective is to determine how much to advertise in each medium to meet the sales goals at a *minimum total cost.* Therefore, the *total cost* of the advertising is entered in the objective cell TotalCost (G14). G14 is a natural location for this cell since it is in the same row as the changing cells. The bottom row of Table 2.2 indicates that the number going into this cell is

$$\text{Cost} = (\$1 \text{ million}) \text{ TV} + (\$2 \text{ million}) \text{ PM} \rightarrow \text{cell G14}$$

6. Use a SUMPRODUCT function to enter the appropriate value into each output cell (including the objective cell). Based on the above expressions for cost and total increases in sales, the SUMPRODUCT functions needed here for the output cells are those shown under the right side of the spreadsheet in Figure 2.21. Note that each of these functions involves the relevant data cells and the changing cells, AdvertisingUnits (C14:D14).

This spreadsheet model is a linear programming model, since it possesses all the characteristics of such models enumerated in Section 2.2.

Applying Solver to This Model

The procedure for using Solver to obtain an optimal solution for this model is basically the same as described in Section 2.5 (for Excel's Solver) or Section 2.6 (for RSPE). The Solver parameters are shown below the left-hand side of the spreadsheet in Figure 2.21. In addition to specifying the objective cell and changing cells, the constraints that IncreasedSales ≥ MinimumIncrease have been specified in this box by using the Add Constraint dialog box. Since the objective is to *minimize* total cost, Min also has been selected. (This is in contrast to the choice of Max for the Wyndor problem.)

Two options are also specified at the bottom of the Solver Parameters box on the lower left-hand side of Figure 2.21. The changing cells need nonnegativity constraints (specified in the main Solver dialog box in Excel's Solver, or on the Engine tab of the Model pane in RSPE) because negative values of advertising levels are not possible alternatives. Choosing the Simplex LP solving method in Excel's Solver (or the Standard LP/Quadratic Engine in RSPE) specifies that this is a linear programming model.

After running Solver, the optimal solution shown in the changing cells of the spreadsheet in Figure 2.21 is obtained.

An Application Vignette

Samsung Electronics Corp., Ltd. (SEC), is a leading merchant of dynamic and static random access memory devices and other advanced digital integrated circuits. Its site at Kiheung, South Korea (probably the largest semiconductor fabrication site in the world), fabricates more than 300,000 silicon wafers per month and employs over 10,000 people.

Cycle time is the industry's term for the elapsed time from the release of a batch of blank silicon wafers into the fabrication process until completion of the devices that are fabricated on those wafers. Reducing cycle times is an ongoing goal since it both decreases costs and enables offering shorter lead times to potential customers, a real key to maintaining or increasing market share in a very competitive industry.

Three factors present particularly major challenges when striving to reduce cycle times. One is that the product mix changes continually. Another is that the company often needs to make substantial changes in the fab-out schedule inside the target cycle time as it revises forecasts

of customer demand. The third is that the machines of a general type are not homogeneous so only a small number of machines are qualified to perform each device step.

A management science team developed a *huge linear programming model with tens of thousands of decision variables and functional constraints* to cope with these challenges. The objective function involved minimizing back-orders and finished-goods inventory.

The ongoing implementation of this model enabled the company to reduce manufacturing cycle times to fabricate dynamic random access memory devices from more than 80 days to less than 30 days. This tremendous improvement and the resulting reduction in both manufacturing costs and sale prices enabled Samsung to capture *an additional* **$200 million** *in annual sales revenue.*

Source: R. C. Leachman, J. Kang, and Y. Lin, "SLIM: Short Cycle Time and Low Inventory in Manufacturing at Samsung Electronics," *Interfaces* 32, no. 1 (January–February 2002), pp. 61–77. (A link to this article is provided on our website, **www.mhhe.com/hillier5e.**)

Optimal Solution

C14 = 4 (Undertake 4 units of advertising on television)

C14 = 3 (Undertake 3 units of advertising in the print media)

The objective cell indicates that the total cost of this advertising plan would be $10 million.

The Mathematical Model in the Spreadsheet

When performing step 5 of the procedure for formulating a spreadsheet model, the total cost of advertising was determined to be

$$\text{Cost} = \text{TV} + 2\,\text{PM} \ (\text{in millions of dollars})$$

where the goal is to choose the values of TV (number of units of advertising on television) and PM (number of units of advertising in the print media) so as to minimize this cost. Step 4 identified three functional constraints:

Stain remover:	1% of PM $\geq$ 3%
Liquid detergent:	3% of TV + 2% of PM $\geq$ 18%
Powder detergent:	-1% of TV + 4% of PM $\geq$ 4%

Choosing the Make Variables Non-Negative option with Solver recognized that TV and PM cannot be negative. Therefore, after dropping the percentage signs from the functional constraints, the complete mathematical model in the spreadsheet can be stated in the following succinct form.

Minimize Cost = TV + 2 PM (in millions of dollars)
subject to

Stain remover increased sales:	PM $\geq$ 3
Liquid detergent increased sales:	3 TV + 2 PM $\geq$ 18
Powder detergent increased sales:	$-$TV + 4 PM $\geq$ 4

and

$$\text{TV} \geq 0 \qquad \text{PM} \geq 0$$

Implicit in this statement is "Choose the values of TV and PM so as to. . . ." The term "subject to" is shorthand for "Choose these values *subject to* the requirement that the values satisfy all the following constraints."

FIGURE 2.22

Graph showing two objective function lines for the Profit & Gambit Co. advertising-mix problem, where the bottom one passes through the optimal solution.

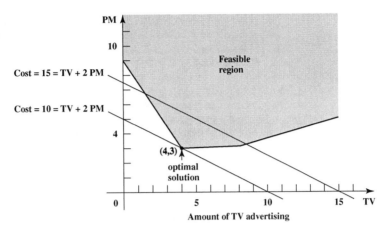

This model is the *algebraic* version of the *linear programming* model in the spreadsheet. Note how the parameters (constants) of this algebraic model come directly from the numbers in Table 2.2. In fact, the entire model could have been formulated directly from this table.

The differences between this algebraic model and the one obtained for the Wyndor problem in Section 2.3 lead to some interesting changes in how the graphical method is applied to solve the model. To further expand your geometric intuition about linear programming, we briefly describe this application of the graphical method next.

Since this linear programming model has only two decision variables, it can be solved by the graphical method described in Section 2.4. The method needs to be adapted in two ways to fit this particular problem. First, because all the functional constraints now have a $\geq$ sign with a positive right-hand side, after obtaining the constraint boundary lines in the usual way, the arrows indicating which side of each line satisfies that constraint now all point *away* from the origin. Second, the method is adapted to *minimization* by moving the objective function lines in the direction that *reduces* Cost and then stopping at the last instant that an objective function line still passes through a point in the feasible region, where such a point then is an optimal solution. The supplement to this chapter includes a description of how the graphical method is applied to the Profit & Gambit problem in this way.

Figure 2.22 shows the resulting *final* graph that identifies the optimal solution as

$$TV = 4 \qquad \text{(use 4 units of TV advertising)}$$
$$PM = 3 \qquad \text{(use 3 units of print media advertising)}$$

Review Questions

1. What kind of product is produced by the Profit & Gambit Co.?
2. Which advertising media are being considered for the three products under consideration?
3. What is management's objective for the problem being addressed?
4. What was the rationale for the placement of the objective cell and the changing cells in the spreadsheet model?
5. The algebraic form of the linear programming model for this problem differs from that for the Wyndor Glass Co. problem in which two major ways?

2.8   LINEAR PROGRAMMING FROM A BROADER PERSPECTIVE

Linear programming is an invaluable aid to managerial decision making in all kinds of companies throughout the world. The emergence of powerful spreadsheet packages has helped to further spread the use of this technique. The ease of formulating and solving small linear programming models on a spreadsheet now enables some managers with a very modest background in management science to do this themselves on their own desktop.

Many linear programming studies are major projects involving decisions on the levels of many hundreds or thousands of activities. For such studies, sophisticated software packages that go beyond spreadsheets generally are used for both the formulation and solution processes. These studies normally are conducted by technically trained teams of management scientists, sometimes called operations research analysts, at the instigation of management. Management needs to keep in touch with the management science team to ensure that the study reflects management's objectives and needs. However, management generally does not get involved with the technical details of the study.

Consequently, there is little reason for a manager to know the details of how linear programming models are solved beyond the rudiments of using Solver. (Even most management science teams will use commercial software packages for solving their models on a computer rather than developing their own software.) Similarly, a manager does not need to know the technical details of how to formulate complex models, how to validate such a model, how to interact with the computer when formulating and solving a large model, how to efficiently perform what-if analysis with such a model, and so forth. Therefore, these technical details are de-emphasized in this book. A student who becomes interested in conducting technical analyses as part of a management science team should plan to take additional, more technically oriented courses in management science.

So what does an enlightened manager need to know about linear programming? A manager needs to have a good intuitive feeling for what linear programming is. One objective of this chapter is to begin to develop that intuition. That's the purpose of studying the graphical method for solving two-variable problems. It is rare to have a *real* linear programming problem with as few as two decision variables. Therefore, the graphical method has essentially no practical value for solving real problems. However, it has great value for conveying the basic notion that linear programming involves pushing up against constraint boundaries and moving objective function values in a favorable direction as far as possible. Chapter 14 on the CD-ROM also demonstrates that this approach provides considerable geometric insight into how to analyze larger models by other methods.

A manager must also have an appreciation for the relevance and power of linear programming to encourage its use where appropriate. For *future* managers using this book, this appreciation is being promoted by using application vignettes and their linked articles to describe *real* applications of linear programming and the resulting impact, as well as by including (in miniature form) various realistic examples and case studies that illustrate what can be done.

Certainly a manager must be able to recognize situations where linear programming is applicable. We focus on developing this skill in Chapter 3, where you will learn how to recognize the *identifying features* for each of the major types of linear programming problems (and their mixtures).

In addition, a manager should recognize situations where linear programming should *not* be applied. Chapter 8 will help to develop this skill by examining certain underlying assumptions of linear programming and the circumstances that violate these assumptions. That chapter also describes other approaches that *can* be applied where linear programming should not.

A manager needs to be able to distinguish between competent and shoddy studies using linear programming (or any other management science technique). Therefore, another goal of the upcoming chapters is to demystify the overall process involved in conducting a management science study, all the way from first studying a problem to final implementation of the managerial decisions based on the study. This is one purpose of the case studies throughout the book.

Finally, a manager must understand how to interpret the results of a linear programming study. He or she especially needs to understand what kinds of information can be obtained through *what-if analysis,* as well as the implications of such information for managerial decision making. Chapter 5 focuses on these issues.

Review
Questions

1. Does management generally get heavily involved with the technical details of a linear programming study?
2. What is the purpose of studying the graphical method for solving problems with two decision variables when essentially all real linear programming problems have more than two?
3. List the things that an enlightened manager should know about linear programming.

2.9 Summary

Linear programming is a powerful technique for aiding managerial decision making for certain kinds of problems. The basic approach is to formulate a mathematical model called a linear programming model to represent the problem and then to analyze this model. Any linear programming model includes decision variables to represent the decisions to be made, constraints to represent the restrictions on the feasible values of these decision variables, and an objective function that expresses the overall measure of performance for the problem.

Spreadsheets provide a flexible and intuitive way of formulating and solving a linear programming model. The data are entered into data cells. Changing cells display the values of the decision variables, and an objective cell shows the value of the objective function. Output cells are used to help specify the constraints. After formulating the model on the spreadsheet, Solver is used to quickly find an optimal solution. Risk Solver Platform for Education also provides a more powerful method for finding an optimal solution.

The graphical method can be used to solve a linear programming model having just two decision variables. This method provides considerable insight into the nature of linear programming models and optimal solutions.

Glossary

absolute reference A reference to a cell (or a column or a row) with a fixed address, as indicated either by using a range name or by placing a $ sign in front of the letter and number of the cell reference. (Section 2.2), 28

changing cells The cells in the spreadsheet that show the values of the decision variables. (Section 2.2), 26

constraint A restriction on the feasible values of the decision variables. (Sections 2.2 and 2.3), 30

constraint boundary equation The equation for the constraint boundary line. (Section 2.4), 35

constraint boundary line For linear programming problems with two decision variables, the line forming the boundary of the solutions that are permitted by the constraint. (Section 2.4), 35

data cells The cells in the spreadsheet that show the data of the problem. (Section 2.2), 26

decision variable An algebraic variable that represents a decision regarding the level of a particular activity. The value of the decision variable appears in a changing cell on the spreadsheet. (Section 2.3), 32

feasible region The geometric region that consists of all the feasible solutions. (Section 2.4), 33

feasible solution A solution that simultaneously satisfies all the constraints in the linear programming model. (Section 2.3), 32

functional constraint A constraint with a function of the decision variables on the left-hand side. All constraints in a linear programming model that are not nonnegativity constraints are called functional constraints. (Section 2.3), 32

graphical method A method for solving linear programming problems with two decision variables on a two-dimensional graph. (Section 2.4), 33

infeasible solution A solution that violates at least one of the constraints in the linear programming model. (Section 2.3), 32

linear programming model The mathematical model that represents a linear programming problem. (Sections 2.2 and 2.3), 26

nonnegativity constraint A constraint that expresses the restriction that a particular decision variable must be nonnegative (greater than or equal to zero). (Section 2.3), 32

objective cell The cell in the spreadsheet that shows the overall measure of performance of the decisions. (Section 2.2), 28

objective function The part of a linear programming model that expresses what needs to be either maximized or minimized, depending on the objective for the problem. The value of the objective function appears in the objective cell on the spreadsheet. (Section 2.3), 32

objective function line For a linear programming problem with two decision variables, a line whose points all have the same value of the objective function. (Section 2.4), 36

optimal solution The best feasible solution according to the objective function. (Section 2.3), 32

output cells The cells in the spreadsheet that provide output that depends on the changing cells. These cells frequently are used to help specify constraints. (Section 2.2), 27

parameter The parameters of a linear programming model are the constants (coefficients or right-hand sides) in the functional constraints and the objective function. Each parameter represents a quantity (e.g., the amount available of a resource) that is of importance for the analysis of the problem. (Section 2.3), 32

product-mix problem A type of linear programming problem where the objective is to find the most profitable mix of production levels for the products under consideration. (Section 2.1), 25

range name A descriptive name given to a cell or range of cells that immediately identifies what is there. (Section 2.2), 26

relative reference A reference to a cell whose address is based upon its position relative to the cell containing the formula. (Section 2.2), 28

solution Any single assignment of values to the decision variables, regardless of whether the assignment is a good one or even a feasible one. (Section 2.3), 32

Solver The spreadsheet tool that is used to specify the model in the spreadsheet and then to obtain an optimal solution for that model. (Section 2.5), 38

Learning Aids for This Chapter in Your MS Courseware

Chapter 2 Excel Files:

Wyndor Example

Profit & Gambit Example

Interactive Management Science Modules:

Module for Graphical Linear Programming and Sensitivity Analysis

Excel Add-in:

Risk Solver Platform for Education (RSPE)

Supplement to Chapter 2 on the CD-ROM:

More About the Graphical Method for Linear Programming

Solved Problems (See the CD-ROM or Website for the Solution)

2.S1. Back Savers Production Problem

Back Savers is a company that produces backpacks primarily for students. They are considering offering some combination of two different models—the Collegiate and the Mini. Both are made out of the same rip-resistant nylon fabric. Back Savers has a long-term contract with a supplier of the nylon and receives a 5,000-square-foot shipment of the material each week. Each Collegiate requires 3 square feet while each Mini requires 2 square feet. The sales forecasts indicate that at most 1,000 Collegiates and 1,200 Minis can be sold per week. Each Collegiate requires 45 minutes of labor to produce and generates a unit profit of $32. Each Mini requires 40 minutes of labor and generates a unit profit of $24. Back Savers has 35 laborers that each provides 40 hours of labor per week. Management wishes to know what quantity of each type of backpack to produce per week.

a. Formulate and solve a linear programming model for this problem on a spreadsheet.

b. Formulate this same model algebraically.

c. Use the graphical method by hand to solve this model.

2.S2. Conducting a Marketing Survey

The marketing group for a cell phone manufacturer plans to conduct a telephone survey to determine consumer attitudes toward a new cell phone that is currently under development.

In order to have a sufficient sample size to conduct the analysis, they need to contact at least 100 young males (under age 40), 150 older males (over age 40), 120 young females (under age 40), and 200 older females (over age 40). It costs $1 to make a daytime phone call and $1.50 to make an evening phone call (because of higher labor costs). This cost is incurred whether or not anyone answers the phone. The table below shows the likelihood of a given customer type answering each phone call. Assume the survey is conducted with whoever first answers the phone. Also, because of limited evening staffing, at most one-third of phone calls placed can be evening phone calls. How should the marketing group conduct the telephone survey so as to meet the sample size requirements at the lowest possible cost?

a. Formulate and solve a linear programming model for this problem on a spreadsheet.

b. Formulate this same model algebraically.

Who Answers?	Daytime Calls	Evening Calls
Young male	10%	20%
Older male	15%	30%
Young female	20%	20%
Older female	35%	25%
No answer	20%	5%

Problems

We have inserted the symbol E* (for Excel) to the left of each problem or part where Excel should be used. The symbol R* is used instead if Risk Solver Platform for Education should be used instead of the Excel Solver to solve the problem. An asterisk on the problem number indicates that at least a partial answer is given in the back of the book.

2.1. Read the referenced article that fully describes the management science study summarized in the application vignette presented in Section 2.1. Briefly describe how linear programming was applied in this study. Then list the various financial and nonfinancial benefits that resulted from this study.

2.2. Reconsider the Wyndor Glass Co. case study introduced in Section 2.1. Suppose that the estimates of the unit profits for the two new products now have been revised to $600 for the doors and $300 for the windows.

E* *a.* Formulate and solve the revised linear programming model for this problem on a spreadsheet.

   b. Formulate this same model algebraically.

   c. Use the graphical method to solve this revised model.

2.3. Reconsider the Wyndor Glass Co. case study introduced in Section 2.1. Suppose that Bill Tasto (Wyndor's vice president for manufacturing) now has found a way to provide a little additional production time in Plant 2 to the new products.

   a. Use the graphical method to find the new optimal solution and the resulting total profit if *one* additional hour per week is provided.

   b. Repeat part *a* if *two* additional hours per week are provided instead.

   c. Repeat part *a* if *three* additional hours per week are provided instead.

   d. Use these results to determine how much each additional hour per week would be worth in terms of increasing the total profit from the two new products.

E*2.4. Use Solver to do Problem 2.3.

2.5. The following table summarizes the key facts about two products, A and B, and the resources, Q, R, and S, required to produce them.

Resource	Resource Usage per Unit Produced		Amount of Resource Available
	Product A	Product B	
Q	2	1	2
R	1	2	2
S	3	3	4
Profit/unit	$3,000	$2,000	

All the assumptions of linear programming hold.

E* *a.* Formulate and solve a linear programming model for this problem on a spreadsheet.

   b. Formulate this same model algebraically.

2.6.* This is your lucky day. You have just won a $20,000 prize. You are setting aside $8,000 for taxes and partying expenses, but you have decided to invest the other $12,000. Upon hearing this news, two different friends have offered you an opportunity to become a partner in two different entrepreneurial ventures, one planned by each friend. In both cases, this investment would involve expending some of your time next summer as well as putting up cash. Becoming a *full* partner in the first friend's venture would require an investment of $10,000 and 400 hours, and your estimated profit (ignoring the value of your time) would be $9,000. The corresponding figures for the second friend's venture are $8,000 and 500 hours, with an estimated profit to you of $9,000. However, both friends are flexible and would allow you to come in at any *fraction* of a full partnership you would like. If you choose a fraction of a full partnership, all the above figures given for a full partnership (money investment, time investment, and your profit) would be multiplied by this same fraction.

Because you were looking for an interesting summer job anyway (maximum of 600 hours), you have decided to participate in one or both friends' ventures in whichever combination would maximize your total estimated profit. You now need to solve the problem of finding the best combination.

   a. Describe the analogy between this problem and the Wyndor Glass Co. problem discussed in Section 2.1. Then construct and fill in a table like Table 2.1 for this problem, identifying both the activities and the resources.

   b. Identify verbally the decisions to be made, the constraints on these decisions, and the overall measure of performance for the decisions.

   c. Convert these verbal descriptions of the constraints and the measure of performance into quantitative expressions in terms of the data and decisions.

E* *d.* Formulate a spreadsheet model for this problem. Identify the data cells, the changing cells, and the objective cell. Also show the Excel equation for each output cell expressed as a SUMPRODUCT function. Then use Solver to solve this model.

   e. Indicate why this spreadsheet model is a linear programming model.

   f. Formulate this same model algebraically.

   g. Identify the decision variables, objective function, nonnegativity constraints, functional constraints, and parameters in both the algebraic version and spreadsheet version of the model.

   h. Use the graphical method by hand to solve this model. What is your total estimated profit?

   i. Use the Graphical Linear Programming and Sensitivity Analysis module in your Interactive Management Science Modules to apply the graphical method to this model.

2.7. You are given the following linear programming model in algebraic form, where x_1 and x_2 are the decision variables and Z is the value of the overall measure of performance.

$$\text{Maximize} \quad Z = x_1 + 2x_2$$

subject to

Constraint on resource 1: $x_1 + x_2 \leq 5$ (amount available)

Constraint on resource 2: $x_1 + 3x_2 \leq 9$ (amount available)

and

$$x_1 \geq 0 \quad x_2 \geq 0$$

   a. Identify the objective function, the functional constraints, and the nonnegativity constraints in this model.

E* *b.* Incorporate this model into a spreadsheet.

   c. Is $(x_1, x_2) = (3, 1)$ a feasible solution?

   d. Is $(x_1, x_2) = (1, 3)$ a feasible solution?

E* *e.* Use Solver to solve this model.

2.8.   You are given the following linear programming model in algebraic form, where x_1 and x_2 are the decision variables and Z is the value of the overall measure of performance.

$$\text{Maximize} \quad Z = 3x_1 + 2x_2$$

subject to

Constraint on resource 1: $3x_1 + x_2 \leq 9$ (amount available)
Constraint on resource 2: $x_1 + 2x_2 \leq 8$ (amount available)

and

$$x_1 \geq 0 \quad x_2 \geq 0$$

     a.   Identify the objective function, the functional constraints, and the nonnegativity constraints in this model.

E*   b.   Incorporate this model into a spreadsheet.

     c.   Is $(x_1, x_2) = (2, 1)$ a feasible solution?

     d.   Is $(x_1, x_2) = (2, 3)$ a feasible solution?

     e.   Is $(x_1, x_2) = (0, 5)$ a feasible solution?

E*   f.   Use Solver to solve this model.

2.9.   The Whitt Window Company is a company with only three employees that makes two different kinds of handcrafted windows: a wood-framed and an aluminum framed window. They earn $60 profit for each wood-framed window and $30 profit for each aluminum-framed window. Doug makes the wood frames and can make 6 per day. Linda makes the aluminum frames and can make 4 per day. Bob forms and cuts the glass and can make 48 square feet of glass per day. Each wood-framed window uses 6 square feet of glass and each aluminum-framed window uses 8 square feet of glass.

The company wishes to determine how many windows of each type to produce per day to maximize total profit.

     a.   Describe the analogy between this problem and the Wyndor Glass Co. problem discussed in Section 2.1. Then construct and fill in a table like Table 2.1 for this problem, identifying both the activities and the resources.

     b.   Identify verbally the decisions to be made, the constraints on these decisions, and the overall measure of performance for the decisions.

     c.   Convert these verbal descriptions of the constraints and the measure of performance into quantitative expressions in terms of the data and decisions.

E*   d.   Formulate a spreadsheet model for this problem. Identify the data cells, the changing cells, and the objective cell. Also show the Excel equation for each output cell expressed as a SUMPRODUCT function. Then use Solver to solve this model.

     e.   Indicate why this spreadsheet model is a linear programming model.

     f.   Formulate this same model algebraically.

     g.   Identify the decision variables, objective function, nonnegativity constraints, functional constraints, and parameters in both the algebraic version and spreadsheet version of the model.

     h.   Use the graphical method to solve this model.

     i.   A new competitor in town has started making wood-framed windows as well. This may force the company to lower the price it charges and so lower the profit made for each wood-framed window. How would the optimal solution change (if at all) if the profit per wood-framed window decreases from $60 to $40? From $60 to $20?

     j.   Doug is considering lowering his working hours, which would decrease the number of wood frames he makes per day. How would the optimal solution change if he only makes 5 wood frames per day?

2.10.   The Apex Television Company has to decide on the number of 27" and 20" sets to be produced at one of its factories. Market research indicates that at most 40 of the 27" sets and 10 of the 20" sets can be sold per month. The maximum number of work-hours available is 500 per month. A 27" set requires 20 work-hours and a 20" set requires 10 work-hours. Each 27" set sold produces a profit of $120 and each 20" set produces a profit of $80. A wholesaler has agreed to purchase all the television sets produced if the numbers do not exceed the maxima indicated by the market research.

E*   a.   Formulate and solve a linear programming model for this problem on a spreadsheet.

     b.   Formulate this same model algebraically.

     c.   Solve this model by using the Graphical Linear Programming and Sensitivity Analysis module in your Interactive Management Science Modules to apply the graphical method.

2.11.   The WorldLight Company produces two light fixtures (Products 1 and 2) that require both metal frame parts and electrical components. Management wants to determine how many units of each product to produce so as to maximize profit. For each unit of Product 1, one unit of frame parts and two units of electrical components are required. For each unit of Product 2, three units of frame parts and two units of electrical components are required. The company has 200 units of frame parts and 300 units of electrical components. Each unit of Product 1 gives a profit of $1, and each unit of Product 2, up to 60 units, gives a profit of $2. Any excess over 60 units of Product 2 brings no profit, so such an excess has been ruled out.

     a.   Identify verbally the decisions to be made, the constraints on these decisions, and the overall measure of performance for the decisions.

     b.   Convert these verbal descriptions of the constraints and the measure of performance into quantitative expressions in terms of the data and decisions.

E*   c.   Formulate and solve a linear programming model for this problem on a spreadsheet.

     d.   Formulate this same model algebraically.

     e.   Solve this model by using the Graphical Linear Programming and Sensitivity Analysis module in your Interactive Management Science Modules to apply the graphical method. What is the resulting total profit?

2.12.   The Primo Insurance Company is introducing two new product lines: special risk insurance and mortgages. The expected profit is $5 per unit on special risk insurance and $2 per unit on mortgages.

Management wishes to establish sales quotas for the new product lines to maximize total expected profit. The work requirements are shown below:

    a. Identify verbally the decisions to be made, the constraints on these decisions, and the overall measure of performance for the decisions.

    b. Convert these verbal descriptions of the constraints and the measure of performance into quantitative expressions in terms of the data and decisions.

Department	Work-Hours per Unit		Work-Hours Available
	Special Risk	Mortgage	
Underwriting	3	2	2,400
Administration	0	1	800
Claims	2	0	1,200

E*   *c.* Formulate and solve a linear programming model for this problem on a spreadsheet.

    d. Formulate this same model algebraically.

2.13.* You are given the following linear programming model in algebraic form, with x_1 and x_2 as the decision variables and constraints on the usage of four resources:

$$\text{Maximize} \quad \text{Profit} = 2x_1 + x_2$$

subject to

$$
\begin{array}{ll}
x_2 \le 10 & \text{(resource 1)} \\
2x_1 + 5x_2 \le 60 & \text{(resource 2)} \\
x_1 + x_2 \le 18 & \text{(resource 3)} \\
3x_1 + x_2 \le 44 & \text{(resource 4)}
\end{array}
$$

and

$$x_1 \ge 0 \quad x_2 \ge 0$$

    a. Use the graphical method to solve this model.

E*   *b.* Incorporate this model into a spreadsheet and then use Solver to solve this model.

R*2.14. Use Risk Solver Platform for Education to formulate and solve the model shown in Problem 2.13 in a spreadsheet.

2.15. Because of your knowledge of management science, your boss has asked you to analyze a product mix problem involving two products and two resources. The model is shown below in algebraic form, where x_1 and x_2 are the production rates for the two products and P is the total profit.

$$\text{Maximize} \quad P = 3x_1 + 2x_2$$

subject to

$$
\begin{array}{ll}
x_1 + x_2 \le 8 & \text{(resource 1)} \\
2x_1 + x_2 \le 10 & \text{(resource 2)}
\end{array}
$$

and

$$x_1 \ge 0 \quad x_2 \ge 0$$

    a. Use the graphical method to solve this model.

E*   *b.* Incorporate this model into a spreadsheet and then use Solver to solve this model.

R*2.16. Use Risk Solver Platform for Education to formulate and solve the model shown in Problem 2.15 in a spreadsheet.

2.17. Independently consider each of the following changes in the Wyndor problem. In each case, apply the graphical method by hand to this new version of the problem, describe your conclusion, and then explain how and why the nature of this conclusion is different from the original Wyndor problem.

    a. The unit profit for the windows now is $200.

    b. To justify introducing these two new products, Wyndor management now requires that the total number of doors and windows produced per week must be at least 10.

    c. The functional constraints for Plants 2 and 3 now have been inadvertently deleted from the model.

2.18. Do Problem 2.17 by using the Graphical Linear Programming and Sensitivity Analysis module in your Interactive Management Science Modules.

2.19. Weenies and Buns is a food processing plant that manufactures hot dogs and hot dog buns. They grind their own flour for the hot dog buns at a maximum rate of 200 pounds per week. Each hot dog bun requires 0.1 pound of flour. They currently have a contract with Pigland, Inc., which specifies that a delivery of 800 pounds of pork product is delivered every Monday. Each hot dog requires 1/4 pound of pork product. All the other ingredients in the hot dogs and hot dog buns are in plentiful supply. Finally, the labor force at Weenies and Buns consists of five employees working full time (40 hours per week each). Each hot dog requires three minutes of labor, and each hot dog bun requires two minutes of labor. Each hot dog yields a profit of $0.20, and each bun yields a profit of $0.10.

Weenies and Buns would like to know how many hot dogs and how many hot dog buns they should produce each week so as to achieve the highest possible profit.

    a. Identify verbally the decisions to be made, the constraints on these decisions, and the overall measure of performance for the decisions.

    b. Convert these verbal descriptions of the constraints and the measure of performance into quantitative expressions in terms of the data and decisions.

E*   *c.* Formulate and solve a linear programming model for this problem on a spreadsheet.

    d. Formulate this same model algebraically.

    e. Use the graphical method to solve this model. Decide yourself whether you would prefer to do this by hand or by using the Graphical Linear Programming and Sensitivity Analysis module in your Interactive Management Science Modules.

2.20. The Oak Works is a family-owned business that makes handcrafted dining room tables and chairs. They obtain the oak from a local tree farm, which ships them 2,500 pounds of oak each month. Each table uses 50 pounds of oak while each chair uses 25 pounds of oak. The family builds all the furniture itself and has 480 hours of labor available each month. Each table or chair requires six hours of labor. Each table nets Oak Works $400 in profit, while each chair nets $100 in profit. Since chairs are often sold with the tables, they want to produce *at least* twice as many chairs as tables.

The Oak Works would like to decide how many tables and chairs to produce so as to maximize profit.

  a. Formulate and solve a linear programming model for this problem on a spreadsheet. by using the Excel Solver.

R* b. Use Risk Solver Platform for Education to formulate and solve this model in a spreadsheet.

  c. Formulate this same model algebraically.

2.21.   Read the referenced article that fully describes the management science study summarized in the application vignette presented in Section 2.6. Briefly describe how linear programming was applied in this study. Then list the various financial and nonfinancial benefits that resulted from this study.

2.22.   Nutri-Jenny is a weight-management center. It produces a wide variety of frozen entrées for consumption by its clients. The entrées are strictly monitored for nutritional content to ensure that the clients are eating a balanced diet. One new entrée will be a beef sirloin tips dinner. It will consist of beef tips and gravy, plus some combination of peas, carrots, and a dinner roll. Nutri-Jenny would like to determine what quantity of each item to include in the entrée to meet the nutritional requirements, while costing as little as possible. The nutritional information for each item and its cost are given in the following table.

Item	Calories (per oz.)	Calories from Fat (per oz.)	Vitamin A (IU per oz.)	Vitamin C (mg per oz.)	Protein (g, per oz.)	Cost (per oz.)
Beef tips	54	19	0	0	8	40¢
Gravy	20	15	0	1	0	35¢
Peas	15	0	15	3	1	15¢
Carrots	8	0	350	1	1	18¢
Dinner roll	40	10	0	0	1	10¢

The nutritional requirements for the entrée are as follows: (1) it must have between 280 and 320 calories, (2) calories from fat should be no more than 30 percent of the total number of calories, and (3) it must have at least 600 IUs of vitamin A, 10 milligrams of vitamin C, and 30 grams of protein. Furthermore, for practical reasons, it must include at least 2 ounces of beef, and it must have at least half an ounce of gravy per ounce of beef.

E* a. Formulate and solve a linear programming model for this problem on a spreadsheet. by using the Excel Solver.

R* b. Use Risk Solver Platform for Education to formulate and solve this model in a spreadsheet.

  c. Formulate this same model algebraically.

2.23.   Ralph Edmund loves steaks and potatoes. Therefore, he has decided to go on a steady diet of only these two foods (plus some liquids and vitamin supplements) for all his meals. Ralph realizes that this isn't the healthiest diet, so he wants to make sure that he eats the right quantities of the two foods to satisfy some key nutritional requirements. He has obtained the following nutritional and cost information.

Grams of Ingredient per Serving			
Ingredient	Steak	Potatoes	Daily Requirement (grams)
Carbohydrates	5	15	≥ 50
Protein	20	5	≥ 40
Fat	15	2	≤ 60
Cost per serving	$4	$2	

Ralph wishes to determine the number of daily servings (may be fractional) of steak and potatoes that will meet these requirements at a minimum cost.

  a. Identify verbally the decisions to be made, the constraints on these decisions, and the overall measure of performance for the decisions.

  b. Convert these verbal descriptions of the constraints and the measure of performance into quantitative expressions in terms of the data and decisions.

E* c. Formulate and solve a linear programming model for this problem on a spreadsheet.

  d. Formulate this same model algebraically.

  e. Use the graphical method by hand to solve this model.

  f. Use the Graphical Linear Programming and Sensitivity Analysis module in your Interactive Management Science Modules to apply the graphical method to this model.

2.24.   Dwight is an elementary school teacher who also raises pigs for supplemental income. He is trying to decide what to feed his pigs. He is considering using a combination of pig feeds available from local suppliers. He would like to feed the pigs at minimum cost while also making sure each pig receives an adequate supply of calories and vitamins. The cost, calorie content, and vitamin content of each feed is given in the table below.

Contents	Feed Type A	Feed Type B
Calories (per pound)	800	1,000
Vitamins (per pound)	140 units	70 units
Cost (per pound)	$0.40	$0.80

Each pig requires at least 8,000 calories per day and at least 700 units of vitamins. A further constraint is that no more than ⅓ of the diet (by weight) can consist of Feed Type A, since it contains an ingredient that is toxic if consumed in too large a quantity.

a. Identify verbally the decisions to be made, the constraints on these decisions, and the overall measure of performance for the decisions.

b. Convert these verbal descriptions of the constraints and the measure of performance into quantitative expressions in terms of the data and decisions.

E* c. Formulate and solve a linear programming model for this problem on a spreadsheet.

d. Formulate this same model algebraically.

2.25.   Reconsider the Profit & Gambit Co. problem described in Section 2.6. Suppose that the estimated data given in Table 2.2 now have been changed as shown in the table that accompanies this problem.

E* a. Formulate and solve a linear programming model on a spreadsheet for this revised version of the problem.

b. Formulate this same model algebraically.

c. Use the graphical method to solve this model.

d. What were the key changes in the data that caused your answer for the optimal solution to change from the one for the original version of the problem?

| Product | Increase in Sales per Unit of Advertising | | Minimum Required Increase |
	Television	Print Media	
Stain remover	0%	1.5%	3%
Liquid detergent	3	4	18
Powder detergent	−1	2	4
Unit cost	$1 million	$2 million	

e. Write a paragraph to the management of the Profit & Gambit Co. presenting your conclusions from the above parts. Include the potential effect of further refining the key data in the below table. Also point out the leverage that your results might provide to management in negotiating a decrease in the unit cost for either of the advertising media.

2.26.   You are given the following linear programming model in algebraic form, with x_1 and x_2 as the decision variables:

$$\text{Minimize} \quad \text{Cost} = 40x_1 + 50x_2$$

subject to

$$\begin{aligned}
\text{Constraint 1:} \quad & 2x_1 + 3x_2 \geq 30 \\
\text{Constraint 2:} \quad & x_1 + x_2 \geq 12 \\
\text{Constraint 3:} \quad & 2x_1 + x_2 \geq 20
\end{aligned}$$

and

$$x_1 \geq 0 \qquad x_2 \geq 0$$

a. Use the graphical method to solve this model.

b. How does the optimal solution change if the objective function is changed to Cost $= 40x_1 + 70x_2$?

c. How does the optimal solution change if the third functional constraint is changed to $2x_1 + x_2 \geq 15$?

E* d. Now incorporate the original model into a spreadsheet and use Solver to solve this model.

E* e. Use Excel to do parts b and c.

2.27.   The Learning Center runs a day camp for 6-10 year olds during the summer. Its manager, Elizabeth Reed, is trying to reduce the center's operating costs to avoid having to raise the tuition fee. Elizabeth is currently planning what to feed the children for lunch. She would like to keep costs to a minimum, but also wants to make sure she is meeting the nutritional requirements of the children. She has already decided to go with peanut butter and jelly sandwiches, and some combination of apples, milk, and/or cranberry juice. The nutritional content of each food choice and its cost are given in the table that accompanies this problem.

The nutritional requirements are as follows. Each child should receive between 300 and 500 calories, but no more than 30 percent of these calories should come from fat. Each child should receive at least 60 milligrams (mg) of vitamin C and at least 10 grams (g) of fiber.

To ensure tasty sandwiches, Elizabeth wants each child to have a minimum of 2 slices of bread, 1 tablespoon (tbsp) of peanut butter, and 1 tbsp of jelly, along with at least 1 cup of liquid (milk and/or cranberry juice).

Elizabeth would like to select the food choices that would minimize cost while meeting all these requirements.

E* a. Formulate and solve a linear programming model for this problem on a spreadsheet.

b. Formulate this same model algebraically.

Food Item	Calories from Fat	Total Calories	Vitamin C (mg)	Fiber (g)	Cost (¢)
Bread (1 slice)	15	80	0	4	6
Peanut butter (1 tbsp)	80	100	0	0	5
Jelly (1 tbsp)	0	70	4	3	8
Apple	0	90	6	10	35
Milk (1 cup)	60	120	2	0	20
Cranberry juice (1 cup)	0	110	80	1	40

60   Chapter Two   *Linear Programming: Basic Concepts*

Case 2-1

Auto Assembly

Automobile Alliance, a large automobile manufacturing company, organizes the vehicles it manufactures into three families: a family of trucks, a family of small cars, and a family of midsized and luxury cars. One plant outside Detroit, Michigan, assembles two models from the family of midsized and luxury cars. The first model, the Family Thrillseeker, is a four-door sedan with vinyl seats, plastic interior, standard features, and excellent gas mileage. It is marketed as a smart buy for middle-class families with tight budgets, and each Family Thrillseeker sold generates a modest profit of $3,600 for the company. The second model, the Classy Cruiser, is a two-door luxury sedan with leather seats, wooden interior, custom features, and navigational capabilities. It is marketed as a privilege of affluence for upper-middle-class families, and each Classy Cruiser sold generates a healthy profit of $5,400 for the company.

Rachel Rosencrantz, the manager of the assembly plant, is currently deciding the production schedule for the next month. Specifically, she must decide how many Family Thrillseekers and how many Classy Cruisers to assemble in the plant to maximize profit for the company. She knows that the plant possesses a capacity of 48,000 labor-hours during the month. She also knows that it takes six labor-hours to assemble one Family Thrillseeker and 10.5 labor-hours to assemble one Classy Cruiser.

Because the plant is simply an assembly plant, the parts required to assemble the two models are not produced at the plant. Instead, they are shipped from other plants around the Michigan area to the assembly plant. For example, tires, steering wheels, windows, seats, and doors all arrive from various supplier plants. For the next month, Rachel knows that she will only be able to obtain 20,000 doors from the door supplier. A recent labor strike forced the shutdown of that particular supplier plant for several days, and that plant will not be able to meet its production schedule for the next month. Both the Family Thrillseeker and the Classy Cruiser use the same door part.

In addition, a recent company forecast of the monthly demands for different automobile models suggests that the demand for the Classy Cruiser is limited to 3,500 cars. There is no limit on the demand for the Family Thrillseeker within the capacity limits of the assembly plant.

a. Formulate and solve a linear programming model to determine the number of Family Thrillseekers and the number of Classy Cruisers that should be assembled.

Before she makes her final production decisions, Rachel plans to explore the following questions independently, except where otherwise indicated.

b. The marketing department knows that it can pursue a targeted $500,000 advertising campaign that will raise the demand for the Classy Cruiser next month by 20 percent. Should the campaign be undertaken?

c. Rachel knows that she can increase next month's plant capacity by using overtime labor. She can increase the plant's labor-hour capacity by 25 percent. With the new assembly plant capacity, how many Family Thrillseekers and how many Classy Cruisers should be assembled?

d. Rachel knows that overtime labor does not come without an extra cost. What is the maximum amount she should be willing to pay for all overtime labor beyond the cost of this labor at regular-time rates? Express your answer as a lump sum.

e. Rachel explores the option of using both the targeted advertising campaign and the overtime labor-hours. The advertising campaign raises the demand for the Classy Cruiser by 20 percent, and the overtime labor increases the plant's labor-hour capacity by 25 percent. How many Family Thrillseekers and how many Classy Cruisers should be assembled using the advertising campaign and overtime labor-hours if the profit from each Classy Cruiser sold continues to be 50 percent more than for each Family Thrillseeker sold?

f. Knowing that the advertising campaign costs $500,000 and the maximum usage of overtime labor-hours costs $1,600,000 beyond regular time rates, is the solution found in part *e* a wise decision compared to the solution found in part *a?*

g. Automobile Alliance has determined that dealerships are actually heavily discounting the price of the Family Thrillseekers to move them off the lot. Because of a profit-sharing agreement with its dealers, the company is not making a profit of $3,600 on the Family Thrillseeker but instead is making a profit of $2,800. Determine the number of Family Thrillseekers and the number of Classy Cruisers that should be assembled given this new discounted profit.

h. The company has discovered quality problems with the Family Thrillseeker by randomly testing Thrillseekers at the end of the assembly line. Inspectors have discovered that in over 60 percent of the cases, two of the four doors on a Thrillseeker do not seal properly. Because the percentage of defective Thrillseekers determined by the random testing is so high, the floor foreman has decided to perform quality control tests on every Thrillseeker at the end of the line. Because of the added tests, the time it takes to assemble one Family Thrillseeker has increased from 6 hours to 7.5 hours. Determine the number of units of each model that should be assembled given the new assembly time for the Family Thrillseeker.

i. The board of directors of Automobile Alliance wishes to capture a larger share of the luxury sedan market and therefore would like to meet the full demand for Classy Cruisers. They ask Rachel to determine by how much the profit of her assembly plant would decrease as compared to the profit found in part *a.* They then ask her to meet the full demand for Classy Cruisers if the decrease in profit is not more than $2,000,000.

j. Rachel now makes her final decision by combining all the new considerations described in parts *f, g,* and *h.* What are her final decisions on whether to undertake the advertising campaign, whether to use overtime labor, the number of Family Thrillseekers to assemble, and the number of Classy Cruisers to assemble?

Case 2-2

Cutting Cafeteria Costs

A cafeteria at **All-State University** has one special dish it serves like clockwork every Thursday at noon. This supposedly tasty dish is a casserole that contains sautéed onions, boiled sliced potatoes, green beans, and cream of mushroom soup. Unfortunately, students fail to see the special quality of this dish, and they loathingly refer to it as the Killer Casserole. The students reluctantly eat the casserole, however, because the cafeteria provides only a limited selection of dishes for Thursday's lunch (namely, the casserole).

Maria Gonzalez, the cafeteria manager, is looking to cut costs for the coming year, and she believes that one sure way to cut costs is to buy less expensive and perhaps lower quality ingredients. Because the casserole is a weekly staple of the cafeteria menu, she concludes that if she can cut costs on the ingredients purchased for the casserole, she can significantly reduce overall cafeteria operating costs. She therefore decides to invest time in determining how to minimize the costs of the casserole while maintaining nutritional and taste requirements.

Maria focuses on reducing the costs of the two main ingredients in the casserole, the potatoes and green beans. These two ingredients are responsible for the greatest costs, nutritional content, and taste of the dish.

Maria buys the potatoes and green beans from a wholesaler each week. Potatoes cost $0.40 per pound (lb), and green beans cost $1.00 per lb.

All-State University has established nutritional requirements that each main dish of the cafeteria must meet. Specifically, the dish must contain 180 grams (g) of protein, 80 milligrams (mg) of iron, and 1,050 mg of vitamin C. (There are 454 g in one lb and 1,000 mg in one g.) For simplicity when planning, Maria assumes that only the potatoes and green beans contribute to the nutritional content of the casserole.

Because Maria works at a cutting-edge technological university, she has been exposed to the numerous resources on the World Wide Web. She decides to surf the Web to find the nutritional content of potatoes and green beans. Her research yields the following nutritional information about the two ingredients.

	Potatoes	Green Beans
Protein	1.5 g per 100 g	5.67 g per 10 ounces
Iron	0.3 mg per 100 g	3.402 mg per 10 ounces
Vitamin C	12 mg per 100 g	28.35 mg per 10 ounces

(There are 28.35 g in one ounce.)

Edson Branner, the cafeteria cook who is surprisingly concerned about taste, informs Maria that an edible casserole must contain at least a six-to-five ratio in the weight of potatoes to green beans.

Given the number of students who eat in the cafeteria, Maria knows that she must purchase enough potatoes and green beans to prepare a minimum of 10 kilograms (kg) of casserole each week. (There are 1,000 g in one kg.) Again, for simplicity in planning, she assumes that only the potatoes and green beans determine the amount of casserole that can be prepared. Maria does not establish an upper limit on the amount of casserole to

prepare since she knows all leftovers can be served for many days thereafter or can be used creatively in preparing other dishes.

a. Determine the amount of potatoes and green beans Maria should purchase each week for the casserole to minimize the ingredient costs while meeting nutritional, taste, and demand requirements.

Before she makes her final decision, Maria plans to explore the following questions independently, except where otherwise indicated.

b. Maria is not very concerned about the taste of the casserole; she is only concerned about meeting nutritional requirements and cutting costs. She therefore forces Edson to change the recipe to allow only for at least a one-to-two ratio in the weight of potatoes to green beans. Given the new recipe, determine the amount of potatoes and green beans Maria should purchase each week.

c. Maria decides to lower the iron requirement to 65 mg since she determines that the other ingredients, such as the onions and cream of mushroom soup, also provide iron. Determine the amount of potatoes and green beans Maria should purchase each week given this new iron requirement.

d. Maria learns that the wholesaler has a surplus of green beans and is therefore selling the green beans for a lower price of $0.50 per lb. Using the same iron requirement from part *c* and the new price of green beans, determine the amount of potatoes and green beans Maria should purchase each week.

e. Maria decides that she wants to purchase lima beans instead of green beans since lima beans are less expensive and provide a greater amount of protein and iron than green beans. Maria again wields her absolute power and forces Edson to change the recipe to include lima beans instead of green beans. Maria knows she can purchase lima beans for $0.60 per lb from the wholesaler. She also knows that lima beans contain 22.68 g of protein and 6.804 mg of iron per 10 ounces of lima beans and no vitamin C. Using the new cost and nutritional content of lima beans, determine the amount of potatoes and lima beans Maria should purchase each week to minimize the ingredient costs while meeting nutritional, taste, and demand requirements. The nutritional requirements include the reduced iron requirement from part *c*.

f. Will Edson be happy with the solution in part *e?* Why or why not?

g. An All-State student task force meets during Body Awareness Week and determines that All-State University's nutritional requirements for iron are too lax and that those for vitamin C are too stringent. The task force urges the university to adopt a policy that requires each serving of an entrée to contain at least 120 mg of iron and at least 500 mg of vitamin C. Using potatoes and lima beans as the ingredients for the dish and using the new nutritional requirements, determine the amount of potatoes and lima beans Maria should purchase each week.

62   Chapter Two   *Linear Programming: Basic Concepts*

Case 2-3

Staffing a Call Center

California Children's Hospital has been receiving numerous customer complaints because of its confusing, decentralized appointment and registration process. When customers want to make appointments or register child patients, they must contact the clinic or department they plan to visit. Several problems exist with this current strategy. Parents do not always know the most appropriate clinic or department they must visit to address their children's ailments. They therefore spend a significant amount of time on the phone being transferred from clinic to clinic until they reach the most appropriate clinic for their needs. The hospital also does not publish the phone numbers of all clinics and departments, and parents must therefore invest a large amount of time in detective work to track down the correct phone number. Finally, the various clinics and departments do not communicate with each other. For example, when a doctor schedules a referral with a colleague located in another department or clinic, that department or clinic almost never receives word of the referral. The parent must contact the correct department or clinic and provide the needed referral information.

In efforts to reengineer and improve its appointment and registration process, the children's hospital has decided to centralize the process by establishing one call center devoted exclusively to appointments and registration. The hospital is currently in the middle of the planning stages for the call center. Lenny Davis, the hospital manager, plans to operate the call center from 7 AM to 9 PM during the weekdays.

Several months ago, the hospital hired an ambitious management consulting firm, Creative Chaos Consultants, to forecast the number of calls the call center would receive each hour of the day. Since all appointment and registration-related calls would be received by the call center, the consultants decided that they could forecast the calls at the call center by totaling the number of appointment and registration-related calls received by all clinics and departments. The team members visited all the clinics and departments, where they diligently recorded every call relating to appointments and registration. They then totaled these calls and altered the totals to account for calls missed during data collection. They also altered totals to account for repeat calls that occurred when the same parent called the hospital many times because of the confusion surrounding the decentralized process. Creative Chaos Consultants determined the average number of calls the call center should expect during each hour of a weekday. The following table provides the forecasts.

Work Shift	Average Number of Calls
7 AM to 9 AM	40 calls per hour
9 AM to 11 AM	85 calls per hour
11 AM to 1 PM	70 calls per hour
1 PM to 3 PM	95 calls per hour
3 PM to 5 PM	80 calls per hour
5 PM to 7 PM	35 calls per hour
7 PM to 9 PM	10 calls per hour

After the consultants submitted these forecasts, Lenny became interested in the percentage of calls from Spanish speakers since the hospital services many Spanish patients. Lenny knows that

he has to hire some operators who speak Spanish to handle these calls. The consultants performed further data collection and determined that, on average, 20 percent of the calls were from Spanish speakers.

Given these call forecasts, Lenny must now decide how to staff the call center during each two-hour shift of a weekday. During the forecasting project, Creative Chaos Consultants closely observed the operators working at the individual clinics and departments and determined the number of calls operators process per hour. The consultants informed Lenny that an operator is able to process an average of six calls per hour. Lenny also knows that he has both full-time and part-time workers available to staff the call center. A full-time employee works eight hours per day, but because of paperwork that must also be completed, the employee spends only four hours per day on the phone. To balance the schedule, the employee alternates the two-hour shifts between answering phones and completing paperwork. Full-time employees can start their day either by answering phones or by completing paperwork on the first shift. The full-time employees speak either Spanish or English, but none of them are bilingual. Both Spanish-speaking and English-speaking employees are paid $10 per hour for work before 5 PM and $12 per hour for work after 5 PM. The full-time employees can begin work at the beginning of the 7 AM to 9 AM shift, 9 AM to 11 AM shift, 11 AM to 1 PM shift, or 1 PM to 3 PM shift. The part-time employees work for four hours, only answer calls, and only speak English. They can start work at the beginning of the 3 PM to 5 PM shift or the 5 PM to 7 PM shift, and, like the full-time employees, they are paid $10 per hour for work before 5 PM and $12 per hour for work after 5 PM.

For the following analysis, consider only the labor cost for the time employees spend answering phones. The cost for paperwork time is charged to other cost centers.

a. How many Spanish-speaking operators and how many English-speaking operators does the hospital need to staff the call center during each two-hour shift of the day in order to answer all calls? Please provide an integer number since half a human operator makes no sense.

b. Lenny needs to determine how many full-time employees who speak Spanish, full-time employees who speak English, and part-time employees he should hire to begin on each shift. Creative Chaos Consultants advises him that linear programming can be used to do this in such a way as to minimize operating costs while answering all calls. Formulate a linear programming model of this problem.

c. Obtain an optimal solution for the linear programming model formulated in part *b* to guide Lenny's decision.

d. Because many full-time workers do not want to work late into the evening, Lenny can find only one qualified English-speaking operator willing to begin work at 1 PM. Given this new constraint, how many full-time English-speaking operators, full-time Spanish-speaking operators, and part-time operators should Lenny hire for each shift to minimize operating costs while answering all calls?

e. Lenny now has decided to investigate the option of hiring bilingual operators instead of monolingual operators. If all the operators are bilingual, how many operators should be working during each two-hour shift to answer all phone calls? As in part *a,* please provide an integer answer.

f. If all employees are bilingual, how many full-time and part-time employees should Lenny hire to begin on each shift to minimize operating costs while answering all calls? As in part *b,* formulate a linear programming model to guide Lenny's decision.

g. What is the maximum percentage increase in the hourly wage rate that Lenny can pay bilingual employees over monolingual employees without increasing the total operating costs?

h. What other features of the call center should Lenny explore to improve service or minimize operating costs?

Source: This case is based on an actual project completed by a team of master's students in what is now the Department of Management Science and Engineering at Stanford University.

Additional Cases

Additional cases for this chapter are also available at the University of Western Ontario Ivey School of Business website, **cases.ivey.uwo.ca/cases**, in the segment of the Case-Mate area designated for this book.

CD S Ch 2-1

SUPPLEMENT TO CHAPTER 2
MORE ABOUT THE GRAPHICAL METHOD FOR
LINEAR PROGRAMMING

Section 2.4 introduced the graphical method for solving two-variable linear programming problems by briefly illustrating its application to the Wyndor problem. For those who would like to see a fuller description of this method, we now will go through this same example in much more detail. (This presentation is self-contained and so will include much of what was said in Section 2.4 in this expanded coverage.) We then will present a second example (the Profit & Gambit Co. advertising-mix problem) where the objective is to *minimize total cost* rather than maximize total profit.

To prepare for going through the Wyndor example again, you might find it helpful to review the description of the problem in Section 2.1, the spreadsheet model for this problem in Section 2.2 (see Figure 2.3), and then (of special importance) the algebraic version of this model in Section 2.3. For your easy reference, this algebraic model is summarized below.

Choose the values of D and W so as to *maximize*
$$P = 300D + 500W$$

subject to satisfying all the following constraints:

$$
\begin{array}{rcll}
D & & \leq & 4 \\
& 2W & \leq & 12 \\
3D & +\ 2W & \leq & 18
\end{array}
$$

and
$$D \geq 0 \qquad W \geq 0$$

where

P = Total profit per week from the special new doors and windows (the number in the target cell G12 in Figure 2.3),

D = Production rate for the special new doors (the number in changing cell C12 in Figure 2.3),

W = Production rate for the special new windows (the number in changing cell D12 in Figure 2.3).

The focus of the graphical method is on solving this algebraic model by using a graph to find the feasible values of D and W that maximize P.

Displaying Solutions as Points on a Graph

The key to the graphical method is the fact that possible solutions can be displayed as points on a two-dimensional graph that has a horizontal axis giving the value of D and a vertical axis giving the value of W. Figure 1 shows some sample points.

Notation: Either $(D, W) = (2, 3)$ or just $(2, 3)$ refers to both the solution and the point in the graph where $D = 2$ and $W = 3$. Similarly, $(D, W) = (4, 6)$ means $D = 4$ and $W = 6$, whereas the origin $(0, 0)$ means $D = 0$ and $W = 0$.

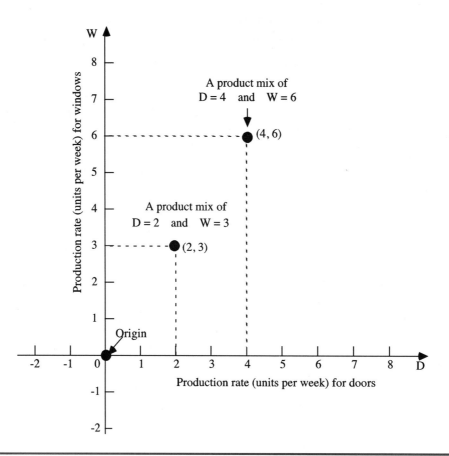

Figure 1   Graph showing the points $(D, W) = (2, 3)$ and $(D, W) = (4, 6)$ for the Wyndor Glass Co. product-mix problem.

To find the optimal solution (the best feasible solution), we first need to display graphically where the feasible solutions are. To do this, we must consider each constraint, identify the solutions graphically that are permitted by that constraint, and then combine this information to identify the solutions permitted by all the constraints.

To begin, the constraint $D \geq 0$ implies that consideration must be limited to points that lie on or to the right of the W axis in Figure 1. Similarly, the constraint, $W \geq 0$ restricts consideration to the points on or above the D axis. Combining these two facts, the region of interest at this juncture is the one shaded in on Figure 2. (This region also includes *larger* values of D and W than can be shown shaded in the available space.)

CD S Ch 2-3

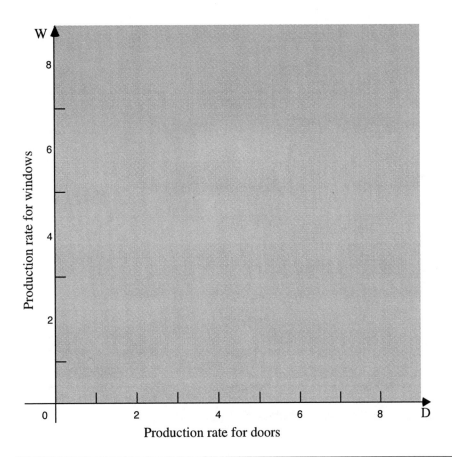

Figure 2	Graph showing that the constraints, $D \geq 0$ and $W \geq 0$, rule out solutions for the Wyndor Glass Co. product-mix problem that are to the left of the vertical axis or under the horizontal axis.

Graphing Nonnegative Solutions Permitted by Each Functional Constraint

We now will look individually at the nonnegative solutions that are permitted by each functional constraint by itself. Later, we will combine all these constraints.

Let us begin with the first functional constraint, $D \leq 4$, which limits the usage of Plant 1 for producing the special new doors to a maximum of 4 hours per week. The solutions permitted by this constraint are those that lie on, or to the left of, the vertical line that intercepts the D axis at $D = 4$ (so $D = 4$ is the equation for the line). Combining this permissible region with the one given in Figure 2 yields the shaded region shown in Figure 3.

CD S Ch 2-4

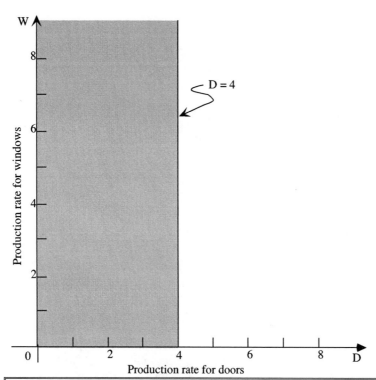

Figure 3   Graph showing that the nonnegative solutions permitted by the constraint $D \leq 4$ lie between the vertical axis and the line where $D = 4$.

The second functional constraint, $2W \leq 12$, has a similar effect, except now the boundary of its permissible region is given by a *horizontal* line with the equation, 2W = 12 (or $W = 6$), as shown in Figure 4. The line forming the boundary of what is permitted by a constraint is sometimes referred to as a **constraint boundary line**, and its equation may be called a **constraint boundary equation**. Frequently, a *constraint boundary line* is identified by its equation.

CD S Ch 2-5

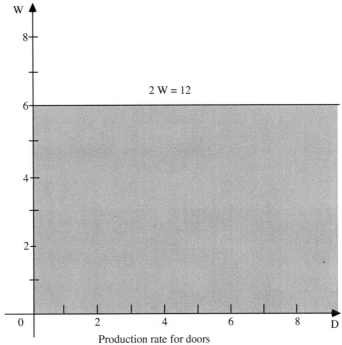

Production rate for windows

Production rate for doors

Figure 4   Graph showing that the nonnegative solutions permitted by the constraint $2W \leq 12$ must lie between the horizontal axis and the constraint boundary line whose equation is $2W = 12$.

For each of the first two functional constraints, $D \leq 4$ and $2W \leq 12$, note that the equation for the constraint boundary line ($D = 4$ and $2W = 12$, respectively) is obtained by replacing the inequality sign with an equality sign. For *any* constraint with an inequality sign (whether a functional constraint or a nonnegativity constraint), the general rule for obtaining its constraint boundary equation is to substitute an equality sign for the inequality sign.

We now need to consider one more functional constraint, $3D + 2W \leq 18$. Its constraint boundary equation,

$$3D + 2W = 18,$$

includes both variables, so the boundary line it represents is neither a vertical line nor a horizontal line. Therefore, the boundary line must intercept (cross through) both axes somewhere. But where?

When a constraint boundary line is neither a vertical line nor a horizontal line, the line *intercepts* the D axis at the point on the line where $W = 0$. Similarly, the line *intercepts* the W axis at the point on the line where $D = 0$.

Hence, the constraint boundary line, $3D + 2W = 18$, intercepts the D axis at the point where $W = 0$.

CD S Ch 2-6

When $W = 0$, $3D + 2W = 18$ becomes $3D = 18$,
so the intercept with the D axis is at $D = 6$.

Similarly, the line intercepts the W axis where $D = 0$.

When $D = 0$, $3D + 2W = 18$ becomes $2W = 18$,
so the intercept with the D axis is at $W = 9$.

Consequently, the constraint boundary line is the line that passes through these two intercept points, as shown in Figure 5.

Another way to find this constraint boundary line is to change the form of the constraint boundary equation so that it expresses W in terms of D.

$3D + 2W = 18$ implies $2W = -3D + 18$,

so

$$W = -\frac{3}{2}D + 9.$$

This form, $W = -\frac{3}{2}D + 9$, is called the **slope-intercept form** of the constraint boundary equation.

The constant term, 9, automatically is the intercept of the line with the W axis (since $W = 9$ when $D = 0$). The coefficient of D, $-\frac{3}{2}$, is the *slope* of the line.

The **slope** of a line is the change in W on the line when D is increased by 1.

Production rate for windows

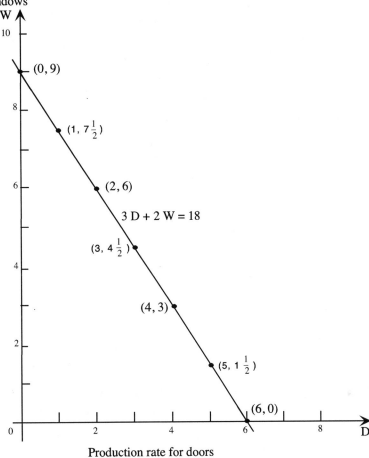

Figure 5   Graph showing that the boundary line for the constraint, $3\,D + 2\,W \le 18$, intercepts the horizontal axis at $D = 6$ and intercepts the vertical axis at $W = 9$.

For example, consider the series of points shown on the constraint boundary line in Figure 5 when moving from (0,9) toward (6,0). Note how W changes by the fixed amount, $-\dfrac{3}{2}$, each time D is increased by 1.

This derivation of the *slope-intercept form* demonstrates that the *only* numbers in the equation, $3D + 2W = 18$, that determine the slope of the line are 3 and 2, the coefficients of D and W. Therefore, if the equation $3D + 2W = 18$ were to be changed *only* by changing the right-hand side (18), the slope of the new line still would be $-\dfrac{3}{2}$. In other words, the new line would be *parallel* to the original line. To illustrate, suppose that the new equation is $3D + 2W = 12$. Since the original line had an intercept with the W axis of $\dfrac{18}{2} = 9$, the new parallel line has an intercept of $\dfrac{12}{2} = 6$, so the new line is closer to the origin, as shown in Figure 6. This figure also shows the parallel line for the equation, $3D + 2W = 24$, which has an intercept with the W axis of $\dfrac{24}{2} = 12$, and so is further from the origin than the original line.

Production rate for windows

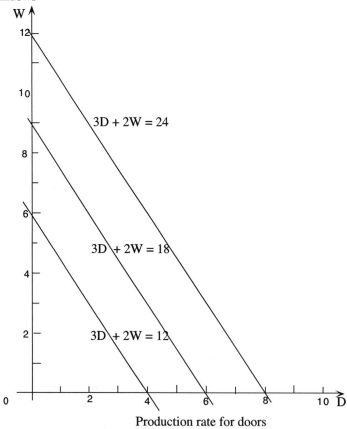

| Figure 6 | Graph showing that changing only the right-hand side of a constraint (such as $3\,D + 2\,W \leq 18$) creates *parallel* constraint boundary lines. |

This analysis also shows that the solutions permitted by the constraint, $3D + 2W \leq 18$, are those that lie on the *origin* side of the constraint boundary line,

CD S Ch 2-9

$3D + 2W = 18$. The easiest way to verify this is to check whether the origin itself, $(D, W) = (0,0)$, satisfies the constraint.[1] If it does, then the permissible region lies on the side of the constraint boundary line where the origin is. Otherwise, it lies on the other side. In this case,

$$3(0) + 2(0) = 0,$$

so $(D, W) = (0, 0)$ satisfies

$$3D + 2W \leq 18.$$

(In fact, the origin satisfies *any* constraint with a $\leq$ sign and a positive right-hand side.) Therefore, the region permitted by this constraint is the one shown in Figure 7.

---

[1] The one case where using the origin to help determine the permissible region does *not* work is if the constraint boundary line passes through the origin. In this case, any other point *not* lying on this line can be used just like the origin.

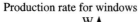

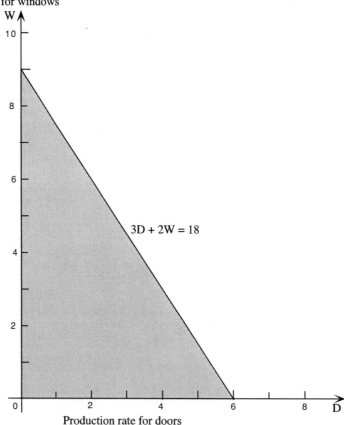

Production rate for doors

Figure 7	Graph showing that nonnegative solutions permitted by the constraint, $3D + 2W \leq 18$, lie within the triangle formed by the two axes and this constraint's boundary line, $3D + 2W = 18$.

Graphing the Feasible Region

We now have graphed the region where solutions are permitted by the *individual* constraints in Figures 2, 3, 4, and 7. However, a feasible solution for a linear programming problem must satisfy *all* the constraints *simultaneously*. To find where these feasible solutions are located, we need to combine all the constraints in one graph and identify the points representing the solutions that are in *every* constraint's permissible region.

Figure 8 shows the constraint boundary line for each of the three functional constraints. We also have added arrows to each line to show which side of the line is permitted by the corresponding constraint (as identified in the preceding figures). Note that the nonnegative solutions permitted by each of these constraints lie on the side of the constraint boundary line where the origin is (or on the line itself). Therefore, the *feasible solutions* are those that lie nearer to the origin than *all three* constraint boundary lines (or on the line nearest the origin). The resulting region of feasible solutions, called the **feasible region**, is the shaded portion of Figure 8.

Production rate for windows

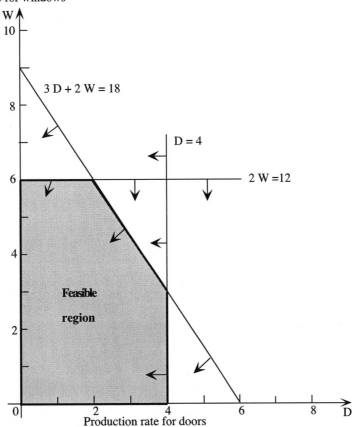

Figure 8	Graph showing how the feasible region is formed by the constraint boundary lines, where the arrows indicate which side of each line is permitted by the corresponding constraint.

Graphing the Objective Function

Having identified the feasible region, the final step is to find which of these feasible solutions is the best one — the *optimal solution*. For the Wyndor problem, the objective happens to be to *maximize* the total profit per week from the two products (denoted by *P*). Therefore, we want to find the feasible solution (*D*, *W*) that makes the value of the objective function,

$$P = 300D + 500W,$$

as large as possible.

CD S Ch 2-12

To accomplish this, we need to be able to locate all the points (D, W) on the graph that give a specified value of the objective function. For example, consider a value of $P = 1,500$ for the objective function. Which points (D, W) give

$$300D + 500W = 1,500?$$

This equation is the equation of a *line*. Just as when plotting constraint boundary lines, the location of this line is found by identifying its intercepts with the two axes. When $W = 0$, this equation yields $D = 5$, and similarly, $W = 3$ when $D = 0$, so these are the two intercepts, as shown in Figure 9.

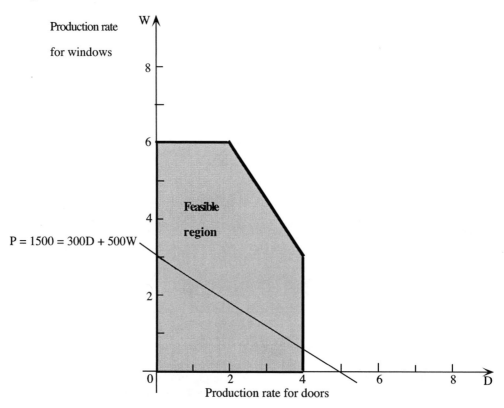

| **Figure 9** | Graph showing the line containing all the points (D, W) that give a value of $P = 1,500$ for the objective function. |

$P = 1,500$ is just one sample value of the objective function. For any other specified value of Z, the points (D, W) that give this value of P also lie on a line called an *objective function line*.

An **objective function line** is a line whose points all have the same value of the objective function.

For the objective function line in Figure 9, the points on this line that lie in the feasible region provide alternate ways of achieving an objective function value of $Z = 1,500$.

CD S Ch 2-13

Can we do better? Let us try doubling the value of Z to $Z = 3,000$. The corresponding objective function line,

$$300D + 500W = 3,000,$$

is shown as the middle line in Figure 10. (Ignore the top line for the moment.) Once again, this line includes points in the feasible region, so $P = 3,000$ is achievable.

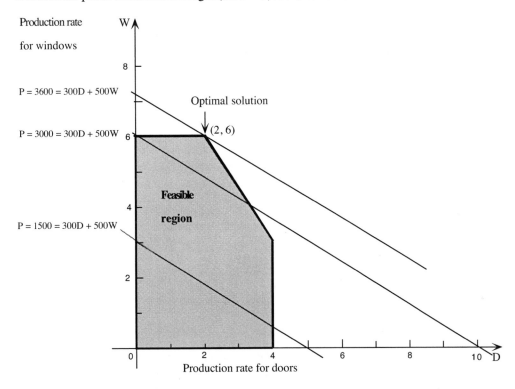

| **Figure 10** | Graph showing the three objective function lines for the Wyndor Glass Co. product-mix problem, where the top one passes through the optimal solution. |

Let us pause to note two interesting features of these objective function lines for $P = 1,500$ and $P = 3,000$. First, these lines are *parallel*. Second, *doubling* the value of P from 1,500 to 3,000 also *doubles* the value of W at which the line intercepts the W axis from $W = 3$ to $W = 6$. These features are no coincidence, as indicated by the following properties.

> **Key Properties of Objective Function Lines**: All objective function lines for the same problem are *parallel*. Furthermore, the value of W at which an objective function line intercepts the W axis is *proportional* to the value of P.

To see why these properties hold, look at the *slope-intercept form* of an objective function line for the Wyndor problem:

$$W = -\frac{300}{500}D + \frac{1}{500}P, \quad \text{which reduces to} \quad W = -\frac{3}{5}D + \frac{1}{500}P.$$

This slope-intercept form indicates that the *slope* of the lines for various values of P always is the same, $-\frac{3}{5}$, so these lines are parallel. Furthermore, this form indicates that the value of W at which a line intercepts the W axis is 1/500 P, so this value of W is *proportional* to P.

These key properties of objective function lines suggest the strategy to follow to find the optimal solution. We already have tried P = 1,500 and P = 3,000 in Figure 10 and found that their objective function lines include points in the feasible region. Increasing Z again will generate another parallel objective function line farther from the origin. The objective function line of special interest is the one farthest from the origin that still includes a point in the feasible region. This is the third objective function line in Figure 10. The point on this line that is in the feasible region, (D, W) = (2, 6), is the optimal solution since no other feasible solution has a larger value of P.

Optimal Solution

$D = 2$ (Produce 2 special new doors per week)
$W = 6$ (Produce 6 special new windows per week)

These values of D and W can be substituted into the objective function to find the value of P.

$$P = 300D + 500W = 300(2) + 500(6) = 3,600$$

You can graphically implement this strategy for finding the optimal solution by using any straight edge, such as a ruler. Rotate the straight edge in the feasible region until it has the slope of the objective function lines. (You can use any objective function line, such as the P = 1,500 line in Figure 9, to obtain this slope.) Then push the straight edge with this fixed slope through the feasible region in the direction that increases P. Stop moving the straight edge at the last instant that it still passes through a point in the feasible region. This point is the optimal solution.

In addition to finding the optimal solution, another important use of the graphical method is to perform *what-if analysis* to determine what would happen to the optimal solution if any of the numbers (parameters) in the model change. The graphical approach provides key insights for answering a variety of what-if questions described in Chapter 5.

The interactive Management Science Modules (available at **www.mhhe.com/hillier5e** or in your CD-ROM) includes a module that is designed to help increase your understanding of the graphical method. This module, called *Graphical Linear Programming and Sensitivity Analysis*, enables you to immediately see the constraint boundary lines and objective function lines that result from any linear programming model with two decision variables. You also can see how the objective function lines lead you to the optimal solution. Another key feature of the module is the ease with which you can perform what-if analysis.

CD S Ch 2-15

Summary of the Graphical Method

The graphical method can be used to solve any linear programming problem having only two variables. The method uses the following steps:

1. Draw the constraint boundary line for each functional constraint. Use the origin (or any point not on the line) to determine which side of the line is permitted by the constraint.
2. Find the feasible region by determining where all constraints are satisfied simultaneously.
3. Determine the slope of one objective function line. All other objective function lines will have the same slope.
4. Move a straight edge with this slope through the feasible region in the direction of improving values of the objective function. Stop at the last instant that the straight edge still passes through a point in the feasible region. This line given by the straight edge is the optimal objective function line.
5. A feasible point on the optimal objective function line is an optimal solution.

The Profit & Gambit Co. Advertising-Mix Example

To illustrate how the graphical method can be applied to a different kind of linear programming problem, we now will address the Profit & Gambit Co. advertising-mix problem described in Section 2.7. For your easy reference, the algebraic model for this problem is repeated below.

Choose the values of TV and PM so as to *minimize*
$$\text{Cost} = \text{TV} + 2\text{PM} \quad \text{(in millions of dollars)}$$

subject to satisfying all the following constraints:

$$
\begin{aligned}
\text{PM} &\geq 3 \\
3\text{TV} + 2\text{PM} &\geq 18 \\
-\text{TV} + 4\text{PM} &\geq 4
\end{aligned}
$$

and

$$\text{TV} \geq 0 \qquad \text{PM} \geq 0$$

where

TV = Number of units of advertising on television,
PM = Number of units of advertising in the print media.

Applying the Graphical Method

Since this linear programming model has only two decision variables, it can be solved by the graphical method described above. The interesting new features here are how this method adapts to *minimization* and to functional constraints with a $\geq$ sign.

Figure 11 shows the feasible region for this model. The three constraint boundary lines are obtained in the manner described above. However, the arrows indicating which side of each line satisfies that constraint now all point away from the origin. The reason is that the origin does not satisfy any functional constraint with a $\geq$ sign and a positive right-hand side.

Amount of print media advertising

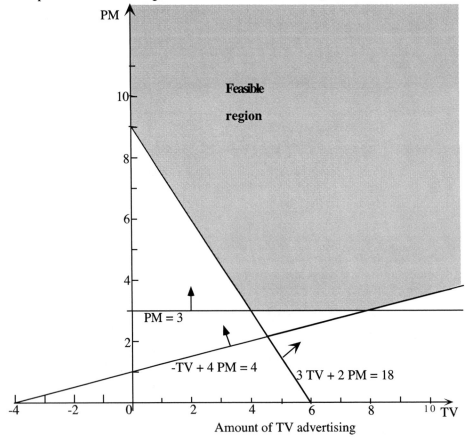

Figure 11 Graph showing the feasible region for the Profit & Gambit Co. advertising-mix problem, where the $\geq$ functional constraints have moved this region up and away from the origin.

To find the *best* solution in this feasible region (one that minimizes Cost = TV + 2 PM), we first construct a sample objective function line for one specific value of the objective function that appears to be attainable, say, Cost = 15. Figure 12 shows that a large segment of this line passes through the feasible region. Since this is a *minimization* problem, we're looking for the *smallest* value of Cost that provides an objective function line that still passes through a point in the feasible region. The origin automatically has an objective function value of Cost = 0, so objective function lines with a positive value of Cost less than 15 will be closer to the origin than the Cost = 15 line. Therefore, we want to move from the Cost =15 line to objective function lines closer to the origin. Figure 12 shows the objective function line with the smallest value of Cost (10) that still passes through a point in the feasible region. This point, (*TV, PM*) = (4, 3), is the optimal solution.

CD S Ch 2-17

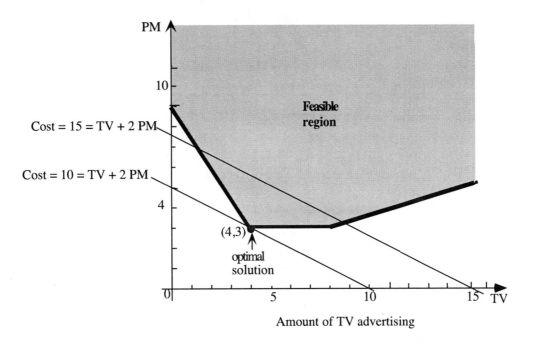

Figure 12   Graph showing two objective function lines for the Profit & Gambit Co. advertising-mix problem, where the bottom one passes through the optimal solution.

Case 5-1 continues this example by performing what-if analysis to see what would happen to the optimal solution and the total advertising cost if management were to change its sales goals for the three products.

Glossary

Constraint boundary equation: The equation for the constraint boundary line.

Constraint boundary line: For linear programming problems with two decision variables, the line forming the boundary of the solutions that are permitted by the constraint.

Feasible region: The geometric region that consists of all the feasible solutions.

Graphical method: A method for solving linear programming problems with two decision variables on a two-dimensional graph.

Objective function line: For a linear programming problem with two decision variables, a line whose points all have the same value of the objective function.

Slope-intercept form: For linear programming problems with two decision variables, the slope-intercept form of a constraint boundary equation displays both the slope of the constraint boundary line and the intercept of this line with the vertical axis.

Slope of a line: For a graph where the horizontal axis represents the variable x and the vertical axis represents y, the slope of a line is the change in y when x is increased by 1.

Problems

Note: The Graphical Linear Programming and Sensitivity Analysis module in your Interactive Management Science Modules on the CD-ROM can be useful on any of these problems.

2s.1. Reconsider Problem 2.5. Use the graphical method to find the optimal solution.

2s.2. Reconsider the model in Problem 2.7.

    a. Use the graphical method to solve this model.

    b. Use the Graphical Linear Programming and Sensitivity Analysis module in your Interactive Management Science Modules to apply the graphical method to this model.

2s.3. Reconsider the model in Problem 2.8.

    a. Use the graphical method to solve this model.

    b. Use the Graphical Linear Programming and Sensitivity Analysis module in your Interactive Management Science Modules to apply the graphical method to this model.

2s.4. You are given the following equation for a line:

$$2x_1 + x_2 = 4$$

    a. Identify the value of x_1 when $x_2 = 0$. Do the same for x_2 when $x_1 = 0$.

    b. Construct a two-dimensional graph with x_1 on the horizontal axis and x_2 on the vertical axis. Then use the information from part *a* to draw the line.

    c. Determine the numerical value of the slope of this line.

    d. Find the slope-intercept form of this equation. Then use this form to identify both the slope of the line and the intercept of the line with the vertical axis.

2s.5. Follow the instructions of Problem 4 for the following equation of a line.

$$2x_1 + 5x_2 = 10$$

2s.6. Follow the instructions of Problem 4 for the following equation of a line.

$$2x_1 - 3x_2 = 12$$

2s.7. For each of the following constraints on the decision variables x_1 and x_2, draw a separate graph to show the nonnegative solutions that satisfy this constraint.

    a. $x_1 + 3x_2 \leq 6$

    b. $4x_1 + 3x_2 \leq 12$

    c. $4x_1 + x_2 \leq 8$

    d. Now combine these constraints into a single graph to show the feasible region for the entire set of functional constraints plus nonnegativity constraints.

2s.8.   For each of the following constraints on the decision variables x_1 and x_2, draw a separate graph to show the nonnegative solutions that satisfy this constraint.

   a. $10x_1 + 20x_2 \leq 40$

   b. $5x_1 + 3x_2 \geq 15$

   c. $5x_1 - x_2 \leq 15$

   d.   Now combine these constraints into a single graph to show the feasible region for the entire set of functional constraints plus nonnegativity constraints.

2s.9.   For each of the following constraints on the decision variables x_1 and x_2, draw a separate graph to show the nonnegative solutions that satisfy this constraint.

   a. $x_1 - x_2 \leq 2$

   b. $-3x_1 + 6x_2 \geq 3$

   c. $4x_1 - 3x_2 \geq 1$

   d.   Now combine these constraints into a single graph to show the feasible region for the entire set of functional constraints plus nonnegativity constraints.

2s.10.   Reconsider Problem 2.12. Find the optimal solution by using the Graphical Linear Programming and Sensitivity Analysis module in your Interactive Management Science Modules.

2s.11.   Consider the following objective function for a linear programming model with decision variables x_1 and x_2:

   Maximize   Profit $= 2x_1 + 3x_2$

   a.   Draw a graph that shows the corresponding objective function lines for Profit $= 6$, Profit $= 12$, and Profit $= 18$.

   b.   Find the slope-intercept form of the equation for each of these three objective function lines. Compare the slope for these three lines. Also compare the intercept with the x_2 axis.

2s.12.   Using the symbol P to represent total profit, you are given the following objective function for a linear programming model with decision variables x_1 and x_2:

   Maximize $P = 25x_1 + 10x_2$

   a.   Draw a graph that shows the corresponding objective function lines for $P = 100$, $P = 200$, and $P = 300$.

   b.   Find the slope-intercept form of the equation for each of these three objective function lines. Compare the slope for these three lines. Also compare the intercept with the x_2 axis.

2s.13.   Consider the following objective function for a linear programming model with decision variables x_1 and x_2:

$$\text{Minimize} \quad \text{Cost} = 5x_1 - x_2$$

    a.   Draw a graph that shows the corresponding objective function lines for Cost = 300, Cost = 200, and Cost = 100.

    b.   Find the slope-intercept form of the equation for each of these three objective function lines. Compare the slope for these three lines. Also compare the intercept with the x_2 axis.

2s.14.   Consider the following equation of a line:

$$20x_1 + 40x_2 = 400$$

    a.   Find the slope-intercept form of this equation.

    b.   Use this form to identify the slope and the intercept with the x_2 axis for this line.

    c.   Use the information from part *b* to draw a graph of this line.

2s.15.   Find the slope-intercept form of the following equation of a line:

$$8x_1 + x_2 = 40$$

2s.16.   Find the slope-intercept form of the following equations of lines:

    a. $10x_1 + 5x_2 = 20$

    b. $-2x_1 + 3x_2 = 6$

    c. $5x_1 - 2x_2 = 10$

2s.17.   Consider the following constraint on the decision variables x_1 and x_2:

$$x_1 - 2x_2 \leq 0$$

    a.   Write the constraint boundary equation for this constraint.

    b.   Find the slope-intercept form of this equation.

    c.   Use this form to identify the slope and the intercept with the x_2 axis for the constraint boundary line.

    d.   Use the information from part *c* to draw a graph of the constraint boundary line.

    e.   Identify which side of this line is permitted by the constraint.

2s.18.   You are given the following linear programming model in algebraic form, where x_1 and x_2 are the decision variables and Z is the value of the overall measure of performance.

$$\text{Maximize} \quad Z = 20x_1 + 10x_2$$

subject to

$$x_1 - x_2 \leq 1$$
$$3x_1 + x_2 \leq 7$$

and

$$x_1 \geq 0 \qquad x_2 \geq 0$$

Use the graphical method to solve this model.

2s.19. You are given the linear programming model in algebraic form shown below, where the objective is to choose the levels of two activities (x_1 and x_2) so as to maximize their total profit, subject to constraints on the amounts of three resources available.

$$\text{Maximize} \qquad \text{Profit} = 10x_1 + 20x_2$$

subject to

$$-x_1 + 2x_2 \leq 15 \text{ (resource 1)}$$
$$x_1 + x_2 \leq 12 \text{ (resource 2)}$$
$$5x_1 + 3x_2 \leq 45 \text{ (resource 3)}$$

and

$$x_1 \geq 0 \qquad x_2 \geq 0$$

Use the graphical method to solve this model.

2s.20. Consider the algebraic form of a linear programming model shown below, where x_1 and x_2 are the decision variables. Use the graphical method to solve this model.

$$\text{Maximize} \quad \text{Profit} = 400x_1 + 500x_2$$

subject to

$$20x_1 + 10x_2 \leq 100$$
$$5x_1 + 10x_2 \leq 50$$
$$3x_1 - x_2 \leq 10$$
$$-x_1 + 4x_2 \leq 15$$

and

$$x_1 \geq 0 \qquad x_2 \geq 0$$

2s.21. Reconsider Problem 2.21. Use the graphical method to find the optimal solution. Decide yourself whether you would prefer to do this by hand or by using the Graphical Linear Programming and Sensitivity Analysis module in your Interactive Management Science Modules.

2s.22. Consider the following algebraic form of a linear programming model, where the value of c_1 has not yet been ascertained.

$$\text{Maximize} \quad Z = c_1 x_1 + x_2$$

subject to

$$x_1 + x_2 \leq 6$$
$$x_1 + 2x_2 \leq 10$$

and

$$x_1 \geq 0 \qquad x_2 \geq 0$$

Use graphical analysis to determine the optimal solution(s) for (x_1, x_2) for the various possible values of c_1 (both positive and negative).

2s.23. Consider the following algebraic form of a linear programming model, where the value of c_1 has not yet been ascertained.

$$\text{Maximize } Z = c_1 x_1 + 2x_2$$

subject to

$$4x_1 + x_2 \leq 12$$
$$x_1 - x_2 \geq 2$$

and

$$x_1 \geq 0 \quad x_2 \geq 0$$

Use graphical analysis to determine the optimal solution(s) for (x_1, x_2) for the various possible values of c_1 (both positive and negative).

2s.24. Consider the following algebraic form of a linear programming model, where the value of k has not yet been ascertained.

$$\text{Maximize } Z = x_1 + 2x_2$$

subject to

$$-x_1 + x_2 \leq 2$$
$$x_2 \leq 3$$
$$kx_1 + x_2 \leq 2k + 3, \quad \text{where } k \geq 0$$

and

$$x_1 \geq 0 \quad x_2 \geq 0$$

The solution currently being used is $(x_1, x_2) = (2, 3)$. Use graphical analysis to determine the values of k such that this solution actually is optimal.

2s.25. Your boss has asked you to use your background in management science to determine what the levels of two activities (x_1 and x_2) should be to minimize their total cost while satisfying some constraints. The algebraic form of the model is shown below.

$$\text{Minimize } \text{Cost} = 15x_1 + 20x_2$$

subject to

Constraint 1:	$x_1 + 2x_2$	≥ 10
Constraint 2:	$2x_1 - 3x_2$	≤ 6
Constraint 3:	$x_1 + x_2$	≥ 6

and

$$x_1 \geq 0 \quad x_2 \geq 0$$

Use the graphical method to solve this model.

2s.26. Reconsider Problem 2.24. Use the graphical method to find the optimal solution.

2s.27. For the following algebraic form of a linear programming model, the objective is to choose the levels of two activities (x_1 and x_2) so as to minimize their total cost while satisfying some constraints.

$$\text{Minimize} \quad \text{Cost} = 3x_1 + 2x_2$$

subject to

Constraint 1:	$x_1 + 2x_2$	≤ 12
Constraint 2:	$2x_1 + 3x_2$	$= 12$
Constraint 3:	$2x_1 + x_2$	≥ 8

and

$$x_1 \geq 0 \qquad x_2 \geq 0$$

Use the graphical method to solve this model.

Chapter **Three**

Linear Programming: Formulation and Applications

Learning Objectives

After completing this chapter, you should be able to

1. Recognize various kinds of managerial problems to which linear programming can be applied.

2. Describe the five major categories of linear programming problems, including their identifying features.

3. Formulate a linear programming model from a description of a problem in any of these categories.

4. Describe the difference between resource constraints and benefit constraints, including the difference in how they arise.

5. Describe fixed-requirement constraints and where they arise.

6. Identify the kinds of Excel functions that linear programming spreadsheet models use for the output cells, including the objective cell.

7. Identify the four components of any linear programming model and the kind of spreadsheet cells used for each component.

8. Recognize managerial problems that can be formulated and analyzed as linear programming problems.

9. Understand the flexibility that managers have in prescribing key considerations that can be incorporated into a linear programming model.

Linear programming problems come in many guises. And their models take various forms. This diversity can be confusing to both students and managers, making it difficult to recognize when linear programming can be applied to address a managerial problem. Since managers instigate management science studies, the ability to recognize the applicability of linear programming is an important managerial skill. This chapter focuses largely on developing this skill.

The usual textbook approach to trying to teach this skill is to present a series of diverse examples of linear programming applications. The weakness of this approach is that it emphasizes differences rather than the common threads between these applications. Our approach will be to emphasize these common threads—the **identifying features**—that tie together linear programming problems even when they arise in very different contexts. We will describe some broad categories of linear programming problems and the identifying features that characterize them. Then we will use diverse examples, but with the purpose of illustrating and emphasizing the common threads among them.

We will focus on five key categories of linear programming problems: resource-allocation problems, cost–benefit–trade-off problems, mixed problems, transportation problems, and assignment problems. In each case, an important identifying feature is the nature of the restrictions on what decisions can be made, and thus the nature of the resulting functional constraints in the linear programming model. For each category, you will see how the basic data for a problem lead directly to a linear programming model with a certain distinctive form. Thus, model formulation becomes a by-product of proper problem formulation.

The chapter begins with a case study that initially involves a resource-allocation problem. We then return to the case study in Section 3.4, where additional managerial considerations turn the problem into a mixed problem.

Sections 3.2 to 3.6 focus on the five categories of linear programming problems in turn. Section 3.7 then takes a broader look at the formulation of linear programming models from a managerial perspective. That section (along with Section 3.4) highlights the importance of having the model accurately reflect the managerial view of the problem. These (and other) sections also describe the flexibility available to managers for having the model structured to best fit their view of the important considerations.

3.1 A CASE STUDY: THE SUPER GRAIN CORP. ADVERTISING-MIX PROBLEM

Claire Syverson, vice president for marketing of the **Super Grain Corporation,** is facing a daunting challenge: how to break into an already overly crowded breakfast cereal market in a big way. Fortunately, the company's new breakfast cereal—*Crunchy Start*—has a lot going for it: Great taste. Nutritious. Crunchy from start to finish. She can recite the litany in her sleep now. It has the makings of a winning promotional campaign.

However, Claire knows that she has to avoid the mistakes she made in her last campaign for a breakfast cereal. That had been her first big assignment since she won this promotion, and what a disaster! She thought she had developed a really good campaign. But somehow it had failed to connect with the most crucial segments of the market—young children and parents of young children. She also has concluded that it was a mistake not to include cents-off coupons in the magazine and newspaper advertising. Oh well. Live and learn.

But she had better get it right this time, especially after the big stumble last time. The company's president, David Sloan, already has impressed on her how important the success of Crunchy Start is to the future of the company. She remembers exactly how David concluded the conversation. "The company's shareholders are not happy. We need to get those earnings headed in the right direction again." Claire had heard this tune before, but she saw in David's eyes how deadly serious he was this time.

Claire often uses spreadsheets to help organize her planning. Her management science course in business school impressed upon her how valuable spreadsheet modeling can be. She regrets that she did not rely more heavily on spreadsheet modeling for the last campaign. That was a mistake that she is determined not to repeat.

Now it is time for Claire to carefully review and formulate the problem in preparation for formulating a spreadsheet model.

The Problem

Claire already has employed a leading advertising firm, Giacomi & Jackowitz, to help design a nationwide promotional campaign that will achieve the largest possible exposure for Crunchy Start. Super Grain will pay this firm a fee based on services performed (not to exceed $1 million) and has allocated an additional $4 million for advertising expenses.

Giacomi & Jackowitz has identified the three most effective advertising media for this product:

Medium 1: Television commercials on Saturday morning programs for children.

Medium 2: Advertisements in food and family-oriented magazines.

Medium 3: Advertisements in Sunday supplements of major newspapers.

TABLE 3.1
Cost and Exposure Data
for the Super Grain
Corp. Advertising-Mix
Problem

	Costs		
Cost Category	**Each TV Commercial**	**Each Magazine Ad**	**Each Sunday Ad**
Ad budget	$300,000	$150,000	$100,000
Planning budget	90,000	30,000	40,000
Expected number of exposures	1,300,000	600,000	500,000

The problem now is to determine which *levels* should be chosen for these *advertising activities* to obtain the most effective *advertising mix.*

To determine the *best mix of activity levels* for this particular advertising problem, it is necessary (as always) to identify the *overall measure of performance* for the problem and then the contribution of each activity toward this measure. An ultimate goal for Super Grain is to maximize its profits, but it is difficult to make a direct connection between advertising exposure and profits. Therefore, as a rough surrogate for profit, Claire decides to use *expected number of exposures* as the overall measure of performance, where each viewing of an advertisement by some individual counts as one exposure.

Giacomi & Jackowitz has made preliminary plans for advertisements in the three media. The firm also has estimated the expected number of exposures for each advertisement in each medium, as given in the bottom row of Table 3.1.

The number of advertisements that can be run in the different media are restricted by both the advertising budget (a limit of $4 million) and the planning budget (a limit of $1 million for the fee to Giacomi & Jackowitz). Another restriction is that there are only five commercial spots available for running different commercials (one commercial per spot) on children's television programs Saturday morning (medium 1) during the time of the promotional campaign. (The other two media have an ample number of spots available.)

Consequently, the three *resources* for this problem are:

Resource 1: Advertising budget ($4 million).

Resource 2: Planning budget ($1 million).

Resource 3: TV commercial spots available (5).

Table 3.1 shows how much of the advertising budget and the planning budget would be used by each advertisement in the respective media.

- The first row gives the cost per advertisement in each medium.
- The second row shows Giacomi & Jackowitz's estimates of its total cost (including overhead and profit) for designing and developing each advertisement for the respective media.[1] (This cost represents the billable fee from Super Grain.)
- The last row then gives the expected number of exposures per advertisement.

Analysis of the Problem

Claire decides to formulate and solve a linear programming model for this problem on a spreadsheet. The formulation procedure summarized at the end of Section 2.2 guides this process. Like any linear programming model, this model will have four components:

1. The data
2. The decisions
3. The constraints
4. The measure of performance

[1] When presenting its estimates in this form, the firm is making two simplifying assumptions. One is that its cost for designing and developing each additional advertisement in a medium is roughly the same as for the first advertisement in that medium. The second is that its cost when working with one medium is unaffected by how much work it is doing (if any) with the other media.

The spreadsheet needs to be formatted to provide the following kinds of cells for these components:

Four kinds of cells are needed for these four components of a spreadsheet model.

Data → data cells

Decisions → changing cells

Constraints → output cells

Measure of performance → objective cell

Figure 3.1 shows the spreadsheet model formulated by Claire. Let us see how she did this by considering each of the components of the model individually.

FIGURE 3.1

The spreadsheet model for the Super Grain problem (Section 3.1), including the objective cell TotalExposures (H13) and the other output cells BudgetSpent (F8:F9), as well as the specifications needed to set up Solver. The changing cells NumberOfAds (C13:E13) show the optimal solution obtained by Solver.

	A	B	C	D	E	F	G	H
1		**Super Grain Corp. Advertising-Mix Problem**						
2								
3			TV Spots	Magazine Ads	SS Ads			
4		Exposures per Ad	1,300	600	500			
5		(thousands)						
6						Budget		Budget
7			Cost per Ad ($thousands)			Spent		Available
8		Ad Budget	300	150	100	4,000	≤	4,000
9		Planning Budget	90	30	40	1,000	≤	1,000
10								
11								Total Exposures
12			TV Spots	Magazine Ads	SS Ads			(thousands)
13		Number of Ads	0	20	10			17,000
14			≤					
15		Max TV Spots	5					

Set Objective Cell: TotalExposures
To: Max
By Changing Variable Cells:
    NumberOfAds
Subject to the Constraints:
    BudgetSpent <= BudgetAvailable
    TVSpots <= MaxTVSpots

Solver Options:
    Make Variables Nonnegative
    Solving Method: Simplex LP

	F
6	Budget
7	Spent
8	=SUMPRODUCT(C8:E8,NumberOfAds)
9	=SUMPRODUCT(C9:E9,NumberOfAds)

	H
11	Total Exposures
12	(thousands)
13	=SUMPRODUCT(ExposuresPerAd,NumberOfAds)

Range Name	Cells
BudgetAvailable	H8: H9
BudgetSpent	F8: F9
CostPerAd	C8: E9
ExposuresPerAd	C4: E4
MaxTVSpots	C15
NumberOfAds	C13: E13
TotalExposures	H13
TVSpots	C13

The Data

One important kind of data is the information given earlier about the amounts available of the three resources for the problem (the advertising budget, the planning budget, and the commercial spots available). Table 3.1 provides the other key data for the problem. Using units of thousands of dollars, these data have been transferred directly into data cells in the spreadsheet in Figure 3.1 and given these range names: ExposuresPerAd (C4:E4), CostPerAd (C8:E9), BudgetAvailable (H8:H9), and MaxTVSpots (C15).

The Decisions

The problem has been defined as determining the most effective advertising mix among the three media selected by Giacomi & Jackowitz. Therefore, there are three decisions:

Decision 1: TV = Number of commercials for separate spots on television.

Decision 2: M = Number of advertisements in magazines.

Decision 3: SS = Number of advertisements in Sunday supplements.

The changing cells to hold these numbers have been placed in row 13 in the columns for these media:

$$TV \rightarrow \text{cell C13} \qquad M \rightarrow \text{cell D13} \qquad SS \rightarrow \text{cell E13}$$

These changing cells are collectively referred to by the range name NumberOfAds (C13:E13).

The Constraints

These changing cells need to be nonnegative. In addition, constraints are needed for the three resources. The first two resources are the ad budget and planning budget. The amounts available for these two budgets are shown in the range BudgetAvailable (H8:H9). As suggested by the $\leq$ signs entered into column G, the corresponding constraints are

Total spending on advertising $\leq$ 4,000   (Ad budget in \$1,000s)

Total cost of planning $\leq$ 1,000   (Planning budget in \$1,000s)

Using the data in columns C, D, and E for the resources, these totals are

Total spending on advertising = $300TV + 150M + 100SS$

Total cost of planning   = $90TV + 30M + 40SS$

These sums of products on the right-hand side are entered into the output cells BudgetSpent (F8:F9) by using the SUMPRODUCT functions shown in the lower right-hand side of Figure 3.1. Although the $\leq$ signs entered in column G are only cosmetic (trial solutions still can be entered in the changing cells that violate these inequalities), they will serve as a reminder later to use these same $\leq$ signs when entering the constraints in Solver.

Excel Tip: Range names may overlap. For instance, we have used NumberOfAds to refer to the whole range of changing cells, C13:E13, and TVSpots to refer to the single cell, C13.

The third resource is TV spots for different commercials. Five such spots are available for purchase. The number of spots used is one of the changing cells (C13). Since this cell will be used in a constraint, we assign the cell its own range name: TVSpots (C13). The maximum number of TV spots available is in the data cell MaxTVSpots (C15). Thus, the required constraint is TVSpots $\leq$ MaxTVSpots.

The Measure of Performance

Claire Syverson is using *expected number of exposures* as the overall measure of performance, so let

Exposure = Expected number of exposures (in thousands) from all the advertising

The data cells ExposuresPerAd (C4:E4) provide the expected number of exposures (in thousands) per advertisement in the respective media and the changing cells NumberOfAds (C13:E13) give the number of each type of advertisement. Therefore,

$$\text{Exposure} = 1,300TV + 600M + 500SS$$

$$= \text{SUMPRODUCT (ExposuresPerAd, NumberOfAds)}$$

is the formula that needs to be entered into the objective cell, TotalExposures (H13).

Summary of the Formulation

The above analysis of the four components of the model has formulated the following linear programming model (in algebraic form) on the spreadsheet:

$$\text{Maximize} \quad \text{Exposure} = 1,300TV + 600M + 500SS$$

subject to

Ad spending:	$300TV + 150M + 100SS \leq 4,000$
Planning costs:	$90TV + 30M + 40SS \leq 1,000$
Number of television spots:	$TV \qquad\qquad\qquad \leq \quad 5$

and

$$TV \geq 0 \quad M \geq 0 \quad SS \geq 0$$

The difficult work of defining the problem and gathering all the relevant data in Table 3.1 leads directly to this formulation.

Solving the Model

Excel Tip: With Excel's Solver, the Solver dialog box is used to tell Solver the location on the spreadsheet of several of the elements of the model: the changing cells, the objective cell, and the constraints. With RSPE, the Decisions, Constraints, and Objective menu on the RSPE ribbon are used along with the Model pane.

To solve the spreadsheet model formulated above, some key information needs to be entered into Solver. The lower left-hand side of Figure 3.1 shows the needed entries: the objective cell (TotalExposures), the changing cells (NumberOfAds), the goal of maximizing the objective cell, and the constraints BudgetSpent ≤ BudgetAvailable and TVSpots ≤ MaxTVSpots. Two options are also specified at the bottom of the Solver Parameters box on the lower left-hand side of Figure 3.1. The changing cells need non-negativity constraints because negative values of advertising are not possible. Choose the Simplex LP (Excel's Solver) or Standard LP/Quadratic Engine (RSPE) solving method, because this is a linear programming model. Running Solver then finds an optimal solution for the model and display it in the changing cells.

The optimal solution given in row 13 of the spreadsheet provides the following plan for the promotional campaign:

Do not run any television commercials.

Run 20 advertisements in magazines.

Run 10 advertisements in Sunday supplements.

Since TotalExposures (H13) gives the expected number of exposures in thousands, this plan would be expected to provide 17,000,000 exposures.

Evaluation of the Adequacy of the Model

When she chose to use a linear programming model to represent this advertising-mix problem, Claire recognized that this kind of model does not provide a perfect match to this problem. However, a mathematical model is intended to be only an approximate representation of the real problem. Approximations and simplifying assumptions generally are required to have a workable model. All that is really needed is that there be a reasonably high correlation between the prediction of the model and what would actually happen in the real problem. The team now needs to check whether this criterion is satisfied.

Linear programming models allow fractional solutions.

One assumption of linear programming is that *fractional* solutions are allowed. For the current problem, this means that a fractional number (e.g., 3½) of television commercials (or of ads in magazines or Sunday supplements) should be allowed. This is technically true, since a commercial can be aired for less than a normal run, or an ad can be run in just a fraction of the usual magazines or Sunday supplements. However, one defect of the model is that it assumes that Giacomi & Jackowitz's cost for planning and developing a commercial or ad that receives only a fraction of its usual run is only that fraction of its usual cost, even though the actual cost would be the same as for a full run. Fortunately, the optimal solution obtained was an *integer* solution (0 television commercials, 20 ads in magazines, and 10 ads in Sunday supplements), so the assumption that fractional solutions are allowed was not even needed.

Although it is possible to have a fractional number of a normal run of commercials or ads, a normal run tends to be much more effective than a fractional run. Therefore, it would have been reasonable for Claire to drop the assumption that fractional solutions are allowed. If Claire had done this and the optimal solution for the linear programming model had not turned out to be integer, constraints can be added to require the changing cells to be integer. (The TBA Airlines example in the next section provides an illustration of this type of constraint.) After adding such constraints, the model is called an *integer programming model* instead of a linear programming model, but it still can be readily solved by Solver.

Linear programming models should use SUM or SUMPRODUCT functions for the output cells, including the objective cell.

Another key assumption of linear programming is that the appropriate equation for each of the output cells, including the objective cell, is one that can be expressed as a SUMPRODUCT of data cells and changing cells (or occasionally just a SUM of changing cells). For the objective cell (cell H13) in Figure 3.1, this implies that the expected number of exposures to be obtained from each advertising medium is *proportional* to the number of advertisements in that medium. This proportionality seems true, since each viewing of the advertisements by some individual counts as another exposure. Another implication of using a SUMPRODUCT function is that the expected number of exposures to be obtained from an advertising medium is unaffected by the number of advertisements in the other media. Again, this implication seems valid, since viewings of advertisements in different media count as separate exposures.

Although a SUMPRODUCT function is appropriate for calculating the expected number of exposures, the choice of this number for the overall measure of performance is somewhat questionable. Management's real objective is to maximize the profit generated as a result of the advertising campaign, but this is difficult to measure so *expected number of exposures* was selected to be a surrogate for profit. This would be valid if profit were proportional to the expected number of exposures. However, proportionality is only an approximation in this case because too many exposures for the same individual reach a saturation level where the impact (potential profit) from one more exposure is substantially less than for the first exposure. (When proportionality is not a reasonable approximation, Chapter 8 will describe nonlinear models that can be used instead.)

To check how reasonable it is to use expected number of exposures as a surrogate for profit, Claire meets with Sid Jackowitz, one of the senior partners of Giacomi & Jackowitz. Sid indicates that the contemplated promotional campaign (20 advertisements in magazines and 10 in Sunday supplements) is a relatively modest one well below saturation levels. Most readers will only notice these ads once or twice, and a second notice is very helpful for reinforcing the first one. Furthermore, the readership of magazines and Sunday supplements is sufficiently different that the interaction of the advertising impact in these two media should be small. Consequently, Claire concludes that using expected number of exposures for the objective cell in Figure 3.1 provides a reasonable approximation. (A continuation of this case study in Case 8-1 will delve into the more complicated analysis that is required in order to use profit directly as the measure of performance to be recorded in the objective cell instead of making this approximation.)

Next, Claire quizzes Sid about his firm's costs for planning and developing advertisements in these media. Is it reasonable to assume that the cost in a given medium is proportional to the number of advertisements in that medium? Is it reasonable to assume that the cost of developing advertisements in one medium would not be substantially reduced if the firm had just finished developing advertisements in another medium that might have similar themes? Sid acknowledges that there is some carryover in ad planning from one medium to another, especially if both are print media (e.g., magazines and Sunday supplements), but that the carryover is quite limited because of the distinct differences in these media. Furthermore, he feels that the proportionality assumption is quite reasonable for any given medium since the amount of work involved in planning and developing each additional advertisement in the medium is nearly the same as for the first one in the medium. The total fee that Super

Grain will pay Giacomi & Jackowitz will eventually be based on a detailed accounting of the amount of work done by the firm. Nevertheless, Sid feels that the cost estimates previously provided by the firm (as entered in cells C9, D9, and E9 in units of thousands of dollars) give a reasonable basis for roughly projecting what the fee will be for any given plan (the entries in the changing cells) for the promotional campaign.

Based on this information, Claire concludes that using a SUMPRODUCT function for cell F9 provides a reasonable approximation. Doing the same for cell F8 is clearly justified. Given her earlier conclusions as well, Claire decides that the linear programming model incorporated into Figure 3.1 (plus any expansions of the model needed later for the detailed planning) is a sufficiently accurate representation of the real advertising-mix problem. It will not be necessary to refine the results from this model by turning next to a more complicated kind of mathematical model (such as those to be described in Chapter 8).

Therefore, Claire sends a memorandum to the company's president, David Sloan, describing a promotional campaign that corresponds to the optimal solution from the linear programming model (no TV commercials, 20 ads in magazines, and 10 ads in Sunday supplements). She also requests a meeting to evaluate this plan and discuss whether some modifications should be made.

We will pick up this story again in Section 3.4.

Review Questions

1. What is the problem being addressed in this case study?
2. What overall measure of performance is being used?
3. What are the assumptions of linear programming that need to be checked to evaluate the adequacy of using a linear programming model to represent the problem under consideration?

3.2 RESOURCE-ALLOCATION PROBLEMS

In the opening paragraph of Chapter 2, we described managerial problems involving the allocation of an organization's resources to its various productive activities. Those were *resource-allocation* problems.

> **Resource-allocation problems** are linear programming problems involving the *allocation of resources to activities*. The *identifying feature* for any such problem is that each functional constraint in the linear programming model is a **resource constraint,** which has the form
>
> Amount of resource used ≤ Amount of resource available
>
> for one of the resources.

The amount of a resource used depends on which activities are undertaken, the levels of those activities, and how heavily those activities need to use the resource. Thus, the resource constraints place limits on the levels of the activities. The objective is to choose the levels of the activities so as to maximize some overall measure of performance (such as total profit) from the activities while satisfying all the resource constraints.

Beginning with the case study and then the Wyndor Glass Co. product-mix problem, we will look at four examples that illustrate the characteristics of resource-allocation problems. These examples also demonstrate how this type of problem can arise in a variety of contexts.

The Super Grain Corp. Advertising-Mix Problem

The linear programming model formulated in Section 3.1 for the Super Grain case study is one example of a resource-allocation problem. The three *activities* under consideration are the advertising in the three types of media chosen by Giacomi & Jackowitz.

Activity 1: TV commercials

Activity 2: Magazine ads

Activity 3: Sunday ads

The decisions being made are the *levels* of these activities, that is, the *number* of TV commercials, magazine ads, and Sunday ads to run.

An initial step in formulating any resource-allocation problem is to identify the activities and the resources.

The *resources* to be allocated to these activities are

Resource 1: Advertising budget ($4 million).
Resource 2: Planning budget ($1 million).
Resource 3: TV spots available for different commercials (5).

where the *amounts available* of these resources are given in parentheses. Thus, this problem has three resource constraints:

1. Advertising budget used   ≤ $4 million
2. Planning budget used   ≤ $1 million
3. TV spots used   ≤ 5

Rows 8–9 and cells C13:C15 in Figure 3.1 show these constraints in a spreadsheet. Cells C8:E9 give the amount of the advertising budget and the planning budget used by *each unit* of each activity, that is, the amount used by one TV spot, one magazine ad, and one Sunday ad, respectively.

Cells C4, D4, and E4 on this spreadsheet give the *contribution per unit of each activity* to the overall measure of performance (expected number of exposures).

Characteristics of Resource-Allocation Problems

For each proposed activity, a decision needs to be made as to how much of the activity to do. In other words, what should the level of the activity be?

Other resource-allocation problems have the same kinds of characteristics as the Super Grain problem. In each case, there are *activities* where the decisions to be made are the *levels* of these activities. The contribution of each activity to the overall measure of performance is proportional to the level of that activity. Commonly, this measure of performance is the *total profit* from the activities, but occasionally it is something else (as in the Super Grain problem).

Every problem of this type has a resource constraint for each resource. The amounts of the resources used depend on the levels of the activities. For each resource, the amount used by each activity is proportional to the level of that activity.

These three kinds of data are needed for any resource-allocation problem.

The manager or management science team studying a resource allocation problem needs to gather (with considerable help) three kinds of data:

1. The *amount available* of each resource.
2. The amount of each resource needed by each activity. Specifically, for each combination of resource and activity, the *amount of the resource used per unit of the activity* must be estimated.
3. The *contribution per unit of each activity* to the overall measure of performance.

Generally there is considerable work involved in developing these data. A substantial amount of digging and consultation is needed to obtain the best estimates available in a timely fashion. This step is critical. Well-informed estimates are needed to obtain a valid linear programming model for guiding managerial decisions. The dangers involved in inaccurate estimates are one reason why *what-if analysis* (Chapter 5) is such an important part of most linear programming studies.

The Wyndor Glass Co. Product-Mix Problem

The product-mix problem facing the management of the Wyndor Glass Co. in Section 2.1 is to determine the most profitable mix of production rates for the two new products, considering the limited availability of spare production capacity in the company's three plants. This is a resource-allocation problem.

The *activities* under consideration are

Activity 1: Produce the special new doors.
Activity 2: Produce the special new windows.

The decisions being made are the *levels* of these activities, that is, the production rates for the doors and windows. Production rate is being measured as the number of units (doors or windows) produced per week. Management's objective is to maximize the total profit generated by the two new products, so the overall measure of performance is total profit. The contribution of each product to profit is proportional to the production rate for that product.

The *resources* to be allocated to these activities are

Resource 1: Production capacity in Plant 1.
Resource 2: Production capacity in Plant 2.
Resource 3: Production capacity in Plant 3.

Each of the three functional constraints in the linear programming model formulated in Section 2.2 (see rows 7–9 of the spreadsheet in Figure 2.3 or 2.4) is a *resource constraint* for one of these three resources. Column E shows the amount of production capacity used in each plant and column G gives the amount available.

Table 2.1 in Section 2.1 provides the data for the Wyndor problem. You already have seen how the numbers in Table 2.1 become the parameters in the linear programming model in either its spreadsheet formulation (Section 2.2) or its algebraic form (Section 2.3).

The TBA Airlines Problem

TBA Airlines is a small regional company that specializes in short flights in small passenger airplanes. The company has been doing well and management has decided to expand its operations.

The Problem

The basic issue facing management now is whether to purchase more small airplanes to add some new short flights or to start moving into the national market by purchasing some large airplanes for new cross-country flights (or both). Many factors will go into management's final decision, but the most important one is which strategy is likely to be most profitable.

The first row of Table 3.2 shows the estimated net annual profit (inclusive of capital recovery costs) from each type of airplane purchased. The second row gives the purchase cost per airplane and also notes that the total amount of capital available for airplane purchases is $250 million. The third row records the fact that management does not want to purchase more than five small airplanes because of limited possibilities for adding lucrative short flights, whereas they have not specified a maximum number for large airplanes (other than that imposed by the limited capital available).

How many airplanes of each type should be purchased to maximize the total net annual profit?

Formulation

This is a *resource-allocation problem.* The activities under consideration are

Activity 1: Purchase small airplanes.
Activity 2: Purchase large airplanes.

The decisions to be made are the levels of these activities, that is,

S = Number of small airplanes to purchase
L = Number of large airplanes to purchase

The one resource to be allocated to these activities is

Resource: Investment capital ($250 million).

Thus, there is a single resource constraint:

$$\text{Investment capital spent} \leq \$250 \text{ million}$$

In addition, management has specified one side constraint:

$$\text{Number of small airplanes purchased} \leq 5$$

Figure 3.2 shows the formulation of a spreadsheet model for this problem, where the data in Table 3.2 have been transferred into the data cells—UnitProfit (C4:D4), CapitalPerUnitPurchased

TABLE 3.2
Data for the TBA
Airlines Problem

	Small Airplane	Large Airplane	Capital Available
Net annual profit per airplane	$7 million	$22 million	
Purchase cost per airplane	$25 million	$75 million	$250 million
Maximum purchase quantity	5	No maximum	

108 Business Decision Models ADM2302

74 Chapter Three *Linear Programming: Formulation and Applications*

FIGURE 3.2

A spreadsheet model for the TBA Airlines integer programming problem where the changing cells, UnitsProduced (C12:D12), show the optimal airplane purchases obtained by Solver, and the objective cell, TotalProfit (G12), gives the resulting total profit in millions of dollars.

	A	B	C	D	E	F	G
1		**TBA Airlines Airplane Purchasing Problem**					
2							
3			Small Airplane	Large Airplane			
4		Unit Profit ($millions)	7	22			
5							
6					Capital		Capital
7			Capital per Unit Purchased		Spent		Available
8		Capital ($millions)	25	75	250	<=	250
9							
10							Total Profit
11			Small Airplane	Large Airplane			($millions)
12		Number Purchased	1	3			73
13			<=				
14		Maximum Small Airplanes	5				

	E
6	Capital
7	Spent
8	=SUMPRODUCT(CapitalPerUnitPurchased,NumberPurchased)

Solver Parameters

Set Objective Cell: TotalProfit
To: Max
By Changing Variable Cells:
NumberPurchased
Subject to the Constraints:
CapitalSpent <= CapitalAvailable
NumberPurchased = integer
SmallAirplanes <= MaxSmallAirplanes

Solver Options:
Make Variables Nonnegative
Solving Method: Simplex LP

	G
10	Total Profit
11	($millions)
12	=SUMPRODUCT(UnitProfit,NumberPurchased)

Range Name	Cells
Capital Available	G8
CapitalPerUnitPurchased	C8:D8
CapitalSpent	E8
MaxSmallAirplanes	C14
NumberPurchased	C12:D12
SmallAirplanes	C12
TotalProfit	G12
UnitProfit	C4:D4

(C8:D8), CapitalAvailable (G8), and MaxSmallAirplanes (C14). The resource constraint then appears in cells C8:G8 while C12:C14 shows the side constraint. The objective for this problem is to maximize the total net annual profit, so the equation for the objective cell is

TotalProfit (G12) = SUMPRODUCT (UnitProfit, UnitsPurchased)

Since the TBA Airlines problem is a resource-allocation problem, this spreadsheet model has essentially the same form as the Super Grain and Wyndor problems except for one small difference. The changing cells in this case must have *integer* values since it is not feasible for the company to purchase and operate a fraction of an airplane. Therefore, constraints that the changing cells need to be integer are added. With Excel's Solver, use the Add Constraint dialog box to choose the range of these cells (C12:D12) as the left-hand side and then choose int from the pop-up menu between the left-hand and right-hand side. In RSPE, choose the changing cells (C12:D12), and then under the Constraint menu on the RSPE ribbon, choose Integer under the Variable Type/Bound submenu.

These changing cells in Figure 3.2 show the optimal solution, (S, L) = (1, 3), obtained after running Solver.

Excel Tip: To constrain a range of changing cells to be integer in Excel's Solver, choose the range of cells in the left-hand side of the Add Constraint dialog box and choose int from the pop-up menu. Clicking OK then enters the constraint that these cells = integer in the Solver dialog box. In RSPE, select the range of cells to be constrained integer, and then under the Constraint menu on the RSPE ribbon, choose Integer under the Variable Type/Bound submenu.

One of the assumptions of linear programming is that the changing cells are allowed to have *any* values, including *fractional* values, that satisfy the functional and nonnegativity constraints. Therefore, technically speaking, the TBA problem is not a linear programming problem because of adding the constraints

$$\text{NumberPurchased} = \text{integer}$$

that are displayed in the Solver Parameters box in Figure 3.2. Such a problem that fits linear programming except for adding such constraints is called an **integer programming problem.** The method used by Solver to solve integer programming problems is quite different from that for solving linear programming problems. In fact, integer programming problems tend to be much more difficult to solve than linear programming problems so there is considerably more limitation on the size of the problem. However, this doesn't matter to a spreadsheet modeler dealing with small problems. From his or her viewpoint, there is virtually no distinction between linear programming and integer programming problems. They are formulated in exactly the same way. Then, at the very end, a decision needs to be made as to whether any of the changing cells need to be restricted to integer values. If so, those constraints are added as described above. Keep this option in mind as we continue to discuss the formulation of various types of linear programming problems throughout the chapter.

Excel Tip: Even when a changing cell is constrained to be integer, rounding errors occasionally will cause Excel to return a non-integer value very close to an integer (e.g., 1.23E-10, meaning 0.000000000123). To make the spreadsheet cleaner, you may replace these "ugly" representations by their proper integer values in the changing cells.

Summary of the Formulation

The above formulation of a model with one resource constraint and one side constraint for the TBA Airlines problem now can be summarized (in algebraic form) as follows:

$$\text{Maximize}\quad \text{Profit} = 7S + 22L$$

subject to

$$25S + 75L \leq 250$$
$$S \qquad \leq 5$$

and

$$S \geq 0 \quad L \geq 0$$

Excel Tip: In Excel's Solver Options, the *Integer Optimality* (%) setting (1 percent by default) causes Solver to stop solving an integer programming problem when it finds a feasible solution whose objective function value is within the specified percentage of being optimal. In RSPE, the equivalent setting is Integer Tolerance under the Engine tab of the Solver model (see Figure 2.19). This is useful to speed up solving large problems. For smaller problems (e.g., homework problems), this option should be set to 0 to guarantee finding an optimal solution.

Capital Budgeting

Financial planning is one of the most important areas of application for resource-allocation problems. The resources being allocated in this area are quite different from those for applications in the *production planning* area (such as the Wyndor Glass Co. product-mix problem), where the resources tend to be *production facilities* of various kinds. For financial planning, the resources tend to be *financial assets* such as cash, securities, accounts receivable, lines of credit, and so forth. Our specific example involves *capital budgeting,* where the resources are amounts of investment capital available at different points in time.

The Problem

The **Think-Big Development Co.** is a major investor in commercial real-estate development projects. It currently has the opportunity to share in three large construction projects:

Project 1: Construct a high-rise office building.
Project 2: Construct a hotel.
Project 3: Construct a shopping center.

Each project requires each partner to make investments at four different points in time: a down payment now, and additional capital after one, two, and three years. Table 3.3 shows for each project the *total* amount of investment capital required from all the partners at these four points in time. Thus, a partner taking a certain percentage share of a project is obligated to invest that percentage of each of the amounts shown in the table for the project.

All three projects are expected to be very profitable in the long run. So the management of Think-Big wants to invest as much as possible in some or all of them. Management is willing to commit all the company's investment capital currently available, as well as all additional

An Application Vignette

A key part of a country's financial infrastructure is its securities markets. By allowing a variety of financial institutions and their clients to trade stocks, bonds, and other financial securities, they help fund both public and private initiatives. Therefore, the efficient operation of its securities markets plays a crucial role in providing a platform for the economic growth of the country.

Each central securities depository and its system for quickly settling security transactions are part of the operational backbone of securities markets and a key component of financial system stability. In Mexico, an institution called **INDEVAL** provides both the central securities depository and its security settlement system for the entire country. This security settlement system uses electronic book entries, modifying cash and securities balances, for the various parties in the transactions.

The total value of the securities transactions the INDEVAL settles averages over **$250 billion** daily. This makes INDEVAL the main liquidity conduit for Mexico's entire financial sector. Therefore, it is extremely important that INDEVAL's system for clearing securities transactions be an exceptionally efficient one that maximizes the amount of cash that can be delivered almost instantaneously after the transactions. Because of past dissatisfaction with this system, INDEVAL's board of directors ordered a major study in 2005 to completely redesign the system.

Following more than 12,000 man-hours devoted to this redesign, the new system was successfully launched in November 2008. The core of the new system is a large linear programming model that is applied many times daily to choose which pending transactions should be settled immediately with the depositor's available balances. Linear programming is ideally suited for this application because it can maximize the value of the transactions settled while taking into account the various relevant constraints.

This application of linear programming has substantially enhanced and strengthened the Mexican financial infrastructure by reducing its daily liquidity requirements by **$130 billion**. It also reduces the intraday financing costs for market participants by more than **$150 million** annually. This application also led to INDEVAL winning the prestigious first prize in the 2010 international competition for the Franz Edelman Award for Achievement in Operations Research and the Management Sciences.

Source: D. Muñoz, M. de Lascurain, O. Romeo-Hernandez, F. Solis, L. de los Santoz, A. Palacios-Brun, F. Herrería, and J. Villaseñor, "INDEVAL Develops a New Operating and Settlement System Using Operations Research," *Interfaces* 41, no. 1 (January–February 2011), pp. 8–17. (A link to this article is provided on our website, **www.mhhe.com/hillier5e.**)

TABLE 3.3
Financial Data for the Projects Being Considered for Partial Investment by the Think-Big Development Co.

Year	Investment Capital Requirements		
	Office Building	**Hotel**	**Shopping Center**
0	$40 million	$80 million	$90 million
1	60 million	80 million	50 million
2	90 million	80 million	20 million
3	10 million	70 million	60 million
Net present value	$45 million	$70 million	$50 million

investment capital expected to become available over the next three years. The objective is to determine the *investment mix* that will be most profitable, based on current estimates of profitability.

Since it will be several years before each project begins to generate income, which will continue for many years thereafter, we need to take into account the *time value of money* in evaluating how profitable it might be. This is done by *discounting* future cash outflows (capital invested) and cash inflows (income), and then adding discounted net cash flows, to calculate a project's *net present value.*

Based on current estimates of future cash flows (not included here except for outflows), the estimated net present value for each project is shown in the bottom row of Table 3.3. All the investors, including Think-Big, then will split this net present value in proportion to their share of the total investment.

For each project, *participation shares* are being sold to major investors, such as Think-Big, who become the partners for the project by investing their proportional shares at the four specified points in time. For example, if Think-Big takes a 10 percent share of the office building, it will need to provide $4 million now, and then $6 million, $9 million, and $1 million in 1 year, 2 years, and 3 years, respectively.

The company currently has $25 million available for capital investment. Projections are that another $20 million will become available after one year, $20 million more after two years, and another $15 million after three years. What share should Think-Big take in the respective projects to maximize the total net present value of these investments?

Formulation

This is a *resource-allocation problem.* The activities under consideration are

Activity 1: Invest in the construction of an office building.

Activity 2: Invest in the construction of a hotel.

Activity 3: Invest in the construction of a shopping center.

Thus, the decisions to be made are the levels of these activities, that is, what participation share to take in investing in each of these projects. A participation share can be expressed as either a fraction or a percentage of the entire project, so the entire project is considered to be one "unit" of that activity.

The resources to be allocated to these activities are the funds available at the four investment points. Funds not used at one point are available at the next point. (For simplicity, we will ignore any interest earned on these funds.) Therefore, the *resource constraint* for each point must reflect the cumulative funds to that point.

Resource 1: Total investment capital available now.

Resource 2: Cumulative investment capital available by the end of one year.

Resource 3: Cumulative investment capital available by the end of two years.

Resource 4: Cumulative investment capital available by the end of three years.

Since the amount of investment capital available is $25 million now, another $20 million in one year, another $20 million in two years, and another $15 million in three years, the amounts available of the resources are the following:

Amount of resource 1 available = $25 million

Amount of resource 2 available = $(25 + 20) million = $45 million

Amount of resource 3 available = $(25 + 20 + 20) million = $65 million

Amount of resource 4 available = $(25 + 20 + 20 + 15) million = $80 million

Table 3.4 shows all the data involving these resources. The rightmost column gives the amounts of resources available calculated above. The middle columns show the *cumulative* amounts of the investment capital requirements listed in Table 3.3. For example, in the Office Building column of Table 3.4, the second number ($100 million) is obtained by adding the first two numbers ($40 million and $60 million) in the Office Building column of Table 3.3.

The Data   As with any resource-allocation problem, three kinds of data need to be gathered. One is the amounts available of the resources, as given in the rightmost column of Table 3.4. A second is the amount of each resource needed by each project, which is given in the middle columns of this table. A third is the contribution of each project to the overall measure of performance (net present value), as given in the bottom row of Table 3.3.

The first step in formulating the spreadsheet model is to enter these data into data cells in the spreadsheet. In Figure 3.3, the data cells (and their range names) are NetPresentValue

TABLE 3.4
Resource Data for the Think-Big Development Co. Investment-Mix Problem

	Cumulative Investment Capital Required for an Entire Project			
Resource	**Office Building**	**Hotel**	**Shopping Center**	**Amount of Resource Available**
1 (Now)	$ 40 million	$ 80 million	$ 90 million	$25 million
2 (End of year 1)	100 million	160 million	140 million	45 million
3 (End of year 2)	190 million	240 million	160 million	65 million
4 (End of year 3)	200 million	310 million	220 million	80 million

78 Chapter Three *Linear Programming: Formulation and Applications*

FIGURE 3.3

The spreadsheet model for the Think-Big problem, including the formulas for the objective cell TotalNPV (H16) and the other output cells CapitalSpent (F9:F12), as well as the specifications needed to set up Solver. The changing cells ParticipationShare (C16:E16) show the optimal solution obtained by Solver.

	A	B	C	D	E	F	G	H
1		**Think-Big Development Co. Capital Budgeting Program**						
2								
3			Office		Shopping			
4			Building	Hotel	Center			
5		Net Present Value	45	70	50			
6		($millions)				Cumulative		Cumulative
7						Capital		Capital
8			Cumulative Capital Required ($millions)			Spent		Available
9		Now	40	80	90	25	≤	25
10		End of Year 1	100	160	140	44.76	≤	45
11		End of Year 2	190	240	160	60.58	≤	65
12		End of Year 3	200	310	220	80	≤	80
13								
14			Office		Shopping			Total NPV
15			Building	Hotel	Center			($millions)
16		Participation Share	0.00%	16.50%	13.11%			18.11

Solver Parameters
Set Objective Cell: TotalNPV
To: Max
By Changing Variable Cells:
  ParticipationShare
Subject to the Constraints:
  CapitalSpent <= CapitalAvailable

Solver Options:
  Make Variables Nonnegative
  Solving Method: Simplex LP

Range Name	Cells
CapitalAvailable	H9:H12
CapitalRequired	C9:E12
CapitalSpent	F9:F12
ParticipationShare	C16:E16
NetPresentValue	C5:E5
TotalNPV	H16

	F
6	Cumulative
7	Capital
8	Spent
9	=SUMPRODUCT(C9:E9,ParticipationShare)
10	=SUMPRODUCT(C10:E10,ParticipationShare)
11	=SUMPRODUCT(C11:E11,ParticipationShare)
12	=SUMPRODUCT C12:E12,ParticipationShare)

	H
14	Total NPV
15	($millions)
16	=SUMPRODUCT(NetPresentValue,ParticipationShare)

(C5:E5), CapitalRequired (C9:E12), and CapitalAvailable (H9:H12). To save space on the spreadsheet, these numbers are entered in units of millions of dollars.

The Decisions With three activities under consideration, there are three decisions to be made.

Decision 1: OB = Participation share in the office building.
Decision 2: H = Participation share in the hotel.
Decision 3: SC = Participation share in the shopping center.

For example, if Think-Big management were to decide to take a one-tenth participation share (i.e., a 10 percent participation share) in each of these projects, then

$OB = 0.1 = 10\%$
$H = 0.1 = 10\%$
$SC = 0.1 = 10\%$

However, it may not be desirable to take the same participation share (expressed as either a fraction or a percentage) in each of the projects, so the idea is to choose the best combination of values of *OB, H,* and *SC.* In Figure 3.3, the participation shares (expressed as percentages) have been placed in changing cells under the data cells (row 16) in the columns for the three projects, so

$$OB \rightarrow \text{cell C16} \quad H \rightarrow \text{D16} \quad SC \rightarrow \text{cell E16}$$

where these cells are collectively referred to by the range name ParticipationShare (C16:E16).

The Constraints The numbers in these changing cells make sense only if they are nonnegative, so the Make Variables Nonnegative option will need to be selected in the Excel's Solver dialog box (or equivalently in RSPE, set the Assume Non-Negative option to True in the Engine tab of the Model pane). In addition, the four resources require resource constraints:

Total invested now	≤ 25 (millions of dollars available)
Total invested within 1 year	≤ 45 (millions of dollars available)
Total invested within 2 years	≤ 65 (millions of dollars available)
Total invested within 3 years	≤ 80 (millions of dollars available)

The data in columns C, D, and E indicate that (in millions of dollars)

Total invested now	=	$40\,OB + 80\,H + 90\,SC$
Total invested within 1 year	=	$100\,OB + 160\,H + 140\,SC$
Total invested within 2 years	=	$190\,OB + 240\,H + 160\,SC$
Total invested within 3 years	=	$200\,OB + 310\,H + 220\,SC$

These totals are calculated in the output cells CapitalSpent (F9:F12) using the SUMPRODUCT function, as shown below the spreadsheet in Figure 3.3. Finally, $\leq$ signs are entered into column G to indicate the resource constraints that will need to be entered in Solver.

The Measure of Performance The objective is to

$$\text{Maximize} \quad NPV = \text{total } \textit{net present value} \text{ of the investments}$$

NetPresentValue (C5:E5) shows the net present value of each entire project, while ParticipationShare (C16:E16) shows the participation share for each of the projects. Therefore, the total net present value of all the participation shares purchased in all three projects is (in millions of dollars)

$$NPV = 45\,OB + 70\,H + 50\,SC$$
$$= \text{SUMPRODUCT (NetPresentValue, ParticipationShare)}$$
$$\rightarrow \text{cell H16}$$

Summary of the Formulation This completes the formulation of the linear programming model on the spreadsheet, as summarized below (in algebraic form).

$$\text{Maximize} \quad NPV = 45\,OB + 70\,H + 50\,SC$$

subject to

Total invested now:	$40\,OB + 80\,H + 90\,SC \leq 25$
Total invested within 1 year:	$100\,OB + 160\,H + 140\,SC \leq 45$
Total invested within 2 years:	$190\,OB + 240\,H + 160\,SC \leq 65$
Total invested within 3 years:	$200\,OB + 310\,H + 220\,SC \leq 80$

and

$$OB \geq 0 \quad H \geq 0 \quad SC \geq 0$$

where all these numbers are in units of millions of dollars.

Note that this model possesses the key *identifying feature* for resource-allocation problems, namely, each functional constraint is a *resource constraint* that has the form

$$\text{Amount of resource used} \leq \text{Amount of resource available}$$

Solving the Model   The lower left-hand side of Figure 3.3 shows the entries needed in Solver to specify the model, along with the selection of the usual two options. The spreadsheet shows the resulting optimal solution in row 16, namely,

> Invest nothing in the office building.
>
> Invest in 16.50 percent of the hotel.
>
> Invest in 13.11 percent of the shopping center.

TotalNPV (H16) indicates that this investment program would provide a total net present value of $18.11 million.

This amount actually is only an estimate of what the total net present value would turn out to be, depending on the accuracy of the financial data given in Table 3.3. There is some uncertainty about the construction costs for the three real estate projects, so the actual investment capital requirements for years 1, 2, and 3 may deviate somewhat from the amounts specified in this table. Because of the risk involved in these projects, the net present value for each one also might deviate from the amounts given at the bottom of the table. Chapter 5 describes one approach to analyzing the effect of such deviations. Chapters 12 and 13 will present another technique, called *computer simulation,* for systematically taking future uncertainties into account. Section 13.5 will focus on further analysis of this same example.

Another Look at Resource Constraints

These examples of resource-allocation problems illustrate a variety of resources: financial allocations for advertising and planning purposes, TV commercial spots available for purchase, available production capacities of different plants, the total amount of capital available for investment, and cumulative investment capital available by certain times. However, these illustrations only scratch the surface of the realm of possible resources that need to be allocated to activities in resource-allocation problems. In fact, by interpreting *resource* sufficiently broadly, *any* restriction on the decisions to be made that has the form

Amount used ≤ Amount available

can be thought of as a *resource constraint,* where the thing whose amount is being measured is the corresponding "resource." Since *any* functional constraint with a ≤ sign in a linear programming model (including the side constraint in the TBA Airlines example) can be verbalized in this form, any such constraint can be thought of as a resource constraint.

> Hereafter, we will use *resource constraint* to refer to *any* functional constraint with a ≤ sign in a linear programming model. The constant on the right-hand side represents the *amount available* of a resource. Therefore, the left-hand side represents the *amount used* of this resource. In the algebraic form of the constraint, the coefficient (positive or negative) of each decision variable is the *resource usage per unit* of the corresponding activity.

Summary of the Formulation Procedure for Resource-Allocation Problems

The four examples illustrate that the following steps are used for any resource-allocation problem to define the specific problem, gather the relevant data, and then formulate the linear programming model.

1. Since any linear programming problem involves finding the *best mix* of levels of various activities, identify these *activities* for the problem at hand. The decisions to be made are the levels of these activities.

2. From the viewpoint of management, identify an appropriate *overall measure of performance* (commonly *profit,* or a surrogate for profit) for solutions of the problem.

3. For each activity, estimate the *contribution per unit of the activity* to this overall measure of performance.

4. Identify the *resources* that must be allocated to the activities.

5. For each resource, identify the *amount available* and then the *amount used per unit of each activity.*

FIGURE 3.4

A template of a spreadsheet model for pure resource-allocation problems.

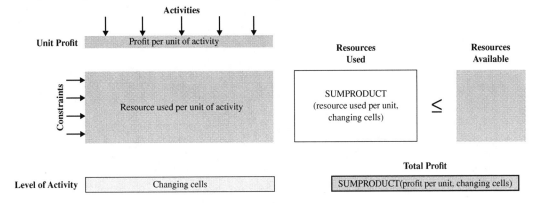

6. Enter the data gathered in steps 3 and 5 into *data cells* in a spreadsheet. A convenient format is to have the data associated with each activity in a separate column, the data for the unit profit and each constraint in a separate row, and to leave two blank columns between the *activity* columns and the *amount of resource available* column. Figure 3.4 shows a template of the overall format of a spreadsheet model for resource-allocation problems.

7. Designate *changing cells* for displaying the decisions on activity levels.

8. For the two blank columns created in step 6, use the left one as a *Totals* column for *output cells* and enter ≤ signs into the right one for all the resources. In the row for each resource, use the SUMPRODUCT function to enter the *total amount used* in the Totals column.

9. Designate an *objective cell* for displaying the overall measure of performance. Use a SUMPRODUCT function to enter this measure of performance.

All the functional constraints in this linear programming model in a spreadsheet are *resource constraints,* that is, constraints with a ≤ sign. This is the *identifying feature* that classifies the problem as being a resource-allocation problem.

Review
Questions

1. What is the identifying feature for a resource-allocation problem?
2. What is the form of a resource constraint?
3. What are the three kinds of data that need to be gathered for a resource-allocation problem?
4. Compare the types of activities for the four examples of resource-allocation problems.
5. Compare the types of resources for the four examples of resource-allocation problems.

3.3   COST–BENEFIT–TRADE-OFF PROBLEMS

Cost–benefit–trade-off problems have a form that is very different from resource-allocation problems. The difference arises from *managerial objectives* that are very different for the two kinds of problems.

For resource-allocation problems, limits are set on the use of various resources (including financial resources), and then the objective is to make the most effective use (according to some overall measure of performance) of these given resources.

For cost–benefit–trade-off problems, management takes a more aggressive stance, prescribing what *benefits* must be achieved by the activities under consideration (regardless of the resulting resource usage), and then the objective is to achieve all these benefits with *minimum cost.* By prescribing a *minimum acceptable level* for each kind of benefit, and then minimizing the cost needed to achieve these levels, management hopes to obtain an appropriate *trade-off* between cost and benefits. (You will see in Chapter 5 that *what-if analysis* plays a key role in providing the additional information needed for management to choose the best trade-off between cost and benefits.)

A cost–benefit–trade-off formulation enables management to specify minimum goals for the benefits that need to be achieved by the activities.

Cost–benefit–trade-off problems are linear programming problems where the mix of levels of various *activities* is chosen to achieve minimum acceptable levels for various *benefits* at a minimum cost. The *identifying feature* is that each functional constraint is a **benefit constraint,** which has the form

Level achieved ≥ Minimum acceptable level

for one of the benefits.

Interpreting *benefit* broadly, we can think of *any* functional constraint with a ≥ sign as a *benefit constraint.* In most cases, the *minimum acceptable level* will be prescribed by management as a policy decision, but occasionally this number will be dictated by other circumstances.

For any cost–benefit–trade-off problem, a major part of the study involves identifying all the activities and benefits that should be considered and then gathering the data relevant to these activities and benefits.

These three kinds of data are needed for any cost–benefit–trade-off problem.

Three kinds of data are needed:

1. The *minimum acceptable level* for each benefit (a managerial policy decision).
2. For each benefit, the *contribution of each activity* to that benefit (per unit of the activity).
3. The *cost* per unit of each activity.

Let's examine two examples of cost–benefit–trade-off problems.

The Profit & Gambit Co. Advertising-Mix Problem

As described in Section 2.7, the Profit & Gambit Co. will be undertaking a major new advertising campaign focusing on three cleaning products. The two kinds of advertising to be used are television and the print media. Management has established minimum goals—the minimum acceptable increase in sales for each product—to be gained by the campaign.

The problem is to determine how much to advertise in each medium to meet all the sales goals at a minimum total cost.

The activities in this cost–benefit–trade-off problem are

Activity 1: Advertise on television.

Activity 2: Advertise in the print media.

An initial step in formulating any cost–benefit–trade-off problem is to identify the activities and the benefits.

The benefits being sought from these activities are

Benefit 1: Increased sales for a spray prewash stain remover.

Benefit 2: Increased sales for a liquid laundry detergent.

Benefit 3: Increased sales for a powder laundry detergent.

Management wants these increased sales to be at least 3 percent, 18 percent, and 4 percent, respectively. As shown in Section 2.7, each benefit leads to a *benefit constraint* that incorporates the managerial goal for the *minimum acceptable level* of increase in the sales for the corresponding product, namely,

Level of benefit 1 achieved ≥ 3%

Level of benefit 2 achieved ≥ 18%

Level of benefit 3 achieved ≥ 4%

The data for this problem are given in Table 2.2 (Section 2.7). Section 2.7 describes how the linear programming model is formulated directly from the numbers in this table.

This example provides an interesting contrast with the Super Grain Corp. case study in Section 3.1, which led to a formulation as a resource-allocation problem. Both are advertising-mix problems, yet they lead to entirely different linear programming models. They differ because of the differences in the managerial view of the key issues in each case:

- As the vice president for marketing of Super Grain, Claire Syverson focused first on how much to spend on the advertising campaign and then set limits (an advertising budget of $4 million and a planning budget of $1 million) that led to resource constraints.

An Application Vignette

Cost control is essential for survival in the airline industry. Therefore, upper management of **United Airlines** initiated a management science study to improve the utilization of personnel at the airline's reservations offices and airports by matching work schedules to customer needs more closely. The number of employees needed at each location to provide the required level of service varies greatly during the 24-hour day and might fluctuate considerably from one half hour to the next.

Trying to design the work schedules for all the employees at a given location to meet these service requirements most efficiently is a nightmare of combinatorial considerations. Once an employee arrives, he or she will be there continuously for the entire shift (2 to 10 hours, depending on the employee), *except* for either a meal break or short rest breaks every two hours. Given the *minimum* number of employees needed on duty for *each* half-hour interval over a 24-hour day (this minimum changes from day to day over a seven-day week), *how many* employees of *each shift length* should begin work at *what start time* over *each* 24-hour day of a seven-day week? Fortunately, linear programming thrives on such combinatorial nightmares. The linear programming model for some of the locations scheduled involves over 20,000 decisions!

This application of linear programming was credited with *saving United Airlines more than* **$6 million** *annually* in just direct salary and benefit costs. Other benefits included improved customer service and reduced workloads for support staff.

Source: T. J. Holloran and J. E. Bryne, "United Airlines Station Manpower Planning System," *Interfaces* 16, no. 1 (January–February 1986), pp. 39–50. (A link to this article is provided on our website, **www.mhhe.com/hillier5e.**)

- The management of Profit & Gambit instead focused on what it wanted the advertising campaign to accomplish and then set goals (minimum required increases in sales) that led to benefit constraints.

From this comparison, we see that it is not the nature of the *application* that determines the classification of the resulting linear programming formulation. Rather, it is the nature of the *restrictions* imposed on the decisions regarding the mix of activity levels. If the restrictions involve *limits* on the usage of resources, that identifies a resource-allocation problem. If the restrictions involve *goals* on the levels of benefits, that characterizes a cost–benefit–trade-off problem. Frequently, the nature of the restrictions arise from the way management frames the problem.

However, we don't want you to get the idea that every linear programming problem falls entirely and neatly into either one type or the other. In the preceding section and this one, we are looking at *pure* resource-allocation problems and *pure* cost–benefit–trade-off problems. Although many *real* problems tend to be either one type or the other, it is fairly common to have *both* resource constraints and benefit constraints, even though one may predominate. (In the next section, you will see an example of how both types of constraints can arise in the same problem when the management of the Super Grain Corp. introduces additional considerations into the analysis of their advertising-mix problem.) Furthermore, we still need to consider additional categories of linear programming problems in the remaining sections of this chapter.

Now, another example of a pure cost–benefit–trade-off problem.

Personnel Scheduling

One of the common applications of cost–benefit–trade-off analysis involves personnel scheduling for a company that provides some kind of service, where the objective is to schedule the work times of the company's employees so as to minimize the cost of providing the level of service specified by management. The following example illustrates how this can be done.

The Problem

Union Airways is adding more flights to and from its hub airport and so needs to hire additional customer service agents. However, it is not clear just how many more should be hired. Management recognizes the need for cost control while also consistently providing a satisfactory level of service to the company's customers, so a desirable trade-off between these two factors is being sought. Therefore, a management science team is studying how to schedule the agents to provide satisfactory service with the smallest personnel cost.

84   Chapter Three   *Linear Programming: Formulation and Applications*

TABLE 3.5
Data for the Union Airways Personnel Scheduling Problem

Time Period	Time Periods Covered by Shift					Minimum Number of Agents Needed
	1	2	3	4	5	
6:00 AM to 8:00 AM	✔					48
8:00 AM to 10:00 AM	✔	✔				79
10:00 AM to noon	✔	✔				65
Noon to 2:00 PM	✔	✔	✔			87
2:00 PM to 4:00 PM		✔	✔			64
4:00 PM to 6:00 PM			✔	✔		73
6:00 PM to 8:00 PM			✔	✔		82
8:00 PM to 10:00 PM				✔		43
10:00 PM to midnight				✔	✔	52
Midnight to 6:00 AM					✔	15
Daily cost per agent	$170	$160	$175	$180	$195	

Based on the new schedule of flights, an analysis has been made of the *minimum* number of customer service agents that need to be on duty at different times of the day to provide a satisfactory level of service. (The queueing models presented in Chapter 11 can be used to determine the minimum numbers of agents needed to keep customer waiting times reasonable.) These numbers are shown in the last column of Table 3.5 for the time periods given in the first column. The other entries in this table reflect one of the provisions in the company's current contract with the union that represents the customer service agents. The provision is that each agent works an eight-hour shift. The authorized shifts are

Shift 1: 6:00 AM to 2:00 PM.
Shift 2: 8:00 AM to 4:00 PM.
Shift 3: Noon to 8:00 PM.
Shift 4: 4:00 PM to midnight.
Shift 5: 10:00 PM to 6:00 AM.

Check marks in the main body of Table 3.5 show the time periods covered by the respective shifts. Because some shifts are less desirable than others, the wages specified in the contract differ by shift. For each shift, the daily compensation (including benefits) for each agent is shown in the bottom row. The problem is to determine how many agents should be assigned to the respective shifts each day to minimize the *total* personnel cost for agents, based on this bottom row, while meeting (or surpassing) the service requirements given in the last column.

Formulation

This problem is, in fact, a pure cost–benefit–trade-off problem. To formulate the problem, we need to identify the *activities* and *benefits* involved.

Activities correspond to shifts.

The *level* of each activity is the number of agents assigned to that shift.

A *unit* of each activity is one agent assigned to that shift.

Thus, the general description of a linear programming problem as finding the *best mix of activity levels* can be expressed for this specific application as finding the *best mix of shift sizes*.

Benefits correspond to time periods.

For each time period, the *benefit* provided by the activities is the service that agents provide customers during that period.

The *level* of a benefit is measured by the number of agents on duty during that time period.

Once again, a careful formulation of the problem, including gathering all the relevant data, leads rather directly to a spreadsheet model. This model is shown in Figure 3.5, and we outline its formulation below.

FIGURE 3.5

The spreadsheet model for the Union Airways problem, including the formulas for the objective cell TotalCost (J21) and the other output cells TotalWorking (H8:H17), as well as the specifications needed to set up Solver. The changing cells NumberWorking (C21:G21) show the optimal solution obtained by Solver.

	A	B	C	D	E	F	G	H	I	J
1		**Union Airways Personnel Scheduling Problem**								
2										
3			6AM–2PM	8AM–4PM	Noon–8PM	4PM–Midnight	10PM–6AM			
4			Shift	Shift	Shift	Shift	Shift			
5		Cost per Shift	$170	$160	$175	$180	$195			
6								Total		Minimum
7		Time Period			Shift Works Time Period? (1=yes, 0=no)			Working		Needed
8		6AM–8AM	1	0	0	0	0	48	≥	48
9		8AM–10AM	1	1	0	0	0	79	≥	79
10		10AM–12PM	1	1	0	0	0	79	≥	65
11		12PM–2PM	1	1	1	0	0	118	≥	87
12		2PM–4PM	0	1	1	0	0	70	≥	64
13		4PM–6PM	0	0	1	1	0	82	≥	73
14		6PM–8PM	0	0	1	1	0	82	≥	82
15		8PM–10PM	0	0	0	1	0	43	≥	43
16		10PM–12AM	0	0	0	1	1	58	≥	52
17		12AM–6AM	0	0	0	0	1	15	≥	15
18										
19			6AM–2PM	8AM–4PM	Noon–8PM	4PM–Midnight	10PM–6AM			
20			Shift	Shift	Shift	Shift	Shift			Total Cost
21		Number Working	48	31	39	43	15			$30,610

Solver Parameters

Set Objective Cell: TotalCost
To: Min
By Changing Variable Cells:
  NumberWorking
Subject to the Constraints:
  NumberWorking = integer
  TotalWorking >= MinimumNeeded

Solver Options:
  Make Variables Nonnegative
  Solving Method: Simplex LP

Range Name	Cells
CostPerShift	C5:G5
MinimumNeeded	J8:J17
NumberWorking	C21:G21
ShiftWorksTimePeriod	C8:G17
TotalCost	J21
TotalWorking	H8:H17

	H
6	Total
7	Working
8	=SUMPRODUCT(C8:G8,NumberWorking)
9	=SUMPRODUCT(C9:G9,NumberWorking)
10	=SUMPRODUCT(C10:G10,NumberWorking)
11	=SUMPRODUCT(C11:G11,NumberWorking)
12	=SUMPRODUCT(C12:G12,NumberWorking)
13	=SUMPRODUCT(C13:G13,NumberWorking)
14	=SUMPRODUCT(C14:G14,NumberWorking)
15	=SUMPRODUCT(C15:G15,NumberWorking)
16	=SUMPRODUCT(C16:G16,NumberWorking)
17	=SUMPRODUCT(C17:G17,NumberWorking)

	J
20	Total Cost
21	=SUMPRODUCT(CostPerShift,NumberWorking)

The Data As indicated in this figure, all the data in Table 3.5 have been entered directly into the data cells CostPerShift (C5:G5), ShiftWorksTimePeriod (C8:G17), and MinimumNeeded (J8:J17). For the ShiftWorksTimePeriod (C8:G17) data, an entry of 1 indicates that the corresponding shift includes that time period whereas 0 indicates not. Like any cost–benefit–trade-off problem, these numbers indicate the contribution of each activity to each benefit. Each agent working a shift contributes either 0 or 1 toward the minimum number of agents needed in a time period.

The Decisions   Since the activities in this case correspond to the five shifts, the decisions to be made are

S_1 = Number of agents to assign to Shift 1 (starts at 6 AM)

S_2 = Number of agents to assign to Shift 2 (starts at 8 AM)

S_3 = Number of agents to assign to Shift 3 (starts at noon)

S_4 = Number of agents to assign to Shift 4 (starts at 4 PM)

S_5 = Number of agents to assign to Shift 5 (starts at 10 PM)

The changing cells to hold these numbers have been placed in the activity columns in row 21, so

$$S_1 \rightarrow \text{cell C21} \qquad S_2 \rightarrow \text{cell D21} \qquad \ldots \qquad S_5 \rightarrow \text{cell G21}$$

where these cells are collectively referred to by the range name NumberWorking (C21:G21).

The Constraints   These changing cells need to be nonnegative. In addition, we need 10 *benefit constraints,* where each one specifies that the *total* number of agents serving in the corresponding time period listed in column B must be no less than the minimum acceptable number given in column J. Thus, these constraints are

Total number of agents serving 6–8 am	≥ 48	(min. acceptable)
Total number of agents serving 8–10 am	≥ 79	(min. acceptable)
	.	
	.	
	.	
Total number of agents serving midnight–6 am	≥ 15	(min. acceptable)

Since columns C to G indicate which of the shifts serve each of the time periods, these totals are

Total number of agents serving 6–8 am	$= S_1$
Total number of agents serving 8–10 am	$= S_1 + S_2$
	.
	.
	.
Total number of agents serving midnight–6 am	$= S_5$

These totals are calculated in the output cells TotalWorking (H8:H17) using the SUMPRODUCT functions shown below the spreadsheet in Figure 3.5.

One other type of constraint is that the number of agents assigned to each shift must have an integer value. These constraints for the five shifts should be added in the same way as described for the TBA Airlines problem in Section 3.2. In particular, with Excel's Solver they are added in the Add Constraint dialog box by entering NumberWorking on the left-hand side and then choosing int from the pop-up menu between the left-hand side and the right-hand side. The set of constraints, NumberWorking = integer, then appears in the Solver Parameters, as shown in Figure 3.5. In RSPE, select the range of cells to be constrained integer, and then under the Constraint menu on the RSPE ribbon, choose Integer under the Variable Type/Bound submenu.

The Measure of Performance   The objective is to

$$\text{Minimize} \quad \text{Cost} = \text{Total daily personnel cost for all agents}$$

Since CostPerShift (C5:G5) gives the daily cost per agent on each shift and NumberWorking (C21:G21) gives the number of agents working each shift,

$$\text{Cost} = 170S_1 + 160S_2 + 175S_3 + 180S_4 + 195S_5 \quad \text{(in dollars)}$$

$$= \text{SUMPRODUCT (CostPerShift, NumberWorking)}$$

$$\rightarrow \text{cell J21}$$

Summary of the Formulation   The above steps provide the complete formulation of the linear programming model on a spreadsheet, as summarized below (in algebraic form).

$$\text{Minimize} \quad \text{Cost} = 170S_1 + 160S_2 + 175S_3 + 180S_4 + 195S_5 \quad \text{(in dollars)}$$

subject to

Total agents 6−8 am:	S_1	≥ 48
Total agents 8−10 am:	$S_1 + S_2$	≥ 79

.

.

.

Total agents midnight−6 am:	$S_5 \geq 15$

and

$$S_1 \geq 0 \quad S_2 \geq 0 \quad S_3 \geq 0 \quad S_4 \geq 0 \quad S_5 \geq 0$$

Solving the Model   The lower left-hand corner of Figure 3.5 shows the entries needed in Solver, along with the selection of the usual two options. After solving, NumberWorking (C21:G21) in the spreadsheet shows the resulting optimal solution for the number of agents that should be assigned to each shift. TotalCost (J21) indicates that this plan would cost $30,610 per day.

Summary of the Formulation Procedure for Cost–Benefit–Trade-Off Problems

The nine steps in formulating any cost–benefit–trade-off problem follow the same pattern as presented at the end of the preceding section for resource-allocation problems, so we will not repeat them here. The main differences are that the overall measure of performance now is the total cost of the activities (or some surrogate of total cost chosen by management) in steps 2 and 3, benefits now replace resources in steps 4 and 5, and ≥ signs now are entered to the right of the output cells for benefits in step 8. Figure 3.6 shows a template of the format of a spreadsheet model for cost–benefit–trade-off problems.

All the functional constraints in the resulting model are *benefit constraints,* that is, constraints with a ≥ sign. This is the *identifying feature* of a pure cost–benefit–trade-off problem.

Review Questions

1. What is the difference in managerial objectives between resource-allocation problems and cost–benefit–trade-off problems?
2. What is the identifying feature of a cost–benefit–trade-off problem?
3. What is the form of a benefit constraint?
4. What are the three kinds of data that need to be gathered for a cost–benefit–trade-off problem?
5. Compare the types of activities for the two examples of cost–benefit–trade-off problems.
6. Compare the types of benefits for the two examples of cost–benefit–trade-off problems.

FIGURE 3.6

A template of a spreadsheet model for pure cost–benefit–trade-off problems.

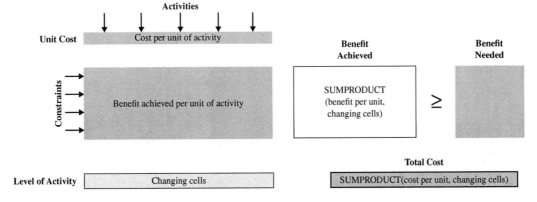

88   Chapter Three   *Linear Programming: Formulation and Applications*

3.4   MIXED PROBLEMS

Sections 3.2 and 3.3 each described a broad category of linear programming problems—resource-allocation and cost–benefit–trade-off problems. As summarized in Table 3.6, each features one of the first two types of functional constraints shown there. In fact, the *identifying feature* of a *pure* resource-allocation problem is that *all* its functional constraints are *resource constraints.* The *identifying feature* of a *pure* cost–benefit–trade-off problem is that *all* its functional constraints are *benefit constraints.* (Keep in mind that the functional constraints include *all* the constraints of a problem *except* its nonnegativity constraints.)

The bottom row of Table 3.6 shows the last of the three types of functional constraints, namely, **fixed-requirement constraints,** which require that the left-hand side of each such constraint must exactly equal some fixed amount. Thus, since the left-hand side represents the amount provided of some quantity, the form of a fixed-requirement constraint is

Amount provided = Required amount

The *identifying feature* of a *pure* **fixed-requirements problem** is that it is a linear programming problem where *all* its functional constraints are fixed-requirement constraints. The next two sections will describe two particularly prominent types of fixed-requirement problems called *transportation problems* and *assignment problems.*

However, before turning to these types of problems, we first will use a continuation of the Super Grain case study from Section 3.1 to illustrate how many linear programming problems fall into another broad category called *mixed problems.*

> Many linear programming problems do not fit completely into any of the previously discussed categories (pure resource-allocation problems, cost–benefit–trade-off problems, and fixed-requirement problems) because the problem's functional constraints include more than one of the types shown in Table 3.6. Such problems are called **mixed problems.**

Now let us see how a more careful analysis of the Super Grain case study turns this resource-allocation problem into a mixed problem that includes all three types of functional constraints shown in Table 3.6.

Super Grain Management Discusses Its Advertising-Mix Problem

The description of the Super Grain case study in Section 3.1 ends with Clair Syverson (Super Grain's vice president for marketing) sending a memorandum to the company's president, David Sloan, requesting a meeting to evaluate her proposed promotional campaign for the company's new breakfast cereal.

Soon thereafter, Claire Syverson and David Sloan meet to discuss plans for the campaign.

David Sloan (president):   Thanks for your memo, Claire. The plan you outline for the promotional campaign looks like a reasonable one. However, I am surprised that it does not make any use of TV commercials. Why is that?

Claire Syverson (vice president for marketing):   Well, as I described in my memo, I used a spreadsheet model to see how to maximize the number of exposures from the

TABLE 3.6
Types of Functional Constraints

Type	Form*	Typical Interpretation	Main Usage
Resource constraint	LHS ≤ RHS	For some resource, Amount used ≤ Amount available	Resource-allocation problems and mixed problems
Benefit constraint	LHS ≥ RHS	For some benefit, Level achieved ≥ Minimum acceptable level	Cost–benefit–trade-off problems and mixed problems
Fixed-requirement constraint	LHS = RHS	For some quantity, Amount provided = Required amount	Fixed-requirements problems and mixed problems

*LHS = Left-hand side (a SUMPRODUCT function).
 RHS = Right-hand side (a constant).

campaign and this turned out to be the plan that does this. I also was surprised that it did not include TV commercials, but the model indicated that introducing commercials would provide less exposures on a dollar-for-dollar basis than magazine ads and Sunday supplement ads. Don't you think it makes sense to use the plan that maximizes the number of exposures?

David: Not necessarily. Some exposures are a lot less important than others. For example, we know that middle-aged adults are not big consumers of our cereals, so we don't care very much how many of those people see our ads. On the other hand, young children are big consumers. Having TV commercials on the Saturday morning programs for children is our primary method of reaching young children. You know how important it will be to get young children to ask their parents for Crunchy Start. That is our best way of generating first-time sales. Those commercials also get seen by a lot of parents who are watching the programs with their kids. What we need is a commercial that is appealing to both parents and kids, and that gets the kids immediately bugging their parents to go buy Crunchy Start. I think that is a real key to a successful campaign.

Claire: Yes, that makes a lot of sense. In fact, I already have set some goals regarding the number of young children and the number of parents of young children that need to be reached by this promotional campaign.

David: Good. Did you include those goals in your spreadsheet model?

Claire: No, I didn't.

David: Well, I suggest that you incorporate them directly into your model. I suspect that maximizing exposures while also meeting your goals will give us a high impact plan that includes some TV commercials.

Claire: Good idea. I'll try it.

David: Are there any other factors that the plan in your memo doesn't take into account as well as you would like?

Claire: Well, yes, one. The plan doesn't take into account my budget for cents-off coupons in magazines and newspapers.

David: You should be able to add that to your model as well. Why don't you go back and see what happens when you incorporate these additional considerations?

Claire: OK, will do. You seem to have had a lot of experience with spreadsheet modeling.

David: Yes. It is a great tool as long as you maintain some healthy skepticism about what comes out of the model. No model can fully take into account everything that we must consider when dealing with managerial problems. This is especially true the first time or two you run the model. You need to keep asking, what are the missing quantitative considerations that I still should add to the model? Then, after you have made the model as complete as possible and obtained a solution, you still need to use your best managerial judgment to weigh intangible considerations that cannot be incorporated into the model.

Incorporating Additional Managerial Considerations into the Super Grain Model

Therefore, David and Claire conclude that the spreadsheet model needs to be expanded to incorporate some additional considerations. In particular, since the promotional campaign is for a breakfast cereal that should have special appeal to young children, they feel that two audiences should be targeted—*young children* and *parents of young children*. (This is why one of the three advertising media recommended by Giacomi & Jackowitz is commercials on children's television programs Saturday morning.) Consequently, Claire now has set two new goals for the campaign.

Goal 1: The advertising should be seen by at least five million young children.

Goal 2: The advertising should be seen by at least five million parents of young children.

In effect, these two goals are *minimum acceptable levels* for two special *benefits* to be achieved by the advertising activities.

Benefit 1: Promoting the new breakfast cereal to young children.
Benefit 2: Promoting the new breakfast cereal to parents of young children.

TABLE 3.7

Benefit Data for the Revised Super Grain Corp. Advertising-Mix Problem

Target Category	Number Reached in Target Category (in millions)			
	Each TV Commercial	Each Magazine Ad	Each Sunday Ad	Minimum Acceptable Level
Young children	1.2	0.1	0	5
Parents of young children	0.5	0.2	0.2	5

Because of the way the goals have been articulated, the *level* of each of these benefits is measured by the *number of people* in the specified category that are reached by the advertising.

To enable constructing the corresponding *benefit constraints* (as described in Section 3.3), Claire asks Giacomi & Jackowitz to estimate how much each advertisement in each of the media will contribute to each benefit, as measured by the number of people reached in the specified category. These estimates are given in Table 3.7.

It is interesting to observe that management wants special consideration given to these two kinds of benefits even though the original spreadsheet model (Figure 3.1) already takes them into account to some extent. As described in Section 3.1, the *expected number of exposures* is the overall measure of performance to be maximized. This measure counts up all the times that an advertisement is seen by any individual, including all those individuals in the target audiences. However, maximizing this *general* measure of performance does *not* ensure that the two *specific goals* prescribed by management (Claire Syverson) will be achieved. Claire feels that achieving these goals is essential to a successful promotional campaign. Therefore, she complements the general objective with specific benefit constraints that *do* ensure that the goals will be achieved. Having benefit constraints added to incorporate managerial goals into the model is a prerogative of management.

Benefit constraints are useful for incorporating managerial goals into the model.

Claire has one more consideration she wants to incorporate into the model. She is a strong believer in the promotional value of *cents-off coupons* (coupons that shoppers can clip from printed advertisements to obtain a refund of a designated amount when purchasing the advertised item). Consequently, she always earmarks a major portion of her annual marketing budget for the redemption of these coupons. She still has $1,490,000 left from this year's allotment for coupon redemptions. Because of the importance of Crunchy Start to the company, she has decided to use this entire remaining allotment in the campaign promoting this cereal.

This *fixed amount* for coupon redemptions is a *fixed requirement* that needs to be expressed as a *fixed-requirement constraint*. As described at the beginning of this section, the form of a fixed-requirement constraint is that, for some type of quantity,

$$\text{Amount provided} = \text{Required amount}$$

In this case, the quantity involved is the amount of money provided for the redemption of cents-off coupons. To specify this constraint in the spreadsheet, we need to estimate how much each advertisement in each of the media will contribute toward fulfilling the required amount for the quantity. Both medium 2 (advertisements in food and family-oriented magazines) and medium 3 (advertisements in Sunday supplements of major newspapers) will feature cents-off coupons. The estimates of the amount of coupon redemption per advertisement in each of these media is given in Table 3.8.

TABLE 3.8

Data for the Fixed-Requirement Constraint for the Revised Super Grain Corp. Advertising-Mix Problem

Requirement	Contribution toward Required Amount			
	Each TV Spot	Each Magazine Ad	Each Sunday Ad	Required Amount
Coupon redemption	0	$40,000	$120,000	$1,490,000

Formulation of the Revised Spreadsheet Model

Figure 3.7 shows one way of formatting the spreadsheet to expand the original spreadsheet model in Figure 3.1 to incorporate the additional managerial considerations. We then outline the four components of the revised model next.

FIGURE 3.7

The spreadsheet model for the revised Super Grain problem, including the formulas for the objective cell TotalExposures (H19) and the other output cells in column F, as well as the specifications needed to set up Solver. The changing cells NumberOfAds (C19:E19) show the optimal solution obtained by Solver.

	A	B	C	D	E	F	G	H
1		**Super Grain Corp. Advertising-Mix Problem**						
2								
3			TV Spots	Magazine Ads	SS Ads			
4		Exposures per Ad	1,300	600	500			
5		(thousands)						
6			Cost per Ad ($thousands)			Budget Spent		Budget Available
7		Ad Budget	300	150	100	3,775	≤	4,000
8		Planning Budget	90	30	40	1,000	≤	1,000
9								
10			Number Reached per Ad (millions)			Total Reached		Minimum Acceptable
11		Young Children	1.2	0.1	0	5	≥	5
12		Parents of Young Children	0.5	0.2	0.2	5.85	≥	5
13								
14			TV Spots	Magazine Ads	SS Ads	Total Redeemed		Required Amount
15		Coupon Redemption	0	40	120	1,490	=	1,490
16		per Ad ($thousands)						
17								Total Exposures
18			TV Spots	Magazine Ads	SS Ads			(thousands)
19		Number of Ads	3	14	7.75			16.175
20			≤					
21		Maximum TV Spots	5					

Solver Parameters
Set Objective Cell: TotalExposures
To: Max
By Changing Variable Cells:
   NumberOfAds
Subject to the Constraints:
   BudgetSpent <= Budget Available
   TVSpots <= MaxTVSpots
   TotalReached >= MinimumAcceptable
   TotalRedeemed = RequiredAmount

Solver Options:
   Make Variables Nonnegative
   Solving Method: Simplex LP

Range Name	Cells
BudgetAvailable	H7:H8
BudgetSpent	F7:F8
CostPerAd	C7:E8
CouponRedemptionPerAd	C15:E15
ExposuresPerAd	C4:E4
MaxTVSpots	C21
MinimumAcceptable	H11:H12
NumberOfAds	C19:E19
NumberReachedPerAd	C11:E12
RequiredAmount	H15
TotalExposures	H19
TotalReached	F11:F12
TotalRedeemed	F15
TVSpots	C19

	F
6	Budget Spent
7	=SUMPRODUCT(C7:E7,NumberOfAds)
8	=SUMPRODUCT(C8:E8,NumberOfAds)
9	
10	Total Reached
11	=SUMPRODUCT(C11:E11,NumberOfAds)
12	=SUMPRODUCT(C12:E12,NumberOfAds)
13	
14	Total Redeemed
15	=SUMPRODUCT(CouponRedemptionPerAd, NumberOfAds)

	H
17	Total Exposures
18	(thousands)
19	=SUMPRODUCT(ExposuresPerAd,NumberOfAds)

The Data

Additional data cells in NumberReachedPerAd (C11:E12), MinimumAcceptable (H11:H12), CouponRedemptionPerAd (C15:E15), and RequiredAmount (H15) give the data in Tables 3.7 and 3.8.

The Decisions

Recall that, as before, the decisions to be made are

    TV = Number of commercials on television

    M = Number of advertisements in magazines

    SS = Number of advertisements in Sunday supplements

The changing cells to hold these numbers continue to be in NumberOfAds (C19:E19).

The Constraints

In addition to the original constraints, we now have two benefit constraints and one fixed-requirement constraint. As specified in rows 11 and 12, columns F to H, the benefit constraints are

Total number of young children reached ≥ 5 (goal 1 in millions)

Total number of parents reached ≥ 5 (goal 2 in millions)

Using the data in columns C to E of these rows,

Total number of young children reached $= 1.2TV + 0.1M + 0SS$

    = SUMPRODUCT (C11:E11, NumberOfAds)

    → cell F11

Total number of parents reached $= 0.5TV + 0.2M + 0.2SS$

    = SUMPRODUCT (C12:E12, NumberOfAds)

    → cell F12

These output cells are given the range name TotalReached (F11:F12).

    The fixed-requirement constraint indicated in row 15 is that

$$\text{Total coupon redemption} = 1{,}490 \quad \text{(allotment in \$1,000s)}$$

CouponRedemptionPerAd (C15:E15) gives the number of coupons redeemed per ad, so

Total coupon redemption $= 0TV + 40M + 120SS$

    = SUMPRODUCT (CouponRedemptionPerAd, NumberOfAds)

    → cell F15

    These same constraints are specified in Solver, along with the original constraints, in Figure 3.7.

The Measure of Performance

The measure of performance continues to be

$$\text{Exposure} = 1{,}300TV + 600M + 500SS$$

    = SUMPRODUCT (ExposuresPerAd, NumberOfAds)

    → cell H19

so the objective cell is again TotalExposures (H19).

Summary of the Formulation

The above steps have resulted in formulating the following linear programming model (in algebraic form) on a spreadsheet.

$$\text{Maximize} \quad \text{Exposure} = 1{,}300TV + 600M + 500SS$$

subject to the following constraints:

1. *Resource constraints:*

$$300TV + 150M + 100SS \leq 4{,}000 \quad \text{(ad budget in \$1,000s)}$$
$$90TV + 30M + 40SS \leq 1{,}000 \quad \text{(planning budget in \$1,000s)}$$
$$TV \leq 5 \quad \text{(television spots available)}$$

2. *Benefit constraints:*

$$1.2TV + 0.1M \geq 5 \quad \text{(millions of young children)}$$
$$0.5TV + 0.2M + 0.2SS \geq 5 \quad \text{(millions of parents)}$$

3. *Fixed-requirement constraint:*

$$40M + 120SS = 1{,}490 \quad \text{(coupon budget in \$1,000s)}$$

4. *Nonnegativity constraints:*

$$TV \geq 0 \quad M \geq 0 \quad SS \geq 0$$

Solving the Model

The lower left-hand corner of Figure 3.7 shows the entries needed in Solver, along with the selection of the usual two options. Solver then finds the optimal solution given in row 19. This optimal solution provides the following plan for the promotional campaign:

Run 3 television commercials.

Run 14 advertisements in magazines.

Run 7.75 advertisements in Sunday supplements (so the eighth advertisement would appear in only 75 percent of the newspapers).

Although the expected number of exposures with this plan is only 16,175,000, versus the 17,000,000 with the first plan shown in Figure 3.1, both Claire Syverson and David Sloan feel that the new plan does a much better job of meeting all of management's goals for this campaign. They decide to adopt the new plan.

A model may need to be modified a number of times before it adequately incorporates all the important considerations.

This case study illustrates a common theme in real applications of linear programming—the continuing evolution of the linear programming model. It is common to make later adjustments in the initial version of the model, perhaps even many times, as experience is gained in using the model. Frequently, these adjustments are made to more adequately reflect some important managerial considerations. This may result in a mixed problem because the new functional constraints needed to incorporate the managerial considerations may be of a different type from those in the original model.

Other Examples

This case study provides a relatively simple example of a small mixed problem. Most of the mixed problems that arise in practice are much larger, sometimes involving hundreds or thousands of activities and hundreds or thousands of constraints. At first glance, these larger problems may seem considerably more complicated than the case study. However, the important thing to remember is that any linear programming problem can have only three types of functional constraints—resource constraints, benefit constraints, and fixed-requirement constraints—where each type is formulated just as illustrated above for the case study.

There are numerous kinds of managerial problems to which linear programming can be applied. We don't have nearly enough space available to give examples of all the most important kinds of applications. However, if you would like to explore this further, we suggest that you go through the five solved problems that are summarized in front of the Problems section for this chapter. Reading the seven cases that follow the Problems section, as well as the application vignettes in both this chapter and the preceding chapter, also will further illustrate the unusually wide applicability of linear programming.

Meanwhile, we soon will turn to two more categories of linear programming problems in the next two sections.

94 Chapter Three *Linear Programming: Formulation and Applications*

Summary of the Formulation Procedure for Mixed Linear Programming Problems

The procedure for formulating mixed problems is similar to the one outlined at the end of Section 3.2 for resource-allocation problems. However, pure resource-allocation problems only have resource constraints whereas mixed problems can include all three types of functional constraints (resource constraints, benefit constraints, and fixed-requirement constraints). Therefore, the following summary for formulating mixed problems includes separate steps for dealing with these different types of constraints. Also see Figure 3.8 for a template of the format for a spreadsheet model of mixed problems. (This format works well for most mixed problems, including those encountered in this chapter, but more flexibility is occasionally needed, as will be illustrated in the next chapter.)

1. Since any linear programming problem involves finding the *best mix* of levels of various activities, identify these *activities* for the problem at hand. The decisions to be made are the *levels* of these activities.

2. From the viewpoint of management, identify an appropriate *overall measure of performance* for solutions of the problem.

3. For each activity, estimate the *contribution per unit* of the activity to this overall measure of performance.

4. Identify any *resources* that must be allocated to the activities (as described in Section 3.2). For each one, identify the *amount available* and then the *amount used per unit of each activity*.

5. Identify any *benefits* to be obtained from the activities (as described in Section 3.3). For each one, identify the *minimum acceptable level* prescribed by management and then the *benefit contribution per unit of each activity*.

6. Identify any *fixed requirements* that, for some type of quantity, the amount provided must equal a required amount (as described in Section 3.4). For each fixed requirement, identify the *required amount* and then the *contribution toward this required amount per unit of each activity*.

FIGURE 3.8

A template of a spreadsheet model for mixed problems.

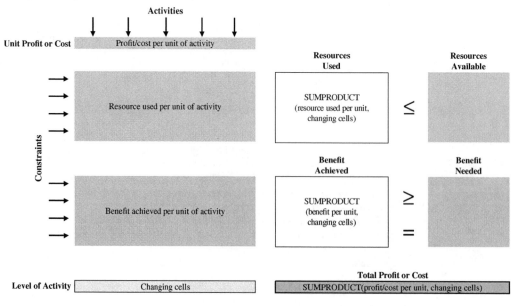

7. Enter the data gathered in steps 3–6 into *data cells* in a spreadsheet.
8. Designate *changing cells* for displaying the decisions on activity levels.
9. Use *output cells* to specify the constraints on resources, benefits, and fixed requirements.
10. Designate an *objective cell* for displaying the overall measure of performance.

Review
Questions

1. What types of functional constraints can appear in a mixed linear programming problem?
2. What managerial goals needed to be incorporated into the expanded linear programming model for the Super Grain Corp. problem?
3. Which categories of functional constraints are included in the new linear programming model?
4. Why did management adopt the new plan even though it provides a smaller expected number of exposures than the original plan recommended by the original linear programming model?

3.5 TRANSPORTATION PROBLEMS

One of the most common applications of linear programming involves optimizing a shipping plan for transporting goods. In a typical application, a company has several plants producing a certain product that needs to be shipped to the company's customers (or perhaps to distribution centers). How much should each plant ship to each customer in order to minimize the total cost? Linear programming can provide the answer. This type of linear programming problem is called a **transportation problem.**

This kind of application normally needs two kinds of functional constraints. One kind specifies that the amount of the product produced at each plant must equal the total amount shipped to customers. The other kind specifies that the total amount received from the plants by each customer must equal the amount ordered. These are *fixed-requirement constraints,* which makes the problem a *fixed-requirements problem.* However, there also are variations of this problem where resource constraints or benefit constraints are needed.

Transportation problems and assignment problems (described in the next section) are such important types of linear programming problems that the entire Chapter 15 on the CD-ROM is devoted to further describing these two related types of problems and providing examples of a wide variety of applications.

We provide below an example of a typical transportation problem.

The Big M Company Transportation Problem

The **Big M Company** produces a variety of heavy duty machines at two factories. One of its products is a large turret lathe. Orders have been received from three customers to purchase some of these turret lathes next month. These lathes will be shipped individually, and Table 3.9 shows what the cost will be for shipping each lathe from each factory to each customer. This table also shows how many lathes have been ordered by each customer and how many will be produced by each factory. The company's distribution manager now wants to determine how many machines to ship from each factory to each customer to minimize the total shipping cost.

Figure 3.9 depicts the distribution network for this problem. This network ignores the geographical layout of the factories and customers and instead lines up the two factories in one column on the left and the three customers in one column on the right. Each arrow shows one of the shipping lanes through this distribution network.

TABLE 3.9
Some Data for the Big M Company Distribution-Network Problem

To	Shipping Cost for Each Lathe			
	Customer 1	Customer 2	Customer 3	Output
From				
Factory 1	$700	$900	$800	12 lathes
Factory 2	800	900	700	15 lathes
Order size	10 lathes	8 lathes	9 lathes	

96   Chapter Three   *Linear Programming: Formulation and Applications*

FIGURE 3.9

The distribution network for the Big M Company problem.

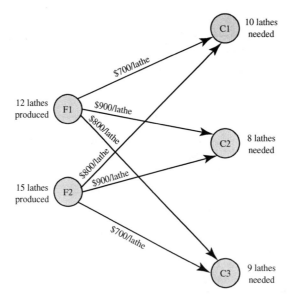

Formulation of the Problem in Linear Programming Terms

We need to identify the *activities* and *requirements* of this transportation problem to formulate it as a linear programming problem. In this case, two kinds of activities have been mentioned—the *production* of the turret lathes at the two factories and the *shipping* of these lathes along the various shipping lanes. However, we know the specific amounts to be produced at each factory, so no decisions need to be made about the production activities. The decisions to be made concern the levels of the *shipping activities*—how many lathes to ship through each shipping lane. Therefore, we need to focus on the shipping activities for the linear programming formulation.

The *activities* correspond to shipping lanes, depicted by arrows in Figure 3.9.

The *level* of each activity is the number of lathes shipped through the corresponding shipping lane.

Just as any linear programming problem can be described as finding the best mix of activity levels, this one involves finding the *best mix of shipping amounts* for the various shipping lanes. The decisions to be made are

$S_{F1\text{-}C1}$ = Number of lathes shipped from Factory 1 to Customer 1

$S_{F1\text{-}C2}$ = Number of lathes shipped from Factory 1 to Customer 2

$S_{F1\text{-}C3}$ = Number of lathes shipped from Factory 1 to Customer 3

$S_{F2\text{-}C1}$ = Number of lathes shipped from Factory 2 to Customer 1

$S_{F2\text{-}C2}$ = Number of lathes shipped from Factory 2 to Customer 2

$S_{F2\text{-}C3}$ = Number of lathes shipped from Factory 2 to Customer 3

so six changing cells will be needed in the spreadsheet.

The objective is to

$$\text{Minimize} \quad \text{Cost} = \text{Total cost for shipping the lathes}$$

Using the shipping costs given in Table 3.9,

$$\text{Cost} = 700S_{F1\text{-}C1} + 900S_{F1\text{-}C2} + 800S_{F1\text{-}C3} + 800S_{F1\text{-}C1} + 900S_{F2\text{-}C2} + 700S_{F2\text{-}C3}$$

is the quantity in dollars to be entered into the objective cell. (We will use a SUMPRODUCT function to do this a little later.)

An Application Vignette

Procter & Gamble (P & G) makes and markets over 300 brands of consumer goods worldwide. The company has grown continuously over its long history tracing back to the 1830s. To maintain and accelerate that growth, a major management science study was undertaken to strengthen P & G's global effectiveness. Prior to the study, the company's supply chain consisted of hundreds of suppliers, over 50 product categories, over 60 plants, 15 distribution centers, and over 1,000 customer zones. However, as the company moved toward global brands, management realized that it needed to consolidate plants to reduce manufacturing expenses, improve speed to market, and reduce capital investment. Therefore, the study focused on redesigning the company's production and distribution system for its North American operations. The result was a reduction in the number of North American plants by almost 20 percent, *saving over* **$200 million** in pretax costs *per year.*

A major part of the study revolved around *formulating and solving transportation problems* for individual product categories. For each option regarding keeping certain plants open, and so forth, solving the corresponding transportation problem for a product category showed what the distribution cost would be for shipping the product category from those plants to the distribution centers and customer zones.

Source: J. D. Camm, T. E. Chorman, F. A. Dill, J. R. Evans, D. J. Sweeney, and G. W. Wegryn, "Blending OR/MS, Judgment, and GIS: Restructuring P & G's Supply Chain," *Interfaces* 27, no. 1 (January–February 1997), pp. 128–142. (A link to this article is provided on our website, **www.mhhe.com/hillier5e.**)

The spreadsheet model also will need five constraints involving *fixed requirements.* Both Table 3.9 and Figure 3.9 show these requirements.

Requirement 1: Factory 1 must ship 12 lathes.

Requirement 2: Factory 2 must ship 15 lathes.

Requirement 3: Customer 1 must receive 10 lathes.

Requirement 4: Customer 2 must receive 8 lathes.

Requirement 5: Customer 3 must receive 9 lathes.

Thus, there is a specific requirement associated with each of the five locations in the distribution network shown in Figure 3.9.

All five of these requirements can be expressed in constraint form as

$$\text{Amount provided} = \text{Required amount}$$

For example, Requirement 1 can be expressed algebraically as

$$S_{\text{F1-C1}} + S_{\text{F1-C2}} + S_{\text{F1-C3}} = 12$$

where the left-hand side gives the total number of lathes shipped from Factory 1, and 12 is the required amount to be shipped from Factory 1. Therefore, this constraint restricts $S_{\text{F1-C1}}, S_{\text{F1-C2}},$ and $S_{\text{F1-C3}}$ to values that sum to the required amount of 12. In contrast to the $\leq$ form for resource constraints and the $\geq$ form for benefit constraints, the constraints express *fixed requirements* that must hold with equality, so this transportation problem falls into the category of fixed-requirements problems introduced in the preceding section. However, Chapter 15 (on the CD-ROM) gives several examples that illustrate how variants of transportation problems can have resource constraints or benefit constraints as well. For example, if 12 lathes represent the manufacturing capacity of Factory 1 (the maximum number that can be shipped) rather than a requirement for how many must be shipped, the constraint just given for Requirement 1 would become a $\leq$ resource constraint instead. Such variations can be incorporated readily into the spreadsheet model.

Formulation of the Spreadsheet Model

Careful *problem* formulation needs to precede *model* formulation.

In preparation for formulating the *model,* the *problem* has been formulated above by identifying the decisions to be made, the constraints on these decisions, and the overall measure of performance, as well as gathering all the important data displayed in Table 3.9. All this information leads to the spreadsheet model shown in Figure 3.10. The data cells include ShippingCost (C5:E6), Output (H11:H12), and OrderSize (C15:E15), incorporating all the data from Table 3.9. The changing cells are UnitsShipped (C11:E12), which give the decisions on the amounts to be shipped through the respective shipping lanes. The output cells are TotalShippedOut (F11:F12) and TotalToCustomer (C13:E13), where the SUM functions

98   Chapter Three   *Linear Programming: Formulation and Applications*

Here is an example where SUM functions are used for output cells instead of SUMPRODUCT functions.

entered into these cells are shown below the spreadsheet in Figure 3.10. The constraints are that TotalShippedOut is required to equal Output and TotalToCustomer is required to equal OrderSize. These constraints have been specified on the spreadsheet and entered into Solver. The objective cell is TotalCost (H15), where its SUMPRODUCT function gives the total shipping cost. The lower left-hand corner of Figure 3.10 shows the entries needed in Solver, along with the selection of the usual two options.

The layout of the spreadsheet is different than for all the prior linear programming examples in the book. Rather than a separate column for each activity and a separate row for each constraint, the cost data and changing cells are laid out in a table format. This format provides a more natural and compact way of displaying the constraints and results.

UnitsShipped (C11:E12) in the spreadsheet in Figure 3.10 shows the result of applying Solver to obtain an optimal solution for the number of lathes to ship through each shipping lane. TotalCost (H15) indicates that the total shipping cost for this shipping plan is $20,500.

Since any transportation problem is a special type of linear programming problem, it makes the standard assumption that fractional solutions are allowed. However, we actually don't want this assumption for this particular application since only *integer* numbers of lathes

FIGURE 3.10

The spreadsheet model for the Big M Company problem, including the formulas for the objective cell TotalCost (H15) and the other output cells TotalShippedOut (F11:F12) and TotalToCustomer (C13:E13), as well as the specifications needed to set up Solver. The changing cells UnitsShipped (C11:E12) show the optimal solution obtained by Solver.

	A	B	C	D	E	F	G	H
1		**Big M Company Distribution Problem**						
2								
3		**Shipping Cost**						
4		**(per Lathe)**	Customer 1	Customer 2	Customer 3			
5		Factory 1	$700	$900	$800			
6		Factory 2	$800	$900	$700			
7								
8						Total		
9						Shipped		
10		**Units Shipped**	Customer 1	Customer 2	Customer 3	Out		Output
11		Factory 1	10	2	0	12	=	12
12		Factory 2	0	6	9	15	=	15
13		Total to Customer	10	8	9			
14			=	=	=			**Total Cost**
15		Order Size	10	8	9			$20,500

Solver Parameters

Set Objective Cell: TotalCost
To: Min
By Changing Variable Cells:
    UnitsShipped
Subject to the Constraints:
    TotalShippedOut = Output
    TotalToCustomer = OrderSize

Solver Options:
    Make Variables Nonnegative
    Solving Method: Simplex LP

Range Name	Cells
OrderSize	C15:E15
Output	H11:H12
ShippingCost	C5:E6
TotalCost	H15
TotalShippedOut	F11:F12
TotalToCustomer	C13:E13
UnitsShipped	C11:E12

	F
8	Total
9	Shipped
10	Out
11	=SUM(C11:E11)
12	=SUM(C12:E12)

	B	C	D	E
13	Total to Customer	=SUM(C11:C12)	=SUM(D11:D12)	=SUM(E11:E12)

	H
14	Total Cost
15	=SUMPRODUCT(ShippingCost,UnitsShipped)

can be shipped from a factory to a customer. Fortunately, even while making the standard assumption, the numbers in the optimal solution shown in UnitsShipped (C11:E12) only have integer values. This is no coincidence. Because of the form of its model, almost any transportation problem (including this one) is guaranteed in advance to have an optimal solution that has only integer values despite the fact that fractional solutions also are allowed. In particular, as long as the data for the problem includes only integer values for all the supplies and demands (which are the outputs and order sizes in the Big M Company problem), any transportation problem with feasible solutions is guaranteed to have an optimal solution with integer values for all its decision variables. Therefore, it is not necessary to add constraints to the model that require these variables to have only integer values.

To summarize, here is the algebraic form of the linear programming model that has been formulated in the spreadsheet:

$$\text{Minimize} \quad \text{Cost} = 700S_{\text{F1-C1}} + 900S_{\text{F1-C2}} + 800S_{\text{F1-C3}} + 800S_{\text{F2-C1}}$$
$$+ 900S_{\text{F2-C2}} + 700S_{\text{F2-C3}}$$

subject to the following constraints:

1. *Fixed-requirement constraints:*

$$
\begin{array}{llll}
S_{\text{F1-C1}} + S_{\text{F1-C2}} + S_{\text{F1-C3}} & & = 12 & \text{(Factory 1)} \\
& S_{\text{F2-C1}} + S_{\text{F2-C2}} + S_{\text{F2-C3}} & = 15 & \text{(Factory 2)} \\
S_{\text{F1-C1}} \quad\quad + S_{\text{F2-C1}} & & = 10 & \text{(Customer 1)} \\
S_{\text{F1-C2}} \quad\quad + S_{\text{F2-C2}} & & = 8 & \text{(Customer 2)} \\
S_{\text{F1-C3}} \quad\quad + S_{\text{F2-C3}} & = 9 & & \text{(Customer 3)}
\end{array}
$$

2. *Nonnegativity constraints:*

$$S_{\text{F1-C1}} \geq 0 \quad S_{\text{F1-C2}} \geq 0 \quad S_{\text{F1-C3}} \geq 0 \quad S_{\text{F2-C1}} \geq 0 \quad S_{\text{F2-C2}} \geq 0 \quad S_{\text{F2-C3}} \geq 0$$

Review Questions

1. Why are transportation problems given this name?
2. What is an identifying feature of transportation problems?
3. How does the form of a fixed-requirement constraint differ from that of a resource constraint? A benefit constraint?
4. What are the quantities with fixed requirements in the Big M Company problem?

3.6 ASSIGNMENT PROBLEMS

We now turn to another special type of linear programming problem called **assignment problems.** As the name suggests, this kind of problem involves making *assignments.* Frequently, these are assignments of people to jobs. Thus, many applications of the assignment problem involve aiding managers in matching up their personnel with tasks to be performed. Other applications might instead involve assigning machines, vehicles, or plants to tasks.

Here is a typical example.

An Example: The Sellmore Company Problem

The marketing manager of the **Sellmore Company** will be holding the company's annual sales conference soon for sales regional managers and personnel. To assist in the administration of the conference, he is hiring four temporary employees (Ann, Ian, Joan, and Sean), where each will handle one of the following four tasks:

1. Word processing of written presentations.
2. Computer graphics for both oral and written presentations.
3. Preparation of conference packets, including copying and organizing written materials.
4. Handling of advance and on-site registrations for the conference.

He now needs to decide which person to assign to each task.

TABLE 3.10
Data for the Sellmore Co. Problem

Temporary Employee	Required Time per Task (Hours)				Hourly Wage
	Word Processing	Graphics	Packets	Registrations	
Ann	35	41	27	40	$14
Ian	47	45	32	51	12
Joan	39	56	36	43	13
Sean	32	51	25	46	15

Decisions need to be made regarding which person to assign to each task.

Although each temporary employee has at least the minimal background necessary to perform any of the four tasks, they differ considerably in how efficiently they can handle the different types of work. Table 3.10 shows how many hours each would need for each task. The rightmost column gives the hourly wage based on the background of each employee.

Formulation of a Spreadsheet Model

Using Cost (D15:G18), the objective is to minimize the total cost of the assignments.

Figure 3.11 shows a spreadsheet model for this problem. Table 3.10 is entered at the top. Combining these required times and wages gives the cost (cells D15:G18) for each possible assignment of a temporary employee to a task, using equations shown at the bottom of Figure 3.11. This *cost table* is just the way that any assignment problem is displayed. The objective is to determine which assignments should be made to minimize the sum of the associated costs.

A value of 1 in a changing cell indicates that the corresponding assignment is being made, whereas 0 means that the assignment is not being made.

The values of 1 in Supply (J24:J27) indicate that each person (assignee) listed in column C must perform exactly one task. The values of 1 in Demand (D30:G30) indicate that each task must be performed by exactly one person. These requirements then are specified in the constraints given in Solver.

Each of the changing cells Assignment (D24:G27) is given a value of 1 when the corresponding assignment is being made, and a value of 0 otherwise. Therefore, the Excel equation for the objective cell, TotalCost = SUMPRODUCT(Cost, Assignment), gives the total cost for the assignments being made. The Solver Parameters box specifies that the goal is to minimize this objective cell.

Excel Tip: When solving an assignment problem, rounding errors occasionally will cause Excel to return a noninteger value very close to 0 (e.g., 1.23 E-10, meaning 0.000000000123) or very close to 1 (e.g., 0.9999912). To make the spreadsheet cleaner, you may replace these "ugly" representations by their proper value of 0 or 1 in the changing cells.

The changing cells in Figure 3.11 show the optimal solution obtained after running Solver. This solution is

Assign Ann to prepare conference packets.

Assign Ian to do the computer graphics.

Assign Joan to handle registrations.

Assign Sean to do the word processing.

The total cost given in cell J30 is $1,957.

Characteristics of Assignment Problems

Note that all the functional constraints of the Sellmore Co. problem (as shown in cells H24:J27 and D28:G30 of Figure 3.11) are fixed-requirement constraints which require each person to perform exactly one task and require each task to be performed by exactly one person. Thus, like the Big M Company transportation problem, the Sellmore Co. is a fixed-requirements problem. This is a characteristic of all pure assignment problems. However, Chapter 15 (on the CD-ROM) gives some examples of variants of assignment problems where this is not the case.

Like the changing cells Assignment (D24:G27) in Figure 3.11, the changing cells in the spreadsheet model for any pure assignment problem gives a value of 1 when the corresponding assignment is being made, and a value of 0 otherwise. Since the fixed-requirement constraints require only each row or column of changing cells to add up to 1 (which could happen, e.g., if two of the changing cells in the same row or column had a value of 0.5 and the rest 0), this would seem to necessitate adding the constraints that each of the changing cells must be *integer*. After choosing the Solver option to make the changing cells nonnegative, this then would force each of the changing cells to be 0 or 1. However, it turned out to be unnecessary to add the constraints that require the changing cells to have values of 0 or 1 in

FIGURE 3.11

A spreadsheet formulation of the Sellmore Co. problem as an assignment problem, including the objective cell TotalCost (J30) and the other output cells Cost (D15:G18), TotalAssignments (H24:H27), and TotalAssigned (D28:G28), as well as the specifications needed to set up the model. The values of 1 in the changing cells Assignment (D24:G27) show the optimal plan obtained by Solver for assigning the people to the tasks.

	A	B	C	D	E	F	G	H	I	J
1		**Sellmore Co. Assignment Problem**								
2										
3					Task					
4		**Required Time**		Word					Hourly	
5		**(Hours)**		Processing	Graphics	Packets	Registrations		Wage	
6			Ann	35	41	27	40		$14	
7		Assignee	Ian	47	45	32	51		$12	
8			Joan	39	56	36	43		$13	
9			Sean	32	51	25	46		$15	
10										
11										
12					Task					
13				Word						
14		**Cost**		Processing	Graphics	Packets	Registrations			
15			Ann	$490	$574	$378	$560			
16		Assignee	Ian	$564	$540	$384	$612			
17			Joan	$507	$728	$468	$559			
18			Sean	$480	$765	$375	$690			
19										
20										
21					Task					
22		**Assignment**		Word				Total		
23				Processing	Graphics	Packets	Registrations	Assignments		Supply
24			Ann	0	0	1	0	1	=	1
25		Assignee	Ian	0	1	0	0	1	=	1
26			Joan	0	0	0	1	1	=	1
27			Sean	1	0	0	0	1	=	1
28			Total Assigned	1	1	1	1			
29				=	=	=	=			Total Cost
30			Demand	1	1	1	1			$1,957

	B	C	D	E	F	G
13			Word			
14	**Cost**		Processing	Graphics	Packets	Registrations
15		Ann	=D6*I6	=E6*I6	=F6*I6	=G6*I6
16	Assignee	Ian	=D7*I7	=E7*I7	=F7*I7	=G7*I7
17		Joan	=D8*I8	=E8*I8	=F8*I8	=G8*I8
18		Sean	=D9*I9	=E9*I9	=F9*I9	=G9*I9

	H
22	Total
23	Assignments
24	=SUM(D24:G24)
25	=SUM(D25:G25)
26	=SUM(D26:G26)
27	=SUM(D27:G27)

Solver Parameters

Set Objective Cell: TotalCost
To: Min
By Changing Variable Cells:
  Assignment
Subject to the Constraints:
  TotalAssigned = Demand
  TotalAssignments = Supply

Solver Options:
  Make Variables Nonnegative
  Solving Method: Simplex LP

	J
29	Total Cost
30	=SUMPRODUCT(Cost,Assignment)

Range Name	Cells
Assignment	D24:G27
Cost	D15:G18
Demand	D30:G30
HourlyWage	I6:I9
RequiredTime	D6:G9
Supply	J24:J27
TotalAssigned	D28:G28
TotalAssignments	H24:H27
TotalCost	J30

	C	D	E	F	G
28	Total Assigned	=SUM(D24:D27)	=SUM(E24:E27)	=SUM(F24:F27)	=SUM(G24:G27)

Figure 3.11 because Solver gave an optimal solution that had only values of 0 or 1 anyway. In fact, a general characteristic of pure assignment problems is that Solver always provides such an optimal solution without needing to add these additional constraints.

As described further in Chapter 15, another interesting characteristic of any pure assignment problem is that it can be viewed as a special type of pure transportation problem. In particular, every fixed-requirement constraint in the corresponding transportation problem would require that either a row or column of changing cells add up to 1. This would result in Solver giving an optimal solution where every changing cell has a value of either 0 or 1, just as for the original assignment problem.

**Review
*Questions***

1. Why are assignment problems given this name?
2. Pure assignment problems have what type of functional constraints?
3. What is the interpretation of the changing cells in the spreadsheet model of a pure assignment problem?

3.7   MODEL FORMULATION FROM A BROADER PERSPECTIVE

Formulating and analyzing a linear programming model provides information to help managers make their decisions. That means the model must accurately reflect the managerial view of the problem:

Both the measure of performance and the constraints in a model need to reflect the managerial view of the problem.

- The overall *measure of performance* must capture what management wants accomplished.
- When management limits the amounts of resources that will be made available to the activities under consideration, these limitations should be expressed as *resource constraints.*
- When management establishes minimum acceptable levels for benefits to be gained from the activities, these managerial goals should be incorporated into the model as *benefit constraints.*
- If management has fixed requirements for certain quantities, then *fixed-requirement constraints* are needed.

With the help of spreadsheets, some managers now are able to formulate and solve small linear programming models themselves. However, larger linear programming models may be formulated by *management science teams,* not managers. When this is done, the management science team must thoroughly understand the managerial view of the problem. This requires clear communication with management from the very beginning of the study and maintaining effective communication as new issues requiring managerial guidance are identified. Management needs to clearly convey its view of the problem and the important issues involved. A manager cannot expect to obtain a helpful linear programming study without making clear just what help is wanted.

Linear programming studies need strong managerial input and support.

As is necessary in any textbook, the examples in this chapter are far smaller, simpler, and more clearly spelled out than is typical of real applications. Many real studies require formulating complicated linear programming models involving hundreds or thousands of decisions and constraints. In these cases, there usually are many ambiguities about just what should be incorporated into the model. Strong managerial input and support are vital to the success of a linear programming study for such complex problems.

When dealing with huge real problems, there is no such thing as "the" correct linear programming model for the problem. The model continually evolves throughout the course of the study. Early in the study, various techniques are used to test initial versions of the model to identify the errors and omissions that inevitably occur when constructing such a large model. This testing process is referred to as **model validation.**

Once the basic formulation has been validated, there are many reasonable variations of the model that might be used. Which variation to use depends on such factors as the assumptions about the problem that seem most reasonable, the estimates of the parameters of the model that seem most reliable, and the degree of detail desired in the model.

In large linear programming studies, a good approach is to begin with a relatively simple version of the model and then use the experience gained with this model to evolve toward more elaborate models that more nearly reflect the complexity of the real problem. This process of **model enrichment** continues only as long as the model remains reasonably easy to solve. It must be curtailed when the study's results are needed by management. Managers often need to curb the natural instinct of management science teams to continue adding "bells and whistles" to the model rather than winding up the study in a timely fashion with a less elegant but adequate model.

When managers study the output of the current model, they often detect some undesirable characteristics that point toward needed model enrichments. These enrichments frequently take the form of new *benefit constraints* to satisfy some managerial goals not previously articulated. (Recall that this is what happened in the Super Grain case study.)

Even though many reasonable variations of the model could be used, an *optimal solution* can be solved for only with respect to one specific version of the model at a time. This is why *what-if analysis* is such an important part of a linear programming study. After obtaining an optimal solution with respect to one specific model, management will have many what-if questions:

- What if the estimates of the parameters in the model are incorrect?
- How do the conclusions change if different plausible assumptions are made about the problem?
- What happens when certain managerial options are pursued that are not incorporated into the current model?

Chapter 5 is devoted primarily to describing how what-if analysis addresses these and related issues, as well as how managers use this information.

Because managers *instigate* management science studies, they need to know enough about linear programming models and their formulation to be able to recognize managerial problems to which linear programming can be applied. Furthermore, since managerial input is so important for linear programming studies, managers need to understand the kinds of managerial concerns that can be incorporated into the model. Developing these two skills have been the most important goals of this chapter.

> What-if analysis addresses some key questions that remain after formulating and solving a model.

Review Questions

1. A linear programming model needs to reflect accurately whose view of the problem?
2. What is meant by *model validation?*
3. What is meant by the process of *model enrichment?*
4. Why is what-if analysis an important part of a linear programming study?

3.8 Summary

Functional constraints with a $\leq$ sign are called *resource constraints*, because they require that the *amount used* of some resource must be *less than or equal to* the *amount available* of that resource. The identifying feature of *resource-allocation problems* is that all their functional constraints are resource constraints.

Functional constraints with a $\geq$ sign are called *benefit constraints*, since their form is that the *level achieved* for some benefit must be *greater than or equal to* the *minimum acceptable level* for that benefit. Frequently, benefit constraints express goals prescribed by management. If every functional constraint is a benefit constraint, then the problem is a *cost–benefit–trade-off problem.*

Functional constraints with an $=$ sign are called *fixed-requirement constraints*, because they express the fixed requirement that, for some quantity, the *amount provided* must be *equal to* the *required amount.* The identifying feature of *fixed-requirements problems* is that their functional constraints are fixed-requirement constraints. One prominent type of fixed-requirements problem is transportation problems, which typically involve finding a shipping plan that minimizes the total cost of transporting a product from a number of plants to a number of customers. Another prominent type is assignment problems, which typically involves assigning people to tasks so as to minimize the total cost of performing these tasks.

Linear programming problems that do not fit into any of these three categories are called *mixed problems.*

In many real applications, management science teams formulate and analyze large linear programming models to help guide managerial decision making. Such teams need strong managerial input and support to help ensure that their work really meets management's needs.

104   Chapter Three   *Linear Programming: Formulation and Applications*

Glossary

assignment problem   A type of linear programming problem that typically involves assigning people to tasks so as to minimize the total cost of performing these tasks. (Section 3.6), 99

benefit constraint   A functional constraint with a $\geq$ sign. The left-hand side is interpreted as the level of some benefit that is achieved by the activities under consideration, and the right-hand side is the minimum acceptable level for that benefit. (Section 3.3), 82

cost–benefit–trade-off problem   A type of linear programming problem involving the trade-off between the total cost of the activities under consideration and the benefits to be achieved by these activities. Its identifying feature is that each functional constraint in the linear programming model is a benefit constraint. (Section 3.3), 82

fixed-requirement constraint   A functional constraint with an $=$ sign. The left-hand side represents the amount provided of some type of quantity, and the right-hand side represents the required amount for that quantity. (Section 3.4), 88

fixed-requirements problem   A type of linear programming problem concerned with optimizing how to meet a number of fixed requirements. Its identifying feature is that each functional constraint in its model is a fixed-requirement constraint. (Section 3.4), 88

identifying feature   A feature of a model that identifies the category of linear programming problem it represents. (Chapter introduction), 64

integer programming problem   A variation of a linear programming problem that has the additional restriction that some or all of the decision variables must have integer values. (Section 3.2), 75

mixed problem   Any linear programming problem that includes at least two of the three types of functional constraints (resource constraints, benefit constraints, and fixed-requirement constraints). (Section 3.4), 88

model enrichment   The process of using experience with a model to identify and add important details that will provide a better representation of the real problem. (Section 3.7), 103

model validation   The process of checking and testing a model to develop a valid model. (Section 3.7), 102

resource-allocation problem   A type of linear programming problem concerned with allocating resources to activities. Its identifying feature is that each functional constraint in its model is a resource constraint. (Section 3.2), 71

resource constraint   A functional constraint with a $\leq$ sign. The left-hand side represents the amount of some resource that is used by the activities under consideration, and the right-hand side represents the amount available of that resource. (Section 3.2), 71

transportation problem   A type of linear programming problem that typically involves finding a shipping plan that minimizes the total cost of transporting a product from a number of plants to a number of customers. (Section 3.5), 95

Learning Aids for This Chapter in Your MS Courseware

Chapter 3 Excel Files:

Super Grain Example

TBA Airlines Example

Think-Big Example

Union Airways Example

Big M Example

Revised Super Grain Example

Sellmore Example

Excel Add-in:

Risk Solver Platform for Education (RSPE)

Solved Problems (See the CD-ROM or Website for the Solutions)

3.S1. Farm Management

Dwight and Hattie have run the family farm for over 30 years. They are currently planning the mix of crops to plant on their 120-acre farm for the upcoming season. The table gives the labor-hours and fertilizer required per acre, as well as the total expected profit per acre for each of the potential crops under consideration. Dwight, Hattie, and their children can work at most 6,500 total hours during the upcoming season. They have 200 tons of fertilizer available. What mix of crops should be planted to maximize the family's total profit?

a. Formulate and solve a linear programming model for this problem in a spreadsheet.

b. Formulate this same model algebraically.

Crop	Labor Required (hours per acre)	Fertilizer Required (tons per acre)	Expected Profit (per acre)
Oats	50	1.5	$500
Wheat	60	2	$600
Corn	105	4	$950

3.S2. Diet Problem

The kitchen manager for Sing Sing prison is trying to decide what to feed its prisoners. She would like to offer some combination of milk, beans, and oranges. The goal is to minimize cost, subject to meeting the minimum nutritional requirements imposed by law. The cost and nutritional content of each food, along with the minimum nutritional requirements, are shown below. What diet should be fed to each prisoner?

a. Formulate and solve a linear programming model for this problem in a spreadsheet.

b. Formulate this same model algebraically.

	Milk (gallons)	Navy Beans (cups)	Oranges (large Calif. Valencia)	Minimum Daily Requirement
Niacin (mg)	3.2	4.9	0.8	13.0
Thiamin (mg)	1.12	1.3	0.19	1.5
Vitamin C (mg)	32.0	0.0	93.0	45.0
Cost ($)	2.00	0.20	0.25	

3.S3. Cutting Stock Problem

Decora Accessories manufactures a variety of bathroom accessories, including decorative towel rods and shower curtain rods. Each of the accessories includes a rod made out of stainless steel. However, many different lengths are needed: 12, 18, 24, 40, and 60 inches. Decora purchases 60-inch rods from an outside supplier and then cuts the rods as needed for their products. Each 60-inch rod can be used to make a number of smaller rods. For example, a 60-inch rod could be used to make a 40-inch and an 18-inch rod (with 2 inches of waste), or five 12-inch rods (with no waste). For the next production period, Decora needs twenty-five 12-inch rods, fifty-two 18-inch rods, forty-five 24-inch rods, thirty 40-inch rods, and twelve 60-inch rods. What is the fewest number of 60-inch rods that can be purchased to meet their production needs? Formulate and solve an integer programming model in a spreadsheet.

3.S4. Producing and Distributing AEDs at Heart Start

Heart Start produces automated external defibrillators in each of two different plants (A and B). The unit production costs and monthly production capacity of the two plants are indicated in the table below. The automated external defibrillators are sold

through three wholesalers. The shipping cost from each plant to the warehouse of each wholesaler along with the monthly demand from each wholesaler are also indicated in the table. The management of Heart Start now has asked their top management scientist (you) to address the following two questions. How many automated external defibrillators should be produced in each plant, and how should they be distributed to each of the three wholesaler warehouses so as to minimize the combined cost of production and shipping? Formulate and solve a linear programming model in a spreadsheet.

3.S5. Bidding for Classes

In the MBA program at a prestigious university in the Pacific Northwest, students bid for electives in the second year of their program. Each student has 100 points to bid (total) and must take two electives. There are four electives available: Management Science (MS), Finance (Fin), Operations Management (OM), and Marketing (Mkt). Each class is limited to 5 students. The bids submitted for each of the 10 students are shown in the table below.

Student Bids for Classes				
Student	MS	Fin	OM	Mkt
George	60	10	10	20
Fred	20	20	40	20
Ann	45	45	5	5
Eric	50	20	5	25
Susan	30	30	30	10
Liz	50	50	0	0
Ed	70	20	10	0
David	25	25	35	15
Tony	35	15	35	15
Jennifer	60	10	10	20

a. Formulate and solve a spreadsheet model to determine an assignment of students to classes so as to maximize the total bid points of the assignments.

b. Does the resulting solution seem like a fair assignment?

c. Which alternative objectives might lead to a fairer assignment?

	Unit Shipping Cost			Unit Production Cost	Monthly Production Capacity
	Warehouse 1	Warehouse 2	Warehouse 3		
Plant A	$22	$14	$30	$600	100
Plant B	$16	$20	$24	$625	120
Monthly Demand	80	60	70		

Problems

We have inserted the symbol E* to the left of each problem (or its parts) where Excel should be used (unless your instructor gives you contrary instructions). Either the Excel's Solver or RSPE may be used to solve such problems. An asterisk on the problem number indicates that at least a partial answer is given in the back of the book.

3.1.   Reconsider the Super Grain Corp. case study as presented in Section 3.1. The advertising firm, Giacomi & Jackowitz, now has suggested a fourth promising advertising medium—radio commercials—to promote the company's new breakfast cereal, Crunchy Start. Young children are potentially major consumers of this cereal, but parents of young children (the major potential purchasers) often are too busy to do much reading (so may miss the company's advertisements in magazines and Sunday supplements) or even to watch the Saturday morning programs for children where the company's television commercials are aired. However, these parents do tend to listen to the radio during the commute to and from work. Therefore, to better reach these parents, Giacomi & Jackowitz suggests giving consideration to running commercials for Crunchy Start on nationally syndicated radio programs that appeal to young adults during typical commuting hours.

Giacomi & Jackowitz estimates that the cost of developing each new radio commercial would be $50,000, and that the expected number of exposures per commercial would be 900,000. The firm has determined that 10 spots are available for different radio commercials, and each one would cost $200,000 for a normal run.

E*   *a.* Formulate and solve a spreadsheet model for the revised advertising-mix problem that includes this fourth advertising medium. Identify the data cells, the changing cells, and the objective cell. Also show the Excel equation for each output cell expressed as a SUMPRODUCT function.

   b. Indicate why this spreadsheet model is a linear programming model.

   c. Express this model in algebraic form.

3.2   Read the referenced article that fully describes the management science study summarized in the application vignette presented in Section 3.2. Briefly describe how linear programming was applied in this study. Then list the various benefits that resulted from this study.

3.3.*   Consider a resource-allocation problem having the following data.

Resource	Resource Usage per Unit of Each Activity		Amount of Resource Available
	1	2	
1	2	1	10
2	3	3	20
3	2	4	20
Contribution per unit	$20	$30	

Contribution per unit = profit per unit of the activity.

E*   *a.* Formulate a linear programming model for this problem on a spreadsheet.

E*   *b.* Use the spreadsheet to check the following solutions: (x_1, x_2) = (2, 2), (3, 3), (2, 4), (4, 2), (3, 4), (4, 3). Which of these solutions are feasible? Which of these feasible solutions has the best value of the objective function?

E*   *c.* Use Solver to find an optimal solution.

   d. Express this model in algebraic form.

   e. Use the graphical method to solve this model.

3.4.   Consider a resource-allocation problem having the following data.

Resource	Resource Usage per Unit of Each Activity			Amount of Resource Available
	1	2	3	
A	30	20	0	500
B	0	10	40	600
C	20	20	30	1,000
Contribution per unit	$50	$40	$70	

Contribution per unit = profit per unit of the activity.

E*   *a.* Formulate and solve a linear programming model for this problem on a spreadsheet.

   b. Express this model in algebraic form.

E*3.5.   Consider a resource-allocation problem having the following data.

Resource	Resource Usage per Unit of Each Activity				Amount of Resource Available
	1	2	3	4	
P	3	5	−2	4	400
Q	4	−1	3	2	300
R	6	3	2	−1	400
S	−2	2	5	3	300
Contribution per unit	$11	$9	$8	$9	

Contribution per unit = profit per unit of the activity.

   a. Formulate a linear programming model for this problem on a spreadsheet.

   b. Make five guesses of your own choosing for the optimal solution. Use the spreadsheet to check each one for feasibility and, if feasible, for the value of the objective function. Which feasible guess has the best objective function value?

   c. Use Solver to find an optimal solution.

3.6.*   The Omega Manufacturing Company has discontinued the production of a certain unprofitable product line. This act created considerable excess production capacity. Management is considering devoting this excess capacity to one or more of three products, Products 1, 2, and 3. The available capacity of the machines that might limit output is summarized in the following table.

Machine Type	Available Time (in Machine-Hours per Week)
Milling machine	500
Lathe	350
Grinder	150

The number of machine-hours required for each unit of the respective products are shown in the next table.

Productivity Coefficient (in Machine-Hours per Unit)

Machine Type	Product 1	Product 2	Product 3
Milling machine	9	3	5
Lathe	5	4	0
Grinder	3	0	2

The Sales Department indicates that the sales potential for Products 1 and 2 exceeds the maximum production rate and that the sales potential for product 3 is 20 units per week. The unit profit would be $50, $20, and $25, respectively, for Products 1, 2, and 3. The objective is to determine how much of each product Omega should produce to maximize profit.

    a. Indicate why this is a resource-allocation problem by identifying both the activities and the limited resources to be allocated to these activities.

    b. Identify verbally the decisions to be made, the constraints on these decisions, and the overall measure of performance for the decisions.

    c. Convert these verbal descriptions of the constraints and the measure of performance into quantitative expressions in terms of the data and decisions.

E*   *d.* Formulate a spreadsheet model for this problem. Identify the data cells, the changing cells, the objective cell, and the other output cells. Also show the Excel equation for each output cell expressed as a SUMPRODUCT function. Then use Solver to solve the model.

    e. Summarize the model in algebraic form.

3.7.   Ed Butler is the production manager for the Bilco Corporation, which produces three types of spare parts for automobiles. The manufacture of each part requires processing on each of two machines, with the following processing times (in hours).

Machine	Part		
	A	B	C
1	0.02	0.03	0.05
2	0.05	0.02	0.04

Each machine is available 40 hours per month. Each part manufactured will yield a unit profit as follows:

	Part		
	A	B	C
Profit	$50	$40	$30

Ed wants to determine the mix of spare parts to produce to maximize total profit.

    a. Identify both the activities and the resources for this resource-allocation problem.

E*   *b.* Formulate a linear programming model for this problem on a spreadsheet.

E*   *c.* Make three guesses of your own choosing for the optimal solution. Use the spreadsheet to check each one for feasibility and, if feasible, for the value of the objective function. Which feasible guess has the best objective function value?

E*   *d.* Use Solver to find an optimal solution.

    e. Express the model in algebraic form.

E*3.8. Consider the following algebraic formulation of a resource-allocation problem with three resources, where the decisions to be made are the levels of three activities (A_1, A_2, and A_3).

$$\text{Maximize} \quad \text{Profit} = 20A_1 + 40A_2 + 30A_3$$

subject to

    Resource 1: $3A_1 + 5A_2 + 4A_3 \leq 400$ (amount available)

    Resource 2: $A_1 + A_2 + A_3 \leq 100$ (amount available)

    Resource 3: $A_1 + 3A_2 + 2A_3 \leq 200$ (amount available)

and

$$A_1 \geq 0 \quad A_2 \geq 0 \quad A_3 \geq 0$$

Formulate and solve the spreadsheet model for this problem.

3.9.   Read the referenced article that fully describes the management science study summarized in the application vignette presented in Section 3.3. Briefly describe how linear programming was applied in this study. Then list the various financial and nonfinancial benefits that resulted from this study.

3.10. Consider a cost–benefit–trade-off problem having the following data.

	Benefit Contribution per Unit of Each Activity		Minimum Acceptable Level
Benefit	1	2	
1	5	3	60
2	2	2	30
3	7	9	126
Unit cost	$60	$50	

E*   *a.* Formulate a linear programming model for this problem on a spreadsheet.

E*   *b.* Use the spreadsheet to check the following solutions: $(x_1, x_2) = (7, 7), (7, 8), (8, 7), (8, 8), (8, 9), (9, 8)$. Which of these solutions are feasible? Which of these feasible solutions has the best value of the objective function?

E*   *c.* Use Solver to find an optimal solution.

    d. Express the model in algebraic form.

    e. Use the graphical method to solve this model.

E*3.11. Consider a cost–benefit–trade-off problem having the following data.

	Benefit Contribution per Unit of Each Activity				Minimum Acceptable Level
Benefit	1	2	3	4	
P	2	−1	4	3	80
Q	1	4	−1	2	60
R	3	5	4	−1	110
Unit cost	$400	$600	$500	$300	

a. Formulate a linear programming model for this problem on a spreadsheet.

b. Make five guesses of your own choosing for the optimal solution. Use the spreadsheet to check each one for feasibility and, if feasible, for the value of the objective function. Which feasible guess has the best objective function value?

c. Use Solver to find an optimal solution.

3.12.* Fred Jonasson manages a family-owned farm. To supplement several food products grown on the farm, Fred also raises pigs for market. He now wishes to determine the quantities of the available types of feed (corn, tankage, and alfalfa) that should be given to each pig. Since pigs will eat any mix of these feed types, the objective is to determine which mix will meet certain nutritional requirements at a *minimum cost*. The number of units of each type of basic nutritional ingredient contained within a kilogram of each feed type is given in the following table, along with the daily nutritional requirements and feed costs.

Maureen wishes to determine the mix of investments in these assets that will cover the cash flow requirements while minimizing the total amount invested.

E* *a.* Formulate a linear programming model for this problem on a spreadsheet.

E* *b.* Use the spreadsheet to check the possibility of purchasing 100 units of asset 1, 100 units of asset 2, and 200 units of asset 3. How much cash flow would this mix of investments generate 5, 10, and 20 years from now? What would be the total amount invested?

E* *c.* Take a few minutes to use a trial-and-error approach with the spreadsheet to develop your best guess for the optimal solution. What is the total amount invested for your solution?

E* *d.* Use Solver to find an optimal solution.

e. Summarize the model in algebraic form.

Nutritional Ingredient	Kilogram of Corn	Kilogram of Tankage	Kilogram of Alfalfa	Minimum Daily Requirement
Carbohydrates	90	20	40	200
Protein	30	80	60	180
Vitamins	10	20	60	150
Cost (¢)	84	72	60	

E* *a.* Formulate a linear programming model for this problem on a spreadsheet.

E* *b.* Use the spreadsheet to check if $(x_1, x_2, x_3) = (1, 2, 2)$ is a feasible solution and, if so, what the daily cost would be for this diet. How many units of each nutritional ingredient would this diet provide daily?

E* *c.* Take a few minutes to use a trial-and-error approach with the spreadsheet to develop your best guess for the optimal solution. What is the daily cost for your solution?

E* *d.* Use Solver to find an optimal solution.

e. Express the model in algebraic form.

3.13.   Maureen Laird is the chief financial officer for the Alva Electric Co., a major public utility in the Midwest. The company has scheduled the construction of new hydroelectric plants 5, 10, and 20 years from now to meet the needs of the growing population in the region served by the company. To cover the construction costs, Maureen needs to invest some of the company's money now to meet these future cash flow needs. Maureen may purchase only three kinds of financial assets, each of which costs $1 million per unit. Fractional units may be purchased. The assets produce income 5, 10, and 20 years from now, and that income is needed to cover minimum cash flow requirements in those years, as shown in the following table.

3.14.   Web Mercantile sells many household products through an online catalog. The company needs substantial warehouse space for storing its goods. Plans now are being made for leasing warehouse storage space over the next five months. Just how much space will be required in each of these months is known. However, since these space requirements are quite different, it may be most economical to lease only the amount needed each month on a month-by-month basis. On the other hand, the additional cost for leasing space for additional months is much less than for the first month, so it may be less expensive to lease the maximum amount needed for the entire five months. Another option is the intermediate approach of changing the total amount of space leased (by adding a new lease and/or having an old lease expire) at least once but not every month.

The space requirement and the leasing costs for the various leasing periods are as follows.

Month	Required Space (Square Feet)
1	30,000
2	20,000
3	40,000
4	10,000
5	50,000

Income per Unit of Asset

Year	Asset 1	Asset 2	Asset 3	Minimum Cash Flow Required
5	$2 million	$1 million	$0.5 million	$400 million
10	0.5 million	0.5 million	1 million	100 million
20	0	1.5 million	2 million	300 million

Leasing Period (Months)	Cost per Sq. Ft. Leased
1	$ 65
2	100
3	135
4	160
5	190

The objective is to minimize the total leasing cost for meeting the space requirements.

   a. Indicate why this is a cost–benefit–trade-off problem by identifying both the activities and the benefits being sought from these activities.

   b. Identify verbally the decisions to be made, the constraints on these decisions, and the overall measure of performance for the decisions.

   c. Convert these verbal descriptions of the constraints and the measure of performance into quantitative expressions in terms of the data and decisions.

E* *d.* Formulate a spreadsheet model for this problem. Identify the data cells, the changing cells, the objective cell, and the other output cells. Also show the Excel equation for each output cell expressed as a SUMPRODUCT function. Then use Solver to solve the model.

   e. Summarize the model in algebraic form.

E*3.15. Consider the following algebraic formulation of a cost–benefit–trade-off problem involving three benefits, where the decisions to be made are the levels of four activities (A_1, A_2, A_3, and A_4):

$$\text{Minimize} \quad \text{Cost} = 2A_1 + A_2 - A_3 + 3A_4$$

subject to

Benefit 1: $3A_1 + 2A_2 - 2A_3 + 5A_4 \geq 80$ (minimum acceptable level)

Benefit 2: $A_1 - A_2 \quad + A_4 \geq 10$ (minimum acceptable level)

Benefit 3: $A_1 + A_2 - A_3 + 2A_4 \geq 30$ (minimum acceptable level)

and

$$A_1 \geq 0 \quad A_2 \geq 0 \quad A_3 \geq 0 \quad A_4 \geq 0$$

Formulate and solve the spreadsheet model for this problem.

Time of Day	Minimum Number of Consultants Required to Be on Duty
8 AM–noon	6
Noon–4 PM	8
4 PM–8 PM	12
8 PM–midnight	6

Two types of computer consultants can be hired: full-time and part-time. The full-time consultants work for eight consecutive hours in any of the following shifts: morning (8 AM–4 PM), afternoon (noon–8 PM), and evening (4 PM–midnight). Full-time consultants are paid $14 per hour.

Part-time consultants can be hired to work any of the four shifts listed in the table. Part-time consultants are paid $12 per hour.

An additional requirement is that during every time period, there must be at least two full-time consultants on duty for every part-time consultant on duty.

Larry would like to determine how many full-time and part-time consultants should work each shift to meet the above requirements at the minimum possible cost.

   a. Which category of linear programming problem does this problem fit? Why?

E* *b.* Formulate and solve a linear programming model for this problem on a spreadsheet.

   c. Summarize the model in algebraic form.

3.17.* The Medequip Company produces precision medical diagnostic equipment at two factories. Three medical centers have placed orders for this month's production output. The following table shows what the cost would be for shipping each unit from each factory to each of these customers. Also shown are the number of units that will be produced at each factory and the number of units ordered by each customer.

A decision now needs to be made about the shipping plan for how many units to ship from each factory to each customer.

   a. Which category of linear programming problem does this problem fit? Why?

E* *b.* Formulate and solve a linear programming model for this problem on a spreadsheet.

   c. Summarize this formulation in algebraic form.

From \ To	Unit Shipping Cost			Output
	Customer 1	Customer 2	Customer 3	
Factory 1	$600	$800	$700	400 units
Factory 2	400	900	600	500 units
Order size	300 units	200 units	400 units	

3.16. Larry Edison is the director of the Computer Center for Buckly College. He now needs to schedule the staffing of the center. It is open from 8 AM until midnight. Larry has monitored the usage of the center at various times of the day and determined that the following number of computer consultants are required.

3.18. The Fagersta Steelworks currently is working two mines to obtain its iron ore. This iron ore is shipped to either of two storage facilities. When needed, it then is shipped on to the company's steel plant. The diagram below depicts this distribution network, where M1 and M2 are the two mines, S1 and S2 are the two storage facilities, and P is the steel plant. The diagram also shows the monthly amounts produced at the mines and needed at the plant, as well as the shipping cost and the maximum amount that can be shipped per month through each shipping lane.

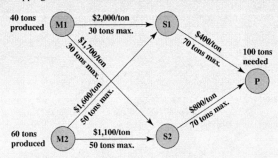

Management now wants to determine the most economical plan for shipping the iron ore from the mines through the distribution network to the steel plant.

    a. Identify all the requirements that will need to be expressed in fixed-requirement constraints.

E*   *b.* Formulate and solve a linear programming model for this problem on a spreadsheet.

    c. Express this model in algebraic form.

3.19.* Al Ferris has $60,000 that he wishes to invest now in order to use the accumulation for purchasing a retirement annuity in five years. After consulting with his financial advisor, he has been offered four types of fixed-income investments, which we will label as investments *A, B, C,* and *D.*

    Investments *A* and *B* are available at the beginning of each of the next five years (call them years 1 to 5). Each dollar invested in *A* at the beginning of a year returns $1.40 (a profit of $0.40) two years later (in time for immediate reinvestment). Each dollar invested in *B* at the beginning of a year returns $1.70 three years later.

    Investments *C* and *D* will each be available at one time in the future. Each dollar invested in *C* at the beginning of year 2 returns $1.90 at the end of year 5. Each dollar invested in *D* at the beginning of year 5 returns $1.30 at the end of year 5.

    Al wishes to know which investment plan maximizes the amount of money that can be accumulated by the beginning of year 6.

    a. For this problem, all its functional constraints can be expressed as fixed-requirement constraints. To do this, let A_t, B_t, C_t, and D_t be the amounts invested in investments *A, B, C,* and *D,* respectively, at the beginning of year *t* for each *t* where the investment is available and will mature by the end of year 5. Also let R_t be the number of available dollars *not* invested at the beginning of year *t* (and so available for investment in a later year). Thus, the amount invested at the beginning of year *t plus* R_t must equal the number of dollars available for investment at that time. Write such an equation in terms of the relevant variables above for the beginning of each of the five years to obtain the five fixed-requirement constraints for this problem.

    b. Formulate a complete linear programming model for this problem in algebraic form.

E*   *c.* Formulate and solve this model on a spreadsheet.

3.20.   The Metalco Company desires to blend a new alloy of 40 percent tin, 35 percent zinc, and 25 percent lead from several available alloys having the following properties.

Property	Alloy				
	1	**2**	**3**	**4**	**5**
Percentage of tin	60	25	45	20	50
Percentage of zinc	10	15	45	50	40
Percentage of lead	30	60	10	30	10
Cost ($/lb)	22	20	25	24	27

    The objective is to determine the proportions of these alloys that should be blended to produce the new alloy at a minimum cost.

    a. Identify all the requirements that will need to be expressed in fixed-requirement constraints.

E*   *b.* Formulate and solve a linear programming model for this problem on a spreadsheet.

    c. Express this model in algebraic form.

3.21.   The Weigelt Corporation has three branch plants with excess production capacity. Fortunately, the corporation has a new product ready to begin production, and all three plants have this capability, so some of the excess capacity can be used in this way. This product can be made in three sizes—large, medium, and small—that yield a net unit profit of $420, $360, and $300, respectively. Plants 1, 2, and 3 have the excess capacity to produce 750, 900, and 450 units per day of this product, respectively, regardless of the size or combination of sizes involved.

    The amount of available in-process storage space also imposes a limitation on the production rates of the new product. Plants 1, 2, and 3 have 13,000, 12,000, and 5,000 square feet, respectively, of in-process storage space available for a day's production of this product. Each unit of the large, medium, and small sizes produced per day requires 20, 15, and 12 square feet, respectively.

    Sales forecasts indicate that if available, 900, 1,200, and 750 units of the large, medium, and small sizes, respectively, would be sold per day.

    At each plant, some employees will need to be laid off unless most of the plant's excess production capacity can be used to produce the new product. To avoid layoffs if possible, management has decided that the plants should use the same percentage of their excess capacity to produce the new product.

    Management wishes to know how much of each of the sizes should be produced by each of the plants to maximize profit.

E*   *a.* Formulate and solve a linear programming model for this mixed problem on a spreadsheet.

    b. Express the model in algebraic form.

3.22.* A cargo plane has three compartments for storing cargo: front, center, and back. These compartments have capacity limits on both *weight* and *space,* as summarized below.

Compartment	Weight Capacity (Tons)	Space Capacity (Cubic Feet)
Front	12	7,000
Center	18	9,000
Back	10	5,000

Furthermore, the weight of the cargo in the respective compartments must be the same proportion of that compartment's weight capacity to maintain the balance of the airplane.

The following four cargoes have been offered for shipment on an upcoming flight as space is available.

Cargo	Weight (Tons)	Volume (Cubic Feet/Ton)	Profit ($/Ton)
1	20	500	320
2	16	700	400
3	25	600	360
4	13	400	290

Any portion of these cargoes can be accepted. The objective is to determine how much (if any) of each cargo should be accepted and how to distribute each among the compartments to maximize the total profit for the flight.

E* *a.* Formulate and solve a linear programming model for this mixed problem on a spreadsheet.

  b. Express the model in algebraic form.

3.23.   Comfortable Hands is a company that features a product line of winter gloves for the entire family—men, women, and children. They are trying to decide what mix of these three types of gloves to produce.

Comfortable Hands's manufacturing labor force is unionized. Each full-time employee works a 40-hour week. In addition, by union contract, the number of full-time employees can never drop below 20. Nonunion, part-time workers also can be hired with the following union-imposed restrictions: (1) each part-time worker works 20 hours per week and (2) there must be at least two full-time employees for each part-time employee.

All three types of gloves are made out of the same 100 percent genuine cowhide leather. Comfortable Hands has a long-term contract with a supplier of the leather and receives a 5,000-square-foot shipment of the material each week. The material requirements and labor requirements, along with the *gross profit* per glove sold (not considering labor costs), are given in the following table.

Glove	Material Required (Square Feet)	Labor Required (Minutes)	Gross Profit (per Pair)
Men's	2	30	$ 8
Women's	1.5	45	10
Children's	1	40	6

Each full-time employee earns $13 per hour, while each part-time employee earns $10 per hour. Management wishes to know what mix of each of the three types of gloves to produce per week, as well as how many full-time and part-time workers

to employ. They would like to maximize their *net profit*—their gross profit from sales minus their labor costs.

E* *a.* Formulate and solve a linear programming model for this problem on a spreadsheet.

  b. Summarize this formulation in algebraic form.

E*3.24. Oxbridge University maintains a powerful mainframe computer for research use by its faculty, Ph.D. students, and research associates. During all working hours, an operator must be available to operate and maintain the computer, as well as to perform some programming services. Beryl Ingram, the director of the computer facility, oversees the operation.

It is now the beginning of the fall semester and Beryl is confronted with the problem of assigning different working hours to her operators. Because all the operators are currently enrolled in the university, they are available to work only a limited number of hours each day.

There are six operators (four undergraduate students and two graduate students). They all have different wage rates because of differences in their experience with computers and in their programming ability. The following table shows their wage rates, along with the maximum number of hours that each can work each day.

		Maximum Hours of Availability				
Operators	Wage Rate	Mon.	Tue.	Wed.	Thurs.	Fri.
K. C.	$10.00/hour	6	0	6	0	6
D. H.	$10.10/hour	0	6	0	6	0
H. B.	$9.90/hour	4	8	4	0	4
S. C.	$9.80/hour	5	5	5	0	5
K. S.	$10.80/hour	3	0	3	8	0
N. K.	$11.30/hour	0	0	0	6	2

Each operator is guaranteed a certain minimum number of hours per week that will maintain an adequate knowledge of the operation. This level is set arbitrarily at 8 hours per week for the undergraduate students (K. C., D. H., H. B., and S. C.) and 7 hours per week for the graduate students (K. S. and N. K.).

The computer facility is to be open for operation from 8 AM to 10 PM Monday through Friday with exactly one operator on duty during these hours. On Saturdays and Sundays, the computer is to be operated by other staff.

Because of a tight budget, Beryl has to minimize cost. She wishes to determine the number of hours she should assign to each operator on each day. Formulate and solve a spreadsheet model for this problem.

3.25.   Slim-Down Manufacturing makes a line of nutritionally complete, weight-reduction beverages. One of its products is a strawberry shake that is designed to be a complete meal. The strawberry shake consists of several ingredients. Some information about each of these ingredients is given next.

Ingredient	Calories from Fat (per tbsp.)	Total Calories (per tbsp.)	Vitamin Content (mg/tbsp.)	Thickeners (mg/tbsp.)	Cost (¢/tbsp.)
Strawberry flavoring	1	50	20	3	10
Cream	75	100	0	8	8
Vitamin supplement	0	0	50	1	25
Artificial sweetener	0	120	0	2	15
Thickening agent	30	80	2	25	6

The nutritional requirements are as follows. The beverage must total between 380 and 420 calories (inclusive). No more than 20 percent of the total calories should come from fat. There must be at least 50 milligrams (mg) of vitamin content. For taste reasons, there must be at least two tablespoons (tbsp.) of strawberry flavoring for each tbsp. of artificial sweetener. Finally, to maintain proper thickness, there must be exactly 15 mg of thickeners in the beverage.

Management would like to select the quantity of each ingredient for the beverage that would minimize cost while meeting the above requirements.

    a. Identify the requirements that lead to resource constraints, to benefit constraints, and to fixed-requirement constraints.

E*   *b.* Formulate and solve a linear programming model for this problem on a spreadsheet.

    c. Summarize this formulation in algebraic form.

3.26.   Joyce and Marvin run a day care for preschoolers. They are trying to decide what to feed the children for lunches. They would like to keep their costs down, but they also need to meet the nutritional requirements of the children. They have already decided to go with peanut butter and jelly sandwiches, and some combination of graham crackers, milk, and orange juice. The nutritional content of each food choice and its cost are given in the table below.

Food Item	Calories from Fat	Total Calories	Vitamin C (mg)	Protein (g)	Cost (¢)
Bread (1 slice)	10	70	0	3	5
Peanut butter (1 tbsp.)	75	100	0	4	4
Strawberry jelly (1 tbsp.)	0	50	3	0	7
Graham cracker (1 cracker)	20	60	0	1	8
Milk (1 cup)	70	150	2	8	15
Juice (1 cup)	0	100	120	1	35

The nutritional requirements are as follows. Each child should receive between 400 and 600 calories. No more than 30 percent of the total calories should come from fat. Each child should consume at least 60 milligrams (mg) of vitamin C and 12 grams (g) of protein. Furthermore, for practical reasons, each child needs exactly 2 slices of bread (to make the sandwich), at least twice as much peanut butter as jelly, and at least 1 cup of liquid (milk and/or juice).

Joyce and Marvin would like to select the food choices for each child that minimize cost while meeting the above requirements.

    a. Identify the requirements that lead to resource constraints, to benefit constraints, and to fixed-requirement constraints.

E*   *b.* Formulate and solve a linear programming model for this problem on a spreadsheet.

    c. Express the model in algebraic form.

3.27.   Read the referenced article that fully describes the management science study summarized in the application vignette presented in Section 3.5. Briefly describe how the model for the transportation problem was applied in this study. Then list the various financial and nonfinancial benefits that resulted from this study.

E*3.28. The Cost-Less Corp. supplies its four retail outlets from its four plants. The shipping cost per shipment from each plant to each retail outlet is given below.

	Unit Shipping Cost			
Retail Outlet:	1	2	3	4
Plant				
1	$500	$600	$400	$200
2	200	900	100	300
3	300	400	200	100
4	200	100	300	200

Plants 1, 2, 3, and 4 make 10, 20, 20, and 10 shipments per month, respectively. Retail outlets 1, 2, 3, and 4 need to receive 20, 10, 10, and 20 shipments per month, respectively.

The distribution manager, Randy Smith, now wants to determine the best plan for how many shipments to send from each plant to the respective retail outlets each month. Randy's objective is to minimize the total shipping cost.

Formulate this problem as a transportation problem on a spreadsheet and then use Solver to obtain an optimal solution.

E*3.29. The Childfair Company has three plants producing child push chairs that are to be shipped to four distribution centers. Plants 1, 2, and 3 produce 12, 17, and 11 shipments per month, respectively. Each distribution center needs to receive 10 shipments per month. The distance from each plant to the respective distribution centers is given below.

	Distance to Distribution Center (Miles)			
	1	2	3	4
Plant				
1	800	1,300	400	700
2	1,100	1,400	600	1,000
3	600	1,200	800	900

The freight cost for each shipment is $100 plus 50 cents/mile.

How much should be shipped from each plant to each of the distribution centers to minimize the total shipping cost?

Formulate this problem as a transportation problem on a spreadsheet and then use Solver to obtain an optimal solution.

E*3.30. The Onenote Co. produces a single product at three plants for four customers. The three plants will produce 60, 80, and 40 units, respectively, during the next week. The firm has made a commitment to sell 40 units to customer 1, 60 units to customer 2, and at least 20 units to customer 3. Both customers 3 and 4 also want to buy as many of the remaining units as possible. The net profit associated with shipping a unit from plant i for sale to customer j is given by the following table.

	Customer			
	1	**2**	**3**	**4**
Plant				
1	$800	$700	$500	$200
2	500	200	100	300
3	600	400	300	500

Management wishes to know how many units to sell to customers 3 and 4 and how many units to ship from each of the plants to each of the customers to maximize profit. Formulate and solve a spreadsheet model for this problem.

E*3.31. The Move-It Company has two plants building forklift trucks that then are shipped to three distribution centers. The production costs are the same at the two plants, and the cost of shipping each truck is shown below for each combination of plant and distribution center.

	Distribution Center		
	1	**2**	**3**
Plant			
A	$800	$700	$400
B	600	800	500

A total of 60 forklift trucks are produced and shipped per week. Each plant can produce and ship any amount up to a maximum of 50 trucks per week, so there is considerable flexibility on how to divide the total production between the two plants so as to reduce shipping costs. However, each distribution center must receive exactly 20 trucks per week.

Management's objective is to determine how many forklift trucks should be produced at each plant, and then what the overall shipping pattern should be to minimize total shipping cost. Formulate and solve a spreadsheet model for this problem.

E*3.32. Redo Problem 3.31 when any distribution center may receive any quantity between 10 and 30 forklift trucks per week in order to further reduce total shipping cost, provided only that the total shipped to all three distribution centers must still equal 60 trucks per week.

E*3.33. Consider the assignment problem having the following cost table.

	Job		
	1	**2**	**3**
Person			
A	$5	$7	$4
B	3	6	5
C	2	3	4

The optimal solution is A-3, B-1, C-2, with a total cost of $10.

Formulate this problem on a spreadsheet and then use Solver to obtain the optimal solution identified above.

3.34.   Four cargo ships will be used for shipping goods from one port to four other ports (labeled 1, 2, 3, 4). Any ship can be used for making any one of these four trips. However, because of differences in the ships and cargoes, the total cost of loading, transporting, and unloading the goods for the different ship–port combinations varies considerably, as shown in the following table.

	Port			
	1	**2**	**3**	**4**
Ship				
1	$500	$400	$600	$700
2	600	600	700	500
3	700	500	700	600
4	500	400	600	600

The objective is to assign the four ships to four different ports in such a way as to minimize the total cost for all four shipments.

    a. Describe how this problem fits into the format for an assignment problem.

E*   *b.* Formulate and solve this problem on a spreadsheet.

E*3.35. Reconsider Problem 3.10. Now distribution centers 1, 2, and 3 must receive exactly 10, 20, and 30 units per week, respectively. For administrative convenience, management has decided that each distribution center will be supplied totally by a single plant, so that one plant will supply one distribution center and the other plant will supply the other two distribution centers. The choice of these assignments of plants to distribution centers is to be made solely on the basis of minimizing total shipping cost.

Formulate and solve a spreadsheet model for this problem.

3.36.   Vincent Cardoza is the owner and manager of a machine shop that does custom order work. This Wednesday afternoon, he has received calls from two customers who would like to place rush orders. One is a trailer hitch company that would like some custom-made heavy-duty tow bars. The other is a mini-car-carrier company that needs some customized stabilizer bars. Both customers would like as many as possible by the end of the week (two working days). Since both products would require the use of the same two machines, Vincent needs to decide and inform the customers this afternoon about how many of each product he will agree to make over the next two days.

Each tow bar requires 3.2 hours on machine 1 and 2 hours on machine 2. Each stabilizer bar requires 2.4 hours on machine 1 and 3 hours on machine 2. Machine 1 will be available for 16 hours over the next two days and machine 2 will be available for 15 hours. The profit for each tow bar produced would be $130 and the profit for each stabilizer bar produced would be $150.

Vincent now wants to determine the mix of these production quantities that will maximize the total profit.

    a. Formulate an integer programming model in algebraic form for this problem.

E*   *b.* Formulate and solve the model on a spreadsheet.

114   Chapter Three *Linear Programming: Formulation and Applications*

3.37.   Pawtucket University is planning to buy new copier machines for its library. Three members of its Management Science Department are analyzing what to buy. They are considering two different models: Model A, a high-speed copier, and Model B, a lower speed but less expensive copier. Model A can handle 20,000 copies a day and costs $6,000. Model B can handle 10,000 copies a day but only costs $4,000. They would like to have at least six copiers so that they can spread them throughout the library. They also would like to have at least one high-speed copier. Finally, the copiers need to be able to handle a capacity of at least 75,000 copies per day. The objective is to determine the mix of these two copiers that will handle all these requirements at minimum cost.

E*   *a.*   Formulate and solve a spreadsheet model for this problem.

    b.   Formulate this same model in algebraic form.

3.38.   Northeastern Airlines is considering the purchase of new long-, medium-, and short-range jet passenger airplanes. The purchase price would be $67 million for each long-range plane, $50 million for each medium-range plane, and $35 million for each short-range plane. The board of directors has authorized a maximum commitment of $1.5 billion for these purchases. Regardless of which airplanes are purchased, air travel of all distances is expected to be sufficiently large that these planes would be utilized at essentially maximum capacity. It is estimated that the net annual profit (after capital recovery costs are subtracted) would be $4.2 million per long-range plane, $3 million per medium-range plane, and $2.3 million per short-range plane.

It is predicted that enough trained pilots will be available to the company to crew 30 new airplanes. If only short-range planes were purchased, the maintenance facilities would be able to handle 40 new planes. However, each medium-range plane is equivalent to 1 1/3 short-range planes, and each long-range plane is equivalent to 1 2/3 short-range planes in terms of their use of the maintenance facilities.

The information given here was obtained by a preliminary analysis of the problem. A more detailed analysis will be conducted subsequently. However, using the preceding data as a first approximation, management wishes to know how many planes of each type should be purchased to maximize profit.

E*   *a.*   Formulate and solve a spreadsheet model for this problem.

    b.   Formulate this model in algebraic form.

Case 3-1

Shipping Wood to Market

Alabama Atlantic is a lumber company that has three sources of wood and five markets to be supplied. The annual availability of wood at sources 1, 2, and 3 is 15, 20, and 15 million board feet, respectively. The amount that can be sold annually at markets 1, 2, 3, 4, and 5 is 11, 12, 9, 10, and 8 million board feet, respectively.

In the past, the company has shipped the wood by train. However, because shipping costs have been increasing, the alternative of using ships to make some of the deliveries is being investigated. This alternative would require the company to invest in some ships. Except for these investment costs, the shipping costs in thousands of dollars per million board feet by rail and by water (when feasible) would be the following for each route.

| Source | Unit Investment for Ships ($1,000s) to Market | | | | |
	1	2	3	4	5
1	275	303	238	—	285
2	293	318	270	250	265
3	—	283	275	268	240

Considering the expected useful life of the ships and the time value of money, the equivalent uniform annual cost of these investments is one-tenth the amount given in the table. The objective is to determine the overall shipping plan that minimizes the total equivalent uniform annual cost (including shipping costs).

| Source | Unit Cost by Rail ($1,000s) to Market | | | | | Unit Cost by Ship ($1,000s) to Market | | | | |
	1	2	3	4	5	1	2	3	4	5
1	61	72	45	55	66	31	38	24	—	35
2	69	78	60	49	56	36	43	28	24	31
3	59	66	63	61	47	—	33	36	32	26

The capital investment (in thousands of dollars) in ships required for each million board feet to be transported annually by ship along each route is given next.

You are the head of the management science team that has been assigned the task of determining this shipping plan for each of the three options listed next.

Option 1: Continue shipping exclusively by rail.

Option 2: Switch to shipping exclusively by water (except where only rail is feasible).

Option 3: Ship by either rail or water, depending on which is less expensive for the particular route.

Present your results for each option. Compare.

Finally, consider the fact that these results are based on current shipping and investment costs, so that the decision on the option to adopt now should take into account management's projection of how these costs are likely to change in the future. For each option, describe a scenario of future cost changes that would justify adopting that option now.

Case 3-2

Capacity Concerns

Bentley Hamilton throws the business section of *The New York Times* onto the conference room table and watches as his associates jolt upright in their overstuffed chairs.

Mr. Hamilton wants to make a point.

He throws the front page of the *The Wall Street Journal* on top of *The New York Times* and watches as his associates widen their eyes once heavy with boredom.

Mr. Hamilton wants to make a big point.

He then throws the front page of the *Financial Times* on top of the newspaper pile and watches as his associates dab the fine beads of sweat off their brows.

Mr. Hamilton wants his point indelibly etched into his associates' minds.

"I have just presented you with three leading financial newspapers carrying today's top business story," Mr. Hamilton declares in a tight, angry voice. "My dear associates, our company is going to hell in a hand basket! Shall I read you the headlines? From *The New York Times*, '**CommuniCorp** stock drops to lowest in 52 weeks.' From *The Wall Street Journal*, 'CommuniCorp loses 25 percent of the pager market in only one year.' Oh, and my favorite, from the *Financial Times*, 'CommuniCorp cannot CommuniCate: CommuniCorp stock drops because of internal communications disarray.' How did our company fall into such dire straits?"

Mr. Hamilton throws a transparency showing a line sloping slightly upward onto the overhead projector. "This is a graph of our productivity over the last 12 months. As you can see from the graph, productivity in our pager production facility has increased steadily over the last year. Clearly, productivity is not the cause of our problem."

Mr. Hamilton throws a second transparency showing a line sloping steeply upward onto the overhead projector. "This is a graph of our missed or late orders over the last 12 months." Mr. Hamilton hears an audible gasp from his associates. "As

you can see from the graph, our missed or late orders have increased steadily and significantly over the past 12 months. I think this trend explains why we have been losing market share, causing our stock to drop to its lowest level in 52 weeks. We have angered and lost the business of retailers, our customers who depend upon on-time deliveries to meet the demand of consumers."

"Why have we missed our delivery dates when our productivity level should have allowed us to fill all orders?" Mr. Hamilton asks. "I called several departments to ask this question."

"It turns out that we have been producing pagers for the hell of it!" Mr. Hamilton says in disbelief. "The marketing and sales departments do not communicate with the manufacturing department, so manufacturing executives do not know what pagers to produce to fill orders. The manufacturing executives want to keep the plant running, so they produce pagers regardless of whether the pagers have been ordered. Finished pagers are sent to the warehouse, but marketing and sales executives do not know the number and styles of pagers in the warehouse. They try to communicate with warehouse executives to determine if the pagers in inventory can fill the orders, but they rarely receive answers to their questions."

Mr. Hamilton pauses and looks directly at his associates. "Ladies and gentlemen, it seems to me that we have a serious internal communications problem. I intend to correct this problem immediately. I want to begin by installing a companywide computer network to ensure that all departments have access to critical documents and are able to easily communicate with each other through e-mail. Because this intranet will represent a large change from the current communications infrastructure, I expect some bugs in the system and some resistance from employees. I therefore want to phase in the installation of the intranet."

Mr. Hamilton passes the following time line and requirements chart to his associates (IN = intranet).

Month 1	Month 2	Month 3	Month 4	Month 5
IN education				
	Install IN in sales			
		Install IN in manufacturing		
			Install IN in warehouse	
				Install IN in marketing

116 Chapter Three *Linear Programming: Formulation and Applications*

Department	Number of Employees
Sales	60
Manufacturing	200
Warehouse	30
Marketing	75

Mr. Hamilton proceeds to explain the time line and requirements chart. "In the first month, I do not want to bring any department onto the intranet; I simply want to disseminate information about it and get buy-in from employees. In the second month, I want to bring the sales department onto the intranet since the sales department receives all critical information from customers. In the third month, I want to bring the manufacturing department onto the intranet. In the fourth month, I want to install the intranet at the warehouse, and in the fifth and final month, I want to bring the marketing department onto the intranet. The requirements chart above lists the number of employees requiring access to the intranet in each department."

Mr. Hamilton turns to Emily Jones, the head of Corporate Information Management. "I need your help in planning for the installation of the intranet. Specifically, the company needs to purchase servers for the internal network. Employees will connect to company servers and download information to their own desktop computers."

Mr. Hamilton passes Emily the following chart detailing the types of servers available, the number of employees each server supports, and the cost of each server.

Type of Server	Number of Employees Server Supports	Cost of Server
Standard Intel Pentium PC	Up to 30 employees	$ 2,500
Enhanced Intel Pentium PC	Up to 80 employees	5,000
SGI Workstation	Up to 200 employees	10,000
Sun Workstation	Up to 2,000 employees	25,000

"Emily, I need you to decide what servers to purchase and when to purchase them to minimize cost and to ensure that the company possesses enough server capacity to follow the intranet implementation timeline," Mr. Hamilton says. "For example, you may decide to buy one large server during the first month to support all employees, or buy several small servers during the first month to support all employees, or buy one small server each month to support each new group of employees gaining access to the intranet."

"There are several factors that complicate your decision," Mr. Hamilton continues. "Two server manufacturers are willing to offer discounts to CommuniCorp. SGI is willing to give you a discount of 10 percent off each server purchased, but only if you purchase servers in the first or second month. Sun is willing to give you a 25 percent discount off all servers purchased in the first two months. You are also limited in the amount of money you can spend during the first month. CommuniCorp has already allocated much of the budget for the next two months, so you only have a total of $9,500 available to purchase servers in months 1 and 2. Finally, the manufacturing department requires at least one of the three more powerful servers. Have your decision on my desk at the end of the week."

a. Emily first decides to evaluate the number and type of servers to purchase on a month-to-month basis. For each month, formulate a spreadsheet model to determine which servers Emily should purchase in that month to minimize costs in that month and support the new users given your results for the preceding months. How many and which types of servers should she purchase in each month? How much is the total cost of the plan?

b. Emily realizes that she could perhaps achieve savings if she bought a larger server in the initial months to support users in the final months. She therefore decides to evaluate the number and type of servers to purchase over the entire planning period. Formulate a spreadsheet model to determine which servers Emily should purchase in which months to minimize total cost and support all new users. How many and which types of servers should she purchase in each month? How much is the total cost of the plan?

c. Why is the answer using the first method different from that using the second method?

d. Are there other costs for which Emily is not accounting in her problem formulation? If so, what are they?

e. What further concerns might the various departments of CommuniCorp have regarding the intranet?

Case 3-3

Fabrics and Fall Fashions

From the 10th floor of her office building, Katherine Rally watches the swarms of New Yorkers fight their way through the streets infested with yellow cabs and the sidewalks littered with hot dog stands. On this sweltering July day, she pays particular attention to the fashions worn by the various women and wonders what they will choose to wear in the fall. Her thoughts are not simply random musings; they are critical to her work since she owns and manages **TrendLines**, an elite women's clothing company.

Today is an especially important day because she must meet with Ted Lawson, the production manager, to decide upon next month's production plan for the fall line. Specifically, she must determine the quantity of each clothing item she should produce given the plant's production capacity, limited resources, and demand forecasts. Accurate planning for next month's production is critical to fall sales since the items produced next month will appear in stores during September and women generally buy the majority of the fall fashions when they first appear in September.

She turns back to her sprawling glass desk and looks at the numerous papers covering it. Her eyes roam across the clothing patterns designed almost six months ago, the lists of material requirements for each pattern, and the lists of demand forecasts for each pattern determined by customer surveys at fashion shows. She remembers the hectic and sometimes nightmarish days of designing the fall line and presenting it at fashion shows in New York, Milan, and Paris. Ultimately, she paid her team of six designers a total of $860,000 for their work on her fall line. With the cost of hiring runway models, hair stylists, and make-up artists; sewing and fitting clothes; building the set; choreographing and rehearsing the show; and renting the conference hall, each of the three fashion shows cost her an additional $2,700,000.

She studies the clothing patterns and material requirements. Her fall line consists of both professional and casual fashions. She determined the price for each clothing item by taking into account the quality and cost of material, the cost of labor and machining, the demand for the item, and the prestige of the TrendLines brand name.

The fall professional fashions include.

Clothing Item	Material Requirements	Price	Labor and Machine Cost
Tailored wool slacks	3 yards of wool 2 yards of acetate for lining	$300	$160
Cashmere sweater	1.5 yards of cashmere	450	150
Silk blouse	1.5 yards of silk	180	100
Silk camisole	0.5 yard of silk	120	60
Tailored skirt	2 yards of rayon 1.5 yards of acetate for lining	270	120
Wool blazer	2.5 yards of wool 1.5 yards of acetate for lining	320	140

The fall casual fashions include.

Clothing Item	Material Requirements	Price	Labor and Machine Cost
Velvet pants	3 yards of velvet 2 yards of acetate for lining	$350	$175
Cotton sweater	1.5 yards of cotton	130	60
Cotton miniskirt	0.5 yard of cotton	75	40
Velvet shirt	1.5 yards of velvet	200	160
Button-down blouse	1.5 yards of rayon	120	90

She knows that for the next month, she has ordered 45,000 yards of wool, 28,000 yards of acetate, 9,000 yards of cashmere, 18,000 yards of silk, 30,000 yards of rayon, 20,000 yards of velvet, and 30,000 yards of cotton for production. The prices of the materials are listed below.

Material	Price per Yard
Wool	$ 9.00
Acetate	1.50
Cashmere	60.00
Silk	13.00
Rayon	2.25
Velvet	12.00
Cotton	2.50

Any material that is not used in production can be sent back to the textile wholesaler for a full refund, although scrap material cannot be sent back to the wholesaler.

She knows that the production of both the silk blouse and cotton sweater leaves leftover scraps of material. Specifically, for the production of one silk blouse or one cotton sweater, 2 yards of silk and cotton, respectively, are needed. From these 2 yards, 1.5 yards are used for the silk blouse or the cotton sweater and 0.5 yard is left as scrap material. She does not want to waste the material, so she plans to use the rectangular scrap of silk or cotton to produce a silk camisole or cotton miniskirt, respectively. Therefore, whenever a silk blouse is produced, a silk camisole is also produced. Likewise, whenever a cotton sweater is produced, a cotton miniskirt is also produced. Note that it is possible to produce a silk camisole without producing a silk blouse and a cotton miniskirt without producing a cotton sweater.

The demand forecasts indicate that some items have limited demand. Specifically, because the velvet pants and velvet shirts are fashion fads, TrendLines has forecasted that it can sell only 5,500 pairs of velvet pants and 6,000 velvet shirts. TrendLines does not want to produce more than the forecasted demand because once the pants and shirts go out of style, the company cannot sell them. TrendLines can produce less than the forecasted demand, however, since the company is not required to meet the demand. The cashmere sweater also has limited demand because it is quite expensive, and TrendLines knows it can sell at most 4,000 cashmere sweaters. The silk blouses and camisoles have limited demand because many women think silk is too hard to care for, and TrendLines projects that it can sell at most 12,000 silk blouses and 15,000 silk camisoles.

The demand forecasts also indicate that the wool slacks, tailored skirts, and wool blazers have a great demand because they are basic items needed in every professional wardrobe. Specifically, the demand is 7,000 pairs of wool slacks and 5,000 wool blazers. Katherine wants to meet at least 60 percent of the demand for these two items to maintain her loyal customer base and not lose business in the future. Although the demand for tailored skirts could not be estimated, Katherine feels she should make at least 2,800 of them.

a. Ted is trying to convince Katherine not to produce any velvet shirts since the demand for this fashion fad is quite low. He argues that this fashion fad alone accounts for $500,000 of the fixed design and other costs. The net contribution (price of clothing item − materials cost − labor cost) from selling the fashion fad should cover these fixed costs. Each velvet shirt generates a net contribution of $22. He argues that given the net contribution, even satisfying the maximum demand will not yield a profit. What do you think of Ted's argument?

b. Formulate and solve a linear programming problem to maximize profit given the production, resource, and demand constraints.

Before she makes her final decision, Katherine plans to explore the following questions independently, except where otherwise indicated.

c. The textile wholesaler informs Katherine that the velvet cannot be sent back because the demand forecasts show that the demand for velvet will decrease in the future. Katherine can

therefore get no refund for the velvet. How does this fact change the production plan?

d. What is an intuitive economic explanation for the difference between the solutions found in parts *b* and *c?*

e. The sewing staff encounters difficulties sewing the arms and lining into the wool blazer since the blazer pattern has an awkward shape and the heavy wool material is difficult to cut and sew. The increased labor time to sew a wool blazer increases the labor and machine cost for each blazer by $80. Given this new cost, how many of each clothing item should TrendLines produce to maximize profit?

f. The textile wholesaler informs Katherine that since another textile customer canceled his order, she can obtain an extra 10,000 yards of acetate. How many of each clothing item should TrendLines now produce to maximize profit?

g. TrendLines assumes that it can sell every item that was not sold during September and October in a big sale in November at 60 percent of the original price. Therefore, it can sell all items in unlimited quantity during the November sale. (The previously mentioned upper limits on demand only concern the sales during September and October.) What should the new production plan be to maximize profit?

Case 3-4

New Frontiers

Rob Richman, president of **AmeriBank**, takes off his glasses, rubs his eyes in exhaustion, and squints at the clock in his study. It reads 3 AM. For the last several hours, Rob has been poring over AmeriBank's financial statements from the last three quarters of operation. AmeriBank, a medium-sized bank with branches throughout the United States, is headed for dire economic straits. The bank, which provides transaction, savings, investment, and loan services, has been experiencing a steady decline in its net income over the past year, and trends show that the decline will continue. The bank is simply losing customers to nonbank and foreign bank competitors.

AmeriBank is not alone in its struggle to stay out of the red. From his daily industry readings, Rob knows that many American banks have been suffering significant losses because of increasing competition from nonbank and foreign bank competitors offering services typically in the domain of American banks. Because the nonbank and foreign bank competitors specialize in particular services, they are able to better capture the market for those services by offering less expensive, more efficient, more convenient services. For example, large corporations now turn to foreign banks and commercial paper offerings for loans, and affluent Americans now turn to money-market funds for investment. Banks face the daunting challenge of distinguishing themselves from nonbank and foreign bank competitors.

Rob has concluded that one strategy for distinguishing AmeriBank from its competitors is to improve services that nonbank and foreign bank competitors do not readily provide: transaction services. He has decided that a more convenient transaction method must logically succeed the automatic teller machine, and he believes that electronic banking over the Internet allows this convenient transaction method. Over the Internet, customers are able to perform transactions on their desktop computers either at home or work. The explosion of the Internet means that many potential customers understand and use the World Wide Web. He therefore feels that if AmeriBank offers Web banking (as the practice of Internet banking is commonly called), the bank will attract many new customers.

Before Rob undertakes the project to make Web banking possible, however, he needs to understand the market for Web banking and the services AmeriBank should provide over the Internet. For example, should the bank only allow customers to access account balances and historical transaction information over the Internet, or should the bank develop a strategy to allow customers to make deposits and withdrawals over the Internet? Should the bank try to recapture a portion of the investment market by continuously running stock prices and allowing customers to make stock transactions over the Internet for a minimal fee?

Because AmeriBank is not in the business of performing surveys, Rob has decided to outsource the survey project to a professional survey company. He has opened the project up for bidding by several survey companies and will award the project to the company that is willing to perform the survey for the least cost. Rob provided each survey company with a list of survey requirements to ensure that AmeriBank receives the needed information for planning the Web banking project.

Because different age groups require different services, AmeriBank is interested in surveying four different age groups. The first group encompasses customers who are 18 to 25 years old. The bank assumes that this age group has limited yearly income and performs minimal transactions. The second group encompasses customers who are 26 to 40 years old. This age group has significant sources of income, performs many transactions, requires numerous loans for new houses and cars, and invests in various securities. The third group encompasses customers who are 41 to 50 years old. These customers typically have the same level of income and perform the same number of transactions as the second age group, but the bank assumes that these customers are less likely to use Web banking since they have not become as comfortable with the explosion of computers or the Internet. Finally, the fourth group encompasses customers who are 51 years of age and over. These customers commonly crave security and require continuous information on retirement funds. The bank believes that it is highly unlikely that customers in this age group will use Web banking, but the bank desires to learn the needs of this age group for the future. AmeriBank wants to interview 2,000 customers with at least 20 percent from the first age group, at least 27.5 percent from the second age group, at least 15 percent from the third age group, and at least 15 percent from the fourth age group.

Rob understands that some customers are uncomfortable with using the Internet. He therefore wants to ensure that the survey includes a mix of customers who know the Internet well and those that have less exposure to the Internet. To ensure that AmeriBank obtains the correct mix, he wants to interview at least 15 percent of customers from the Silicon Valley where Internet use is high, at least 35 percent of customers from big cities where Internet use is medium, and at least 20 percent of customers from small towns where Internet use is low.

Sophisticated Surveys is one of three survey companies competing for the project. It has performed an initial analysis of these survey requirements to determine the cost of surveying different populations. The costs per person surveyed are listed in the following table.

	Age Group			
Region	**18 to 25**	**26 to 40**	**41 to 50**	**51 and over**
Silicon Valley	$4.75	$6.50	$6.50	$5.00
Big cities	5.25	5.75	6.25	6.25
Small towns	6.50	7.50	7.50	7.25

Sophisticated Surveys explores the following options cumulatively.

a. Formulate a linear programming model to minimize costs while meeting all survey constraints imposed by AmeriBank.

b. If the profit margin for Sophisticated Surveys is 15 percent of cost, what bid will it submit?

c. After submitting its bid, Sophisticated Surveys is informed that it has the lowest cost but that AmeriBank does not like the solution. Specifically, Rob feels that the selected survey population is not representative enough of the banking customer population. Rob wants at least 50 people of each age group surveyed in each region. What is the new bid made by Sophisticated Surveys?

d. Rob feels that Sophisticated Surveys oversampled the 18-to-25-year-old population and the Silicon Valley population. He imposes a new constraint that no more than 600 individuals can be surveyed from the 18-to-25-year-old population and no more than 650 individuals can be surveyed from the Silicon Valley population. What is the new bid?

e. When Sophisticated Surveys calculated the cost of reaching and surveying particular individuals, the company thought that reaching individuals in young populations would be easiest. In a recently completed survey, however, Sophisticated Surveys learned that this assumption was wrong. The new costs for surveying the 18-to-25-year-old population are listed below.

Region	Cost per Person
Silicon Valley	$6.50
Big cities	6.75
Small towns	7.00

Given the new costs, what is the new bid?

f. To ensure the desired sampling of individuals, Rob imposes even stricter requirements. He fixes the exact percentage of people that should be surveyed from each population. The requirements are listed next.

Population	Percentage of People Surveyed
18 to 25	25%
26 to 40	35
41 to 50	20
51 and over	20
Silicon Valley	20
Big cities	50
Small towns	30

By how much would these new requirements increase the cost of surveying for Sophisticated Surveys? Given the 15 percent profit margin, what would Sophisticated Surveys bid?

Case 3-5

Assigning Students to Schools

The **Springfield School Board** has made the decision to close one of its middle schools (sixth, seventh, and eighth grades) at the end of this school year and reassign all of next year's middle school students to the three remaining middle schools. The school district provides busing for all middle school students who must travel more than approximately a mile, so the school

120 Chapter Three *Linear Programming: Formulation and Applications*

board wants a plan for reassigning the students that will minimize the total busing cost. The annual cost per student for busing from each of the six residential areas of the city to each of the schools is shown in the following table (along with other basic data for next year), where 0 indicates that busing is not needed and a dash indicates an infeasible assignment.

How much does this increase the total busing cost? (This line of analysis will be pursued more rigorously in Case 7-3.)

The school board is considering eliminating some busing to reduce costs. Option 1 is to only eliminate busing for students traveling 1 to 1.5 miles, where the cost per student is given in the table

Area	Number of Students	Percentage in 6th Grade	Percentage in 7th Grade	Percentage in 8th Grade	Busing Cost per Student		
					School 1	School 2	School 3
1	450	32	38	30	$300	$ 0	$700
2	600	37	28	35	—	400	500
3	550	30	32	38	600	300	200
4	350	28	40	32	200	500	—
5	500	39	34	27	0	—	400
6	450	34	28	38	500	300	0
				School capacity:	900	1,100	1,000

The school board also has imposed the restriction that each grade must constitute between 30 and 36 percent of each school's population. The above table shows the percentage of each area's middle school population for next year that falls into each of the three grades. The school attendance zone boundaries can be drawn so as to split any given area among more than one school, but assume that the percentages shown in the table will continue to hold for any partial assignment of an area to a school.

You have been hired as a management science consultant to assist the school board in determining how many students in each area should be assigned to each school.

a. Formulate and solve a linear programming model for this problem.
b. What is your resulting recommendation to the school board?

After seeing your recommendation, the school board expresses concern about all the splitting of residential areas among multiple schools. They indicate that they "would like to keep each neighborhood together."

c. Adjust your recommendation as well as you can to enable each area to be assigned to just one school. (Adding this restriction may force you to fudge on some other constraints.)

as $200. Option 2 is to also eliminate busing for students traveling 1.5 to 2 miles, where the estimated cost per student is $300.

d. Revise the model from part *a* to fit Option 1, and solve. Compare these results with those from part *b,* including the reduction in total busing cost.
e. Repeat part *d* for Option 2.

The school board now needs to choose among the three alternative busing plans (the current one or Option 1 or Option 2). One important factor is busing costs. However, the school board also wants to place equal weight on a second factor: the inconvenience and safety problems caused by forcing students to travel by foot or bicycle a substantial distance (more than a mile, and especially more than 1.5 miles). Therefore, they want to choose a plan that provides the best trade-off between these two factors.

f. Use your results from parts *b, d,* and *e* to summarize the key information related to these two factors that the school board needs to make this decision.
g. Which decision do you think should be made? Why?

Note: This case will be continued in later chapters (Cases 5-4 and 7-3), so we suggest that you save your analysis, including your basic spreadsheet model.

120 Chapter Three *Linear Programming: Formulation and Applications*

Case 3-6
Reclaiming Solid Wastes

The **Save-It Company** operates a reclamation center that collects four types of solid waste materials and then treats them so that they can be amalgamated (treating and amalgamating are separate processes) into a salable product. Three different grades of this product can be made, depending on the mix of the materials used. (See the first table.) Although there is some flexibility in the mix for each grade, quality standards specify the minimum or maximum amount of the materials allowed in that product grade. (This minimum or maximum amount is the weight of the material expressed as a percentage of the total weight for that product grade.) For each of the two higher grades, a fixed percentage is specified for one of the materials. These specifications are given in the first table along with the cost of amalgamation and the selling price for each grade.

The reclamation center collects its solid waste materials from some regular sources and so is normally able to maintain a steady rate for treating them. The second table gives the quantities available for collection and treatment each week, as well as the cost of treatment, for each type of material.

Grade	Specification	Amalgamation Cost per Pound	Selling Price per Pound
A	Material 1: Not more than 30% of the total Material 2: Not less than 40% of the total Material 3: Not more than 50% of the total Material 4: Exactly 20% of the total	$3.00	$8.50
B	Material 1: Not more than 50% of the total Material 2: Not less than 10% of the total Material 4: Exactly 10% of the total	2.50	7.00
C	Material 1: Not more than 70% of the total	2.00	5.50

Material	Available Pounds/Week	Treatment Cost per Pound	Additional Restrictions
1	3,000	$3.00	1. For each material, at least half
2	2,000	6.00	of the pounds/week available
3	4,000	4.00	should be collected and treated.
4	1,000	5.00	2. $30,000 per week should be used to treat these materials.

The Save-It Company is solely owned by Green Earth, an organization that is devoted to dealing with environmental issues; Save-It's profits are all used to help support Green Earth's activities. Green Earth has raised contributions and grants, amounting to $30,000 per week, to be used exclusively to cover the entire treatment cost for the solid waste materials. The board of directors of Green Earth has instructed the management of Save-It to divide this money among the materials in such a way that *at least half* of the amount available of each material is actually collected and treated. These additional restrictions are listed in the second table.

Within the restrictions specified in the two tables, management wants to allocate the materials to product grades so as to maximize the total weekly profit (total sales income *minus* total amalgamation cost).

a. Formulate this problem in linear programming terms by identifying all the activities, resources, benefits, and fixed requirements that lurk within it.

b. Formulate and solve a spreadsheet model for this linear programming problem.

c. Express this linear programming model in the spreadsheet in algebraic form.

Case 3-7

Project Pickings

Tazer, a pharmaceutical manufacturing company, entered the pharmaceutical market 15 years ago with the introduction of six new drugs. Five of the six drugs were simply permutations of existing drugs and therefore did not sell very heavily. The sixth drug, however, addressed hypertension and was a huge success. Since Tazer had a patent on the hypertension drug, it experienced no competition, and profits from the hypertension drug alone kept Tazer in business. Pharmaceutical patents remain in force for 20 years, so this one has five more years before it expires.

During the past 15 years, Tazer continued a moderate amount of research and development, but it never stumbled upon a drug as successful as the hypertension drug. One reason is that the company never had the motivation to invest heavily in innovative research and development. The company was riding the profit wave generated by its hypertension drug and did not feel the need to commit significant resources to finding new drug breakthroughs.

Now Tazer is beginning to fear the pressure of competition. Tazer knows that once the patent expires in five years, generic drug manufacturing companies will swarm into the market like vultures. Historical trends show that generic drugs decrease sales of branded drugs by 75 percent.

Tazer is therefore looking to invest significant amounts of money in research and development this year to begin the search for a new breakthrough drug that will offer the company the same success as the hypertension drug. Tazer believes that if the company begins extensive research and development now, the probability of finding a successful drug shortly after the expiration of the hypertension patent will be high.

As head of research and development at Tazer, you are responsible for choosing potential projects and assigning project directors to lead each of the projects. After researching the needs of the market, analyzing the shortcomings of current drugs,

122 Chapter Three *Linear Programming: Formulation and Applications*

and interviewing numerous scientists concerning the promising areas of medical research, you have decided that your department will pursue five separate projects, which are listed below:

Project Up: Develop a more effective antidepressant that does not cause serious mood swings.

Project Stable: Develop a drug that addresses manic-depression.

Project Choice: Develop a less intrusive birth control method for women.

Project Hope: Develop a vaccine to prevent HIV infection.

Project Release: Develop a more effective drug to lower blood pressure.

For each of the five projects, you are only able to specify the medical ailment the research should address since you do not know what compounds will exist and be effective without research.

You also have five senior scientists to lead the five projects. You know that scientists are very temperamental people and will only work well if they are challenged and motivated by the project. To ensure that the senior scientists are assigned to projects they find motivating, you have established a bidding system for the projects. You have given each of the five scientists 1,000 bid points. They assign bids to each project, giving a higher number of bid points to projects they most prefer to lead.

The following table provides the bids from the five senior scientists for the five individual projects.

Project Up: 20
Project Stable: 450
Project Choice: 451
Project Hope: 39
Project Release: 40

Under these new conditions with just four senior scientists, which scientists will lead which projects to maximize preferences?

e. Do you support the assignments found in part *d?* Why or why not?

f. Now you again consider all five scientists. You decide, however, that several scientists cannot lead certain projects. In particular, Dr. Mickey does not have experience with research on the immune system, so he cannot lead Project Hope. His family also has a history of manic-depression, and you feel that he would be too personally involved in Project Stable to serve as an effective project leader. Dr. Mickey therefore cannot lead Project Stable. Dr. Kvaal also does not have experience with research on the immune system and cannot lead Project Hope. In addition, Dr. Kvaal cannot lead Project Release because he does not have experience with research on the cardiovascular system. Finally, Dr. Rollins cannot lead Project Up because her family has a history of depression and you feel she would be too personally involved in the project to serve as an effective leader. Because Dr. Mickey and Dr. Kvaal cannot lead two of the five projects, they each have only 600 bid points.

Project	Dr. Kvaal	Dr. Zuner	Dr. Tsai	Dr. Mickey	Dr. Rollins
Project Up	100	0	100	267	100
Project Stable	400	200	100	153	33
Project Choice	200	800	100	99	33
Project Hope	200	0	100	451	34
Project Release	100	0	600	30	800

You decide to evaluate a variety of scenarios you think are likely.

a. Given the bids, you need to assign one senior scientist to each of the five projects to maximize the preferences of the scientists. What are the assignments?

b. Dr. Rollins is being courted by Harvard Medical School to accept a teaching position. You are fighting desperately to keep her at Tazer, but the prestige of Harvard may lure her away. If this were to happen, the company would give up the project with the least enthusiasm. Which project would not be done?

c. You do not want to sacrifice any project since researching only four projects decreases the probability of finding a breakthrough new drug. You decide that either Dr. Zuner or Dr. Mickey could lead two projects. Under these new conditions with just four senior scientists, which scientists will lead which projects to maximize preferences?

d. After Dr. Zuner was informed that she and Dr. Mickey are being considered for two projects, she decided to change her bids. Dr. Zuner's new bids for each of the projects are shown next.

Dr. Rollins has only 800 bid points because she cannot lead one of the five projects. The following table provides the new bids of Dr. Mickey, Dr. Kvaal, and Dr. Rollins.

Project	Dr. Mickey	Dr. Kvaal	Dr. Rollins
Project Up	300	86	Can't lead
Project Stable	Can't lead	343	50
Project Choice	125	171	50
Project Hope	Can't lead	Can't lead	100
Project Release	175	Can't lead	600

Which scientists should lead which projects to maximize preferences?

g. You decide that Project Hope and Project Release are too complex to be led by only one scientist. Therefore, each of these projects will be assigned two scientists as project leaders. You decide to hire two more scientists in order to staff all projects: Dr. Arriaga and Dr. Santos. Because of religious reasons, neither of them want to lead Project Choice and so they assign 0 bid points to this project. The next table lists all projects, scientists, and their bids.

Project	Dr. Kvaal	Dr. Zuner	Dr. Tsai	Dr. Mickey	Dr. Rollins	Dr. Arriaga	Dr. Santos
Project Up	86	0	100	300	Can't lead	250	111
Project Stable	343	200	100	Can't lead	50	250	1
Project Choice	171	800	100	125	50	0	0
Project Hope	Can't lead	0	100	Can't lead	100	250	333
Project Release	Can't lead	0	600	175	600	250	555

Which scientists should lead which projects to maximize preferences?

h. Do you think it is wise to base your decision in part *g* only on an optimal solution for a variant of an assignment problem?

Additional Cases

Additional cases for this chapter are also available at the University of Western Ontario Ivey School of Business website, **cases.ivey.uwo.ca/cases**, in the segment of the CaseMate area designated for this book.

Chapter **Four**

The Art of Modeling with Spreadsheets

Learning Objectives

After completing this chapter, you should be able to

1. Describe the general process for modeling in spreadsheets.
2. Describe some guidelines for building good spreadsheet models.
3. Apply both the general process for modeling in spreadsheets and the guidelines in this chapter to develop your own spreadsheet model from a description of the problem.
4. Identify some deficiencies in a poorly formulated spreadsheet model.
5. Apply a variety of techniques for debugging a spreadsheet model.

Nearly all managers now make extensive use of spreadsheets to analyze business problems. What they are doing is *modeling* with spreadsheets.

Spreadsheet modeling is a major emphasis throughout this book. Section 1.2 in Chapter 1 introduced a spreadsheet model for performing break-even analysis. Section 2.2 in Chapter 2 described how to use spreadsheets to formulate linear programming models. Chapter 3 focused on spreadsheet models for five key categories of linear programming problems: resource-allocation problems, cost–benefit–trade-off problems, mixed problems, transportation problems, and assignment problems. Many kinds of spreadsheet models are discussed in subsequent chapters as well. However, those presentations focus mostly on the characteristics of spreadsheet models that fit the management science techniques (such as linear programming) being covered in those chapters. We devote this chapter instead to the general *process* of building models with spreadsheets.

Modeling in spreadsheets is more an art than a science. There is no systematic procedure that invariably will lead to a single correct spreadsheet model. For example, if two people were given exactly the same business problem to analyze with a spreadsheet, their spreadsheet models would likely look quite different. There is no one right way of modeling any given problem. However, some models will be better than others.

Although no completely systematic procedure is available for modeling in spreadsheets, there is a general process that should be followed. This process has four major steps: (1) *plan* the spreadsheet model, (2) *build* the model, (3) *test* the model, and (4) *analyze* the model and its results. After introducing a case study in Section 4.1, the next section will describe this plan-build-test-analyze process in some detail and illustrate the process in the context of the case study. Section 4.2 also will discuss some ways of overcoming common stumbling blocks in the modeling process.

Unfortunately, despite its logical approach, there is no guarantee that the plan-build-test-analyze process will lead to a "good" spreadsheet model. A good spreadsheet model is easy to understand, easy to debug, and easy to modify. Section 4.3 presents some guidelines for building such models. This section also uses the case study in Section 4.1 to illustrate the difference between appropriate formulations and poor formulations of a model.

Even with an appropriate formulation, the initial versions of large spreadsheet models commonly will include some small but troublesome errors, such as inaccurate references to cell addresses or typographical errors when entering equations into cells. Indeed, some studies have shown that a surprisingly large number of errors typically occur in the first version of such models. These errors often can be difficult to track down. Section 4.4 presents some helpful ways to debug a spreadsheet model and root out such errors.

The overriding goal of this chapter is to provide a solid foundation for becoming a successful spreadsheet modeler. However, this chapter by itself will not turn you into a highly skilled modeler. Ultimately, to reach this point you also will need to study various examples of good spreadsheet models in the different areas of management science and then have lots of practice in formulating your own models. This process will continue throughout the remainder of this book.

4.1 A CASE STUDY: THE EVERGLADE GOLDEN YEARS COMPANY CASH FLOW PROBLEM

The **Everglade Golden Years Company** operates upscale retirement communities in certain parts of southern Florida. The company was founded in 1946 by Alfred Lee, who was in the right place at the right time to enjoy many successful years during the boom in the Florida economy as many wealthy retirees flooded into the area. Today, the company continues to be run by the Lee family, with Alfred's grandson, Sheldon Lee, as the CEO.

The past few years have been difficult ones for Everglade. The demand for retirement community housing has been light and Everglade has been unable to maintain full occupancy. However, this market has picked up recently and the future is looking brighter. Everglade has recently broken ground for the construction of a new retirement community and has more new construction planned over the next 10 years (2014 through 2023).

With only $1 million in cash reserves and negative cash flows looming soon, loans will be needed to observe the company policy of maintaining a balance of at least $500,000 at all times.

Julie Lee is the chief financial officer (CFO) at Everglade. She has spent the last week in front of her computer trying to come to grips with the company's imminent cash flow problem. Julie has projected Everglade's net cash flows over the next 10 years as shown in Table 4.1. With less money currently coming in than would be provided by full occupancy and with all the construction costs for the new retirement community, Everglade will have negative cash flow for the next few years. With only $1 million in cash reserves, it appears that Everglade will need to take out some loans in order to meet its financial obligations. Also, to protect against uncertainty, company policy dictates maintaining a balance of at least $500,000 in cash reserves at all times.

The company's bank has offered two types of loans to Everglade. The first is a 10-year loan with interest-only payments made annually and then the entire principal repaid in a single balloon payment after 10 years. The interest rate on this long-term loan is a favorable 5 percent per year. The second option is a series of one-year loans. These loans can be taken out each year as needed, but each must be repaid (with interest) the following year. Each new loan can be used to help repay the loan for the preceding year if needed. The interest rate for these short-term loans currently is projected to be 7 percent per year.

Armed with her cash flow projections and the loan options from the bank, Julie schedules a meeting with the CEO, Sheldon Lee. Their discussion is as follows:

Julie: Well, we really seem to be in a pickle. There is no way to meet our cash flow problems without borrowing money.

TABLE 4.1

Projected Net Cash Flows for the Everglade Golden Years Company over the Next Ten Years

Year	Projected Net Cash Flow (millions of dollars)
2014	−8
2015	−2
2016	−4
2017	3
2018	6
2019	3
2020	−4
2021	7
2022	−2
2023	10

Sheldon: I was afraid of that. What are our options?

Julie: I've talked to the bank, and we can take out a 10-year loan with an interest rate of 5 percent, or a series of one-year loans at a projected rate of 7 percent.

Sheldon: Wow. That 5 percent rate sounds good. Can we just borrow all that we need using the 10-year loan?

Julie: That was my initial reaction as well. However, after looking at the cash flow projections, I'm not sure the answer is so clear-cut. While we have negative cash flow for the next few years, the situation looks much brighter down the road. With a 10-year loan, we are obligated to keep the loan and make the interest payments for 10 years. The one-year loans are more flexible. We can borrow the money only in the years we need it. This way we can save on interest payments in the future.

Sheldon: Okay. I can see how the flexibility of the one-year loans could save us some money. Those loans also will look better if interest rates come down in future years.

Julie: Or they could go higher instead. There's no way to predict future interest rates, so we might as well just plan on the basis of the current projection of 7 percent per year.

Sheldon: Yes, you're right. So which do you recommend, a 10-year loan or a series of one-year loans?

Julie: Well, there's actually another option as well. We could consider a combination of the two types of loans. We could borrow some money long-term to get the lower interest rate and borrow some money short-term to retain flexibility.

> The objective is to develop a financial plan that will keep the company solvent and then maximize the cash balance in 2024, after all the loans are paid off.

Sheldon: That sounds complicated. What we want is a plan that will keep us solvent throughout the 10 years and then leave us with as large a cash balance as possible at the end of the 10 years after paying off all the loans. Could you set this up on a spreadsheet to figure out the best plan?

Julie: You bet. I'll try that and get back to you.

Sheldon: Great. Let's plan to meet again next week when you have your report ready.

You'll see in the next two sections how Julie carefully develops her spreadsheet model for this cash flow problem.

Review
Questions

1. What is the advantage of the long-term loan for Everglade?
2. What is the advantage of the series of short-term loans for Everglade?
3. What is the objective for the financial plan that needs to be developed?

4.2   OVERVIEW OF THE PROCESS OF MODELING WITH SPREADSHEETS

You will see later that a linear programming model can be incorporated into a spreadsheet to solve this problem. However, you also will see that the format of this spreadsheet model does not fit readily into any of the categories of linear programming models described in Chapter 3. Even the template given in Figure 3.8 that shows the format for a spreadsheet model of *mixed problems* (the broadest category of linear programming problems) does not help in formulating the model for the current problem. The reason is that the Everglade cash flow management problem is an example of a more complicated type of linear programming problem (a *dynamic problem* with many time periods) that requires starting from scratch in carefully formulating the spreadsheet model. Therefore, this example will nicely illustrate the process of modeling with spreadsheets when dealing with complicated problems of any type, including those discussed later in the book that do not fit linear programming.

> *Spaghetti code* is a term from computer programming. It refers to computer code that is not logically organized and thus jumps all over the place, so it is jumbled like a plate of spaghetti.

When presented with a problem like the Everglade problem, the temptation is to jump right in, launch Excel, and start entering a model. Resist this urge. Developing a spreadsheet model without proper planning inevitably leads to a model that is poorly organized and filled with "spaghetti code."

Part of the challenge of planning and developing a spreadsheet model is that there is no standard procedure to follow. It is more an art than a science. However, to provide you with

FIGURE 4.1

A flow diagram for the general plan-build-test-analyze process for modeling with spreadsheets.

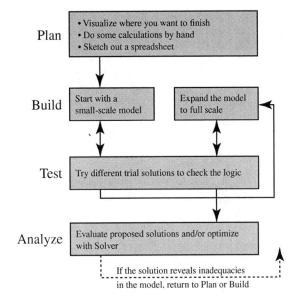

some structure as you begin learning this art, we suggest that you follow the modeling process depicted in Figure 4.1.

As suggested by the figure, the four major steps in this process are to (1) plan, (2) build, (3) test, and (4) analyze the spreadsheet model. The process mainly flows in this order. However, the two-headed arrows between Build and Test indicate a back-and-forth process where testing frequently results in returning to the Build step to fix some problems discovered during the Test step. This back and forth movement between Build and Test may occur several times until the modeler is satisfied with the model. At the same time that this back and forth movement is occurring, the modeler may be involved with further building of the model. One strategy is to begin with a small version of the model to establish its basic logic and then, after testing verifies its accuracy, to expand to a full-scale model. Even after completing the testing and then the analyzing of the model, the process may return to the Build step or even the Plan step if the Analysis step reveals inadequacies in the model.

A modeler might go back and forth between the Build and Test steps several times.

Each of these four major steps may also include some detailed steps. For example, Figure 4.1 lists three detailed steps within the Plan step. Initially, when dealing with a fairly complicated problem, it is helpful to take some time to perform each of these detailed steps manually one at a time. However, as you become more experienced with modeling in spreadsheets, you may find yourself merging some of the detailed steps and quickly performing them mentally. An experienced modeler often is able to do some of these steps mentally, without working them out explicitly on paper. However, if you find yourself getting stuck, it is likely that you are missing a key element from one of the previous detailed steps. You then should go back a step or two and make sure that you have thoroughly completed those preceding steps.

We now describe the various components of the modeling process in the context of the Everglade cash flow problem. At the same time, we also point out some common stumbling blocks encountered while building a spreadsheet model and how these can be overcome.

Plan: Visualize Where You Want to Finish

One common stumbling block in the modeling process occurs right at the very beginning. Given a complicated situation like the one facing Julie at Everglade, sometimes it can be difficult to decide how to even get started. At this point, it can be helpful to think about where you want to end up. For example, what information should Julie provide in her report to Sheldon? What should the "answer" look like when presenting the recommended approach to the problem?

What kinds of numbers need to be included in the recommendation? The answers to these questions can quickly lead you to the heart of the problem and help get the modeling process started.

The question that Julie is addressing is *which loan,* or combination of loans, to use and in *what amounts.* The long-term loan is taken in a single lump sum. Therefore, the "answer" should include a single number indicating how much money to borrow now at the long-term rate. The short-term loan can be taken in any or all of the 10 years, so the "answer" should include 10 numbers indicating how much to borrow at the short-term rate in each given year. These will be the changing cells in the spreadsheet model.

What other numbers should Julie include in her report to Sheldon? The key numbers would be the projected cash balance each year, the amount of the interest payments, and when loan payments are due. These will be output cells in the spreadsheet model.

It is important to distinguish between the numbers that represent decisions (changing cells) and those that represent results (output cells). For instance, it may be tempting to include the cash balances as changing cells. These cells clearly change depending on the decisions made. However, the cash balances are a *result* of how much is borrowed, how much is paid, and all of the other cash flows. They cannot be chosen independently but instead are a function of the other numbers in the spreadsheet. The distinguishing characteristic of changing cells (the loan amounts) is that they do not depend on anything else. They represent the independent decisions being made. They impact the other numbers, but not vice versa.

At this point, you should know what changing cells and output cells are needed.

At this stage in the process, you should have a clear idea of what the answer will look like, including what and how many changing cells are needed, and what kind of results (output cells) should be obtained.

Plan: Do Some Calculations by Hand

When building a model, another common stumbling block can arise when trying to enter a formula in one of the output cells. For example, just how does Julie keep track of the cash balances in the Everglade cash flow problem? What formulas need to be entered? There are a lot of factors that enter into this calculation, so it is easy to get overwhelmed.

If you are getting stuck at this point, it can be a very useful exercise to do some calculations by hand. Just pick some numbers for the changing cells and determine with a calculator or pencil and paper what the results should be. For example, pick some loan amounts for Everglade and then calculate the company's resulting cash balance at the end of the first couple of years. Let's say Everglade takes a long-term loan of $6 million and then adds short-term loans of $2 million in 2014 and $5 million in 2015. How much cash would the company have left at the end of 2014 and at the end of 2015?

These two quantities can be calculated by hand as follows. In 2014, Everglade has some initial money in the bank ($1 million), a negative cash flow from its business operations (−$8 million), and a cash inflow from the long-term and short-term loans ($6 million and $2 million, respectively). Thus, the ending balance for 2014 would be:

Ending balance (2014) = Starting balance	$1 million
+ Cash flow (2014)	−$8 million
+ LT loan (2014)	+$6 million
+ ST loan (2014)	+$2 million
	$1 million

The calculations for the year 2015 are a little more complicated. In addition to the starting balance left over from 2014 ($1 million), negative cash flow from business operations for 2015 (−$2 million), and a new short-term loan for 2015 ($5 million), the company will need to make interest payments on its 2014 loans as well as pay back the short-term loan from 2014. The ending balance for 2015 is therefore:

Ending balance (2015) = Starting balance (from end of 2014)	$1 million
+Cash flow (2015)	−$2 million
+ST loan (2015)	+$5 million
−LT interest payment	−(5%)($6 million)

−ST interest payment	−(7%)($2 million)
−ST loan payback (2014)	−$2 million
	$1.56 million

Doing calculations by hand can help in a couple of ways. First, it can help clarify what formula should be entered for an output cell. For instance, looking at the by-hand calculations above, it appears that the formula for the ending balance for a particular year should be

$$\text{Ending balance} = \text{Starting balance} + \text{Cash flow} + \text{Loans} \\ -\text{Interest payments} - \text{Loan paybacks}$$

Hand calculations can clarify what formulas are needed for the output cells.

It now will be a simple exercise to enter the proper cell references in the formula for the ending balance in the spreadsheet model. Second, hand calculations can help to verify the spreadsheet model. By plugging in a long-term loan of $6 million, along with short-term loans of $2 million in 2014 and $5 million in 2015, into a completed spreadsheet, the ending balances should be the same as calculated above. If they're not, this suggests an error in the spreadsheet model (assuming the hand calculations are correct).

Plan: Sketch Out a Spreadsheet

Any model typically has a large number of different elements that need to be included on the spreadsheet. For the Everglade problem, these would include some data cells (interest rates, starting balance, minimum balances, and cash flows), some changing cells (loan amounts), and a number of output cells (interest payments, loan paybacks, and ending balances). Therefore, a potential stumbling block can arise when trying to organize and lay out the spreadsheet model. Where should all the pieces fit on the spreadsheet? How do you begin putting together the spreadsheet?

Before firing up Excel and blindly entering the various elements, it can be helpful to sketch a layout of the spreadsheet. Is there a logical way to arrange the elements? A little planning at this stage can go a long way toward building a spreadsheet that is well organized. Don't bother with numbers at this point. Simply sketch out blocks on a piece of paper for the various data cells, changing cells, and output cells, and label them. Concentrate on the layout. Should a block of numbers be laid out in a row or a column, or as a two-dimensional table? Are there common row or column headings for different blocks of cells? If so, try to arrange the blocks in consistent rows or columns so they can utilize a single set of headings. Try to arrange the spreadsheet so that it starts with the data at the top and progresses logically toward the objective cell at the bottom. This will be easier to understand and follow than if the data cells, changing cells, output cells, and objective cell are all scattered throughout the spreadsheet.

Plan where the various blocks of data cells, changing cells, and output cells should go on the spreadsheet by sketching your layout ideas on paper.

A sketch of a potential spreadsheet layout for the Everglade problem is shown in Figure 4.2. The data cells for the interest rates, starting balance, and minimum cash balance are at the

FIGURE 4.2

Sketch of the spreadsheet for Everglade's cash flow problem.

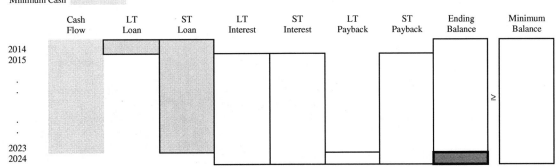

top of the spreadsheet. All of the remaining elements in the spreadsheet then follow the same structure. The rows represent the different years (from 2014 through 2024). All the various cash inflows and outflows are then broken out in the columns, starting with the projected cash flow from the business operations (with data for each of the 10 years), continuing with the loan inflows, interest payments, and loan paybacks, and culminating with the ending balance (calculated for each year). The long-term loan is a one-time loan (in 2014), so it is sketched as a single cell. The short-term loan can occur in any of the 10 years (2014 through 2023), so it is sketched as a block of cells. The interest payments start one year after the loans. The long-term loan is paid back 10 years later (2024).

Organizing the elements with a consistent structure, like in Figure 4.2, not only saves having to retype the year labels for each element, but also makes the model easier to understand. Everything that happens in a given year is arranged together in a single row.

It is generally easiest to start sketching the layout with the data. The structure of the rest of the model should then follow the structure of the data cells. For example, once the projected cash flows data are sketched as a vertical column (with each year in a row), then it follows that the other cash flows should be structured the same way.

There is also a logical progression to the spreadsheet. The data for the problem are located at the top and left of the spreadsheet. Then, since the cash flow, loan amounts, interest payments, and loan paybacks are all part of the calculation for the ending balance, the columns are arranged this way, with the ending balance directly to the right of all these other elements. Since Sheldon has indicated that the objective is to maximize the ending balance in 2024, this cell is designated to be the objective cell.

The sketch of a spreadsheet in Figure 4.2 has a logical progression, starting with the data on the top left and then moving through the calculations toward the objective cell on the bottom right.

Each year, the balance must be greater than the minimum required balance (\$500,000). Since this will be a constraint in the model, it is logical to arrange the balance and minimum balance blocks of numbers adjacent to each other in the spreadsheet. You can put the $\geq$ signs on the sketch to remind yourself that these will be constraints.

Build: Start with a Small Version of the Spreadsheet

Once you've thought about a logical layout for the spreadsheet, it is finally time to open a new worksheet in Excel and start building the model. If it is a complicated model, you may want to start by building a small, readily manageable version of the model. The idea is to first make sure that you've got the logic of the model worked out correctly for the small version before expanding the model to full scale.

Work out the logic for a small version of the spreadsheet model before expanding to full size.

For example, in the Everglade problem, we could get started by building a model for just the first two years (2014 and 2015), like the spreadsheet shown in Figure 4.3.

This spreadsheet is set up to follow the layout suggested in the sketch of Figure 4.2. The loan amounts are in columns D and E. Since the interest payments are not due until the following year, the formulas in columns F and G refer to the loan amounts from the preceding year (LTLoan, or D11, for the long-term loan, and E11 for the short-term loan). The loan payments are calculated in columns H and I. Column H is blank because the long-term loan does not need to be repaid until 2024. The short-term loan is repaid one year later, so the formula in cell I12 refers to the short-term loan taken the preceding year (cell E11). The ending balance in 2014 is the starting balance plus the sum of all the various cash flows that occur in 2014 (cells C11:I11). The ending balance in 2015 is the ending balance in 2014 (cell J11) plus the sum of all the various cash flows that occur in 2015 (cells C12:I12). All these formulas are summarized below the spreadsheet in Figure 4.3.

Building a small version of the spreadsheet works very well for spreadsheets that have a time dimension. For example, instead of jumping right into a 10-year planning problem, we can start with the simpler problem of just looking at a couple of years. Once this smaller model is working correctly, you then can expand the model to 10 years.

Even if a spreadsheet model does not have a time dimension, the same concept of starting small can be applied. For example, if certain constraints considerably complicate a problem, start by working on a simpler problem without the difficult constraints. Get the simple model working and then move on to tackle the difficult constraints. If a model has many sets of output cells, you can build up a model piece by piece by working on one set of output cells at a time, making sure each set works correctly before moving on to the next.

FIGURE 4.3

A small version (years 2014 and 2015 only) of the spreadsheet for the Everglade cash flow management problem.

	A	B	C	D	E	F	G	H	I	J	K	L
1		Everglade Cash Flow Management Problem (Years 2014 and 2015)										
2												
3		LT Rate	5%									
4		ST Rate	7%									
5					(all cash figures in millions of dollars)							
6		Start Balance	1									
7		Minimum Cash	0.5									
8												
9			Cash	LT	ST	LT	ST	LT	ST	Ending		Minimum
10		Year	Flow	Loan	Loan	Interest	Interest	Payback	Payback	Balance		Balance
11		2014	–8	6	2					1.00	≥	0.50
12		2015	–2		5	–0.30	–0.14		–2.00	1.56	≥	0.50

	F	G	H	I	J	K	L
9	LT	ST	LT	ST	Ending		Minimum
10	Interest	Interest	Payback	Payback	Balance		Balance
11					=StartBalance+SUM(C11:I11)	≥	=MinimumCash
12	= –LTRate*LTLoan	= –STRate*E11		= –E11	=J11+SUM(C12:I12)	≥	=MinimumCash

Range Name	Cell
LTLoan	D11
LTRate	C3
MinimumCash	C7
StartBalance	C6
STRate	C4

Test: Test the Small Version of the Model

If you do start with a small version of the model first, be sure to test this version thoroughly to make sure that all the logic is correct. It is far better to fix a problem early, while the spreadsheet is still a manageable size, rather than later after an error has been propagated throughout a much larger spreadsheet.

Try entering numbers in the changing cells for which you know what the values of the output cells should be.

To test the spreadsheet, try entering values in the changing cells for which you know what the values of the output cells should be, and then see if the spreadsheet gives the results that you expect. For example, in Figure 4.3, if zeroes are entered for the loan amounts, then the interest payments and loan payback quantities also should be zero. If $1 million is borrowed for both the long-term loan and the short-term loan, then the interest payments the following year should be $50,000 and $70,000, respectively. (Recall that the interest rates are 5 percent and 7 percent, respectively.) If Everglade takes out a $6 million long-term loan and a $2 million short-term loan in 2014, plus a $5 million short-term loan in 2015, then the ending balances should be $1 million for 2014 and $1.56 million for 2015 (based on the calculations done earlier by hand). All these tests work correctly for the spreadsheet in Figure 4.3, so we can be fairly certain that it is correct.

If the output cells are not giving the results that you expect, then carefully look through the formulas to see if you can determine and fix the problem. Section 4.4 will give further guidance on some ways to debug a spreadsheet model.

Build: Expand the Model to Full-Scale Size

Once a small version of the spreadsheet has been tested to make sure all the formulas are correct and everything is working properly, the model can be expanded to full-scale size. Excel's fill commands often can be used to quickly copy the formulas into the remainder of

Excel Tip: A shortcut for filling down or filling across to the right is to select the cell you want to copy, click on the fill handle (the small box in the lower right-hand corner of the selection rectangle), and drag through the cells you want to fill.

the model. For Figure 4.3, the formulas in columns F, G, I, J, and L can be copied using the Fill Down command in the Editing Group of the Home tab to obtain all the formulas shown in Figure 4.4. For example, selecting cells G12:G21 and choosing Fill Down will take the formula in cell G12 and copy it (after adjusting the cell address in Column E for the formula) into cells G13 through G21.

Before using the fill commands to copy formulas, be sure that the relative and absolute references have been used appropriately. (Appendix A provides details about relative and absolute references.) For example, in G12 ($= -$STRate* E11) using a range name for STRate makes this an absolute reference. When copied into cells G13:G21, the short-term loan interest rate used will always be the value in STRate (C4). The reference to E11 (the loan amount from the previous year) is a relative reference. E11 is two cells to the left and one cell up. When the formula is copied from G12 into G13:G21, the reference in each of these cells will continue to be two cells to the left and one cell up. This is exactly what we want, since we always want the interest payment to be based on the short-term loan that was taken one year ago (two cells to the left and one cell up).

Excel Tip: A shortcut for changing a cell reference from relative to absolute is to press the F4 key on a PC or command-T on a Mac.

After using the Fill Down command to copy the formulas in columns F, G, I, J, and L and entering the LT loan payback into cell H21, the complete model appears as shown in Figure 4.4.

Test: Test the Full-Scale Version of the Model

Just as it was important to test the small version of the model, it needs to be tested again after it is expanded to full-scale size. The procedure is the same one followed for testing the small version, including the ideas that will be presented in Section 4.4 for debugging a spreadsheet model.

Analyze: Analyze the Model

Before using Solver, the spreadsheet in Figure 4.4 is merely an evaluative model for Everglade. It can be used to evaluate any proposed solution, including quickly determining what interest and loan payments will be required and what the resulting balances will be at the end of each year. For example, LTLoan (D11) and STLoan (E11:E20) in Figure 4.4 show one possible plan, which turns out to be unacceptable because EndingBalance (J11:J21) indicates that a negative ending balance would result in three of the years.

To optimize the model, Solver is used as shown in Figure 4.5 to specify the objective cell, the changing cells, and the constraints. Everglade management wants to find a combination of loans that will keep the company solvent throughout the next 10 years (2014–2023) and then will leave as large a cash balance as possible in 2024 after paying off all the loans. Therefore, the objective cell to be maximized is EndBalance (J21) and the changing cells are the loan amounts LTLoan (D11) and STLoan (E11:E20). To assure that Everglade maintains a minimum balance of at least $500,000 at the end of each year, the constraints for the model are EndingBalance (J11:J21) $\geq$ MinimumBalance (L11:L21).

After running Solver, the optimal solution is shown in Figure 4.5. The changing cells, LTLoan (D11) and STLoan (E11:E20) give the loan amounts in the various years. The objective cell EndBalance (J21) indicates that the ending balance in 2024 will be $5.39 million.

Conclusion of the Case Study

The spreadsheet model developed by Everglade's CFO, Julie Lee, is the one shown in Figure 4.5. Her next step is to submit a report to her CEO, Sheldon Lee, that recommends the plan obtained by this model.

Soon thereafter, Sheldon and Julie meet to discuss her report.

Sheldon: Thanks for your report, Julie. Excellent job. Your spreadsheet really lays everything out in a very understandable way.

Julie: Thanks. It took a little while to get the spreadsheet organized properly and to make sure it was operating correctly, but I think the time spent was worthwhile.

Sheldon: Yes, it was. You can't rush those things. But one thing is still bothering me.

Julie: What's that?

Sheldon: It has to do with our forecasts for the company's future cash flows. We have been assuming that the cash flows in the coming years will be the ones shown in column C

FIGURE 4.4

A complete spreadsheet model for the Everglade cash flow management problem, including the equations entered into the objective cell EndBalance (J21) and all the other output cells, to be used before calling on Solver. The entries in the changing cells, LTLoan (D11) and STLoan (E11:E20), are only a trial solution at this stage.

	A	B	C	D	E	F	G	H	I	J	K	L
1		**Everglade Cash Flow Management Problem**										
2												
3		LT Rate	5%									
4		ST Rate	7%									
5						(all cash figures in millions of dollars)						
6		Start Balance	1									
7		Minimum Cash	0.5									
8												
9			Cash	LT	ST	LT	ST	LT	ST	Ending		Minimum
10		Year	Flow	Loan	Loan	Interest	Interest	Payback	Payback	Balance		Balance
11		2014	−8	6	2					1.00	≥	0.5
12		2015	−2		5	−0.30	−0.14		−2	1.56	≥	0.5
13		2016	−4		0	−0.30	−0.35		−5	−8.09	≥	0.5
14		2017	3		0	−0.30	0		0	−5.39	≥	0.5
15		2018	6		0	−0.30	0		0	0.31	≥	0.5
16		2019	3		0	−0.30	0		0	3.01	≥	0.5
17		2020	−4		0	−0.30	0		0	−1.29	≥	0.5
18		2021	7		0	−0.30	0		0	5.41	≥	0.5
19		2022	−2		0	−0.30	0		0	3.11	≥	0.5
20		2023	10		0	−0.30	0		0	12.81	≥	0.5
21		2024				−0.30	0	−6	0	6.51	≥	0.5

	F	G	H	I	J	K	L
9	LT	ST	LT	ST	Ending		Minimum
10	Interest	Interest	Payback	Payback	Balance		Balance
11					=StartBalance+SUM(C11:I11)	≥	=MinimumCash
12	=−LTRate*LTLoan	=−STRate*E11		=−E11	=J11+SUM(C12:I12)	≥	=MinimumCash
13	=−LTRate*LTLoan	=−STRate*E12		=−E12	=J12+SUM(C13:I13)	≥	=MinimumCash
14	=−LTRate*LTLoan	=−STRate*E13		=−E13	=J13+SUM(C14:I14)	≥	=MinimumCash
15	=−LTRate*LTLoan	=−STRate*E14		=−E14	=J14+SUM(C15:I15)	≥	=MinimumCash
16	=−LTRate*LTLoan	=−STRate*E15		=−E15	=J15+SUM(C16:I16)	≥	=MinimumCash
17	=−LTRate*LTLoan	=−STRate*E16		=−E16	=J16+SUM(C17:I17)	≥	=MinimumCash
18	=−LTRate*LTLoan	=−STRate*E17		=−E17	=J17+SUM(C18:I18)	≥	=MinimumCash
19	=−LTRate*LTLoan	=−STRate*E18		=−E18	=J18+SUM(C19:I19)	≥	=MinimumCash
20	=−LTRate*LTLoan	=−STRate*E19		=−E19	=J19+SUM(C20:I20)	≥	=MinimumCash
21	=−LTRate*LTLoan	=−STRate*E20	=−LTLoan	=−E20	=J20+SUM(C21:I21)	≥	=MinimumCash

Range Name	Cells
CashFlow	C11:C20
EndBalance	J21
EndingBalance	J11:J21
LTLoan	D11
LTRate	C3
MinimumBalance	L11:L21
MinimumCash	C7
StartBalance	C6
STLoan	E11:E20
STRate	C4

134 Chapter Four *The Art of Modeling with Spreadsheets*

FIGURE 4.5

A complete spreadsheet model for the Everglade cash flow management problem after calling on Solver to obtain the optimal solution shown in the changing cells, LTLoan (D11) and STLoan (E11:E20). The objective cell EndBalance (J21) indicates that the resulting cash balance in 2024 will be $5.39 million if all the data cells prove to be accurate.

	A	B	C	D	E	F	G	H	I	J	K	L
1		**Everglade Cash Flow Management Problem**										
2												
3		LT Rate	5%									
4		ST Rate	7%									
5						(all cash figures in millions of dollars)						
6		Start Balance	1									
7		Minimum Cash	0.5									
8												
9			Cash	LT	ST	LT	ST	LT	ST	Ending		Minimum
10		Year	Flow	Loan	Loan	Interest	Interest	Payback	Payback	Balance		Balance
11		2014	−8	4.65	2.85					0.50	≥	0.50
12		2015	−2		5.28	−0.23	−0.20		−2.85	0.50	≥	0.50
13		2016	−4		9.88	−0.23	−0.37		−5.28	0.50	≥	0.50
14		2017	3		7.81	−0.23	−0.69		−9.88	0.50	≥	0.50
15		2018	6		2.59	−0.23	−0.55		−7.81	0.50	≥	0.50
16		2019	3		0	−0.23	−0.18		−2.59	0.50	≥	0.50
17		2020	−4		4.23	−0.23	0		0	0.50	≥	0.50
18		2021	7		0	−0.23	−0.30		−4.23	2.74	≥	0.50
19		2022	−2		0	−0.23	0		0	0.51	≥	0.50
20		2023	10		0	−0.23	0		0	10.27	≥	0.50
21		2024				−0.23	0	−4.65	0	5.39	≥	0.50

	F	G	H	I	J	K	L
9	LT	ST	LT	ST	Ending		Minimum
10	Interest	Interest	Payback	Payback	Balance		Balance
11					= StartBalance+SUM(C11:I11)	≥	=MinimumCash
12	=−LTRate*LTLoan	=−STRate*E11		=−E11	=J11+SUM(C12:I12)	≥	=MinimumCash
13	=−LTRate*LTLoan	=−STRate*E12		=−E12	=J12+SUM(C13:I13)	≥	=MinimumCash
14	=−LTRate*LTLoan	=−STRate*E13		=−E13	=J13+SUM(C14:I14)	≥	=MinimumCash
15	=−LTRate*LTLoan	=−STRate*E14		=−E14	=J14+SUM(C15:I15)	≥	=MinimumCash
16	=−LTRate*LTLoan	=−STRate*E15		=−E15	=J15+SUM(C16:I16)	≥	=MinimumCash
17	=−LTRate*LTLoan	=−STRate*E16		=−E16	=J16+SUM(C17:I17)	≥	=MinimumCash
18	=−LTRate*LTLoan	=−STRate*E17		=−E17	=J17+SUM(C18:I18)	≥	=MinimumCash
19	=−LTRate*LTLoan	=−STRate*E18		=−E18	=J18+SUM(C19:I19)	≥	=MinimumCash
20	=−LTRate*LTLoan	=−STRate*E19		=−E19	=J19+SUM(C20:I20)	≥	=MinimumCash
21	=−LTRate*LTLoan	=−STRate*E20	=−LTLoan	=−E20	=J20+SUM(C21:I21)	≥	=MinimumCash

Solver Parameters

Set Objective Cell: EndBalance
To: Max
By Changing Variable Cells:
  LTLoan, STLoan
Subject to the Constraints:
  EndingBalance >= MinimumBalance

Solver Options:
  Make Variables Nonnegative
  Solving Method: Simplex LP

Range Name	Cells
CashFlow	C11:C20
EndBalance	J21
EndingBalance	J11:J21
LTLoan	D11
LTRate	C3
MinimumBalance	L11:L21
MinimumCash	C7
StartBalance	C6
STLoan	E11:E20
STRate	C4

of your spreadsheet. Those are good estimates, but we both know that they are only estimates. A lot of changes that we can't foresee now are likely to occur over the next 10 years. When there is a shift in the economy, or when other unexpected developments occur that impact the company, those cash flows can change a lot. How do we know if your recommended plan will still be a good one if those kinds of changes occur?

Julie: A very good question. To answer it, we should do some *what-if analysis* to see what would happen if those kinds of changes occur. Now that the spreadsheet is set up properly, it will be very easy to do that by simply changing some of the cash flows in column C and seeing what would happen with the current plan. You can try out any change or changes you want and immediately see the effect. Each time you change a future cash flow, you also have the option of trying out changes on short-term loan amounts to see what kind of adjustments would be needed to maintain a balance of at least $500,000 in every year.

OK, are you ready? Shall we do some what-if analysis now?

Sheldon: Let's do.

Fortunately, Julie had set up the spreadsheet properly (providing a data cell for the cash flow in each of the next 10 years) to enable performing *what-if analysis* immediately by simply trying different numbers in some of these data cells. (The next chapter will focus on describing the importance of what-if analysis and alternative ways of performing this kind of analysis.) After spending half an hour trying different numbers, Sheldon and Julie conclude that the plan in Figure 4.5 will be a sound initial financial plan for the next 10 years, even if future cash flows deviate somewhat from current forecasts. If deviations do occur, adjustments will of course need to be made in the short-term loan amounts. At any point, Julie also will have the option of returning to the company's bank to try to arrange another long-term loan for the remainder of the 10 years at a lower interest rate than that offered for short-term loans. If so, essentially the same spreadsheet model as in Figure 4.5 can be used, along with Solver, to find the optimal adjusted financial plan for the remainder of the 10 years.

A management science technique called *computer simulation* provides another effective way of taking the uncertainty of future cash flows into account. Chapters 12 and 13 will describe this technique and Section 13.4 will be devoted to continuing the analysis of this same case study.

> Providing a data cell for each piece of data makes it easy to check what would happen if the correct value for a piece of data differs from its initial estimate.

Review Questions

1. What is a good way to get started with a spreadsheet model if you don't even know where to begin?
2. What are two ways in which doing calculations by hand can help you?
3. Describe a useful way to get started organizing and laying out a spreadsheet.
4. What types of values should be put into the changing cells to test the model?
5. What is the difference between an absolute cell reference and a relative cell reference?

4.3   SOME GUIDELINES FOR BUILDING "GOOD" SPREADSHEET MODELS

There are many ways to set up a model on a spreadsheet. While one of the benefits of spreadsheets is the flexibility they offer, this flexibility also can be dangerous. Although Excel provides many features (such as range names, shading, borders, etc.) that allow you to create "good" spreadsheet models that are easy to understand, easy to debug, and easy to modify, it is also easy to create "bad" spreadsheet models that are difficult to understand, difficult to debug, and difficult to modify. The goal of this section is to provide some guidelines that will help you to create "good" spreadsheet models.

Enter the Data First

> All the data should be laid out on the spreadsheet before beginning to formulate the rest of the spreadsheet model.

Any spreadsheet model is driven by the data in the spreadsheet. The form of the entire model is built around the structure of the data. Therefore, it is always a good idea to enter and carefully lay out all the data before you begin to set up the rest of the model. The model structure then can conform to the layout of the data as closely as possible.

An Application Vignette

Welch's, Inc., is the world's largest processor of Concord and Niagara grapes with annual sales surpassing $550 million per year. Such products as Welch's grape jelly and Welch's grape juice have been enjoyed by generations of American consumers.

Every September, growers begin delivering grapes to processing plants that then press the raw grapes into juice. Time must pass before the grape juice is ready for conversion into finished jams, jellies, juices, and concentrates.

Deciding how to use the grape crop is a complex task given changing demand and uncertain crop quality and quantity. Typical decisions include what recipes to use for major product groups, the transfer of grape juice between plants, and the mode of transportation for these transfers.

Because Welch's lacked a formal system for optimizing raw material movement and the recipes used for production, a management science team developed a preliminary linear programming model. This was a large model with 8,000 decision variables that focused on the component level of detail. Small-scale testing proved that the model worked.

To make the model more useful, the team then revised it by aggregating demand by product group rather than by component. This reduced its size to 324 decision variables and 361 functional constraints. *The model then was incorporated into a spreadsheet.*

The company has run the continually updated version of this *spreadsheet model* each month since 1994 to provide senior management with information on the optimal logistics plan generated by Solver. The *savings* from using and optimizing this model were *approximately $150,000 in the first year alone.* A major advantage of incorporating the linear programming model into a spreadsheet has been the ease of explaining the model to managers with differing levels of mathematical understanding. This has led to a widespread appreciation of the management science approach for both this application and others.

Source: E. W. Schuster and S. J. Allen, "Raw Material Management at Welch's, Inc.," *Interfaces* 28, no. 5 (September–October 1998), pp. 13–24. (A link to this article is provided on our website, **www.mhhe.com/hillier5e.**)

Often, it is easier to set up the rest of the model when the data are already on the spreadsheet. In the Everglade problem (see Figure 4.5), the data for the cash flows have been laid out in the first columns of the spreadsheet (B and C), with the year labels in column B and the data in cells C11:C20. Once the data are in place, the layout for the rest of the model quickly falls into place around the structure of the data. It is only logical to lay out the changing cells and output cells using the same structure, with each of the various cash flows in columns that utilize the same row labels from column B.

Now reconsider the spreadsheet model developed in Section 2.2 for the Wyndor Glass Co. problem. The spreadsheet is repeated here in Figure 4.6. The data for the Hours Used per Unit Produced have been laid out in the center of the spreadsheet in cells C7:D9. The output cells, HoursUsed (E7:E9), then have been placed immediately to the right of these data and to the left of the data on HoursAvailable(G7:G9), where the row labels for these output cells are the same as for all these data. This makes it easy to interpret the three constraints being laid out in rows 7–9 of the spreadsheet model. Next, the changing cells and objective cell have been placed together in row 12 below the data, where the column labels for the changing cells are the same as for the columns of data above.

The locations of the data occasionally will need to be shifted somewhat to better accommodate the overall model. However, with this caveat, the model structure generally should conform to the data as closely as possible.

Organize and Clearly Identify the Data

Provide labels in the spreadsheet that clearly identify all the data.

Related data should be grouped together in a convenient format and entered into the spreadsheet with labels that clearly identify the data. For data that are laid out in tabular form, the table should have a heading that provides a general description of the data and then each row and column should have a label that will identify each entry in the table. The units of the data also should be identified. Different types of data should be well separated in the spreadsheet. However, if two tables need to use the same labels for either their rows or columns, then be consistent in making them either rows in both tables or columns in both tables.

In the Wyndor Glass Co. problem (Figure 4.6), the three sets of data have been grouped into tables and clearly labeled Unit Profit, Hours Used per Unit Produced, and Hours Available. The units of the data are identified (dollar signs are included in the unit profit data and hours are indicated in the labels of the time data). Finally, all three data tables make consistent use of rows and columns. Since the Unit Profit data have their product labels (Doors and Windows) in columns C and D, the Hours Used per Unit Produced data use this same structure.

FIGURE 4.6

The spreadsheet model formulated in Section 2.2 for the Wyndor Glass Co. product-mix problem.

	A	B	C	D	E	F	G
1		**Wyndor Glass Co. Product-Mix Problem**					
2							
3			Doors	Windows			
4		Unit Profit	$300	$500			
5					Hours		Hours
6			Hours Used per Unit Produced		Used		Available
7		Plant 1	1	0	2	≤	4
8		Plant 2	0	2	12	≤	12
9		Plant 3	3	2	18	≤	18
10							
11			Doors	Windows			Total Profit
12		Units Produced	2	6			$3,600

Solver Parameters

Set Objective Cell: TotalProfit
To: Max
By Changing Variable Cells:
   UnitsProduced
Subject to the Constraints:
   HoursUsed <= HoursAvailable

Solver Options:
   Make Variables Nonnegative
   Solving Method: Simplex LP

	E
5	Hours
6	Used
7	=SUMPRODUCT(C7:D7,UnitsProduced)
8	=SUMPRODUCT(C8:D8,UnitsProduced)
9	=SUMPRODUCT(C9:D9,UnitsProduced)

	G
11	Total Profit
12	=SUMPRODUCT(Unit Profit,UnitsProduced)

Range Name	Cells
HoursAvailable	G7:G9
HoursUsed	E7:E9
HoursUsedPerUnitProduced	C7:D9
TotalProfit	G12
UnitProfit	C4:D4
UnitsProduced	C12:D12

This structure also is carried through to the changing cells (Units Produced). Similarly, the data for each plant (rows 7–9) are in the rows for both the Hours Used per Unit Produced data *and* the Hours Available data. Keeping the data oriented the same way is not only less confusing, but it also makes it possible to use the SUMPRODUCT function. Recall that the SUMPRODUCT function assumes that the two ranges are exactly the same shape (i.e., the same number of rows *and* columns). If the Unit Profit data and the Units Produced data had not been oriented the same way (e.g., one in a column and the other in a row), it would not have been possible to use the SUMPRODUCT function in the Total Profit calculation.

Similarly, for the Everglade problem (Figure 4.5), the five sets of data have been grouped into cells and tables and clearly labeled ST Rate, LT Rate, Start Balance, Cash Flow, and Minimum Cash. The units of the data are identified (cells F5:I5 specify that all cash figures are in millions of dollars), and all the tables make consistent use of rows and columns (years in the rows).

Enter Each Piece of Data into One Cell Only

Every formula using the same piece of data should refer to the same single data cell.

If a piece of data is needed in more than one formula, then refer to the original data cell rather than repeating the data in additional places. This makes the model much easier to modify. If the value of that piece of data changes, it only needs to be changed in one place. You do not need to search through the entire model to find all the places where the data value appears.

For example, in the Everglade problem (Figure 4.5), there is a company policy of maintaining a cash balance of at least $500,000 at all times. This translates into a constraint for the minimum balance of $500,000 at the end of each year. Rather than entering the minimum cash position of 0.5 (in millions of dollars) into all the cells in column L, it is entered once in MinimumCash (C7) and then referred to by the cells in MinimumBalance (L11:L21). Then, if this policy were to change to, say, a minimum of $200,000 cash, the number would need to be changed in only one place.

Separate Data from Formulas

Formulas should refer to data cells for any needed numbers.

Avoid using numbers directly in formulas. Instead, enter any needed numbers into data cells and then refer to the data cells as needed. For example, in the Everglade problem (Figure 4.5), all the data (the interest rates, starting balance, minimum cash, and projected cash flows) are entered into separate data cells on the spreadsheet. When these numbers are needed to calculate the interest charges (in columns F and G), loan payments (in column H and I), ending balances (column J), and minimum balances (column L), the data cells are referred to rather than entering these numbers directly in the formulas.

Separating the data from the formulas has a couple advantages. First, all the data are visible on the spreadsheet rather than buried in formulas. Seeing all the data makes the model easier to interpret. Second, the model is easier to modify since changing data only requires modifying the corresponding data cells. You don't need to modify any formulas. This proves to be very important when it comes time to perform what-if analysis to see what the effect would be if some of the estimates in the data cells were to take on other plausible values.

Keep It Simple

Make the spreadsheet as easy to interpret as possible.

Avoid the use of powerful Excel functions when simpler functions are available that are easier to interpret. As much as possible, stick to SUMPRODUCT or SUM functions. This makes the model easier to understand and also helps to ensure that the model will be linear. (Linear models are considerably easier to solve than others.) Try to keep formulas short and simple. If a complicated formula is required, break it out into intermediate calculations with subtotals. For example, in the Everglade spreadsheet, each element of the loan payments is broken out explicitly: LT Interest, ST Interest, LT Payback, and ST Payback. Some of these columns could have been combined (e.g., into two columns with LT Payments and ST Payments, or even into one column for all Loan Payments). However, this makes the formulas more complicated and also makes the model harder to test and debug. As laid out, the individual formulas for the loan payments are so simple that their values can be predicted easily without even looking at the formula. This simplifies the testing and debugging of the model.

Use Range Names

Range names make formulas much easier to interpret.

One way to refer to a block of related cells (or even a single cell) in a spreadsheet formula is to use its cell address (e.g., L11:L21 or C3). However, when reading the formula, this requires looking at that part of the spreadsheet to see what kind of information is given there. As mentioned previously in Sections 1.2 and 2.2, a better alternative is to assign a descriptive **range name** to the block of cells that immediately identifies what is there. (This is done by selecting the block of cells, clicking on the name box on the left of the formula bar above the spreadsheet, and then typing a name.) This is especially helpful when writing a formula for an output cell. Writing the formula in terms of range names instead of cell addresses makes the formula much easier to interpret. Range names also make the description of the model in Solver much easier to understand.

Figure 4.5 illustrates the use of range names for the Everglade spreadsheet model. For example, consider the formula for long-term interest in cell F12. Since the long-term rate is given in cell C3 and the long-term loan amount is in cell D11, the formula for the long-term interest could have been written as $= -C3*D11$. However, by using the range name LTRate for cell C3 and the range name LTLoan for cell D11, the formula instead becomes $= -LTRate*LTLoan$, which is much easier to interpret at a glance.

On the other hand, be aware that it is easy to get carried away with defining range names. Defining too many range names can be more trouble than it is worth. For example, when related data are grouped together in a table, we recommend giving a range name only for the entire table rather than for the individual rows and columns. In general, we suggest defining range names only for each group of data cells, the changing cells, the objective cell, and both sides of each group of constraints (the left-hand side and the right-hand side).

Spaces are not allowed in range names. When a range name has more than one word, we have used capital letters to distinguish the start of each new word in a range name (e.g., MinimumBalance). Another way is to use the underscore character (e.g., Minimum_Balance).

Care also should be taken to assure that it is easy to quickly identify which cells are referred to by a particular range name. Use a name that corresponds exactly to the label on the spreadsheet. For example, in Figure 4.5, columns J and L are labeled Ending Balance and Minimum Balance on the spreadsheet, so we use the range names EndingBalance and MinimumBalance. Using exactly the same name as the label on the spreadsheet makes it quick and easy to find the cells that are referred to by a range name.

When desired, a list of all the range names and their corresponding cell addresses can be pasted directly into the spreadsheet by choosing Paste from the Use in Formula menu on the Formulas tab, and then clicking Paste List. Such a list (after reformatting) is included below essentially all the spreadsheets displayed in this text.

When modifying an existing model that utilizes range names, care should be taken to assure that the range names continue to refer to the correct range of cells. When inserting a row or column into a spreadsheet model, it is helpful to insert the row or column into the middle of a range rather than at the end. For example, to add another product to a product-mix model with four products, add a column between Products 2 and 3 rather than after Product 4. This will automatically extend the relevant range names to span across all five columns since these range names will continue to refer to everything between Product 1 and Product 4, including the newly inserted column for the fifth product. Similarly, deleting a row or column from the middle of a range will contract the span of the relevant range names appropriately. You can double-check the cells that are referred to by a range name by choosing that range name from the name box (on the left of the formula bar above the spreadsheet). This will highlight the cells that are referred to by the chosen range name.

Use Relative and Absolute References to Simplify Copying Formulas

Excel's fill commands provide a quick and reliable way to replicate a formula into multiple cells.

Whenever multiple related formulas will be needed, try to enter the formula just once and then use Excel's fill commands to replicate the formula. Not only is this quicker than retyping the formula, but it is also less prone to error.

We saw a good example of this when discussing the expansion of the model to full-scale size in the preceding section. Starting with the two-year spreadsheet in Figure 4.3, fill commands were used to copy the formulas in columns F, G, I, J, and L for the remaining years to create the full-scale, 10-year spreadsheet in Figure 4.4.

Using relative and absolute references for related formulas not only aids in building a model but also makes it easier to modify an existing model or template. For example, suppose that you have formulated a spreadsheet model for a product-mix problem but now wish to modify the model to add another resource. This requires inserting a row into the spreadsheet. If the output cells are written with proper relative and absolute references, then it is simple to copy the existing formulas into the inserted row.

Use Borders, Shading, and Colors to Distinguish between Cell Types

Make it easy to spot all the cells of the same type.

It is important to be able to easily distinguish between the data cells, changing cells, output cells, and objective cell in a spreadsheet. One way to do this is to use different borders and cell shading for each of these different types of cells. In the text, data cells appear lightly shaded, changing cells are shaded a medium amount with a light border, output cells appear with no shading, and the objective cell is shaded darkly with a heavy border.

In the spreadsheet files in MS Courseware, data cells are light blue, changing cells are yellow, and the objective cell is orange. Obviously, you may use any scheme that you like. The important thing is to be consistent, so that you can quickly recognize the types of cells. Then, when you want to examine the cells of a certain type, the color will immediately guide you there.

Show the Entire Model on the Spreadsheet

Solver uses a combination of the spreadsheet and the Solver dialog box (or the model pane in RSPE) to specify the model to be solved. Therefore, it is possible to include certain elements of the model (such as the ≤, =, or ≥ signs and/or the right-hand sides of the constraints) in

Solver without displaying them in the spreadsheet. However, we strongly recommend that *every* element of the model be displayed *on the spreadsheet*. Every person using or adapting the model, or referring back to it later, needs to be able to interpret the model. This is much easier to do by viewing the model on the spreadsheet than by trying to decipher it from Solver. Furthermore, a printout of the spreadsheet does not include information from Solver.

In particular, all the elements of a constraint should be displayed on the spreadsheet. For each constraint, three adjacent cells should be used for the total of the left-hand side, the $\leq$, $=$, or $\geq$ sign in the middle, and the right-hand side. (Note in Figure 4.5 that this was done in columns J, K, and L of the spreadsheet for the Everglade problem.) As mentioned earlier, the changing cells and objective cell should be highlighted in some manner (e.g., with borders and/or cell shading). A good test is that you should not need to go to Solver to determine any element of the model. You should be able to identify the changing cells, the objective cell, and all the constraints in the model just by looking at the spreadsheet.

Display every element of the model on the spreadsheet rather than relying on only Solver to include certain elements.

A Poor Spreadsheet Model

It is certainly possible to set up a linear programming spreadsheet model without utilizing any of these ideas. Figure 4.7 shows an alternative spreadsheet formulation for the Everglade problem that violates nearly every one of these guidelines. This formulation can still be solved using Solver, which in fact yields the same optimal solution as in Figure 4.5. However, the

FIGURE 4.7

A poor formulation of the spreadsheet model for the Everglade cash flow management problem.

	A	B	C	D	E	F
1		**A Poor Formulation of the Everglade Cash Flow Problem**				
2						
3			LT	ST	Ending	
4		Year	Loan	Loan	Balance	
5		2014	4.65	2.85	0.50	
6		2015		5.28	0.50	
7		2016		9.88	0.50	
8		2017		7.81	0.50	
9		2018		2.59	0.50	
10		2019		0	0.50	
11		2020		4.23	0.50	
12		2021		0	2.74	
13		2022		0	0.51	
14		2023		0	10.27	
15		2024			5.39	

Solver Parameters

Set Objective Cell: E15
To: Max
By Changing Variable Cells:
   C5, D5:D14
Subject to the Constraints:
   E5:E15 >= 0.5

Solver Options:
   Make Variables Nonnegative
   Solving Method: Simplex LP

	E
3	Ending
4	Balance
5	=1–8+C5+D5
6	=E5–2+D6–$C$5*(0.05)–D5*(1.07)
7	=E6–4+D7–$C$5*(0.05)–D6*(1.07)
8	=E7+3+D8–$C$5*(0.05)–D7*(1.07)
9	=E8+6+D9–$C$5*(0.05)–D8*(1.07)
10	=E9+3+D10–$C$5*(0.05)–D9*(1.07)
11	=E10–4+D11–$C$5*(0.05)–D10*(1.07)
12	=E11+7+D12–$C$5*(0.05)–D11*(1.07)
13	=E12–2+D13–$C$5*(0.05)–D12*(1.07)
14	=E13+10+D14–$C$5*(0.05)–D13*(1.07)
15	=E14+D15–$C$5*(1.05)–D14*(1.07)

formulation has many problems. It is not clear which cells yield the solution (borders and/ or shading are not used to highlight the changing cells and objective cell). Without going to Solver, the constraints in the model cannot be identified (the spreadsheet does not show the entire model). The spreadsheet also does not show most of the data. For example, to determine the data used for the projected cash flows, the interest rates, or the starting balance, you need to dig into the formulas in column E (the data are not separate from the formulas). If any of these data change, the actual formulas need to be modified rather than simply changing a number on the spreadsheet. Furthermore, the formulas and the model in Solver are difficult to interpret (range names are not utilized).

Compare Figures 4.5 and 4.7. Applying the guidelines for good spreadsheet models (as is done for Figure 4.5) results in a model that is easier to understand, easier to debug, and easier to modify. This is especially important for models that will have a long life span. If this model is going to be reused months later, the "good" model of Figure 4.5 immediately can be understood, modified, and reapplied as needed, whereas deciphering the spreadsheet model of Figure 4.7 again would be a great challenge.

Review
Questions

1. Which part of the model should be entered first on the spreadsheet?
2. Should numbers be included in formulas or entered separately in data cells?
3. How do range names make formulas and the model in Solver easier to interpret? How should range names be chosen?
4. What are some ways to distinguish data cells, changing cells, output cells, and objective cells on a spreadsheet?
5. How many cells are needed to completely specify a constraint on a spreadsheet?

4.4 DEBUGGING A SPREADSHEET MODEL

Debugging a spreadsheet model sometimes is as challenging as debugging a computer program.

If you have added rows or columns to the spreadsheet, make sure that each of the range names still refers to the correct cells.

toggle
The toggle feature in Excel is a great way to check the formulas for the output cells.

Excel Tip: Pressing control-~ on a PC (or command-~ on a Mac) toggles the worksheet between viewing values and viewing formulas in all the output cells.

No matter how carefully it is planned and built, even a moderately complicated model usually will not be error-free the first time it is run. Often the mistakes are immediately obvious and quickly corrected. However, sometimes an error is harder to root out. Following the guidelines in Section 4.3 for developing a good spreadsheet model can make the model *much* easier to debug. Even so, much like debugging a computer program, debugging a spreadsheet model can be a difficult task. This section presents some tips and a variety of Excel features that can make debugging easier.

As a first step in debugging a spreadsheet model, test the model using the principles discussed in the first subsection on testing in Section 4.2. In particular, try different values for the changing cells for which you can predict the correct result in the output cells and see if they calculate as expected. Values of 0 are good ones to try initially because usually it is then obvious what should be in the output cells. Try other simple values, such as all 1s, where the correct results in the output cells are reasonably obvious. For more complicated values, break out a calculator and do some manual calculations to check the various output cells. Include some very large values for the changing cells to ensure that the calculations are behaving reasonably for these extreme cases.

If you have defined range names, be sure that they still refer to the correct cells. Sometimes they can become disjointed when you add rows or columns to the spreadsheet. To test the range names, you can either select the various range names in the name box, which will highlight the selected range in the spreadsheet, or paste the entire list of range names and their references into the spreadsheet.

Carefully study each formula to be sure it is entered correctly. A very useful feature in Excel for checking formulas is the **toggle** to switch back and forth between viewing the formulas in the worksheet and viewing the resulting values in the output cells. By default, Excel shows the values that are calculated by the various output cells in the model. Typing control-~ switches the current worksheet to instead display the formulas in the output cells, as shown in Figure 4.8. Typing control-~ again switches back to the standard view of displaying the values in the output cells (like Figure 4.5).

142 Chapter Four *The Art of Modeling with Spreadsheets*

FIGURE 4.8

The spreadsheet obtained by toggling the spreadsheet in Figure 4.5 once to replace the values in the output cells by the formulas entered into those cells. Using the toggle feature in Excel once more will restore the view of the spreadsheet shown in Figure 4.5.

	A	B	C	D	E	F	G	H	I	J	K	L
1	**Everglade Cash Flow Management Problem**											
2												
3		LT Rate	0.05									
4		ST Rate	0.07									
5						(all cash figures in millions of dollars)						
6		Start Balance	1									
7		Minimum Cash	0.5									
8												
9			Cash	LT	ST					Ending		Minimum
10		Year	Flow	Loan	Loan	LT Interest	ST Interest	LT Payback	ST Payback	Balance		Balance
11		2014	−8	4.65124	2.84759	=−LTRate*LTLoan	=−STRate*E11			=StartBalance+SUM(C11:I11)	≥	=MinimumCash
12		2015	−2		5.28073	=−LTRate*LTLoan	=−STRate*E12		=−E11	=J11+SUM(C12:I12)	≥	=MinimumCash
13		2016	−4		9.88295	=−LTRate*LTLoan	=−STRate*E13		=−E12	=J12+SUM(C13:I13)	≥	=MinimumCash
14		2017	3		7.80732	=−LTRate*LTLoan	=−STRate*E14		=−E13	=J13+SUM(C14:I14)	≥	=MinimumCash
15		2018	6		2.58639	=−LTRate*LTLoan	=−STRate*E15		=−E14	=J14+SUM(C15:I15)	≥	=MinimumCash
16		2019	3		0	=−LTRate*LTLoan	=−STRate*E16		=−E15	=J15+SUM(C16:I16)	≥	=MinimumCash
17		2020	−4		4.23256	=−LTRate*LTLoan	=−STRate*E17		=−E16	=J16+SUM(C17:I17)	≥	=MinimumCash
18		2021	7		0	=−LTRate*LTLoan	=−STRate*E18		=−E17	=J17+SUM(C18:I18)	≥	=MinimumCash
19		2022	−2		0	=−LTRate*LTLoan	=−STRate*E19		=−E18	=J18+SUM(C19:I19)	≥	=MinimumCash
20		2023	10		0	=−LTRate*LTLoan	=−STRate*E20	=−LTLoan	=−E19	=J19+SUM(C20:I20)	≥	=MinimumCash
21		2024								=J20+SUM(C21:I21)	≥	=MinimumCash

Excel's auditing tools enable you to either trace forward or backward to see the linkages between cells.

Another useful set of features built into Excel are the **auditing tools.** The auditing tools are available in the Formula Auditing group of the Formulas Tab.

The auditing tools can be used to graphically display which cells make direct links to a given cell. For example, selecting LTLoan (D11) in Figure 4.5 and then Trace Dependents generates the arrows on the spreadsheet shown in Figure 4.9.

You now can immediately see that LTLoan (D11) is used in the calculation of LT Interest for every year in column F, in the calculation of LTPayback (H21), and in the calculation of the ending balance in 2014 (J11). This can be very illuminating. Think about what output cells LTLoan should impact directly. There should be an arrow to each of these cells. If, for example, LTLoan is missing from any of the formulas in column F, the error will be immediately revealed by the missing arrow. Similarly, if LTLoan is mistakenly entered in any of the short-term loan output cells, this will show up as extra arrows.

You also can trace backward to see which cells provide the data for any given cell. These can be displayed graphically by choosing Trace Precedents. For example, choosing Trace Precedents for the ST Interest cell for 2015 (G12) displays the arrows shown in Figure 4.10. These arrows indicate that the ST Interest cell for 2015 (G12) refers to the ST Loan in 2014 (E11) and to STRate (C4).

When you are done, choose Remove Arrows.

Review Questions

1. What is a good first step for debugging a spreadsheet model?
2. How do you toggle between viewing formulas and viewing values in output cells?
3. Which Excel tool can be used to trace the dependents or precedents for a given cell?

FIGURE 4.9

The spreadsheet obtained by using the Excel auditing tools to trace the dependents of the LT Loan value in cell D11 of the spreadsheet in Figure 4.5.

	A	B	C	D	E	F	G	H	I	J	K	L
1		**Everglade Cash Flow Management Problem**										
2												
3		LT Rate	5%									
4		ST Rate	7%									
5						(all cash figures in millions of dollars)						
6		Start Balance	1									
7		Minimum Cash	0.5									
8												
9			Cash	LT	ST	LT	ST	LT	ST	Ending		Minimum
10		Year	Flow	Loan	Loan	Interest	Interest	Payback	Payback	Balance		Balance
11	2014		−8	4.55	2.85					0.50	≥	0.5
12	2015		−2		5.28	−0.23	−0.20		−2.85	0.50	≥	0.5
13	2016		−4		9.88	−0.23	−0.37		−5.28	0.50	≥	0.5
14	2017		3		7.81	−0.23	−0.69		−9.88	0.50	≥	0.5
15	2018		6		2.59	−0.23	−0.55		−7.81	0.50	≥	0.5
16	2019		3		0	−0.23	−0.18		−2.59	0.50	≥	0.5
17	2020		−4		4.23	−0.23	0		0	0.50	≥	0.5
18	2021		7		0	−0.23	−0.30		−4.23	2.74	≥	0.5
19	2022		−2		0	−0.23	0		0	0.51	≥	0.5
20	2023		10		0	−0.23	0		0	10.27	≥	0.5
21	2024					−0.23	0	−4.65	0	5.39	≥	0.5

144   Chapter Four   *The Art of Modeling with Spreadsheets*

FIGURE 4.10

The spreadsheet obtained by using the Excel auditing tools to trace the precedents of the ST Interest (2015) calculation in cell G12 of the spreadsheet in Figure 4.5.

	A	B	C	D	E	F	G	H	I	J	K	L
1		**Everglade Cash Flow Management Problem**										
2												
3		LT Rate	5%									
4		ST Rate	7%									
5						(all cash figures in millions of dollars)						
6		Start Balance	1									
7		Minimum Cash	0.5									
8												
9			Cash	LT	ST	LT	ST	LT	ST	Ending		Minimum
10		Year	Flow	Loan	Loan	Interest	Interest	Payback	Payback	Balance		Balance
11		2014	−8	4.65	2.85					0.50	≥	0.5
12		2015	−2		5.28	−0.23	−0.20		−2.85	0.50	≥	0.5
13		2016	−4		9.88	−0.23	−0.37		−5.28	0.50	≥	0.5
14		2017	3		7.81	−0.23	−0.69		−9.88	0.50	≥	0.5
15		2018	6		2.59	−0.23	−0.55		−7.81	0.50	≥	0.5
16		2019	3		0	−0.23	−0.18		−2.59	0.50	≥	0.5
17		2020	−4		4.23	−0.23	0		0	0.50	≥	0.5
18		2021	7		0	−0.23	−0.30		−4.23	2.74	≥	0.5
19		2022	−2		0	−0.23	0		0	0.51	≥	0.5
20		2023	10		0	−0.23	0		0	10.27	≥	0.5
21		2024				−0.23	0	−6.65	0	5.39	≥	0.5

4.5 Summary

There is a considerable art to modeling well with spreadsheets. This chapter focuses on providing a foundation for learning this art.

The general process of modeling in spreadsheets has four major steps: (1) plan the spreadsheet model, (2) build the model, (3) test the model, and (4) analyze the model and its results. During the planning step, it is helpful to begin by visualizing where you want to finish and then doing some calculations by hand to clarify the needed computations before starting to sketch out a logical layout for the spreadsheet. Then, when you are ready to undertake the building step, it is a good idea to start by building a small, readily manageable version of the model before expanding the model to full-scale size. This enables you to test the small version first to get all the logic straightened out correctly before expanding to a full-scale model and undertaking a final test. After completing all of this, you are ready for the analysis step, which involves applying the model to evaluate proposed solutions and perhaps using Solver to optimize the model.

Using this plan-build-test-analyze process should yield a spreadsheet model, but it doesn't guarantee that you will obtain a good one. Section 4.3 describes in detail the following guidelines for building "good" spreadsheet models:

- Enter the data first.
- Organize and clearly identify the data.
- Enter each piece of data into one cell only.
- Separate data from formulas.
- Keep it simple.
- Use range names.
- Use relative and absolute references to simplify copying formulas.
- Use borders, shading, and colors to distinguish between cell types.
- Show the entire model on the spreadsheet.

Even if all these guidelines are followed, a thorough debugging process may be needed to eliminate the errors that lurk within the initial version of the model. It is important to check whether the output cells are giving correct results for various values of the changing cells. Other items to check include whether range names refer to the appropriate cells and whether formulas have been entered into output cells correctly. Excel provides a number of useful features to aid in the debugging process. One is the ability to toggle the worksheet between viewing the results in the output cells and the formulas entered into those output cells. Several other helpful features are available with Excel's auditing tools.

Glossary

auditing tools   A set of tools provided by Excel to aid in debugging a spreadsheet model. (Section 4.4), 143

range name   A descriptive name given to a range of cells that immediately identifies what is there. (Section 4.3), 138

toggle   The act of switching back and forth between viewing the results in the output cells and viewing the formulas entered into those output cells. (Section 4.4), 141

Learning Aids for This Chapter in Your MS Courseware

Chapter 4 Excel Files:

Everglade Case Study

Wyndor Example

Everglade Problem 4.12

Everglade Problem 4.13

Excel Add-in:

Risk Solver Platform for Education (RSPE)

Solved Problems (See the CD-ROM or Website for the Solutions)

4.S1. Production and Inventory Planning Model

Surfs Up produces high-end surfboards. A challenge faced by Surfs Up is that their demand is highly seasonal. Demand exceeds production capacity during the warm summer months, but is very low in the winter months. To meet the high demand during the summer, Surfs Up typically produces more surfboards than are needed in the winter months and then carries inventory into the summer months. Their production facility can produce at most 50 boards per month using regular labor at a cost of $125 each. Up to 10 additional boards can be produced by utilizing overtime labor at a cost of $135 each. The boards are sold for $200. Because of storage cost and the opportunity cost of capital, each board held in inventory from one month to the next incurs a cost of $5 per board. Since demand is uncertain, Surfs Up would like to maintain an ending inventory (safety stock) of at least 10 boards during the warm months (May–September) and at least 5 boards during the other months (October–April). It is now the start of January and Surfs Up has 5 boards in inventory. The forecast of demand over the next 12 months is shown in the table below. Formulate and solve a linear programming model in a spreadsheet to determine how many surfboards should be produced each month to maximize total profit.

4.S2. Aggregate Planning: Manpower Hiring/ Firing/Training

Cool Power produces air-conditioning units for large commercial properties. Because of the low cost and efficiency of its products, the company has been growing from year to year. Also, seasonality in construction and weather conditions create production requirements that vary from month to month. Cool Power currently has 10 fully trained employees working in manufacturing. Each trained employee can work 160 hours per month and is paid a monthly wage of $4,000. New trainees can be hired at the beginning of any month. Because of their lack of initial skills and required training, a new trainee provides only 100 hours of useful labor in the first month, but is still paid a full monthly wage of $4,000. Furthermore, because of required interviewing and training, there is a $2,500 hiring cost for each employee hired. After one month, a trainee is considered fully trained. An employee can be fired at the beginning of any month, but must be paid two weeks of severance pay ($2,000). Over the next 12 months, Cool Power forecasts the labor requirements shown in the table on the next page. Since management anticipates higher requirements next year, Cool Power would like to end the year with at least 12 fully trained employees. How many trainees should be hired and/or workers fired in each month to meet the labor requirements at the minimum possible cost? Formulate and solve a linear programming spreadsheet model.

					Forecasted Demand							
Jan.	**Feb.**	**Mar.**	**Apr.**	**May**	**June**	**July**	**Aug.**	**Sept.**	**Oct.**	**Nov.**	**Dec.**
10	14	15	20	45	65	85	85	40	30	15	15

146 Chapter Four   *The Art of Modeling with Spreadsheets*

Labor Requirements (hours)

Jan.	Feb.	Mar.	Apr.	May	June	July	Aug.	Sept.	Oct.	Nov.	Dec.
1,600	2,000	2,000	2,000	2,800	3,200	3,600	3,200	1,600	1,200	800	800

Problems

We have inserted the symbol E* (for Excel) to the left of each problem or part where Excel should be used. An asterisk on the problem number indicates that at least a partial answer is given in the back of the book.

E*4.1. Consider the Everglade cash flow problem discussed in this chapter. Suppose that extra cash is kept in an interest-bearing savings account. Assume that any cash left at the end of a year earns 3 percent interest the following year. Make any necessary modifications to the spreadsheet and re-solve. (The original spreadsheet for this problem is available on the CD-ROM.)

4.2.*   The Pine Furniture Company makes fine country furniture. The company's current product lines consist of end tables, coffee tables, and dining room tables. The production of each of these tables requires 8, 15, and 80 pounds of pine wood, respectively. The tables are handmade and require one hour, two hours, and four hours, respectively. Each table sold generates $50, $100, and $220 profit, respectively. The company has 3,000 pounds of pine wood and 200 hours of labor available for the coming week's production. The chief operating officer (COO) has asked you to do some spreadsheet modeling with these data to analyze what the product mix should be for the coming week and make a recommendation.

   a. Visualize where you want to finish. What numbers will the COO need? What are the decisions that need to be made? What should the objective be?

   b. Suppose that Pine Furniture were to produce three end tables and three dining room tables. Calculate by hand the amount of pine wood and labor that would be required, as well as the profit generated from sales.

   c. Make a rough sketch of a spreadsheet model, with blocks laid out for the data cells, changing cells, output cells, and objective cell.

E*   *d.* Build a spreadsheet model and then solve it.

4.3.   Reboot, Inc., is a manufacturer of hiking boots. Demand for boots is highly seasonal. In particular, the demand in the next year is expected to be 3,000, 4,000, 8,000, and 7,000 pairs of boots in quarters 1, 2, 3, and 4, respectively. With its current production facility, the company can produce at most 6,000 pairs of boots in any quarter. Reboot would like to meet all the expected demand, so it will need to carry inventory to meet demand in the later quarters. Each pair of boots sold generates a profit of $20 per pair. Each pair of boots in inventory at the end of a quarter incurs $8 in storage and capital recovery costs. Reboot has 1,000 pairs of boots in inventory at the start of quarter 1. Reboot's top management has given you the assignment of doing some spreadsheet modeling to analyze what the production schedule should be for the next four quarters and make a recommendation.

   a. Visualize where you want to finish. What numbers will top management need? What are the decisions that need to be made? What should the objective be?

   b. Suppose that Reboot were to produce 5,000 pairs of boots in each of the first two quarters. Calculate by hand the ending inventory, profit from sales, and inventory costs for quarters 1 and 2.

   c. Make a rough sketch of a spreadsheet model, with blocks laid out for the data cells, changing cells, output cells, and objective cell.

E*   *d.* Build a spreadsheet model for quarters 1 and 2, and then thoroughly test the model.

E*   *e.* Expand the model to full scale and then solve it.

E*4.4.* The Fairwinds Development Corporation is considering taking part in one or more of three different development projects—A, B, and C—that are about to be launched. Each project requires a significant investment over the next few years and then would be sold upon completion. The projected cash flows (in millions of dollars) associated with each project are shown in the table below.

Year	Project A	Project B	Project C
1	−4	−8	−10
2	−6	−8	−7
3	−6	−4	−7
4	24	−4	−5
5	0	30	−3
6	0	0	44

Fairwinds has $10 million available now and expects to receive $6 million from other projects by the end of each year (1 through 6) that would be available for the ongoing investments the following year in projects A, B, and C. By acting now, the company may participate in each project either fully, fractionally (with other development partners), or not at all. If Fairwinds participates at less than 100 percent, then all the cash flows associated with that project are reduced proportionally. Company policy requires ending each year with a cash balance of at least $1 million.

   a. Visualize where you want to finish. What numbers are needed? What are the decisions that need to be made? What should the objective be?

   b. Suppose that Fairwinds were to participate in Project A fully and in Project C at 50 percent. Calculate by hand what the ending cash positions would be after year 1 and year 2.

   c. Make a rough sketch of a spreadsheet model, with blocks laid out for the data cells, changing cells, output cells, and objective cell.

E*   *d.* Build a spreadsheet model for years 1 and 2, and then thoroughly test the model.

E*   *e.* Expand the model to full scale, and then solve it.

4.5. Read the referenced article that fully describes the management science study summarized in the application vignette presented in Section 4.3. Briefly describe how spreadsheet modeling was applied in this study. Then list the various financial and nonfinancial benefits that resulted from this study.

4.6. Decorum, Inc., manufactures high-end ceiling fans. Their sales are seasonal with higher demand in the warmer summer months. Typically, sales average 400 units per month. However, in the hot summer months (June, July, and August), sales spike up to 600 units per month. Decorum can produce up to 500 units per month at a cost of $300 each. By bringing in temporary workers, Decorum can produce up to an additional 75 units at a cost of $350 each. Decorum sells the ceiling fans for $500 each. Decorum can carry inventory from one month to the next, but at a cost of $20 per ceiling fan per month. Decorum has 25 units in inventory at the start of January. Assuming Decorum must produce enough ceiling fans to meet demand, how many ceiling fans should Decorum produce each month (using their regular labor force and/or temporary workers) over the course of the next year so as to maximize their total profit?

a. Visualize where you want to finish. What numbers will Decorum require? What are the decisions that need to be made? What should the objective be?

b. Suppose Decorum builds 450 ceiling fans in January and 550 (utilizing temporary workers) in February. Calculate by hand the total costs for January and February.

c. Make a rough sketch of a spreadsheet model, with blocks laid out for the data cells, changing cells, output cells, and objective cell.

E* d. Build a spreadsheet model for January and February and thoroughly test the model.

E* e. Build and solve a linear programming spreadsheet model to maximize the profit over all 12 months.

4.7. Allen Furniture is a manufacturer of hand-crafted furniture. At the start of January, Allen employs 20 trained craftspeople. They have forecasted their labor needs over the next 12 months as shown in the table below. Each trained craftsperson provides 200 labor-hours per month and is paid a wage of $3,000 per month. Hiring new craftspeople requires advertising, interviewing, and then training at a cost of $2,500 per hire. New hires are called apprentices for their first month. Apprentices spend their first month observing and learning. They are paid $2,000 for the month, but provide no labor. In their second month, apprentices are reclassified as trained craftspeople. The union contract allows for firing a craftsperson at the beginning of a month, but $1,500 must be given in severance pay. Moreover, at most 10% of the trained craftspeople can be fired in any month. Allen would like to start next year with at least 25 trained craftspeople. How many apprentices should be hired and how many craftspeople should be fired in each month to meet the labor requirements at the minimum possible cost?

a. Visualize where you want to finish. What numbers will Allen require? What are the decisions that need to be made? What should the objective be?

b. Suppose one apprentice is hired in January. Calculate by hand how many labor-hours would be available in January and February. Calculate by hand the total costs in January and February.

c. Make a rough sketch of a spreadsheet model, with blocks laid out for the data cells, changing cells, output cells, and objective cell.

E* d. Build a spreadsheet model for January and February and thoroughly test the model.

E* e. Build and solve a linear programming spreadsheet model to maximize the profit over all 12 months.

4.8. Refer to the scenario described in Problem 3.14 (Chapter 3), but ignore the instructions given there. Focus instead on using spreadsheet modeling to address Web Mercantile's problem by doing the following.

a. Visualize where you want to finish. What numbers will Web Mercantile require? What are the decisions that need to be made? What should the objective be?

b. Suppose that Web Mercantile were to lease 30,000 square feet for all five months and then 20,000 additional square feet for the last three months. Calculate the total costs by hand.

c. Make a rough sketch of a spreadsheet model, with blocks laid out for the data cells, changing cells, output cells, and objective cell.

E* d. Build a spreadsheet model for months 1 and 2, and then thoroughly test the model.

E* e. Expand the model to full scale, and then solve it.

4.9.* Refer to the scenario described in Problem 3.16 (Chapter 3), but ignore the instructions given there. Focus instead on using spreadsheet modeling to address Larry Edison's problem by doing the following.

a. Visualize where you want to finish. What numbers will Larry require? What are the decisions that need to be made? What should the objective be?

b. Suppose that Larry were to hire three full-time workers for the morning shift, two for the afternoon shift, and four for the evening shift, as well as three part-time workers for each of the four shifts. Calculate by hand how many workers would be working at each time of the day and what the total cost would be for the entire day.

c. Make a rough sketch of a spreadsheet model, with blocks laid out for the data cells, changing cells, output cells, and objective cell.

E* d. Build a spreadsheet model and then solve it.

4.10. Refer to the scenario described in Problem 3.19 (Chapter 3), but ignore the instructions given there. Focus instead on using spreadsheet modeling to address Al Ferris's problem by doing the following.

Labor Requirements (hours)

Jan.	Feb.	Mar.	Apr.	May	June	July	Aug.	Sept.	Oct.	Nov.	Dec.
3,400	4,000	4,200	4,200	3,000	2,800	3,000	4,000	4,500	5,000	5,200	4,800

a. Visualize where you want to finish. What numbers will Al require? What are the decisions that need to be made? What should the objective be?

b. Suppose that Al were to invest $20,000 each in investment A (year 1), investment B (year 2), and investment C (year 2). Calculate by hand what the ending cash position would be after each year.

c. Make a rough sketch of a spreadsheet model, with blocks laid out for the data cells, changing cells, output cells, and objective cell.

E* d. Build a spreadsheet model for years 1 through 3, and then thoroughly test the model.

E* e. Expand the model to full scale, and then solve it.

4.11. In contrast to the spreadsheet model for the Wyndor Glass Co. product-mix problem shown in Figure 4.6, the spreadsheet given below is an example of a poorly formulated spreadsheet model for this same problem. Referring to Section 4.3, identify the guidelines violated by the model below. Then, explain how each guideline has been violated and why the model in Figure 4.6 is a better alternative.

E*4.12. Refer to the spreadsheet file named "Everglade Problem 4.12" contained on the CD-ROM. This file contains a formulation of the Everglade problem considered in this chapter. However, three errors are included in this formulation. Use the ideas presented in Section 4.4 for debugging a spreadsheet model to find the errors. In particular, try different trial values for which you can predict the correct results, use the toggle to examine all the formulas, and use the auditing tools to check precedence and dependence relationships among the various changing cells, data cells, and output cells. Describe the errors found and how you found them.

E*4.13. Refer to the spreadsheet file named "Everglade Problem 4.13" contained on the CD-ROM. This file contains a formulation of the Everglade problem considered in this chapter. However, three errors are included in this formulation. Use the ideas presented in Section 4.4 for debugging a spreadsheet model to find the errors. In particular, try different trial values for which you can predict the correct results, use the toggle to examine all the formulas, and use the auditing tools to check precedence and dependence relationships among the various changing cells, data cells, and output cells. Describe the errors found and how you found them.

	A	B	C	D
1		**Wyndor Glass Co. (Poor Formulation)**		
2				
3		Doors Produced	2	
4		Windows Produced	6	
5		Hours Used (Plant 1)	2	
6		Hours Used (Plant 2)	12	
7		Hours Used (Plant 3)	18	
8		Total Profit	$3,600	

Solver Parameters

Set Objective Cell: C8
To: Max
By Changing Variable Cells:
   C3:C4
Subject to the Constraints:
   C5 <= 4
   C6 <= 12
   C7 <= 18
Solver Options:
   Make Variables Nonnegative
   Solving Method: Simplex LP

	B	C
5	Hours Used (Plant 1)	=1*C3+0*C4
6	Hours Used (Plant 2)	=0*C3+2*C4
7	Hours Used (Plant 3)	=3*C3+2*C4
8	Total Profit	=300*C3+500*C4

Case 4-1

Prudent Provisions for Pensions

Among its many financial products, the Prudent Financial Services Corporation (normally referred to as PFS) manages a well-regarded pension fund that is used by a number of companies to provide pensions for their employees. PFS's management takes pride in the rigorous professional standards used in operating the fund. Since the near-collapse of the financial markets during the protracted Great Recession that began in late 2007, PFS has redoubled its efforts to provide prudent management of the fund.

It is now December 2013. The total pension payments that will need to be made by the fund over the next 10 years are shown in the following table.

Year	Pension Payments ($ millions)
2014	8
2015	12
2016	13
2017	14
2018	16
2019	17
2020	20
2021	21
2022	22
2023	24

By using interest as well, PFS currently has enough liquid assets to meet all these pension payments. Therefore, to safeguard the pension fund, PFS would like to make a number of investments whose payouts would match the pension payments over the next 10 years. The only investments that PFS trusts for the pension fund are a money market fund and bonds. The money market fund pays an annual interest rate of 2 percent. The characteristics of each unit of the four bonds under consideration are shown in the table below.

	Current Price	Coupon Rate	Maturity Date	Face Value
Bond 1	$980	4%	Jan. 1, 2015	$1,000
Bond 2	920	2	Jan. 1, 2017	1,000
Bond 3	750	0	Jan. 1, 2019	1,000
Bond 4	800	3	Jan. 1, 2022	1,000

All of these bonds will be available for purchase on January 1, 2014, in as many units as desired. The coupon rate is the percentage of the face value that will be paid in interest on January 1 of each year, starting one year after purchase and continuing until (and including) the maturity date. Thus, these interest payments on January 1 of each year are in time to be used toward the pension payments for that year. Any excess interest payments will be deposited into the money market fund. To be conservative in its financial planning, PFS assumes that all the pension payments for the year occur at the beginning of the year immediately after these interest payments (including a year's interest from the money market fund) are received. The entire face value of a bond also will be received on its maturity date. Since the current price of each bond is less than its face value, the actual yield of the bond exceeds its coupon rate. Bond 3 is a zero-coupon bond, so it pays no interest but instead pays a face value on the maturity date that greatly exceeds the purchase price.

PFS would like to make the smallest possible investment (including any deposit into the money market fund) on January 1, 2014, to cover all its required pension payments through 2023. Some spreadsheet modeling needs to be done to see how to do this.

a. Visualize where you want to finish. What numbers are needed by PFS management? What are the decisions that need to be made? What should the objective be?

b. Suppose that PFS were to invest $30 million in the money market fund and purchase 10,000 units each of bond 1 and bond 2 on January 1, 2014. Calculate by hand the payments received from bonds 1 and 2 on January 1 of 2015 and 2016. Also calculate the resulting balance in the money market fund on January 1 of 2014, 2015, and 2016 after receiving these payments, making the pension payments for the year, and depositing any excess into the money market fund.

c. Make a rough sketch of a spreadsheet model, with blocks laid out for the data cells, changing cells, output cells, and objective cell.

d. Build a spreadsheet model for years 2014 through 2016, and then thoroughly test the model.

e. Expand the model to consider all years through 2023, and then solve it.

Additional Case

Additional cases for this chapter also are available at the University of Western Ontario Ivey School of Business website, **cases.ivey.uwo.ca/cases,** in the segment of the CaseMate area designated for this book.

Chapter **Five**

What-If Analysis for Linear Programming

Learning Objectives

After completing this chapter, you should be able to

1. Explain what is meant by *what-if analysis.*
2. Summarize the benefits of what-if analysis.
3. Enumerate the different kinds of changes in the model that can be considered by what-if analysis.
4. Describe how the spreadsheet formulation of the problem can be used to perform any of these kinds of what-if analysis.
5. Use Parameters with Risk Solver Platform for Education (RSPE) to systematically investigate the effect of changing either one or two data cells to various other trial values.
6. Find how much any single coefficient in the objective function can change without changing the optimal solution.
7. Evaluate simultaneous changes in objective function coefficients to determine whether the changes are small enough that the original optimal solution must still be optimal.
8. Predict how the value in the objective cell would change if a small change were to be made in the right-hand side of one or more of the functional constraints.
9. Find how much the right-hand side of a single functional constraint can change before this prediction becomes no longer valid.
10. Evaluate simultaneous changes in right-hand sides to determine whether the changes are small enough that this prediction must still be valid.

Chapters 2 to 4 have described and illustrated how to formulate a linear programming model on a spreadsheet to represent a variety of managerial problems, and then how to use Solver to find an optimal solution for this model. You might think that this would finish our story about linear programming: Once the manager learns the optimal solution, she would immediately implement this solution and then turn her attention to other matters. However, this is not the case. The enlightened manager demands much more from linear programming, and linear programming has much more to offer her—as you will discover in this chapter.

An optimal solution is only optimal with respect to a particular mathematical model that provides only a rough representation of the real problem. A manager is interested in much more than just finding such a solution. The purpose of a linear programming study is to help guide management's final decision by providing insights into the likely consequences of pursuing various managerial options under a variety of assumptions about future conditions. Most of the important insights are gained while conducting analysis *after* finding an optimal solution for the original version of the basic model. This analysis is commonly referred to as **what-if analysis** because it involves addressing some questions about *what* would happen to the optimal solution *if* different assumptions were made about future conditions. Spreadsheets play a central role in addressing these *what-if questions.*

This chapter focuses on the types of information provided by what-if analysis and why it is valuable to managers. The first section provides an overview. Section 5.2 returns to the Wyndor Glass Co. product-mix case study (Section 2.1) to describe the what-if analysis that is needed in this situation. The subsequent sections then perform this what-if analysis, using a variety of procedures that are applicable to any linear programming problem.

5.1 THE IMPORTANCE OF WHAT-IF ANALYSIS TO MANAGERS

In real applications, many of the numbers in the model may be only rough estimates.

The examples and problems in the preceding chapters on linear programming have provided the data needed to determine precisely all the numbers that should go into the data cells for the spreadsheet formulation of the linear programming model. (Recall that these numbers are referred to as the **parameters of the model.**) Real applications seldom are this straightforward. Substantial time and effort often are needed to track down the needed data. Even then, it may be possible to develop only rough estimates of the parameters of the model.

For example, in the Wyndor case study, two key parameters of the model are the coefficients in the objective function that represent the unit profits of the two new products. These parameters were estimated to be $300 for the doors and $500 for the windows. However, these unit profits depend on many factors—the costs of raw materials, production, shipping, advertising, and so on, as well as such things as the market reception to the new products and the amount of competition encountered. Some of these factors cannot be estimated with real accuracy until long after the linear programming study has been completed and the new products have been on the market for some time.

Therefore, before Wyndor's management makes a decision on the product mix, it will want to know what the effect would be if the unit profits turn out to differ significantly from the estimates. For example, would the optimal solution change if the unit profit for the doors turned out to be $200 instead of the estimate of $300? How inaccurate can the estimate be in either direction before the optimal solution changes?

Such questions are addressed in Section 5.3 when only one estimate is inaccurate. Section 5.4 will address similar questions when multiple estimates are inaccurate.

What happens to the optimal solution if an error is made in estimating a parameter of the model?

If the optimal solution will remain the same over a wide range of values for a particular coefficient in the objective function, then management will be content with a fairly rough estimate for this coefficient. On the other hand, if even a small error in the estimate would change the optimal solution, then management will want to take special care to refine this estimate. Management sometimes will get involved directly in adjusting such estimates to its satisfaction.

Here then is a summary of the first benefit of what-if analysis:

1. Typically, many of the parameters of a linear programming model are only *estimates* of quantities (e.g., unit profits) that cannot be determined precisely at this time. What-if analysis reveals how close each of these estimates needs to be to avoid obtaining an erroneous optimal solution, and therefore pinpoints the **sensitive parameters** (those parameters where extra care is needed to refine their estimates because even small changes in their values can change the optimal solution).

Several sections describe how what-if analysis provides this benefit for the most important parameters. Sections 5.3 and 5.4 do this for the coefficients in the objective function (these numbers typically appear in the spreadsheet in the row for the unit contribution of each activity toward the overall measure of performance). Sections 5.5 and 5.6 do the same for the *right-hand sides of the functional constraints* (these are the numbers that typically are in the right-hand column of the spreadsheet just to the right of the $\leq$, $\geq$, or $=$ signs).

Businesses operate in a dynamic environment. Even when management is satisfied with the current estimates and implements the corresponding optimal solution, conditions may change later. For example, suppose that Wyndor's management is satisfied with $300 as the estimate of the unit profit for the doors, but increased competition later forces a price reduction that reduces this unit profit. Does this change the optimal product mix? The what-if analysis shown in Section 5.3 immediately indicates in advance which new unit profits would leave the optimal product mix unchanged, which can help guide management in its new

What happens to the optimal solution if conditions change in the future?

pricing decision. Furthermore, if the optimal product mix is unchanged, then there is no need to solve the model again with the new coefficient. Avoiding solving the model again is no big deal for the tiny two-variable Wyndor problem, but it is extremely welcome for real applications that may have hundreds or thousands of constraints and variables. In fact, for such large models, it may not even be practical to re-solve the model repeatedly to consider the many possible changes of interest.

Thus, here is the second benefit of what-if analysis:

2. If conditions change after the study has been completed (a common occurrence), what-if analysis leaves signposts that indicate (without solving the model again) whether a resulting change in a parameter of the model changes the optimal solution.

Again, several subsequent sections describe how what-if analysis does this.

These sections focus on studying how changes in the parameters of a linear programming model affect the optimal solution. This type of what-if analysis commonly is referred to as **sensitivity analysis,** because it involves checking how *sensitive* the optimal solution is to the value of each parameter. Sensitivity analysis is a vital part of what-if analysis.

However, rather than being content with the passive sensitivity analysis approach of checking the effect of parameter estimates being inaccurate, what-if analysis often goes further to take a proactive approach. An analysis may be made of various possible managerial actions that would result in changes to the model.

A prime example of this proactive approach arises when certain parameters of the model represent *managerial policy decisions* rather than quantities that are largely outside the control of management. For example, for the Wyndor product-mix problem, the right-hand sides of the three functional constraints (4, 12, 18) represent the number of hours of production time in the three respective plants being made available per week for the production of the two new products. Management can change these three resource amounts by altering the production levels for the old products in these plants. Therefore, after learning the optimal solution, management will want to know the impact on the profit from the new products if these resource amounts are changed in certain ways. One key question is how much this profit can be increased by increasing the available production time for the new products in just one of the plants. Another is how much this profit can be increased by simultaneously making helpful changes in the available production times in all the plants. If the profit from the new products can be increased enough to more than compensate for the profit lost by decreasing the production levels for certain old products, management probably will want to make the change.

What happens if managerial policy decisions change?

We now can summarize the third benefit of what-if analysis:

3. When certain parameters of the model represent managerial policy decisions, what-if analysis provides valuable guidance to management regarding the impact of altering these policy decisions.

Sections 5.5 and 5.6 will explore this benefit further.

What-if analysis sometimes goes even further in providing helpful guidance to management, such as when analyzing alternate scenarios for how business conditions might evolve. However, this chapter will focus on the three benefits summarized above.

Review *Questions*

1. What are the *parameters* of a linear programming model?
2. How can inaccuracies arise in the parameters of a model?
3. What does what-if analysis reveal about the parameters of a model that are only estimates?
4. Is it always inappropriate to make only a fairly rough estimate for a parameter of a model? Why?
5. How is it possible for the parameters of a model to be accurate initially and then become inaccurate at a later date?
6. How does what-if analysis help management prepare for changing conditions?
7. What is meant by *sensitivity analysis?*
8. For what kinds of managerial policy decisions does what-if analysis provide guidance?

5.2 CONTINUING THE WYNDOR CASE STUDY

We now return to the case study introduced in Section 2.1 involving the Wyndor Glass Co. product-mix problem.

To review briefly, recall that the company is preparing to introduce two new products:

- An 8-foot glass door with aluminum framing.
- A 4-foot × 6-foot double-hung wood-framed window.

To analyze which mix of the two products would be most profitable, the company's Management Science Group introduced two decision variables:

D = Production rate of this new kind of door

W = Production rate of this new kind of window

where this rate measures the number of units produced per week. Three plants will be involved in the production of these products. Based on managerial decisions regarding how much these plants will continue to be used to produce current products, the number of hours of production time per week being made available in Plants 1, 2, and 3 for the new products is 4, 12, and 18, respectively. After obtaining rough estimates that the profit per unit will be $300 for the doors and $500 for the windows, the Management Science Group then formulated the linear programming model shown in Figure 2.13 and repeated here in Figure 5.1, where the objective is to choose the values of D and W in the changing cells UnitsProduced (C12:D12) so as to maximize the total profit (per week) given in the objective cell TotalProfit (G12). Applying Solver to this model yielded the optimal solution shown on this spreadsheet and summarized as follows.

Optimal Solution

$D = 2$ (Produce 2 doors per week.)

$W = 6$ (Produce 6 windows per week.)

Profit = 3,600   (The estimated total weekly profit is $3,600.)

However, this optimal solution assumes that all the estimates that provide the parameters of the model (as shown in the UnitProfit (C4:D4), HoursUsedPerUnitProduced (C7:D9), and HoursAvailable (G7:G9) data cells) are accurate.

The head of the Management Science Group, Lisa Taylor, now is ready to meet with management to discuss the group's recommendation that the above product mix be used.

Management's Discussion of the Recommended Product Mix

Lisa Taylor (head of Management Science Group): I asked for this meeting so we could explore what questions the two of you would like us to pursue further. In particular, I am especially concerned that we weren't able to better pin down just what the numbers should be to go into our model. Which estimates do you think are the shakiest?

Bill Tasto (vice president for manufacturing): Without question, the estimates of the unit profits for the two products. Since the products haven't gone into production yet, all we could do is analyze the data from similar current products and then try to project what the changes would be for these new products. We have some numbers, but they are pretty rough. We would need to do a lot more work to pin down the numbers better.

John Hill (president): We may need to do that. Lisa, do you have a way of checking how far off one of these estimates can be without changing the optimal product mix?

The allowable range for a unit profit indicates how far its estimate can be off without affecting the optimal product mix.

Lisa: Yes, we do. We can quickly find what we call the *allowable range* for each unit profit. As long as the true value of the unit profit is within this allowable range, and the other unit profit is correct, the optimal product mix will not change. If this range is pretty wide, you don't need to worry about refining the estimate of the unit profit. However, if the range is quite narrow, then it is important to pin down the estimate more closely.

154   Chapter Five   *What-If Analysis for Linear Programming*

FIGURE 5.1

The spreadsheet model and its optimal solution for the original Wyndor problem before beginning what-if analysis.

	A	B	C	D	E	F	G
1		**Wyndor Glass Co. Product-Mix Problem**					
2							
3			Doors	Windows			
4		Unit Profit	$300	$500			
5					Hours		Hours
6			Hours Used per Unit Produced		Used		Available
7		Plant 1	1	0	2	≤	4
8		Plant 2	0	2	12	≤	12
9		Plant 3	3	2	18	≤	18
10							
11			Doors	Windows			Total Profit
12		Units Produced	2	6			$3,600

Solver Parameters

Set Objective Cell: TotalProfit
To: Max
By Changing Variable Cells:
    UnitsProduced
Subject to the Constraints:
    HoursUsed <= HoursAvailable

Solver Options:
    Make Variables Nonnegative
    Solving Method: Simplex LP

	E
5	Hours
6	Used
7	=SUMPRODUCT(C7:D7, UnitsProduced)
8	=SUMPRODUCT(C8:D8, UnitsProduced)
9	=SUMPRODUCT(C9:D9, UnitsProduced)

	G
11	Total Profit
12	=SUMPRODUCT(UnitProfit, UnitsProduced)

Range Name	Cells
DoorsProduced	C12
HoursAvailable	G7:G9
HoursUsed	E7:E9
HoursUsedPerUnitProduced	C7:D9
TotalProfit	G12
UnitProfit	C4:D4
UnitsProduced	C12:D12
WindowsProduced	D12

John: What happens if both estimates are off?

Lisa: We can provide a way of checking whether the optimal product mix might change for any new combination of unit profits you think might be the true one.

John: Great. That's what we need. There's also one more thing. Bill gave you the numbers for how many hours of production time we're making available per week in the three plants for these new products. I noticed you used these numbers on your spreadsheet.

Lisa: Yes. They're the right-hand sides of our constraints. Is something wrong with these numbers?

John: No, not at all. I just wanted to let you know that we haven't made a final decision on whether these are the numbers we want to use. We would like your group to provide us with some analysis of what the effect would be if we change any of those numbers. How much more profit could we get from the new products for each additional hour of production time per week we provide in one of the plants? That sort of thing.

Lisa: Yes, we can get that analysis to you right away also.

John: We might also be interested in changing the available production hours for two or three of the plants.

Lisa: No problem. We'll give you information about that as well.

Summary of Management's What-If Questions

Here is a summary of John Hill's what-if questions that Lisa and her group will be addressing in the coming sections.

1. What happens if the estimate of the unit profit of one of Wyndor's new products is inaccurate? (Section 5.3)
2. What happens if the estimates of the unit profits of both of Wyndor's new products are inaccurate? (Section 5.4)
3. What happens if a change is made in the number of hours of production time per week being made available to Wyndor's new products in one of the plants? (Section 5.5)
4. What happens if simultaneous changes are made in the number of hours of production time per week being made available to Wyndor's new products in all the plants? (Section 5.6)

Review
Questions

1. Which estimates of the parameters in the linear programming model for the Wyndor problem are most questionable?
2. Which numbers in this model represent tentative managerial decisions that management might want to change after receiving the Management Science Group's analysis?

5.3 THE EFFECT OF CHANGES IN ONE OBJECTIVE FUNCTION COEFFICIENT

Section 5.1 began by discussing the fact that many of the parameters of a linear programming model typically are only *estimates* of quantities that cannot be determined precisely at the time. What-if analysis (or *sensitivity analysis* in particular) reveals how close each of these estimates needs to be to avoid obtaining an erroneous optimal solution.

We focus in this section on how sensitivity analysis does this when the parameters involved are *coefficients in the objective function*. (Recall that each of these coefficients gives the *unit contribution* of one of the activities toward the overall measure of performance.) In the process, we will address the first of the what-if questions posed by Wyndor management in the preceding section.

Question 1: What happens if the estimate of the unit profit of one of Wyndor's new products is inaccurate?

To start this process, first consider the question of what happens if the estimate of $300 for the unit profit for Wyndor's new kind of door is inaccurate. To address this question, let

P_D = Unit profit for the new kind of door

= Cell C4 in the spreadsheet (see Figure 5.1)

Although $P_D = \$300$ in the current version of Wyndor's linear programming model, we now want to explore how much larger or how much smaller P_D can be and still have $(D, W) = (2, 6)$ as the optimal solution. In other words, how much can the estimate of $300 for the unit profit for these doors be off before the model will give an erroneous optimal solution?

Using the Spreadsheet to Do Sensitivity Analysis

One of the great strengths of a spreadsheet is the ease with which it can be used interactively to perform various kinds of what-if analysis, including the sensitivity analysis being considered in this section. Once Solver has been set up to obtain an optimal solution, you can immediately find out what would happen if one of the parameters of the model were to be changed to some other value. All you have to do is make this change on the spreadsheet and then run Solver again.

Run Solver again and the spreadsheet immediately reveals the effect of changing any values in the data cells.

To illustrate, Figure 5.2 shows what would happen if the unit profit for doors were to be decreased from $P_D = \$300$ to $P_D = \$200$. Comparing with Figure 5.1, there is no change at all in the optimal solution. In fact, the *only* changes in the new spreadsheet are the new value of P_D in cell C4 and a decrease of $200 in the total profit shown in cell G12 (because each

FIGURE 5.2

The revised Wyndor problem where the estimate of the unit profit for doors has been decreased from $P_D = \$300$ to $P_D = \$200$, but no change occurs in the optimal solution.

	A	B	C	D	E	F	G
1		**Wyndor Glass Co. Product-Mix Problem**					
2							
3			Doors	Windows			
4		Unit Profit	$200	$500			
5					Hours		Hours
6			Hours Used per Unit Produced		Used		Available
7		Plant 1	1	0	2	≤	4
8		Plant 2	0	2	12	≤	12
9		Plant 3	3	2	18	≤	18
10							
11			Doors	Windows			Total Profit
12		Units Produced	2	6			$3,400

FIGURE 5.3

The revised Wyndor problem where the estimate of the unit profit for doors has been increased from $P_D = \$300$ to $P_D = \$500$, but no change occurs in the optimal solution.

	A	B	C	D	E	F	G
1		**Wyndor Glass Co. Product-Mix Problem**					
2							
3			Doors	Windows			
4		Unit Profit	$500	$500			
5					Hours		Hours
6			Hours Used per Unit Produced		Used		Available
7		Plant 1	1	0	2	≤	4
8		Plant 2	0	2	12	≤	12
9		Plant 3	3	2	18	≤	18
10							
11			Doors	Windows			Total Profit
12		Units Produced	2	6			$4,000

of the two doors produced per week provides $100 less profit). Because the optimal solution does not change, we now know that the original estimate of $P_D = \$300$ can be considerably *too high* without invalidating the model's optimal solution.

But what happens if this estimate is *too low* instead? Figure 5.3 shows what would happen if P_D were to be increased to $P_D = \$500$. Again, there is no change in the optimal solution.

Because the original value of $P_D = \$300$ can be changed considerably in either direction without changing the optimal solution, P_D is said to be *not a sensitive parameter.* It is not necessary to pin down this estimate with great accuracy to have confidence that the model is providing the correct optimal solution.

This may be all the information that is needed about P_D. However, if there is a good possibility that the true value of P_D will turn out to be outside this broad range from $200 to $500, further investigation would be desirable. How much higher or lower can P_D be before the optimal solution would change?

Figure 5.4 demonstrates that the optimal solution would indeed change if P_D were increased all the way up to $P_D = \$1,000$. Thus, we now know that this change occurs somewhere between $500 and $1,000 during the process of increasing P_D.

Using a Parameter Analysis Report (RSPE) to Do Sensitivity Analysis Systematically

To pin down just when the optimal solution will change, we could continue selecting new values of P_D at random. However, a better approach is to systematically consider a range of values of P_D.

FIGURE 5.4

The revised Wyndor problem where the estimate of the unit profit for doors has been increased from $P_D = \$300$ to $P_D = \$1,000$, which results in a change in the optimal solution.

	A	B	C	D	E	F	G
1		**Wyndor Glass Co. Product-Mix Problem**					
2							
3			Doors	Windows			
4		Unit Profit	$1,000	$500			
5					Hours		Hours
6			Hours Used per Unit Produced		Used		Available
7		Plant 1	1	0	4	≤	4
8		Plant 2	0	2	6	≤	12
9		Plant 3	3	2	18	≤	18
10							
11			Doors	Windows			Total Profit
12		Units Produced	4	3			$5,500

The Risk Solver Platform for Education (RSPE), first introduced in Section 2.6, can generate a *parameter analysis report* that is designed to do just this sort of analysis. Instructions for installing RSPE are on a supplementary insert included with the book and also on the book's website, **www.mhhe.com/hillier5e**.

The data cell containing a parameter that will be systematically varied (C4 in this case) is referred to as a **parameter cell**. A parameter analysis report is used to show the results in the changing cells and/or the objective cell for various trial values in the parameter cell. For each trial value, these results are obtained by using Solver to re-solve the problem.

To generate a parameter analysis report, the first step is to define the parameter cell. In this case, select cell C4 (the unit profit for doors) and choose Optimization under the Parameters menu on the RSPE ribbon. In the parameter cell dialog box, shown in Figure 5.5, enter the range of trial values for the parameter cell. The entries shown specify that P_D will be systematically varied from $100 to $1,000. If desired, additional parameter cells could be defined in this same way, but we will not do so at this point.

Next choose Optimization > Parameter Analysis under the Reports menu on the RSPE ribbon. This brings up the dialog box shown in Figure 5.6 that allows you to specify which parameter cells to vary and which results to show. The choice of which parameter cells to vary is made under Parameters in the bottom half of the dialog box. Clicking on (>>) will select all of the parameter cells defined so far (moving them to the box on the right). In the Wyndor example, only one parameter has been defined, so this causes the single parameter cell (UnitProfitPerDoor) to appear on the right. If more parameter cells had been defined, particular parameter cells can be chosen for immediate analysis by clicking on the + next

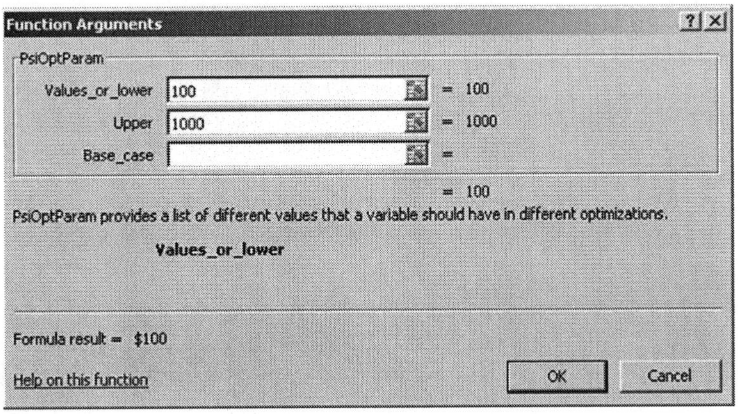

FIGURE 5.5

The parameter cell dialog box for P_D specifies here that this parameter cell for the Wyndor problem will be systematically varied from $100 to $1,000.

FIGURE 5.6

The dialog box for the parameter analysis report specifies here for the Wyndor problem that the UnitProfitPerDoor parameter cell will be varied and that results from all the changing cells (DoorsProduced and WindowsProduced) and the objective cell (Total-Profit) will be shown.

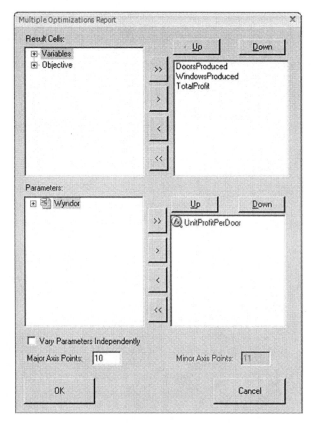

to Wyndor to reveal the list of parameter cells that have been defined in the Wyndor spreadsheet. Clicking on (>) then moves individual parameter cells to the list on the right.

The choice of which results to show as the parameter cell is varied is made in the upper half of the dialog box. Clicking on (>>) will cause *all* of the changing cells (DoorsProduced and WindowsProduced) and the objective cell (Total Profit) to appear in the list on the right. To instead choose a subset of these cells, click on the small + next to Variables (or Objective) to reveal a list of all the changing cells (or objective cell) and then click on > to move that changing cell (or objective cell) to the right.

Finally, enter the number of Major Axis Points to specify how many different values of the parameter cell will be shown in the parameter analysis report. The values will be spread evenly between the lower and upper values specified in the parameters cell dialog box in Figure 5.5. With 10 major axis points, a lower value of $100, and an upper value of $1000, the parameter analysis report will show results for P_D of $100, $200, $300,. . . , $1000.

Clicking on the OK button generates the parameter analysis report shown in Figure 5.7. One at a time, the trial values listed in the first column of the table are put into the parameter cell (UnitProfitPerDoor) and then Solver is called on to re-solve the problem. The optimal results for that particular trial value of the parameter cell are then shown in the remaining columns—DoorsProduced, WindowsProduced, and TotalProfit. This is repeated automatically for each remaining trial value of the parameter cell. The end result (which happens very quickly for small problems) is the completely-filled-in parameter analysis report shown in Figure 5.7.

The allowable range for a coefficient in the objective function is the range of values for this coefficient over which the optimal solution for the original model remains optimal.

The parameter analysis report reveals that the optimal solution remains the same all the way from $P_D = $100 (and perhaps lower) to $P_D = $700, but that a change occurs somewhere between $700 and $800. We next could systematically consider values of P_D between $700 and $800 to determine more closely where the optimal solution changes. However, here is a shortcut. The range of values of P_D over which $(D, W) = (2, 6)$ remains as the optimal solution is referred to as the **allowable range for an objective function coefficient,** or

FIGURE 5.7
The parameter analysis report that shows the effect of systematically varying the estimate of the unit profit for doors for the Wyndor problem.

	A	B	C	D
1	UnitProfitPerDoor	DoorsProduced	WindowsProduced	TotalProfit
2	$100	2	6	$3,200
3	$200	2	6	$3,400
4	$300	2	6	$3,600
5	$400	2	6	$3,800
6	$500	2	6	$4,000
7	$600	2	6	$4,200
8	$700	2	6	$4,400
9	$800	4	3	$4,700
10	$900	4	3	$5,100
11	$1,000	4	3	$5,500

FIGURE 5.8
Part of the sensitivity report generated by Solver for the original Wyndor problem (Figure 5.1), where the last three columns enable identifying the allowable ranges for the unit profits for doors and windows.

Variable Cells

Cell	Name	Final Value	Reduced Cost	Objective Coefficient	Allowable Increase	Allowable Decrease
$C$12	DoorsProduced	2	0	300	450	300
$D$12	WindowsProduced	6	0	500	1E + 30	300

just the **allowable range** for short. Upon request, Solver will provide a report called the *sensitivity report* that reveals exactly what this allowable range is.

Using the Sensitivity Report to Find the Allowable Range

As was shown in Figure 2.12, when Solver gives the message that it has found a solution, it also gives on the right a list of three reports that can be provided. By selecting the second one (labeled Sensitivity), you will obtain the sensitivity report.

Reduced costs are described in the supplement to this chapter on the CD-ROM. Don't worry about this relatively technical subject (unless your instructor assigns this supplement).

Figure 5.8 shows the relevant part of this report for the Wyndor problem. The Final Value column indicates the optimal solution. The next column gives the *reduced costs,* which can provide some useful information when any of the changing cells equal zero in the optimal solution, which is not the case here. (For a zero-valued changing cell, the corresponding reduced cost can be used to determine what the effect would be of either increasing that changing cell or making a change in its coefficient in the objective function. Because of the relatively technical nature of these interpretations of reduced costs, we will not discuss them further here, but will provide a full explanation in the supplement to this chapter on the CD-ROM.) The next three columns provide the information needed to identify the *allowable range* for each coefficient in the objective function. The Objective Coefficient column gives the current value of each coefficient, and then the next two columns give the *allowable increase* and the *allowable decrease* from this value to remain within the allowable range.

The sensitivity report generated by Solver reveals the allowable range for each coefficient in the objective function.

For example, consider P_D, the coefficient of D in the objective function. Since D is the production rate for these special doors, the Doors row in the table provides the following information (without the dollar sign) about P_D:

Current value of P_D:	300	
Allowable increase in P_D:	450	So $P_D \leq 300 + 450 = 750$
Allowable decrease in P_D:	300	So $P_D \geq 300 - 300 = 0$
Allowable range for P_D:	$0 \leq P_D \leq 750$	

FIGURE 5.9

The two dashed lines that pass through solid constraint boundary lines are the objective function lines when P_D (the unit profit for doors) is at an endpoint of its allowable range, $0 \leq P_D \leq 750$, since either line or any objective function line in between still yields $(D, W) = (2, 6)$ as an optimal solution for the Wyndor problem.

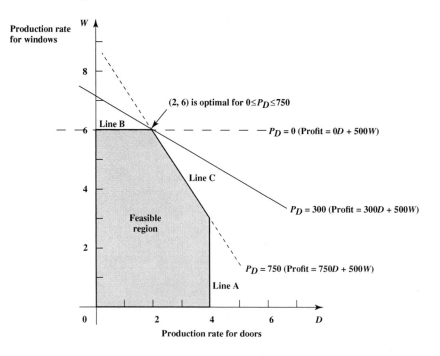

Therefore, if P_D is changed from its current value (without making any other change in the model), the current solution $(D, W) = (2, 6)$ will remain optimal so long as the new value of P_D is within this allowable range.

Figure 5.9 provides graphical insight into this allowable range. For the original value of $P_D = 300$, the solid line in the figure shows the slope of the objective function line passing through $(2, 6)$. At the lower end of the allowable range, when $P_D = 0$, the objective function line that passes through $(2, 6)$ now is line B in the figure, so every point on the line segment between $(0, 6)$ and $(2, 6)$ is an optimal solution. For any value of $P_D < 0$, the objective function line will have rotated even further so that $(0, 6)$ becomes the only optimal solution. At the upper end of the allowable range, when $P_D = 750$, the objective function line that passes through $(2, 6)$ becomes line C, so every point on the line segment between $(2, 6)$ and $(4, 3)$ becomes an optimal solution. For any value of $P_D > 750$, the objective function line is even steeper than line C, so $(4, 3)$ becomes the only optimal solution.

Check out this module in the Interactive Management Science Modules to gain graphical insight into the allowable range.

The module called *Graphical Linear Programming and Sensitivity Analysis* in the Interactive Management Science Modules (available at **www.mhhe.com/hillier5e/** or in your CD-ROM) is designed to help you perform this kind of graphical analysis. After you enter the model for the original Wyndor problem, the module provides you with the graph shown in Figure 5.9 (without the dashed lines). You then can simply drag one end of the objective function line up or down to see how far you can increase or decrease P_D before $(D, W) = (2, 6)$ will no longer be optimal.

Conclusion: The allowable range for P_D is $0 \leq P_D \leq 750$, because $(D, W) = (2, 6)$ remains optimal over this range but not beyond. (When $P_D = 0$ or $P_D = 750$, there are multiple optimal solutions, but $(D, W) = (2, 6)$ still is one of them.) With the range this wide around the original estimate of \$300 $(P_D = 300)$ for the unit profit for doors, we can be quite confident of obtaining the correct optimal solution for the true unit profit even though the discussion in Section 5.2 indicates that this estimate is fairly rough.

The sensitivity report also can be used to find the allowable range for the unit profit for Wyndor's other new product. In particular, let

P_W = Unit profit for Wyndor's new kind of window

= Cell D4 in the spreadsheet

Referring to the Windows row of the sensitivity report (Figure 5.8), this row indicates that the allowable decrease in P_W is 300 (so $P_W \geq 500 - 300 = 200$) and the allowable increase is 1E + 30. What is meant by 1E + 30? This is shorthand in Excel for 10^{30} (1 with 30 zeroes after it). This tremendously huge number is used by Excel to represent *infinity*. Therefore, the allowable range of P_W is obtained from the sensitivity report as follows:

Current value of P_W:	500	
Allowable increase in P_W:	Unlimited	So P_W has no upper limit
Allowable decrease in P_W:	300	So $P_W \geq 500 - 300 = 200$
Allowable range:	$P_W \geq 200$	

The allowable range is quite wide for both objective function coefficients. Thus, even though $P_D = \$300$ and $P_W = \$500$ were only rough estimates of the true unit profit for the doors and windows, respectively, we can still be confident that we have obtained the correct optimal solution.

We are not always so lucky. For some linear programming problems, even a small change in the value of certain coefficients in the objective function can change the optimal solution. Such coefficients are referred to as *sensitive parameters*. The sensitivity report will immediately indicate which of the objective function coefficients (if any) are sensitive parameters. These are parameters that have a small allowable increase and/or a small allowable decrease. Hence, extra care should be taken to refine these estimates.

> A parameter is considered sensitive if even a small change in its value can change the optimal solution.

Once this has been done and the final version of the model has been solved, the allowable ranges continue to serve an important purpose. As indicated in Section 5.1, the second benefit of what-if analysis is that if conditions change after the study has been completed (a common occurrence), what-if analysis leaves signposts that indicate (without solving the model again) whether a resulting change in a parameter of the model changes the optimal solution. Thus, if weeks, months, or even years later, the unit profit for one of Wyndor's new products changes substantially, its allowable range indicates immediately whether the old optimal product mix still is the appropriate one to use. Being able to draw an affirmative conclusion without reconstructing and solving the revised model is extremely helpful for any linear programming problem, but especially so when the model is a large one.

Review Questions

1. What is meant by the *allowable range* for a coefficient in the objective function?
2. What is the significance if the true value for a coefficient in the objective function turns out to be so different from its estimate that it lies outside its allowable range?
3. In Solver's sensitivity report, what is the interpretation of the Objective Coefficient column? The Allowable Increase column? The Allowable Decrease column?

5.4   THE EFFECT OF SIMULTANEOUS CHANGES IN OBJECTIVE FUNCTION COEFFICIENTS

The coefficients in the objective function typically represent quantities (e.g., unit profits) that can only be estimated because of considerable uncertainty about what their true values will turn out to be. The allowable ranges described in the preceding section deal with this uncertainty by focusing on just one coefficient at a time. In effect, the allowable range for a particular coefficient assumes that the original estimates for all the other coefficients are completely accurate so that this coefficient is the only one whose true value may differ from its original estimate.

In actuality, the estimates for *all* the coefficients (or at least more than one of them) may be inaccurate simultaneously. The crucial question is whether this is likely to result in obtaining the wrong optimal solution. If so, greater care should be taken to refine these estimates as much as possible, at least for the more crucial coefficients. On the other hand, if what-if analysis reveals that the anticipated errors in estimating the coefficients are unlikely to affect the optimal solution, then management can be reassured that the current linear programming model and its results are providing appropriate guidance.

An Application Vignette

The **Pacific Lumber Company (PALCO)** is a large timber-holding company with headquarters in Scotia, California. The company has over 200,000 acres of highly productive forest lands that support five mills located in Humboldt County in northern California. The lands include some of the most spectacular redwood groves in the world that have been given or sold at low cost to be preserved as parks. PALCO manages the remaining lands intensively for sustained timber production, subject to strong forest practice laws. Since PALCO's forests are home to many species of wildlife, including endangered species such as spotted owls and marbled murrelets, the provisions of the federal Endangered Species Act also need to be carefully observed.

To obtain a sustained yield plan for the entire land-holding, PALCO management contracted with a team of management science consultants to develop a 120-year, 12-period, long-term forest ecosystem management plan. The management science team performed this task by formulating and applying a linear programming model to optimize the company's overall timberland operations and profitability after satisfying the various constraints. The model was a huge one with approximately 8,500 functional constraints and 353,000 decision variables.

A major challenge in applying the linear programming model was the many uncertainties in estimating what the parameters of the model should be. The major factors causing these uncertainties were the continuing fluctuations in market supply and demand, logging costs, and environmental regulations. Therefore, the management science team made extensive use of *detailed sensitivity analysis*. The resulting sustained yield plan *increased the company's present net worth by over* **$398 million** while also generating a better mix of wildlife habitat acres.

Source: L. R. Fletcher, H. Alden, S. P. Holmen, D. P. Angelis, and M. J. Etzenhouser, "Long-Term Forest Ecosystem Planning at Pacific Lumber," *Interfaces* 29, no. 1 (January–February 1999), pp. 90–112. (A link to this article is provided on our website, **www.mhhe.com/hillier5e.**)

This section focuses on how to determine, without solving the problem again, whether the optimal solution might change if certain changes occur simultaneously in the coefficients of the objective function (due to their true values differing from their estimates). In the process, we will address the second of Wyndor management's what-if questions.

Question 2: What happens if the estimates of the unit profits of both of Wyndor's new products are inaccurate?

Using the Spreadsheet for This Analysis

Once again, a quick-and-easy way to address this kind of question is to simply try out different estimates on the spreadsheet formulation of the model and see what happens each time after running Solver again.

In this case, the optimal product mix indicated by the model is heavily weighted toward producing the windows (6 per week) rather than the doors (only 2 per week). Since there is equal enthusiasm for both new products, management is concerned about this imbalance. Therefore, management has raised a what-if question. What would happen if the estimate of the unit profit for the doors ($300) were too low and the corresponding estimate for the windows ($500) were too high? Management feels that the estimates could easily be off in these directions. If this were the case, would this lead to a more balanced product mix being the most profitable one?

This question can be answered in a matter of seconds simply by substituting new estimates of the unit profits in the original spreadsheet in Figure 5.1 and running Solver again. Figure 5.10 shows that new estimates of $450 for doors and $400 for windows causes no change at all in the solution for the optimal product mix. (The total profit does change, but this occurs only because of the changes in the unit profits.) Would even larger changes in the estimates of unit profits finally lead to a change in the optimal product mix? Figure 5.11 shows that this does happen, yielding a relatively balanced product mix of $(D, W) = (4, 3)$, when estimates of $600 for doors and $300 for windows are used.

Using a Two-Way Parameter Analysis Report (RSPE) for This Analysis

Using RPSE, a two-way parameter analysis report provides a way of systematically investigating the effect if the estimates of both unit profits are inaccurate. This kind of parameter analysis table shows the results in a single output cell for various trial values in two parameter

FIGURE 5.10

The revised Wyndor problem where the estimates of the unit profits for doors and windows have been changed to $P_D = \$450$ and $P_W = \$400$, respectively, but no change occurs in the optimal solution.

	A	B	C	D	E	F	G
1		Wyndor Glass Co. Product-Mix Problem					
2							
3			Doors	Windows			
4		Unit Profit	$450	$400			
5					Hours		Hours
6			Hours Used per Unit Produced		Used		Available
7		Plant 1	1	0	2	≤	4
8		Plant 2	0	2	12	≤	12
9		Plant 3	3	2	18	≤	18
10							
11			Doors	Windows			Total Profit
12		Units Produced	2	6			$3,300

FIGURE 5.11

The revised Wyndor problem where the estimates of the unit profits for doors and windows have been changed to $600 and $300, respectively, which results in a change in the optimal solution.

	A	B	C	D	E	F	G
1		Wyndor Glass Co. Product-Mix Problem					
2							
3			Doors	Windows			
4		Unit Profit	$600	$300			
5					Hours		Hours
6			Hours Used per Unit Produced		Used		Available
7		Plant 1	1	0	4	≤	4
8		Plant 2	0	2	6	≤	12
9		Plant 3	3	2	18	≤	18
10							
11			Doors	Windows			Total Profit
12		Units Produced	4	3			$3,300

cells. Therefore, for example, it can be used to show how TotalProfit (G12) in Figure 5.1 varies over a range of trial values in the two parameter cells, UnitProfitPerDoor (C4) and UnitProfitPerWindow (D4). For each pair of trial values in these data cells, Solver is called on to re-solve the problem.

To create such a two-way parameter analysis report for the Wyndor problem, both Unit-ProfitPerDoor (C4) and UnitProfitPerWindow (D4) need to be defined as parameter cells. In turn, select cell C4 and D4, then choose Optimization under the Parameters menu on the RSPE ribbon, and then enter the range of trial values for each parameter cell (as was done in Figure 5.5 in the previous section). For this example, UnitProfitPerDoor (C4) will be varied from $300 to $600 while UnitProfitPerWindow (D4) will be varied from $100 to $500.

Next, choose Optimization > Parameter Analysis under the reports menu on the RSPE ribbon to bring up the dialog box shown in Figure 5.12. For a two-way parameter analysis report, two parameter cells are chosen, but only a single result can be shown. Under Parameters, clicking on (>>) chooses both of the defined parameter cells, UnitProfitPerDoor and UnitProfitPerWindow. Under Results, click on (<<) to clear out the list of cells on the right, click on the + next to Objective to reveal the objective cell (TotalProfit), select TotalProfit, and then click on > to move this cell to the right.

The next step is to turn on the option called Vary Parameters Independently. This will allow both parameter cells to be varied independently over their entire ranges. The number of different values of the first parameter cell and the second parameter cell to be shown in the parameter analysis report are entered in Major Axis Points and Minor Axis Points, respectively. These values will be spread evenly over the range of values specified in the parameter

164   Chapter Five   *What-If Analysis for Linear Programming*

FIGURE 5.12

The dialog box for the parameter analysis report specifies here that the UnitProfitPerDoor and UnitProfitPerWindow parameter cells will be varied and results from the objective cell (Total-Profit) will be shown for the Wyndor problem.

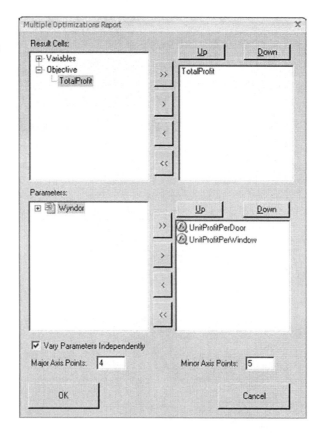

FIGURE 5.13

The parameter analysis report that shows how the optimal total profit changes when systematically varying the estimate of both the unit profit for doors and the unit profit for windows for the Wyndor problem.

	A	B	C	D	E	F
1	TotalProfit	UnitProfitPerWindow				
2	UnitProfitPerDoor	$100	$200	$300	$400	$500
3	$300	$1,500	$1,800	$2,400	$3,000	$3,600
4	$400	$1,900	$2,200	$2,600	$3,200	$3,800
5	$500	$2,300	$2,600	$2,900	$3,400	$4,000
6	$600	$2,700	$3,000	$3,300	$3,600	$4,200

dialog box for each parameter cell. Therefore, choosing 4 and 5 for the respective number of values, as shown in Figure 5.12, will vary UnitProfitPerDoor over the four values of $300, $400, $500, and $600 while simultaneously varying UnitProfitPerWindow over the five values of $100, $200, $300, $400, and $500.

Clicking on the OK button generates the parameter analysis report shown in Figure 5.13. The trial values for the respective parameter cells are listed in the first column and first row of the table. For each combination of a trial value from the first column and from the first row, Solver has solved for the value of the output cell of interest (the objective cell for this example) and entered it into the corresponding column and row of the table.

It also is possible to choose either DoorsProduced or WindowsProduced instead of Total-Profit as the result to show in the dialog box in Figure 5.12. A similar parameter analysis report then could have been generated to show either the optimal number of doors to produce or the optimal number of windows to produce for each combination of values for the unit profits. These two parameter analysis reports are shown in Figure 5.14. The upper right-hand corner (cell F3) of both reports, taken together, gives the optimal solution of $(D, W) = (2, 6)$ when using the original unit-profit estimates of $300 for doors and $500 for windows.

FIGURE 5.14

The pair of parameter analysis reports that show how the optimal number of doors to produce (top report) and the optimal number of windows to produce (bottom report) change when systematically varying the estimate of both the unit profit for doors and the unit profit for windows for the Wyndor problem.

	A	B	C	D	E	F
1	DoorsProduced	UnitProfitPerWindow				
2	UnitProfitPerDoor	$100	$200	$300	$400	$500
3	$300	4	2	2	2	2
4	$400	4	4	2	2	2
5	$500	4	4	4	2	2
6	$600	4	4	4	2	2

	A	B	C	D	E	F
1	WindowsProduced	UnitProfitPerWindow				
2	UnitProfitPerDoor	$100	$200	$300	$400	$500
3	$300	3	6	6	6	6
4	$400	3	3	6	6	6
5	$500	3	3	3	6	6
6	$600	3	3	3	6	6

What-if analysis shows that there is no need to refine Wyndor's estimates of the unit profits for doors and windows.

Moving down from this cell corresponds to increasing this estimate for doors, while moving to the left amounts to decreasing the estimate for windows. (The cells when moving up or to the right of H26 are not shown because these changes would only increase the attractiveness of (D, W) = (2, 6) as the optimal solution.) Note that (D, W) = (2, 6) continues to be the optimal solution for all the cells near H26. This indicates that the original estimates of unit profit would need to be very inaccurate indeed before the optimal product mix would change. Although the estimates are fairly rough, management is confident that they are not that inaccurate. Therefore, there is no need to expend the considerable effort that would be needed to refine the estimates.

At this point, it continues to appear that (D, W) = (2, 6) is the best product mix for initiating the production of the two new products (although additional what-if questions remain to be addressed in subsequent sections). However, we also now know from Figure 5.14 that as conditions change in the future, if the unit profits for both products change enough, it may be advisable to change the product mix later. We still need to leave clear signposts behind to signal when a future change in the product mix should be considered, as described next.

Gleaning Additional Information from the Sensitivity Report

A sum ≤ 100 percent guarantees that the original optimal solution is still optimal.

The preceding section described how the data in the sensitivity report enable finding the allowable range for an individual coefficient in the objective function when that coefficient is the only one that changes from its original value. These same data (the allowable increase and allowable decrease in each coefficient) also can be used to analyze the effect of *simultaneous* changes in these coefficients. Here is how.

The 100 Percent Rule for Simultaneous Changes in Objective Function Coefficients: If simultaneous changes are made in the coefficients of the objective function, calculate for each change the percentage of the allowable change (increase or decrease) for that coefficient to remain within its allowable range. If the *sum* of the percentage changes does *not* exceed 100 percent, the original optimal solution definitely will still be optimal. (If the sum *does* exceed 100 percent, then we cannot be sure.)

This rule does not spell out what happens if the sum of the percentage changes *does* exceed 100 percent. The consequence depends on the directions of the changes in the coefficients. Exceeding 100 percent may or may not change the optimal solution, but so long as 100 percent is not exceeded, the original optimal solution *definitely* will still be optimal.

Keep in mind that we can safely use the entire allowable increase or decrease in a single objective function coefficient only if none of the other coefficients have changed at all. With simultaneous changes in the coefficients, we focus on the *percentage* of the allowable increase or decrease that is being used for each coefficient.

To illustrate, consider the Wyndor problem again, along with the information provided by the sensitivity report in Figure 5.8. Suppose conditions have changed after the initial study, and the unit profit for doors (P_D) has increased from \$300 to \$450 while the unit profit for windows (P_W) has decreased from \$500 to \$400. The calculations for the 100 percent rule then are

P_D: \$300 → \$450

$$\text{Percentage of allowable increase} = 100\left(\frac{450 - 300}{450}\right)\% = 33\tfrac{1}{3}\%$$

P_W: \$500 → \$400

$$\text{Percentage of allowable decrease} = 100\left(\frac{500 - 400}{300}\right)\% = 33\tfrac{1}{3}\%$$

$$\text{Sum} = \overline{66\tfrac{2}{3}\%}$$

Since the sum of the percentages does not exceed 100 percent, the original optimal solution $(D, W) = (2, 6)$ definitely is still optimal, just as we found earlier in Figure 5.10.

Now suppose conditions have changed even further, so P_D has increased from \$300 to \$600 while P_W has decreased from \$500 to \$300. The calculations for the 100 percent rule now are

P_D: \$300 → \$600

$$\text{Percentage of allowable increase} = 100\left(\frac{600 - 300}{450}\right)\% = 66\tfrac{2}{3}\%$$

P_W: \$500 → \$300

$$\text{Percentage of allowbale decrease} = 100\left(\frac{500 - 300}{300}\right)\% = 66\tfrac{2}{3}\%$$

$$\text{Sum} = \overline{133\tfrac{1}{3}\%}$$

Since the sum of the percentages now exceeds 100 percent, the 100 percent rule says that we can no longer guarantee that $(D, W) = (2, 6)$ is still optimal. In fact, we found earlier in both Figures 5.11 and 5.14 that the optimal solution has changed to $(D, W) = (4, 3)$.

These results suggest how to find just where the optimal solution changes while P_D is being increased and P_W is being decreased in this way. Since 100 percent is midway between 66⅔ percent and 133⅓ percent, the sum of the percentage changes will equal 100 percent when the values of P_D and P_W are midway between their values in the above cases. In particular, $P_D = \$525$ is midway between \$450 and \$600 and $P_W = \$350$ is midway between \$400 and \$300. The corresponding calculations for the 100 percent rule are

P_D: \$300 → \$525

$$\text{Percentage of allowable increase} = 100\left(\frac{525 - 300}{450}\right)\% = 50\%$$

P_W: \$500 → \$350

$$\text{Percentage of allowable decrease} = 100\left(\frac{500 - 350}{300}\right)\% = 50\%$$

$$\text{Sum} = \overline{100\%}$$

Although the sum of the percentages equals 100 percent, the fact that it does not *exceed* 100 percent guarantees that $(D, W) = (2, 6)$ is still optimal. Figure 5.15 shows graphically that *both* (2, 6) and (4, 3) are now optimal, as well as all the points on the line segment connecting these two points. However, if P_D and P_W were to be changed any further from their original values (so that the sum of the percentages exceeds 100 percent), the objective function line would be rotated so far toward the vertical that $(D, W) = (4, 3)$ would become the only optimal solution.

FIGURE 5.15

When the estimates of the unit profits for doors and windows change to $P_D = \$525$ and $P_W = \$350$, which lies at the edge of what is allowed by the 100 percent rule, the graphical method shows that $(D, W) = (2, 6)$ still is an optimal solution, but now every other point on the line segment between this solution and $(4, 3)$ also is optimal.

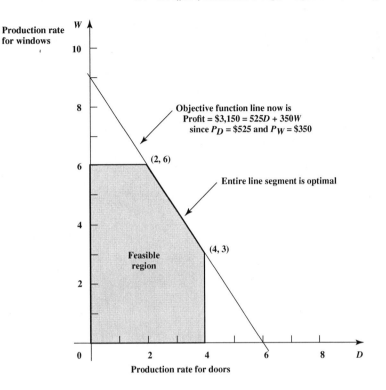

Here is an example where the original optimal solution is still optimal even though the sum exceeds 100 percent.

At the same time, keep in mind that having the sum of the percentages of allowable changes exceed 100 percent does not automatically mean that the optimal solution will change. For example, suppose that the estimates of both unit profits are halved. The resulting calculations for the 100 percent rule are

P_D: $\$300 \rightarrow \$150$

$$\text{Percentage of allowable decrease} = 100\left(\frac{300 - 150}{300}\right)\% = 50\%$$

P_W: $\$500 \rightarrow \$250$

$$\text{Percentage of allowable decrease} = 100\left(\frac{500 - 250}{300}\right)\% = 83\%$$

$$\text{Sum} = \overline{133\%}$$

Even though this sum exceeds 100 percent, Figure 5.16 shows that the original optimal solution is still optimal. In fact, the objective function line has the same slope as the original objective function line (the solid line in Figure 5.9). This happens whenever *proportional changes* are made to all the unit profits, which will automatically lead to the same optimal solution.

Comparisons

You now have seen three approaches to investigating what happens if simultaneous changes occur in the coefficients of the objective function: (1) try out changes directly on a spreadsheet, (2) use a two-way parameter analysis report and (3) apply the 100 percent rule.

The spreadsheet approach is a good place to start, especially for less experienced modelers, because it is simple and quick. If you are only interested in checking one specific set of changes in the coefficients, you can immediately see what happens after making the changes in the spreadsheet.

168   Chapter Five   *What-If Analysis for Linear Programming*

FIGURE 5.16

When the estimates of the unit profits for doors and windows change to $P_D = \$150$ and $P_W = \$250$ (half their original values), the graphical method shows that the optimal solution still is $(D, W) = (2, 6)$, even though the 100 percent rule says that the optimal solution might change.

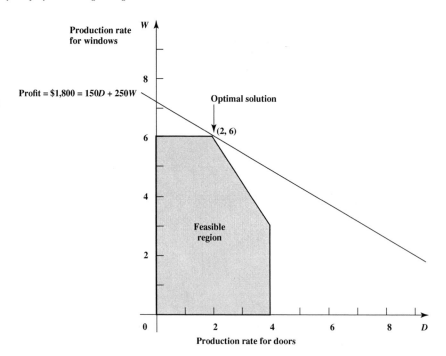

More often, there will be numerous possibilities for what the true values of the coefficients will turn out to be, because of uncertainty in the original estimates of these coefficients. The parameter analysis report is useful for systematically checking a variety of possible changes in one or two objective function coefficients. Trying out representative possibilities on the spreadsheet may provide all the insight that is needed. Perhaps the optimal solution for the original model will remain optimal over nearly all these possibilities, so this solution can be confidently used. Or perhaps it will become clear that the original estimates need to be refined before selecting a solution.

When the spreadsheet approach and/or parameter analysis report does not provide a clear conclusion, the 100 percent rule can usefully complement this approach in the following ways:

- The 100 percent rule can be used to determine just how large the changes in the objective function coefficients need to be before the original optimal solution may no longer be optimal.

- When the model has a large number of decision variables (as is common for real problems), it may become impractical to use the spreadsheet approach to systematically try out a variety of simultaneous changes in many or all of the coefficients in the objective function because of the huge number of representative possibilities. The parameter analysis report can only be used to systematically check possible changes in—at most—two coefficients at a time. However, by dividing each coefficient's allowable increase or allowable decrease by the number of decision variables, the 100 percent rule immediately indicates how much each coefficient can be safely changed without invalidating the current optimal solution.

- After completing the study, if conditions change in the future that cause some or all of the coefficients in the objective function to change, the 100 percent rule quickly indicates whether the original optimal solution must remain optimal. If the answer is affirmative, there is no need to take all the time that may be required to reconstruct the (revised) spreadsheet model. The time saved can be very substantial for large models.

Review
Questions

1. In the 100 percent rule for simultaneous changes in objective function coefficients, what are the percentage changes that are being considered?
2. In this 100 percent rule, if the sum of the percentage changes does not exceed 100 percent, what does this say about the original optimal solution?
3. In this 100 percent rule, if the sum of the percentage changes exceeds 100 percent, does this mean that the original optimal solution is no longer optimal?

5.5   THE EFFECT OF SINGLE CHANGES IN A CONSTRAINT

We now turn our focus from the coefficients in the objective function to the effect of changing the functional constraints. The changes might occur either in the coefficients on the left-hand sides of the constraints or in the values of the right-hand sides.

We might be interested in the effect of such changes for the same reason we are interested in this effect for objective function coefficients, namely, that these parameters of the model are only *estimates* of quantities that cannot be determined precisely at this time so we want to determine the effect if these estimates are inaccurate.

When the right-hand sides represent managerial policy decisions, what-if analysis provides guidance regarding the effect of altering these decisions.

However, a more common reason for this interest is the one discussed at the end of Section 5.1, namely, that the right-hand sides of the functional constraints may well represent *managerial policy decisions* rather than quantities that are largely outside the control of management. Therefore, after the model has been solved, management will want to analyze the effect of altering these policy decisions in a variety of ways to see if these decisions can be improved. What-if analysis provides valuable guidance to management in determining the effect of altering these policy decisions. (Recall that this was cited as the third benefit of what-if analysis in Section 5.1.)

This section describes how to perform what-if analysis when making changes in just one spot (a coefficient or a right-hand side) of a single constraint. The next section then will deal with simultaneous changes in the constraints.

The procedure for determining the effect if a single change is made in a constraint is the same regardless of whether the change is in a coefficient on the left-hand side or in the value on the right-hand side. (The one exception is that the Solver sensitivity report provides information about changes in the right-hand side but does not do so for the left-hand side.) Therefore, we will illustrate the procedure by making changes in a right-hand side.

In particular, we return to the Wyndor case study to address the third what-if question posed by Wyndor management in Section 5.2.

Question 3: What happens if a change is made in the number of hours of production time per week being made available to Wyndor's new products in one of the plants?

The number of hours available in each plant is the value of the right-hand side for the corresponding constraint, so we want to investigate the effect of changing this right-hand side for one of the plants. With the original optimal solution, $(D, W) = (2, 6)$, only 2 of the 4 available hours in Plant 1 are used, so changing this number of available hours (barring a large decrease) would have no effect on either the optimal solution or the resulting total profit from the two new products. However, it is unclear what would happen if the number of available hours in either Plant 2 or Plant 3 were to be changed. Let's start with Plant 2.

Using the Spreadsheet for This Analysis

Referring back to Section 5.2, Figure 5.1 shows the spreadsheet model for the original Wyndor problem before beginning what-if analysis. The optimal solution is $(D, W) = (2, 6)$ with a total profit of $3,600 per week from the two new products. Cell G8 shows that 12 hours of production time per week are being made available for the new products in Plant 2.

To see what happens if a specific change is made in this number of hours, all you need to do is substitute the new number in cell G8 and run Solver again. For example, Figure 5.17 shows the result if the number of hours is increased from 12 to 13. The corresponding optimal solution in C12:D12 gives a total profit of $3,750. Thus, the resulting change in profit would be

$$\text{Incremental profit} = \$3,750 - \$3,600$$
$$= \$150$$

170   Chapter Five   *What-If Analysis for Linear Programming*

FIGURE 5.17

The revised Wyndor problem where the hours available in Plant 2 per week have been increased from 12 (as in Figure 5.1) to 13, which results in an increase of $150 in the total profit per week from the two new products.

	A	B	C	D	E	F	G
1		Wyndor Glass Co. Product-Mix Problem					
2							
3			Doors	Windows			
4		Unit Profit	$300	$500			
5					Hours		Hours
6			Hours Used per Unit Produced		Used		Available
7		Plant 1	1	0	1.66667	≤	4
8		Plant 2	0	2	13	≤	13
9		Plant 3	3	2	18	≤	18
10							
11			Doors	Windows			Total Profit
12		Units Produced	1.667	6.5			$3,750

FIGURE 5.18

A further revision of the Wyndor problem in Figure 5.17 to further increase the hours available in Plant 2 from 13 to 18, which results in a further increase in total profit of $750 (which is the $150 per hour added in Plant 2).

	A	B	C	D	E	F	G
1		Wyndor Glass Co. Product-Mix Problem					
2							
3			Doors	Windows			
4		Unit Profit	$300	$500			
5					Hours		Hours
6			Hours Used per Unit Produced		Used		Available
7		Plant 1	1	0	0	≤	4
8		Plant 2	0	2	18	≤	18
9		Plant 3	3	2	18	≤	18
10							
11			Doors	Windows			Total Profit
12		Units Produced	0	9			$4,500

Since this increase in profit is obtained by adding just one more hour in Plant 2, it would be interesting to see the effect of adding several more hours. Figure 5.18 shows the effect of adding five more hours. Comparing Figure 5.18 to Figure 5.17, the additional profit from providing five more hours would be

So far, each additional hour provided in Plant 2 adds $150 to profit.

$$\text{Incremental profit} = \$4,500 - \$3,750$$
$$= \$750 \text{ from adding 5 hours}$$
$$= \$150 \text{ per hour added}$$

Would adding even more hours increase profit even further? Figure 5.19 shows what would happen if a total of 20 hours per week were made available to the new products in Plant 2. Both the optimal solution and the total profit are the same as in Figure 5.18, so increasing from 18 to 20 hours would not help. (The reason is that the 18 hours available in Plant 3 prevent producing more than 9 windows per week, so only 18 hours can be used in Plant 2.) Thus, it appears that 18 hours is the maximum that should be considered for Plant 2.

Now management needs to consider the trade-off between adding production time for the new products and decreasing it for other products.

However, the fact that the total profit from the two new products can be increased substantially by increasing the number of hours per week made available to the new products from 12 to 18 does not mean that these additional hours should be provided automatically. The production time made available for these two new products can be increased only if it is decreased for other products. Therefore, management will need to assess the disadvantages of decreasing the production time for any other products (including both lost profit

FIGURE 5.19
A further revision of the Wyndor problem in Figure 5.18 to further increase the hours available in Plant 2 from 18 to 20, which results in no change in total profit because the optimal solution cannot make use of these additional hours.

	A	B	C	D	E	F	G
1		**Wyndor Glass Co. Product-Mix Problem**					
2							
3			Doors	Windows			
4		Unit Profit	$300	$500			
5					Hours		Hours
6			Hours Used per Unit Produced		Used		Available
7		Plant 1	1	0	0	≤	4
8		Plant 2	0	2	18	≤	20
9		Plant 3	3	2	18	≤	18
10							
11			Doors	Windows			Total Profit
12		Units Produced	0	9			$4,500

and less tangible disadvantages) before deciding whether to increase the production time for the new products. This analysis also might lead to *decreasing* the production time made available to the two new products in one or more of the plants.

Using a Parameter Analysis Report (RSPE) for This Analysis

Using RPSE, a parameter analysis report can be used to systematically determine the effect of making various changes in one of the parameters in a constraint. For example, Figure 5.20 displays a parameter analysis report (obtained by following the same procedure used to generate a parameter analysis report in Section 5.3) to show how the changing cells and total profit change as the number of available hours in Plant 2 range between 4 and 20.

An interesting pattern is apparent in the incremental profit column. Starting at 12 hours available at Plant 2 (the current allotment), each additional hour allocated yields an additional $150 in profit (up to making 18 hours available). Similarly, if hours are taken away from

FIGURE 5.20
The parameter analysis report that shows the effect of varying the number of hours of production time being made available per week in Plant 2 for Wyndor's new products.

	A	B	C	D	E
1	HoursAvailableInPlant2	DoorsProduced	WindowsProduced	TotalProfit	Incremental Profit
2	4	4	2	$2,200	
3	5	4	2.5	$2,450	$250
4	6	4	3	$2,700	$250
5	7	3.666666667	3.5	$2,850	$150
6	8	3.333333333	4	$3,000	$150
7	9	3	4.5	$3,150	$150
8	10	2.666666667	5	$3,300	$150
9	11	2.333333333	5.5	$3,450	$150
10	12	2	6	$3,600	$150
11	13	1.666666667	6.5	$3,750	$150
12	14	1.333333333	7	$3,900	$150
13	15	1	7.5	$4,050	$150
14	16	0.666666667	8	$4,200	$150
15	17	0.333333333	8.5	$4,350	$150
16	18	0	9	$4,500	$150
17	19	0	9	$4,500	$0
18	20	0	9	$4,500	$0

Plant 2, each hour lost causes a loss of $150 profit (down to making six hours available). This rate of change in the profit for increases or decreases in the right-hand side of a constraint is known as the **shadow price**.

In general, the shadow price for a constraint reveals the rate at which the objective cell can be increased by increasing the right-hand side of that constraint. This remains valid as long as the right-hand side is within its allowable range.

> Given an optimal solution and the corresponding value of the objective function for a linear programming model, the **shadow price** for a functional constraint is the *rate* at which the value of the objective function can be increased by increasing the right-hand side of the constraint by a small amount.

However, the shadow price of $150 for the Plant 2 constraint is valid only within a range of values near 12 (in particular, between 6 hours and 18 hours). If the number of available hours is increased beyond 18 hours, then the incremental profit drops to zero. If the available hours are reduced below six hours, then profit drops at a faster rate of $250 per hour. Therefore, letting RHS denote the value of the right-hand side, the shadow price of $150 is valid for

$$6 \leq RHS \leq 18$$

This allowable range focuses on a right-hand side and the corresponding shadow price. In contrast to the allowable range for objective function coefficients described in Section 5.3, it does not *indicate whether the original solution is still optimal, just whether the shadow price remains valid.*

This range is known as the **allowable range for the right-hand side** (or just **allowable range** for short).

> The *allowable range for the right-hand side* of a functional constraint is the range of values for this right-hand side over which this constraint's shadow price remains valid.

Unlike the allowable range for objective function coefficients described in Section 5.3, a change that is within the allowable range for the right-hand side does *not* mean the original solution is still optimal. In fact, any time the shadow price is not zero, a change to a right-hand side leads to a change in the optimal solution. The shadow price indicates how much the value of the objective function will change as the optimal solution changes.

Using the Sensitivity Report to Obtain the Key Information

As illustrated earlier, it is straightforward to use a parameter analysis report to calculate the *shadow price* for a functional constraint, as well as to find (or at least closely approximate) the *allowable range* for the right-hand side of this constraint over which the shadow price remains valid. However, this same information also can be obtained immediately from Solver's sensitivity report for all the functional constraints. Figure 5.21 shows the full sensitivity report provided by Solver for the original Wyndor problem after obtaining the optimal solution given in Figure 5.1. The top half is the part already shown in Figure 5.8 for finding allowable ranges for the objective function coefficients. The bottom half focuses on the functional constraints, including providing the shadow prices for these constraints in the fourth column. The first three columns remind us that (1) the output cells for these constraints in Figure 5.1 are cells E7 to E9, (2) these cells give the number of production hours used per week in the three plants, and (3) the final values in these cells are 2, 12, and 18 (as shown in column E of Figure 5.1). (We will discuss the last three columns a little later.)

The shadow price given in the fourth column for each constraint tells us how much the value of the objective function [objective cell (G12) in Figure 5.1] would increase if the

FIGURE 5.21

The complete sensitivity report generated by Solver for the original Wyndor problem as formulated in Figure 5.1.

Variable Cells

Cell	Name	Final Value	Reduced Cost	Objective Coefficient	Allowable Increase	Allowable Decrease
$C$12	DoorsProduced	2	0	300	450	300
$D$12	WindowsProduced	6	0	500	1E + 30	300

Constraints

Cell	Name	Final Value	Shadow Price	Constraint R. H. Side	Allowable Increase	Allowable Decrease
$E$7	Plant 1 Used	2	0	4	1E + 30	2
$E$8	Plant 2 Used	12	150	12	6	6
$E$9	Plant 3 Used	18	100	18	6	6

right-hand side of that constraint (cell G7, G8, or G9) were to be increased by 1. Conversely, it also tells us how much the value of the objective function would *decrease* if the right-hand side were to be decreased by 1. The shadow price for the Plant 1 constraint is 0, because this plant already is using less hours (2) than are available (4) so there would be no benefit to making an additional hour available. However, Plants 2 and 3 are using all the hours available to them for the two new products (with the product mix given by the changing cells). Thus, it is not surprising that the shadow prices indicate that the objective cell would increase if the hours available in either Plant 2 or Plant 3 were to be increased.

The shadow prices reveal the relationship between profit and the amount of production time made available in the plants.

To express this information in the language of management, the value of the objective function for this problem [objective cell (G12) in Figure 5.1] represents the *total profit* in dollars per week from the two new products under consideration. The right-hand side of each functional constraint represents the number of hours of production time being made available per week for these products in the plant that corresponds to this constraint. Therefore, the shadow price for a functional constraint informs management as to how much the total profit from the two new products could be increased for each additional hour of production time made available to these products per week in the corresponding plant. Conversely, the shadow price indicates how much this profit would decrease for each reduction of an hour of production time in that plant. This interpretation of the shadow price remains valid as long as the change in the number of hours of production time is not very large.

Here is how to find the allowable ranges for the right-hand sides from the sensitivity report.

Specifically, this interpretation of the shadow price remains valid as long as the number of hours of production time remains within its *allowable range*. Solver's sensitivity report provides all the data needed to identify the allowable range of each functional constraint. Refer back to the bottom of this report given in Figure 5.21. The final three columns enable calculation of this range. The "Constraint R. H. Side" column indicates the original value of the right-hand side before any change is made. Adding the number in the "Allowable Increase" column to this original value then gives the upper endpoint of the allowable range. Similarly, subtracting the number in the "Allowable Decrease" column from this original value gives the lower endpoint. Using the fact that 1E + 30 represents infinity (∞), these calculations of the allowable ranges are shown below, where a subscript has been added to each RHS to identify the constraint involved.

Plant 1 constraint: $4 - 2 \leq RHS_1 \leq 4 + \infty$,   so $2 \leq RHS_1$ (no upper limit)

Plant 2 constraint: $12 - 6 \leq RHS_2 \leq 12 + 6$,   so $6 \leq RHS_2 \leq 18$

Plant 3 constraint: $18 - 6 \leq RHS_3 \leq 18 + 6$,   so $12 \leq RHS_3 \leq 24$

In the case of the Plant 2 constraint, Figure 5.22 provides graphical insight into why $6 \leq RHS \leq 18$ is the range of validity for the shadow price. The optimal solution for the original problem, $(D, W) = (2, 6)$, lies at the intersection of line B and line C. The equation for line B is $2W = 12$ because this is the constraint boundary line for the Plant 2 constraint ($2W \leq 12$). However, if the value of this right-hand side ($RHS_2 = 12$) is changed, line B will either shift upward (for a larger value of RHS_2) or downward (for a smaller value of RHS_2). As line B shifts, the boundary of the feasible region shifts accordingly and the optimal solution continues to lie at the intersection of the shifted line B and line C—provided the shift in line B is not so large that this intersection is no longer feasible. Each time RHS_2 is increased (or decreased) by 1, this intersection shifts enough to increase (or decrease) Profit by the amount of the shadow price ($150). Figure 5.22 indicates that this intersection remains feasible (and so optimal) as RHS_2 increases from 12 to 18, because the feasible region expands upward as line B shifts upward. However, for values of RHS_2 larger than 18, this intersection is no longer feasible because it gives a negative value of D (the production rate for doors). Thus, each increase of 1 above 18 no longer increases Profit by the amount of the shadow price. Similarly, as RHS_2 decreases from 12 to 6, this intersection remains feasible (and so optimal) as line B shifts down accordingly. However, for values of RHS_2 less than 6, this intersection is no longer feasible because it violates the Plant 1 constraint ($D \leq 4$) whose boundary line is line A. Hence, each decrease of 1 below 6 no longer decreases Profit by the amount of the shadow price. Consequently, $6 \leq RHS \leq 18$ is the allowable range over which the shadow price is valid.

174   Chapter Five   *What-If Analysis for Linear Programming*

FIGURE 5.22

A graphical interpretation of the allowable range, $6 \le RHS_2 \le 18$, for the right-hand side of Wyndor's Plant 2 constraint.

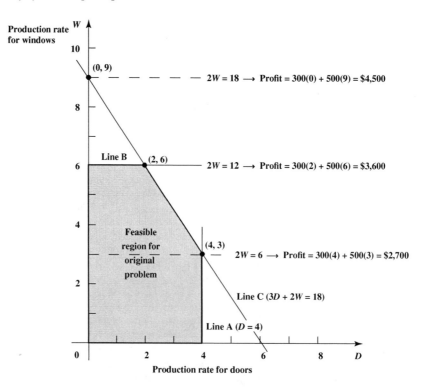

Summary

Recall again that the right-hand side of each functional constraint for the Wyndor problem represents the number of hours of production time per week in the corresponding plant that is being made available to the two new products. The *shadow price* for each constraint reveals how much the total profit from these new products would increase for each additional hour of production time made available in the corresponding plant for these products. This interpretation of the shadow price remains valid as long as the number of hours remains within its *allowable range*. Therefore, each shadow price can be applied by management to evaluate a change in its original decision regarding the number of hours as long as the new number is within the corresponding allowable range. This evaluation also would need to take into account how the change in the number of hours made available to the new products would impact the production rates and profits for the company's other products.

Review Questions

1. Why might it be of interest to investigate the effect of making changes in a functional constraint?
2. Why might it be possible to alter the right-hand side of a functional constraint?
3. What is meant by a *shadow price*?
4. How can a shadow price be found by using the spreadsheet? By using a parameter analysis report? By using Solver's sensitivity report?
5. Why are shadow prices of interest to managers?
6. Can shadow prices be used to determine the effect of *decreasing* rather than increasing the right-hand side of a functional constraint?
7. What does a shadow price of 0 tell a manager?
8. Which columns of Solver's sensitivity report are used to find the allowable range for the right-hand side of a functional constraint?
9. Why are these allowable ranges of interest to managers?

5.6   THE EFFECT OF SIMULTANEOUS CHANGES IN THE CONSTRAINTS

The preceding section described how to perform what-if analysis to investigate the effect of changes in a single spot of a constraint. We now turn our consideration to the effect of simultaneous changes in the constraints.

Managerial policy decisions involving right-hand sides frequently are interrelated, so changes in these decisions should be considered simultaneously.

The need to consider these simultaneous changes arises frequently. There may be considerable uncertainty about the estimates for a number of the parameters in the functional constraints, so questions will arise as to the effect if the true values of the parameters simultaneously deviate significantly from the estimates. Since the right-hand sides of the constraints often represent managerial policy decisions, questions will arise about what would happen if some of these decisions were to be changed. These decisions frequently are interrelated and so need to be considered simultaneously.

We outline next how the usual three methods for performing what-if analysis can be applied to considering simultaneous changes in the constraints. The third one (using Solver's sensitivity report) is only helpful for changing right-hand sides. For the first two (using the spreadsheet and using a parameter analysis report), the procedure is the same regardless of whether the changes are in the coefficients on the left-hand sides or in the right-hand sides of the constraints (or both). Since changing the right-hand sides is the more important case, we will focus on this case.

In particular, we now will deal with the last of Wyndor management's what-if questions.

Question 4: What happens if simultaneous changes are made in the number of hours of production time per week being made available to Wyndor's new products in all the plants?

In particular, after seeing that the Plant 2 constraint has the largest shadow price (150), versus a shadow price of 100 for the Plant 3 constraint, management now is interested in exploring a specific type of simultaneous change in these production hours. By shifting the production of one of the company's current products from Plant 2 to Plant 3, it is possible to increase the number of production hours available to the new products in Plant 2 by decreasing the number of production hours available in Plant 3 by the same amount. Management wonders what would happen if these simultaneous changes in production hours were made.

Using the Spreadsheet for This Analysis

According to the shadow prices, the effect of shifting one hour of production time per week from Plant 3 to Plant 2 would be as follows.

RHS_2: $12 \rightarrow 13$ Change in total profit $=$ Shadow price $= \$150$

RHS_3: $18 \rightarrow 17$ Change in total profit $= -$ Shadow price $= \underline{-100}$

Net increase in total profit $=$ $\$50$

We now are checking to see whether the shadow prices remain valid for evaluating specific simultaneous changes in the right-hand sides.

However, we don't know if these shadow prices remain valid if *both* right-hand sides are changed by this amount.

A quick way to check this is to substitute the new right-hand sides into the original spreadsheet in Figure 5.1 and run Solver again. The resulting spreadsheet in Figure 5.23 shows that the net increase in total profit (from \$3,600 to \$3,650) is indeed \$50, so the shadow prices are valid for these particular simultaneous changes in right-hand sides.

How long will these shadow prices remain valid if we continue shifting production hours from Plant 3 to Plant 2? We could continue checking this by substituting other combinations of right-hand sides into the spreadsheet and re-solving each time. However, a more systematic way of doing this is to use a parameter analysis report, as described below.

Using a Parameter Analysis Report for This Analysis

Since it can become tedious, or even impractical, to use the spreadsheet to investigate a large number of simultaneous changes in the right-hand sides, let us see how a parameter analysis report can be used to do this analysis more systematically.

We could use a two-way parameter analysis report to investigate how the profit and optimal production rates vary for different combinations of the number of hours available in Plant 2 and Plant 3. However, in this case we aren't interested in *all* combinations of hours in the two plants,

FIGURE 5.23

The revised Wyndor problem where column G in Figure 5.1 has been changed by shifting one of the hours available in Plant 3 to Plant 2 and then re-solving.

	A	B	C	D	E	F	G
1		**Wyndor Glass Co. Product-Mix Problem**					
2							
3			Doors	Windows			
4		Unit Profit	$300	$500			
5					Hours		Hours
6			Hours Used per Unit Produced		Used		Available
7		Plant 1	1	0	1.33333	≤	4
8		Plant 2	0	2	13	≤	13
9		Plant 3	3	2	17	≤	17
10							
11			Doors	Windows			Total Profit
12		Units Produced	1.333	6.5			$3.650

By entering a formula into one data cell in terms of another one, a one-way parameter analysis report is able to investigate inter-related trial values in both data cells.

but rather only those combinations that involve a simple *shifting* of available hours from Plant 3 to Plant 2. For this analysis, we will see that a one-way parameter analysis table is sufficient.

For each hour reduced in Plant 3, an additional hour is made available in Plant 2. Thus, the number of available hours in Plant 2 is a function of the number of available hours in Plant 3. In particular, since there are 30 total hours available at the two plants ($RHS_2 + RHS_3 = 30$), the number of available hours in Plant 2 (RHS_2) is

$$RHS_2 = 30 - RHS_3$$

Figure 5.24 shows the Wyndor Glass Co. spreadsheet with the data cell for the number of available hours in Plant 2 replaced by the above formula. Because of this formula, whenever the number of available hours in Plant 3 is reduced, the number of available hours in Plant 2 will automatically increase by the same amount. Now a one-way parameter analysis report can be used to investigate various numbers of available hours in Plant 3 (with the corresponding automatic adjustment made to the available hours at Plant 2). HoursAvailableInPlant3 (G9) is specified as a parameter cell with a range of trial values from 18 down to 12. A parameter analysis table is then generated in Figure 5.25 to show how DoorsProduced (C12), WindowsProduced (D12), and TotalProfit (G12) vary as HoursAvailableInPlant3 (G9) varies from 18 down to 12. A column was added to the left of the parameter analysis table to show how HoursAvailableInPlant2 varies correspondingly with the different values of HoursAvailableInPlant3. Also, we have calculated the incremental profit (in column F) for each hour shifted from Plant 3 to Plant 2.

Again there is a pattern to the incremental profit. For each hour shifted from Plant 3 to Plant 2 (up to 3 hours), an additional profit of $50 is achieved. However, if more than 3 hours are shifted, the incremental profit becomes −$250. Thus, it appears worthwhile to shift up to 3 available hours from Plant 3 to Plant 2, but no more.

Although a one-way parameter analysis report is limited to enumerating trial values for only one data cell, you have just seen how such a parameter analysis report still can systematically investigate a large number of simultaneous changes in two data cells by entering a formula for the second data cell in terms of the first one. The two data cells considered above happened to be right-hand sides of constraints, but either or both could have been coefficients on the left-hand side instead. It is even possible to enter formulas for multiple data cells in terms of the one whose trial values are being enumerated. Furthermore, by using a two-way parameter analysis report, trial values can be enumerated simultaneously for two data cells, with the possibility of entering formulas for additional data cells in terms of these two.

Gleaning Additional Information from the Sensitivity Report

Despite the versatility of a parameter analysis report, it cannot handle a number of important cases. The most important one is where management wants to explore various possibilities for changing its policy decisions that correspond to changing several right-hand sides

FIGURE 5.24

By inserting a formula into cell G8 that keeps the total number of hours available in Plant 2 and Plant 3 equal to 30, it will be possible to generate a one-way parameter analysis report (see Figure 5.25) that shows the effect of shifting more and more of the hours available from Plant 3 to Plant 2.

	A	B	C	D	E	F	G	H
1		**Wyndor Glass Co. Product-Mix Problem**						
2								
3			Doors	Windows				
4		Unit Profit	$300	$500				
5					Hours		Hours	
6			Hours Used per Unit Produced		Used		Available	
7		Plant 1	1	0	2	≤	4	Total (Plants 2 & 3)
8		Plant 2	0	2	12	≤	12	30
9		Plant 3	3	2	18	≤	18	
10								
11			Doors	Windows			Total Profit	
12		Units Produced	2	6			$3,600	

	G	H
5	Hours	
6	Available	
7	4	Total (Plants 2 & 3)
8	=H8-G9	30
9	18	

FIGURE 5.25

The parameter analysis report that shows the effect of shifting more and more of the hours available from Plant 3 to Plant 2 for the Wyndor problem.

	A	B	C	D	E	F
1	HoursAvailableInPlant2	HoursAvailableInPlant3	DoorsProduced	WindowsProduced	TotalProfit	Incremental Profit
2	12	18	2	6	$3,600	
3	13	17	1.333	6.5	$3,650	$50
4	14	16	0.667	7	$3,700	$50
5	15	15	0	7.5	$3,750	$50
6	16	14	0	7	$3,500	-$250
7	17	13	0	6.5	$3,250	-$250
8	18	12	0	6	$3,000	-$250

simultaneously in a variety of ways. Although the spreadsheet can be used to see the effect of any combination of simultaneous changes, it can take an exorbitant amount of time to systematically investigate a large number of simultaneous changes in right-hand sides in this way. Fortunately, Solver's sensitivity report provides valuable information for guiding such an investigation. In particular, there is a *100 percent rule* (analogous to the one presented in Section 5.4) that uses this information to conduct this kind of investigation.

Recall that the 100 percent rule described in Section 5.4 is used to investigate simultaneous changes in *objective function coefficients*. The new 100 percent rule presented next investigates simultaneous changes in *right-hand sides* in a similar way.

The data needed to apply the new 100 percent rule for the Wyndor problem are given by the last three columns in the bottom part of the sensitivity report in Figure 5.21. Keep in mind that we can safely use the entire allowable decrease or increase from the current value of a right-hand side only if none of the other right-hand sides are changed at all. With simultaneous changes in the right-hand sides, we focus for each change on the *percentage* of the allowable decrease or increase that is being used. As detailed next, the 100 percent rule basically says that we can safely make the simultaneous changes only if the *sum* of these percentages does not exceed 100 percent.

This 100 percent rule reveals whether the simultaneous changes in the right-hand sides are small enough to guarantee that the shadow prices are still valid.

The 100 Percent Rule for Simultaneous Changes in Right-Hand Sides: The shadow prices remain valid for predicting the effect of simultaneously changing the right-hand sides of some of the functional constraints as long as the changes are not too large. To check whether the changes are small enough, calculate for each change the percentage of the allowable change (decrease or increase) for that right-hand side to remain within its allowable range. If the *sum* of the percentage changes does *not* exceed 100 percent, the shadow prices definitely will still be valid. (If the sum *does* exceed 100 percent, then we cannot be sure.)

To illustrate this rule, consider again the simultaneous changes (shifting one hour of production time per week from Plant 3 to Plant 2) that led to Figure 5.23. The calculations for the 100 percent rule in this case are

RHS$_2$: 12 → 13

$$\text{Percentage of allowable increase} = 100\left(\frac{13 - 12}{6}\right) = 16\tfrac{2}{3}\%$$

RHS$_3$: 18 → 17

$$\text{Percentage of allowable decrease} = 100\left(\frac{18 - 17}{6}\right) = 16\tfrac{2}{3}\%$$

$$\text{Sum} = \overline{33\tfrac{1}{3}\%}$$

Since the sum of 33⅓ percent is less than 100 percent, the shadow prices definitely are valid for predicting the effect of these changes, as was illustrated with Figure 5.23.

The fact that 33⅓ percent is one-third of 100 percent suggests that the changes can be three times as large as above without invalidating the shadow prices. To check this, let us apply the 100 percent rule with these larger changes.

RHS$_2$: 12 → 15

$$\text{Percentage of allowable increase} = \left(\frac{15 - 12}{6}\right)\% = 50\%$$

RHS$_3$: 18 → 15

$$\text{Percentage of allowable decrease} = \left(\frac{18 - 15}{6}\right)\% = 50\%$$

$$\text{Sum} = \overline{100\%}$$

Because the sum does *not exceed* 100 percent, the shadow prices are still valid, but these are the largest changes in the right-hand sides that can provide this guarantee. In fact, Figure 5.25 demonstrated that the shadow prices become invalid for larger changes.

Review Questions

1. Why might it be of interest to investigate the effect of making simultaneous changes in the functional constraints?
2. How can the spreadsheet be used to investigate simultaneous changes in the functional constraints?
3. What are the capabilities of a parameter analysis report for investigating simultaneous changes in the functional constraints?
4. Why might a manager be interested in considering simultaneous changes in right-hand sides?
5. What is the 100 percent rule for simultaneous changes in right-hand sides?
6. What are the data needed to apply the 100 percent rule for simultaneous changes in right-hand sides?
7. What is guaranteed if the sum of the percentages of allowable changes in the right-hand sides does not exceed 100 percent?
8. What is the conclusion if the sum of the percentages of allowable changes in the right-hand sides does exceed 100 percent?

5.7 Summary

What-if analysis is analysis done *after* finding an optimal solution for the original version of the basic model. This analysis provides important insights to help guide managerial decision making. This chapter describes how this is done when the basic model is a linear programming model. The spreadsheet for the model, the parameter analysis report available with RSPE, and the sensitivity report generated by Solver all play a central role in this process.

The coefficients in the objective function typically represent quantities that can only be roughly estimated when the model is formulated. Will the optimal solution obtained from the model be the correct one if the true value of one of these coefficients is significantly different from the estimate used in the model? The spreadsheet can be used to quickly check specific changes in the coefficient. The parameter analysis report enables the systematic investigation of many trial values for this coefficient. For a broader investigation, the *allowable range* for each coefficient identifies the interval within which the true value must lie in order for this solution to still be the correct optimal solution. These ranges are easily calculated from the data in the sensitivity report provided by Solver.

What happens if there are significant inaccuracies in the estimates of two or more coefficients in the objective function? Specific simultaneous changes can be checked with the spreadsheet. A two-way parameter analysis report can systematically investigate various simultaneous changes in two coefficients. To go further, the *100 percent rule for simultaneous changes in objective function coefficients* provides a convenient way of checking whole ranges of simultaneous changes, again by using the data in Solver's sensitivity report.

What-if analysis usually extends to considering the effect of changes in the functional constraints as well. Occasionally, changes in the coefficients of these constraints will be considered because of the uncertainty in their original estimates. More frequently, the changes considered will be in the right-hand sides of the constraints. The right-hand sides frequently represent managerial policy decisions. In such cases, *shadow prices* provide valuable guidance to management about the potential effects of altering these policy decisions. The shadow price for each constraint is easily found by using the spreadsheet, a parameter analysis report, or the sensitivity report.

Shadow price analysis can be validly applied to investigate possible changes in right-hand sides as long as these changes are not too large. The *allowable range* for each right-hand side indicates just how far it can be changed, assuming no other changes are made. If other right-hand sides are changed as well, the *100 percent rule for simultaneous changes in right-hand sides* enables checking whether the changes definitely are not too large. Solver's sensitivity report provides the key information needed to find each allowable range or to apply this 100 percent rule. Both the spreadsheet and the parameter analysis report also can sometimes be used to help investigate these simultaneous changes.

Glossary

allowable range for an objective function coefficient The range of values for a particular coefficient in the objective function over which the optimal solution for the original model remains optimal. (Section 5.3), 158

allowable range for the right-hand side The range of values for the right-hand side of a functional constraint over which this constraint's shadow price remains valid. (Section 5.5), 172

parameter cell A data cell containing a parameter that will be systematically varied when generating a parameter analysis report. (Section 5.3), 157

parameters of the model The parameters of a linear programming model are the constants (coefficients or right-hand sides) in the functional constraints and the objective function. (Section 5.1), 151

sensitive parameter A parameter is considered sensitive if even a small change in its value can change the optimal solution. (Section 5.1), 151

sensitivity analysis The part of what-if analysis that focuses on individual parameters of the model. It involves checking how sensitive the optimal solution is to the value of each parameter. (Section 5.1), 152

shadow price The shadow price for a functional constraint is the rate at which the optimal value of the objective function can be increased by increasing the right-hand side of the constraint by a small amount. (Section 5.5), 172

what-if analysis Analysis that addresses questions about what would happen to the optimal solution if different assumptions were made about future conditions. (Chapter introduction), 150

180   Chapter Five   *What-If Analysis for Linear Programming*

Learning Aids for This Chapter in Your MS Courseware

Chapter 5 Excel Files:
Wyndor Example
Profit & Gambit Example

Excel Add-in:
Risk Solver Platform for Education (RSPE)

Interactive Management Science Modules:
Module for Graphical Linear Programming and Sensitivity Analysis

Supplement to Chapter 5 on the CD-ROM:
Reduced Costs

Solved Problem (See the CD-ROM or Website for the Solution)

5.S1. Sensitivity Analysis at Stickley Furniture

Stickley Furniture is a manufacturer of fine hand-crafted furniture. During the next production period, management is considering producing dining room tables, dining room chairs, and/or bookcases. The time required for each item to go through the two stages of production (assembly and finishing), the amount of wood required (fine cherry wood), and the corresponding unit profits are given in the following table, along with the amount of each resource available in the upcoming production period.

	Tables	Chairs	Bookcases	Available
Assembly (minutes)	80	40	50	8,100
Finishing) (minutes)	30	20	30	4,500
Wood (pounds)	80	10	50	9,000
Unit profit	$360	$125	$300	

After formulating a linear programming model to determine the production levels that would maximize profit, the solved model and the corresponding sensitivity report are shown below.

a. Suppose the profit per table increases by $100. Will this change the optimal production quantities? What can be said about the change in total profit?

b. Suppose the profit per chair increases by $100. Will this change the optimal production quantities? What can be said about the change in total profit?

c. Suppose the profit per table increases by $90 and the profit per bookcase decreases by $50. Will this change the optimal production quantities? What can be said about the change in total profit?

d. Suppose a worker in the assembly department calls in sick, so eight fewer hours now are available in the assembly department. How much would this affect total profit? Would it change the optimal production quantities?

e. Explain why the shadow price for the wood constraint is zero.

f. A new worker has been hired who is trained to do both assembly and finishing. She will split her time between the two areas, so there now are four additional hours available in both assembly and finishing. How much would this affect total profit? Would this change the optimal production quantities?

g. Based on the sensitivity report, is it wise to have the new worker in part *f* split her time equally between assembly and finishing, or would some other plan be better?

	B	C	D	E	F	G	H
3		Tables	Chairs	Bookcases			
4	Unit Profit	$360	$125	$300			
5							
6		Resources Required per Unit			Used		Available
7	Assembly (minutes)	80	40	50	8,100	<=	8,100
8	Finishing (minutes)	30	20	30	4,500	<=	4,500
9	Woods (pounds)	80	10	50	8,100	<=	9,000
10							
11		Tables	Chairs	Bookcases			Total Profit
12	Production	20	0	130			$46,200

Variable Cells

Cell	Name	Final Value	Reduced Cost	Objective Coefficient	Allowable Increase	Allowable Decrease
$C$12	Production Tables	20	0	360	120	60
$D$12	Production Chairs	0	−88.333	125	88.333	1E + 30
$E$12	Production Bookcases	130	0	300	60	75

Constraints

Cell	Name	Final Value	Shadow Price	Constraint R. H. Side	Allowable Increase	Allowable Decrease
$F$7	Assembly (minutes) Used	8,100	2	8,100	900	600
$F$8	Finishing (minutes) Used	4,500	6.67	4,500	360	1,462.5
$F$9	Wood (pounds) Used	8,100	0	9,000	1E + 30	900

h. Use a parameter analysis report to determine how the optimal production quantities and total profit will change depending on how the new worker in part *f* allocates her time between assembly and finishing. In particular, assume 0, 1, 2, . . . , or 8 hours are added to assembly, with a corresponding 8, 7, 6, . . . , or 0 hours added to finishing. (The original spreadsheet is contained on the CD included with the textbook.)

Problems

We have inserted the symbol E* to the left of each problem (or its parts) where Excel should be used (unless your instructor gives you contrary instructions). An asterisk on the problem number indicates that at least a partial answer is given in the back of the book.

5.1.* One of the products of the G. A. Tanner Company is a special kind of toy that provides an estimated unit profit of $3. Because of a large demand for this toy, management would like to increase its production rate from the current level of 1,000 per day. However, a limited supply of two subassemblies (A and B) from vendors makes this difficult. Each toy requires two subassemblies of type A, but the vendor providing these subassemblies would only be able to increase its supply rate from the current 2,000 per day to a maximum of 3,000 per day. Each toy requires only one subassembly of type B, but the vendor providing these subassemblies would be unable to increase its supply rate above the current level of 1,000 per day.

Because no other vendors currently are available to provide these subassemblies, management is considering initiating a new production process internally that would simultaneously produce an equal number of subassemblies of the two types to supplement the supply from the two vendors. It is estimated that the company's cost for producing one subassembly of each type would be $2.50 more than the cost of purchasing these subassemblies from the two vendors. Management wants to determine both the production rate of the toy and the production rate of each pair of subassemblies (one A and one B) that would maximize the total profit.

Viewing this problem as a resource-allocation problem, one of the company's managers has organized its data as follows:

Resource	Produce Toys	Produce Subassemblies	Amount of Resource Available
	Resource Usage per Unit of Each Activity		
Subassembly A	2	−1	3,000
Subassembly B	1	−1	1,000
Unit profit	$3	−$2.50	

E* *a.* Formulate and solve a spreadsheet model for this problem.

E* *b.* Since the stated unit profits for the two activities are only estimates, management wants to know how much

each of these estimates can be off before the optimal solution would change. Begin exploring this question for the first activity (producing toys) by using the spreadsheet and Solver to manually generate a table that gives the optimal solution and total profit as the unit profit for this activity increases in 50¢ increments from $2.00 to $4.00. What conclusion can be drawn about how much the estimate of this unit profit can differ in each direction from its original value of $3.00 before the optimal solution would change?

E* *c.* Repeat part *b* for the second activity (producing subassemblies) by generating a table as the unit profit for this activity increases in 50¢ increments from −$3.50 to −$1.50 (with the unit profit for the first activity fixed at $3).

E* *d.* Use a parameter analysis report to systematically generate all the data requested in parts *b* and *c*, except use 25¢ increments instead of 50¢ increments. Use these data to refine your conclusions in parts *b* and *c*.

E* *e.* Use Solver's sensitivity report to find the allowable range for the unit profit of each activity.

E* *f.* Use a two-way parameter analysis report to systematically generate the total profit as the unit profits of the two activities are changed simultaneously as described in parts *b* and *c*.

g. Use the information provided by Solver's sensitivity report to describe how far the unit profits of the two activities can change simultaneously before the optimal solution might change.

5.2. Consider a resource-allocation problem having the following data:

Resource	1	2	Amount of Resource Available
	Resource Usage per Unit of Each Activity		
1	1	2	10
2	1	3	12
Unit profit	$2	$5	

The objective is to determine the number of units of each activity to undertake so as to maximize the total profit.

While doing what-if analysis, you learn that the estimates of the unit profits are accurate only to within ± 50 percent. In other words, the ranges of *likely values* for these unit profits are $1 to $3 for activity 1 and $2.50 to $7.50 for activity 2.

E* *a.* Formulate a spreadsheet model for this problem based on the original estimates of the unit profits. Then use Solver to find an optimal solution and to generate the sensitivity report.

E* *b.* Use the spreadsheet and Solver to check whether this optimal solution remains optimal if the unit profit for activity 1 changes from $2 to $1. From $2 to $3.

E* *c.* Also check whether the optimal solution remains optimal if the unit profit for activity 1 still is $2 but the unit profit for activity 2 changes from $5 to $2.50. From $5 to $7.50.

E* *d.* Use a parameter analysis report to systematically generate the optimal solution and total profit as the unit profit of activity 1 increases in 20¢ increments from $1 to $3 (without changing the unit profit of activity 2). Then do the same as the unit profit of activity 2 increases in 50¢ increments from $2.50 to $7.50 (without changing the unit profit of activity 1). Use these results to estimate the allowable range for the unit profit of each activity.

E* *e.* Use the Graphical Linear Programming and Sensitivity Analysis module in your Interactive Management Science Modules to estimate the allowable range for the unit profit of each activity.

E* *f.* Use the sensitivity report to find the allowable range for the unit profit of each activity. Then use these ranges to check your results in parts *b-e*.

E* *g.* Use a two-way parameter analysis report to systematically generate the optimal total profit as the unit profits of the two activities are changed simultaneously as described in part *d*.

h. Use the Graphical Linear Programming and Sensitivity Analysis module to interpret the results in part *g* graphically.

E*5.3. Consider the Big M Co. problem presented in Section 3.5, including the spreadsheet in Figure 3.10 showing its formulation and optimal solution.

There is some uncertainty about what the unit costs will be for shipping through the various shipping lanes. Therefore, before adopting the optimal solution in Figure 3.10, management wants additional information about the effect of inaccuracies in estimating these unit costs.

Use Solver to generate the sensitivity report preparatory to addressing the following questions.

a. Which of the unit shipping costs given in Table 3.9 has the smallest margin for error without invalidating the optimal solution given in Figure 3.10? Where should the greatest effort be placed in estimating the unit shipping costs?

b. What is the allowable range for each of the unit shipping costs?

c. How should the allowable range be interpreted to management?

d. If the estimates change for more than one of the unit shipping costs, how can you use the sensitivity report to determine whether the optimal solution might change?

E*5.4.* Consider the Union Airways problem presented in Section 3.3, including the spreadsheet in Figure 3.5 showing its formulation and optimal solution.

Management is about to begin negotiations on a new contract with the union that represents the company's customer service agents. This might result in some small changes in the daily costs per agent given in Table 3.5 for the various shifts. Several possible changes listed below are being considered separately. In each case, management would like to know whether the change might result in the solution in Figure 3.5 no longer being optimal. Answer this question in parts *a* to *e* by using the spreadsheet and Solver directly. If the optimal solution changes, record the new solution.

a. The daily cost per agent for shift 2 changes from $160 to $165.

b. The daily cost per agent for shift 4 changes from $180 to $170.

c. The changes in parts *a* and *b* both occur.

d. The daily cost per agent increases by $4 for shifts 2, 4, and 5, but decreases by $4 for shifts 1 and 3.

e. The daily cost per agent increases by 2 percent for each shift.

f. Use Solver to generate the sensitivity report for this problem. Suppose that the above changes are being considered later without having the spreadsheet model immediately available on a computer. Show in each case how the sensitivity report can be used to check whether the original optimal solution must still be optimal.

g. For each of the five shifts in turn, use a parameter analysis report to systematically generate the optimal solution and total cost when the only change is that the daily cost per agent on that shift increases in $3 increments from $15 less than the current cost up to $15 more than the current cost.

E*5.5. Consider the Think-Big Development Co. problem presented in Section 3.2, including the spreadsheet in Figure 3.3 showing its formulation and optimal solution. In parts *a-g*, use the spreadsheet and Solver to check whether the optimal solution would change and, if so, what the new optimal solution would be, if the estimates in Table 3.3 of the net present values of the projects were to be changed in each of the following ways. (Consider each part by itself.)

a. The net present value of project 1 (a high-rise office building) increases by $200,000.

b. The net present value of project 2 (a hotel) increases by $200,000.

c. The net present value of project 1 decreases by $5 million.

d. The net present value of project 3 (a shopping center) decreases by $200,000.

e. All three changes in parts *b, c,* and *d* occur simultaneously.

f. The net present values of projects 1, 2, and 3 change to $46 million, $69 million, and $49 million, respectively.

g. The net present values of projects 1, 2, and 3 change to $54 million, $84 million, and $60 million, respectively.

h. Use Solver to generate the sensitivity report for this problem. For each of the preceding parts, suppose that the change occurs later without having the spreadsheet model immediately available on a computer. Show in each case how the sensitivity report can be used to check whether the original optimal solution must still be optimal.

i. For each of the three projects in turn, use a parameter analysis report to systematically generate the optimal solution and the total net present value when the only change is that the net present value of that project increases in $1 million increments from $5 million less than the current value up to $5 million more than the current value.

5.6. Read the referenced article that fully describes the management science study summarized in the application vignette presented in Section 5.4. Briefly describe how what-if analysis was applied in this study. Then list the various financial and nonfinancial benefits that resulted from this study.

5.7. University Ceramics manufactures plates, mugs, and steins that include the campus name and logo for sale in campus bookstores. The time required for each item to go through the two stages of production (molding and finishing), the material required (clay), and the corresponding unit profits are given in the following table, along with the amount of each resource available in the upcoming production period.

	Plates	Mugs	Steins	Available
Molding (minutes)	4	6	3	2,400
Finishing (minutes)	8	14	12	7,200
Clay (ounces)	5	4	3	3,000
Unit Profit	$3.10	$4.75	$4.00	

A linear programming model has been formulated in a spreadsheet to determine the production levels that would maximize profit. The solved spreadsheet model and corresponding sensitivity report are shown below.

For each of the following parts, answer the question as specifically and completely as is possible without re-solving the problem with Solver. *Note:* Each part is independent (i.e., any change made in one part does not apply to any other parts).

a. Suppose the profit per plate decreases from $3.10 to $2.80. Will this change the optimal production quantities? What can be said about the change in total profit?

b. Suppose the profit per stein *increases* by $0.30 and the profit per plate *decreases* by $0.25. Will this change the optimal production quantities? What can be said about the change in total profit?

	A	B	C	D	E	F	G
1		Plates	Mugs	Steins			
2	Unit Profit	$3.10	$4.75	$4.00			
3							
4		Resource Required per Unit			Used		Available
5	Molding (minutes)	4	6	3	2,400	<=	2,400
6	Finishing (minutes)	8	14	12	7,200	<=	7,200
7	Clay (ounces)	5	4	3	2,700	<=	3,000
8							
9		Plates	Mugs	Steins			Total Profit
10	Production	300	0	400			$2,530

Variable Cells

Cell	Name	Final Value	Reduced Cost	Objective Coefficient	Allowable Increase	Allowable Decrease
$B$10	Production Plates	300	0	3.10	2.23	0.37
$C$10	Production Mugs	0	−0.46	4.75	0.46	
$D$10	Production Steins	400	0	4.00	0.65	1.37

Constraints

Cell	Name	Final Value	Shadow Price	Constraint R. H. Side	Allowable Increase	Allowable Decrease
$E$5	Molding (minutes) Used	2,400	0.22	2400	200	600
$E$6	Finishing (minutes) Used	7,200	0.28	7200	2400	2400
$E$7	Cream (ounces) Used	2,700	0	3000	1E + 30	

c. Suppose a worker in the molding department calls in sick. Now eight fewer hours are available that day in the molding department. How much would this affect total profit? Would it change the optimal production quantities?

d. Suppose one of the workers in the molding department is also trained to do finishing. Would it be a good idea to have this worker shift some of her time from the molding department to the finishing department? Indicate the rate at which this would increase or decrease total profit per minute shifted. How many minutes can be shifted before this rate might change?

e. The allowable decrease for the mugs' objective coefficient and for the available clay constraint are both missing from the sensitivity report. What numbers should be there? Explain how you were able to deduce each number.

5.8. Ken and Larry, Inc., supplies its ice cream parlors with three flavors of ice cream: chocolate, vanilla, and banana. Due to extremely hot weather and a high demand for its products, the company has run short of its supply of ingredients: milk, sugar, and cream. Hence, they will not be able to fill all the orders received from their retail outlets, the ice cream parlors. Due to these circumstances, the company has decided to choose the amount of each flavor to produce that will maximize total profit, given the constraints on the supply of the basic ingredients.

The chocolate, vanilla, and banana flavors generate, respectively, $1.00, $0.90, and $0.95 of profit per gallon sold. The

company has only 200 gallons of milk, 150 pounds of sugar, and 60 gallons of cream left in its inventory. The linear programming formulation for this problem is shown below in algebraic form.

Let

C = Gallons of chocolate ice cream produced

V = Gallons of vanilla ice cream produced

B = Gallons of banana ice cream produced

Maximize   Profit = $1.00C + 0.90V + 0.95B$

subject to

Milk: $0.45C + 0.50V + 0.40B \leq 200$ gallons

Sugar: $0.50C + 0.40V + 0.40B \leq 150$ pounds

Cream: $0.10C + 0.15V + 0.20B \leq 60$ gallons

and

$$C \geq 0 \quad V \geq 0 \quad B \geq 0$$

This problem was solved using Solver. The spreadsheet (already solved) and the sensitivity report are shown below. (*Note:* The numbers in the sensitivity report for the milk constraint are missing on purpose, since you will be asked to fill in these numbers in part *f*.)

For each of the following parts, answer the question as specifically and completely as possible without solving the problem again with Solver. *Note:* Each part is independent (i.e., any change made to the model in one part does not apply to any other parts).

	A	B	C	D	E	F	G
1		Chocolate	Vanilla	Banana			
2	Unit Profit	$1.00	$0.90	$0.95			
3							
4	Resource	Resources Used per Gallon Produced			Used		Available
5	Milk	0.45	0.5	0.4	180	≤	200
6	Sugar	0.5	0.4	0.4	150	≤	150
7	Cream	0.1	0.15	0.2	60	≤	60
8							
9		Chocolate	Vanilla	Banana			Total Profit
10	Gallons Produced	0	300	75			$341.25

Variable Cells

Cell	Name	Final Value	Reduced Cost	Objective Coefficient	Allowable Increase	Allowable Decrease
$B$10	Gallons Produced Chocolate	0	−0.0375	1	0.0375	1E + 30
$C$10	Gallons Produced Vanilla	300	0	0.9	0.05	0.0125
$D$10	Gallons Produced Banana	75	0	0.95	0.0214	0.05

Constraints

Cell	Name	Final Value	Shadow Price	Constraint R. H. Side	Allowable Increase	Allowable Decrease
$E$5	Milk Used					
$E$6	Sugar Used	150	1.875	150	10	30
$E$7	Cream Used	60	1	60	15	3.75

a. What is the optimal solution and total profit?

b. Suppose the profit per gallon of banana changes to $1.00. Will the optimal solution change and what can be said about the effect on total profit?

c. Suppose the profit per gallon of banana changes to 92¢. Will the optimal solution change and what can be said about the effect on total profit?

d. Suppose the company discovers that three gallons of cream have gone sour and so must be thrown out. Will the optimal solution change and what can be said about the effect on total profit?

e. Suppose the company has the opportunity to buy an additional 15 pounds of sugar at a total cost of $15. Should it do so? Explain.

f. Fill in all the sensitivity report information for the milk constraint, given just the optimal solution for the problem. Explain how you were able to deduce each number.

5.9.   Colonial Furniture produces hand-crafted colonial style furniture. Plans are now being made for the production of rocking chairs, dining room tables, and/or armoires over the next week. These products go through two stages of production (assembly and finishing). The following table gives the time required for each item to go through these two stages, the amount of wood required (fine cherry wood), and the corresponding unit profits, along with the amount of each resource available next week.

	Rocking Chair	Dining Room Table	Armoire	Available
Assembly (minutes)	100	180	120	3,600
Finishing (minutes)	60	80	80	2,000
Wood (pounds)	30	180	120	4,000
Unit Profit	$240	$720	$600	

A linear programming model has been formulated in a spreadsheet to determine the production levels that would maximize profit. The solved spreadsheet model and corresponding sensitivity report are shown below.

For each of the following parts, answer the question as specifically and completely as is possible without re-solving the problem with Solver. *Note*: Each part is independent (i.e., any change made in one problem part does not apply to any other parts).

a. Suppose the profit per armoire decreases by $50. Will this change the optimal production quantities? What can be said about the change in total profit?

b. Suppose the profit per table decreases by $60 and the profit per armoire increases by $90. Will this change the optimal production quantities? What can be said about the change in total profit?

	A	B	C	D	E	F	G
1		Rocking	Dining Room				
2		Chair	Table	Armoire			
3	Unit Profit	$240	$720	$600			
4							
5		Resource Required per Unit			Used		Available
6	Assembly (minutes)	100	180	120	3,600	<=	3,600
7	Finishing (minutes)	60	80	80	2,000	<=	2,000
8	Wood (pounds)	30	180	120	3,600	<=	4,000
9							
10		Rocking	Dining Room				
11		Chair	Table	Armoire			Total Profit
12	Production	0	10	15			$16,200

Variable Cells

Cell	Name	Final Value	Reduced Cost	Objective Coefficient	Allowable Increase	Allowable Decrease
$B$12	Production Chair	0	−230	240	230	1E + 30
$C$12	Production Table	10	0	720	180	120
$D$12	Production Armoire	15	0	600	120	120

Constraints

Cell	Name	Final Value	Shadow Price	Constraint R. H. Side	Allowable Increase	Allowable Decrease
$E$6	Assembly (minutes) Used	3,600	2.00	3,600	400	600
$E$7	Finishing (minutes) Used	2,000	4.50	2,000	400	400
$E$8	Wood (pounds) Used	3,600		4,000		

c. Suppose a part-time worker in the assembly department calls in sick, so that now four fewer hours are available that day in the assembly department. How much would this affect total profit? Would it change the optimal production quantities?

d. Suppose one of the workers in the assembly department is also trained to do finishing. Would it be a good idea to have this worker shift some of his time from the assembly department to the finishing department? Indicate the rate at which this would increase or decrease total profit per minute shifted. How many minutes can be shifted before this rate might change?

e. The shadow price and allowable range for the wood constraint are missing from the sensitivity report. What numbers should be there? Explain how you were able to deduce each number.

5.10.   David, LaDeana, and Lydia are the sole partners and workers in a company that produces fine clocks. David and LaDeana are each available to work a maximum of 40 hours per week at the company, while Lydia is available to work a maximum of 20 hours per week.

The company makes two different types of clocks: a grandfather clock and a wall clock. To make a clock, David (a mechanical engineer) assembles the inside mechanical parts of the clock while LaDeana (a woodworker) produces the hand-carved wood casings. Lydia is responsible for taking orders and shipping the clocks. The amount of time required for each of these tasks is shown next.

	Time Required	
	---	---
Task	**Grandfather Clock**	**Wall Clock**
Assemble clock mechanism	6 hours	4 hours
Carve wood casing	8 hours	4 hours
Shipping	3 hours	3 hours

Each grandfather clock built and shipped yields a profit of $300, while each wall clock yields a profit of $200.

The three partners now want to determine how many clocks of each type should be produced per week to maximize the total profit.

a. Formulate a linear programming model in algebraic form for this problem.

b. Use the Graphical Linear Programming and Sensitivity Analysis module in your Interactive Management Science Modules to solve the model. Then use this module to check if the optimal solution would change if the unit profit for grandfather clocks were changed from $300 to $375 (with no other changes in the model). Then check if the optimal solution would change if, in addition to this change in the unit profit for grandfather clocks, the estimated unit profit for wall clocks also changed from $200 to $175.

E*   *c.* Formulate and solve the original version of this model on a spreadsheet.

E*   *d.* Use Solver to check the effect of the changes specified in part *b*.

E*   *e.* Use a parameter analysis report to systematically generate the optimal solution and total profit as the unit profit for grandfather clocks is increased in $20 increments from $150 to $450 (with no change in the unit profit for wall clocks). Then do the same as the unit profit for wall clocks is increased in $20 increments from $50 to $350 (with no change in the unit profit for grandfather clocks). Use this information to estimate the allowable range for the unit profit of each type of clock.

E*   *f.* Use a two-way parameter analysis report to systematically generate the optimal total profit as the unit profits for the two types of clocks are changed simultaneously as specified in part *e*, except use $50 increments instead of $20 increments.

E*   *g.* For each of the three partners in turn, use Solver to determine the effect on the optimal solution and the total profit if that partner alone were to increase his or her maximum number of work hours available per week by 5 hours.

E*   *h.* Use a parameter analysis report to systematically generate the optimal solution and the total profit when the only change is that David's maximum number of hours available to work per week changes to each of the following values: 35, 37, 39, 41, 43, 45. Then do the same when the only change is that LaDeana's maximum number of hours available to work per week changes in the same way. Then do the same when the only change is that Lydia's maximum number of hours available to work per week changes to each of the following values: 15, 17, 19, 21, 23, 25.

E*   *i.* Generate a sensitivity report and use it to determine the allowable range for the unit profit for each type of clock and the allowable range for the maximum number of hours each partner is available to work per week.

j. To increase the total profit, the three partners have agreed that one of them will slightly increase the maximum number of hours available to work per week. The choice of which one will be based on which one would increase the total profit the most. Use the sensitivity report to make this choice. (Assume no change in the original estimates of the unit profits.)

k. Explain why one of the shadow prices is equal to zero.

l. Can the shadow prices in the sensitivity report be validly used to determine the effect if Lydia were to change her maximum number of hours available to work per week from 20 to 25? If so, what would be the increase in the total profit?

m. Repeat part *l* if, in addition to the change for Lydia, David also were to change his maximum number of hours available to work per week from 40 to 35.

n. Use graphical analysis to verify your answer in part *m*.

E*5.11.* Reconsider Problem 5.1. After further negotiations with each vendor, management of the G. A. Tanner Company has learned that either of them would be willing to consider increasing their supply of their respective subassemblies over the previously stated maxima (3,000 subassemblies of type A per day and 1,000 of type B per day) if the company would pay a small premium over the regular price for the extra subassemblies. The size of the premium for each type of subassembly remains to be negotiated. The demand for the toy being produced is sufficiently high that 2,500 per day could be sold if the supply of subassemblies could be increased enough to support this production rate. Assume that the original estimates of unit profits given in Problem 5.1 are accurate.

    a. Formulate and solve a spreadsheet model for this problem with the original maximum supply levels and the additional constraint that no more than 2,500 toys should be produced per day.

    b. Without considering the premium, use the spreadsheet and Solver to determine the shadow price for the subassembly A constraint by solving the model again after increasing the maximum supply by one. Use this shadow price to determine the maximum premium that the company should be willing to pay for each subassembly of this type.

    c. Repeat part *b* for the subassembly B constraint.

    d. Estimate how much the maximum supply of subassemblies of type A could be increased before the shadow price (and the corresponding premium) found in part *b* would no longer be valid by using a parameter analysis report to generate the optimal solution and total profit (excluding the premium) as the maximum supply increases in increments of 100 from 3,000 to 4,000.

    e. Repeat part *d* for subassemblies of type B by using a parameter analysis report as the maximum supply increases in increments of 100 from 1,000 to 2,000.

    f. Use Solver's sensitivity report to determine the shadow price for each of the subassembly constraints and the allowable range for the right-hand side of each of these constraints.

E*5.12. Reconsider the model given in Problem 5.2. While doing what-if analysis, you learn that the estimates of the right-hand sides of the two functional constraints are accurate only to within ± 50 percent. In other words, the ranges of *likely values* for these parameters are 5 to 15 for the first right-hand side and 6 to 18 for the second right-hand side.

    a. After solving the original spreadsheet model, determine the shadow price for the first functional constraint by increasing its right-hand side by one and solving again.

    b. Use a parameter analysis report to generate the optimal solution and total profit as the right-hand side of the first functional constraint is incremented by 1 from 5 to 15. Use this table to estimate the allowable range for this right-hand side, that is, the range over which the shadow price obtained in part *a* is valid.

    c. Repeat part *a* for the second functional constraint.

    d. Repeat part *b* for the second functional constraint where its right-hand side is incremented by 1 from 6 to 18.

    e. Use Solver's sensitivity report to determine the shadow price for each functional constraint and the allowable range for the right-hand side of each of these constraints.

5.13. Consider a resource-allocation problem having the following data:

Resource	Resource Usage per Unit of Each Activity		Amount of Resource Available
	1	2	
1	1	3	8
2	1	1	4
Unit profit	$1	$2	

    The objective is to determine the number of units of each activity to undertake so as to maximize the total profit.

    a. Use the graphical method to solve this model.

    b. Use graphical analysis to determine the shadow price for each of these resources by solving again after increasing the amount of the resource available by one.

E*   *c.* Use the spreadsheet model and Solver instead to do parts *a* and *b*.

E*   *d.* For each resource in turn, use a parameter analysis report to systematically generate the optimal solution and the total profit when the only change is that the amount of that resource available increases in increments of 1 from 4 less than the original value up to 6 more than the original value. Use these results to estimate the allowable range for the amount available for each resource.

E*   *e.* Use Solver's sensitivity report to obtain the shadow prices. Also use this report to find the range for the amount of each resource available over which the corresponding shadow price remains valid.

    f. Describe why these shadow prices are useful when management has the flexibility to change the amounts of the resources being made available.

5.14. Follow the instructions of Problem 5.13 for a resource-allocation problem that again has the objective of maximizing total profit and that has the following data:

Resource	Resource Usage per Unit of Each Activity		Amount of Resource Available
	1	2	
1	1	0	4
2	1	3	15
3	2	1	10
Unit profit	$3	$2	

188   Chapter Five   *What-If Analysis for Linear Programming*

E*5.15.* Consider the Super Grain Corp. case study as presented in Section 3.1, including the spreadsheet in Figure 3.1 showing its formulation and optimal solution. Use Solver to generate the sensitivity report. Then use this report to independently address each of the following questions.

    a. How much could the total expected number of exposures be increased for each additional $1,000 added to the advertising budget?

    b. Your answer in part *a* would remain valid for how large of an increase in the advertising budget?

    c. How much could the total expected number of exposures be increased for each additional $1,000 added to the planning budget?

    d. Your answer in part *c* would remain valid for how large of an increase in the planning budget?

    e. Would your answers in parts *a* and *c* definitely remain valid if *both* the advertising budget and planning budget were increased by $100,000 each?

    f. If only $100,000 can be added to *either* the advertising budget or the planning budget, where should it be added to do the most good?

    g. If $100,000 must be *removed* from either the advertising budget or the planning budget, from which budget should it be removed to do the least harm?

E*5.16.* Follow the instructions of Problem 5.15 for the continuation of the Super Grain Corp. case study as presented in Section 3.4 including the spreadsheet in Figure 3.7 showing its formulation and optimal solution.

E*5.17.* Consider the Union Airways problem presented in Section 3.3, including the spreadsheet in Figure 3.5 showing its formulation and optimal solution.

Management now is considering increasing the level of service provided to customers by increasing one or more of the numbers in the rightmost column of Table 3.5 for the minimum number of agents needed in the various time periods. To guide them in making this decision, they would like to know what impact this change would have on total cost.

Use Solver to generate the sensitivity report in preparation for addressing the following questions.

    a. Which of the numbers in the rightmost column of Table 3.5 can be increased without increasing total cost? In each case, indicate how much it can be increased (if it is the only one being changed) without increasing total cost.

    b. For each of the other numbers, how much would the total cost increase per increase of 1 in the number? For each answer, indicate how much the number can be increased (if it is the only one being changed) before the answer is no longer valid.

    c. Do your answers in part *b* definitely remain valid if all the numbers considered in part *b* are simultaneously increased by 1?

    d. Do your answers in part *b* definitely remain valid if all 10 numbers are simultaneously increased by 1?

    e. How far can all 10 numbers be simultaneously increased by the same amount before your answers in part *b* may no longer be valid?

Case 5-1

Selling Soap

Reconsider the **Profit & Gambit Co.** advertising-mix problem presented in Section 2.7. Recall that a major advertising campaign is being planned that will focus on three key products: a stain remover, a liquid detergent, and a powder detergent. Management has made the following policy decisions about what needs to be achieved by this campaign.

• Sales of the stain remover should increase by at least 3 percent.

• Sales of the liquid detergent should increase by at least 18 percent.

• Sales of the powder detergent should increase by at least 4 percent.

The spreadsheet in Figure 2.21 shows the linear programming model that was formulated for this problem. The minimum required increases in the sales of the three products are given in the data cells Minimum Increase (G8:G10). The changing cells Advertising Units (C14:D14) indicate that an optimal solution for the model is to undertake four units of advertising on television and three units of advertising in the print media. The objective cell TotalCost (G14) shows that the total cost for this advertising campaign would be $10 million.

After receiving this information, Profit & Gambit management now wants to analyze the trade-off between the total advertising cost and the resulting benefits achieved by increasing the sales of the three products. Therefore, a management science team (you) has been given the assignment of developing the information that management will need to analyze this trade-off and decide whether it should change any of its policy decisions regarding the required minimum increases in the sales of the three products. In particular, management needs some detailed information about how the total advertising cost would change if it were to change any or all of these policy decisions.

a. For each of the three products in turn, use graphical analysis to determine how much the total advertising cost would change if the required minimum increase in the sales of that product were to be increased by 1 percent (without changing the required minimum increases for the other two products).

b. Use the spreadsheet shown in Figure 2.21 (available on the CD-ROM) to obtain the information requested in part *a*.

c. For each of the three products in turn, use a parameter analysis report to determine how the optimal solution for the model and the resulting total advertising cost would change if the required minimum increase in the sales of that product were to be systematically varied over a range of values (without changing the required minimum increases for the other two products). In each case, start the range of values at 0 percent and increase by 1 percent increments up to double the original minimum required increase.

d. Use Solver to generate the sensitivity report and indicate how the report is able to provide the information requested in part *a*. Also use the report to obtain the allowable range for the required minimum increase in the sales of each product. Interpret how each of these allowable ranges relates to the results obtained in part *c*.

e. Suppose that all the original numbers in Minimum Increase (G8:G10) were to be increased simultaneously by the same amount. How large can this amount be before the shadow prices provided by the sensitivity report may no longer be valid?

f. Below is the beginning of a memorandum from the management science team to Profit & Gambit management that is intended to provide management with the information it needs to perform its trade-off analysis. Write the rest of this memorandum based on a summary of the results obtained in the preceding parts. Present your information in clear, simple terms that use the language of management. Avoid technical terms such as shadow prices, allowable ranges, and so forth.

MEMORANDUM

To: Profit & Gambit management
From: The Management Science Team
Subject: The trade-off between advertising expenditures and increased sales

As instructed, we have been continuing our analysis of the plans for the major new advertising campaign that will focus on our spray prewash stain remover, our liquid formulation laundry detergent, and our powder laundry detergent.

Our recent report presented our preliminary conclusions on how much advertising to do in the different media to meet the sales goals at a minimum total cost:

Allocate $4 million to advertising on television.

Allocate $6 million to advertising in the print media.

Total advertising cost: $10 million.

We estimate that the resulting increases in sales will be

Stain remover:	3 percent increase in sales
Liquid detergent:	18 percent increase in sales
Powder detergent:	8 percent increase in sales

You had specified that these increases should be at least 3 percent, 18 percent, and 4 percent, respectively, so we have met the minimum levels for the first two products and substantially exceeded it for the third.

However, you also indicated that your decisions on these minimum required increases in sales (3 percent, 18 percent, and 4 percent) had been tentative ones. Now that we have more specific information on what the advertising costs and the resulting increases in sales will be, you plan to reevaluate these decisions to see if small changes might improve the trade-off between advertising cost and increased sales.

To assist you in reevaluating your decisions, we now have analyzed this trade-off for each of the three products. Our best estimates are the following.

Case 5-2

Controlling Air Pollution

The **Nori & Leets Co.** is one of the major producers of steel in its part of the world. It is located in the city of Steeltown and is the only large employer there. Steeltown has grown and prospered along with the company, which now employs nearly 50,000 residents. Therefore, the attitude of the townspeople always has been, "What's good for Nori & Leets is good for the town." However, this attitude is now changing; uncontrolled air pollution from the company's furnaces is ruining the appearance of the city and endangering the health of its residents.

A recent stockholders' revolt resulted in the election of a new enlightened board of directors for the company. These directors are determined to follow socially responsible policies, and they have been discussing with Steeltown city officials and citizens' groups what to do about the air pollution problem. Together they have worked out stringent air quality standards for the Steeltown airshed.

The three main types of pollutants in this airshed are particulate matter, sulfur oxides, and hydrocarbons. The new standards require that the company reduce its annual emission of these pollutants by the amounts shown in the following table.

Pollutant	Required Reduction in Annual Emission Rate (million pounds)
Particulates	60
Sulfur oxides	150
Hydrocarbons	125

The board of directors has instructed management to have the engineering staff determine how to achieve these reductions in the most economical way.

The steelworks have two primary sources of pollution, namely, the blast furnaces for making pig iron and the open-hearth furnaces for changing iron into steel. In both cases, the engineers have decided that the most effective abatement methods are (1) increasing the height of the smokestacks,[1] (2) using filter devices (including gas traps) in the smokestacks, and (3) including cleaner, high-grade materials among the fuels for the furnaces. Each of these methods has a technological limit on how heavily it can be used (e.g., a maximum feasible increase in the height of the smokestacks), but there also is considerable flexibility for using the method at a fraction of its technological limit.

The next table shows how much emissions (in millions of pounds per year) can be eliminated from each type of furnace by fully using any abatement method to its technological limit.

is not substantially affected by whether or not the other methods also are used.

After these data were developed, it became clear that no single method by itself could achieve all the required reductions. On the other hand, combining all three methods at full capacity on both types of furnaces (which would be prohibitively expensive if the company's products are to remain competitively priced) is much more than adequate. Therefore, the engineers concluded that they would have to use some combination of the methods, perhaps with fractional capacities, based on their relative costs. Furthermore, because of the differences between the blast and the open-hearth furnaces, the two types probably should not use the same combination.

An analysis was conducted to estimate the total annual cost that would be incurred by each abatement method. A method's annual cost includes increased operating and maintenance expenses, as well as reduced revenue due to any loss in the efficiency of the production process caused by using the method. The other major cost is the start-up cost (the initial capital outlay) required to install the method. To make this one-time cost commensurable with the ongoing annual costs, the time value of money was used to calculate the annual expenditure that would be equivalent in value to this start-up cost.

This analysis led to the total annual cost estimates given in the next table for using the methods at their full abatement capacities.

Total Annual Cost from the Maximum Feasible Use of an Abatement Method

Abatement Method	Blast Furnaces	Open-Hearth Furnaces
Taller smokestacks	$8 million	$10 million
Filters	7 million	6 million
Better fuels	11 million	9 million

Reduction in Emission Rate from the Maximum Feasible Use of an Abatement Method

Pollutant	Taller Smokestacks Blast Furnaces	Taller Smokestacks Open-Hearth Furnaces	Filters Blast Furnaces	Filters Open-Hearth Furnaces	Better Fuels Blast Furnaces	Better Fuels Open-Hearth Furnaces
Particulates	12	9	25	20	17	13
Sulfur oxides	35	42	18	31	56	49
Hydrocarbons	37	53	28	24	29	20

For purposes of analysis, it is assumed that each method also can be used to less fully used to achieve any fraction of the abatement capacities shown in this table. Furthermore, the fractions can be different for blast furnaces and open-hearth furnaces. For either type of furnace, the emission reduction achieved by each method

It also was determined that the cost of a method being used at a lower level is roughly proportional to the fraction of the abatement capacity (given in the preceding table) that is achieved. Thus, for any given fraction achieved, the total annual cost would be roughly that fraction of the corresponding quantity in the cost table.

The stage now is set to develop the general framework of the company's plan for pollution abatement. This plan needs to specify which types of abatement methods will be used and at what fractions of their abatement capacities for (1) the blast furnaces and (2) the open-hearth furnaces.

You have been asked to head a management science team to analyze this problem. Management wants you to begin by

[1] Subsequent to this study, this particular abatement method has become a controversial one. Because its effect is to reduce ground-level pollution by spreading emissions over a greater distance, environmental groups contend that this creates more acid rain by keeping sulfur oxides in the air longer. Consequently, the U.S. Environmental Protection Agency adopted new rules to remove incentives for using tall smokestacks.

determining which plan would minimize the total annual cost of achieving the required reductions in annual emission rates for the three pollutants.

a. Identify verbally the components of a linear programming model for this problem.

b. Display the model on a spreadsheet.

c. Obtain an optimal solution and generate the sensitivity report.

Management now wants to conduct some what-if analysis with your help. Since the company does not have much prior experience with the pollution abatement methods under consideration, the cost estimates given in the third table are fairly rough, and each one could easily be off by as much as 10 percent in either direction. There also is some uncertainty about the values given in the second table, but less so than for the third table. By contrast, the values in the first table are policy standards and so are prescribed constants.

However, there still is considerable debate about where to set these policy standards on the required reductions in the emission rates of the various pollutants. The numbers in the first table actually are preliminary values tentatively agreed upon before learning what the total cost would be to meet these standards. Both the city and company officials agree that the final decision on these policy standards should be based on the *trade-off* between costs and benefits. With this in mind, the city has concluded that each 10 percent increase in the policy standards over the current values (all the numbers in the first table) would be worth $3.5 million to the city. Therefore, the city has agreed to reduce the company's tax payments to the city by $3.5 million for *each* 10 percent increase in the policy standards (up to 50 percent) that is accepted by the company.

Finally, there has been some debate about the *relative* values of the policy standards for the three pollutants. As indicated in the first table, the required reduction for particulates now is less than half of that for either sulfur oxides or hydrocarbons. Some have argued for decreasing this disparity. Others contend that an even greater disparity is justified because sulfur oxides and hydrocarbons cause considerably more damage than particulates. Agreement has been reached that this issue will be reexamined after information is obtained about which trade-offs in

policy standards (increasing one while decreasing another) are available without increasing the total cost.

d. Identify the parameters of the linear programming model that should be classified as *sensitive parameters*. Make a resulting recommendation about which parameters should be estimated more closely, if possible.

e. Analyze the effect of an inaccuracy in estimating each cost parameter given in the third table. If the true value were 10 percent less than the estimated value, would this change the optimal solution? Would it change if the true value were 10 percent more than the estimated value? Make a resulting recommendation about where to focus further work in estimating the cost parameters more closely.

f. For each pollutant, specify the rate at which the total cost of an optimal solution would change with any small change in the required reduction in the annual emission rate of the pollutant. Also specify how much this required reduction can be changed (up or down) without affecting the rate of change in the total cost.

g. For each unit change in the policy standard for particulates given in the first table, determine the change in the opposite direction for sulfur oxides that would keep the total cost of an optimal solution unchanged. Repeat this for hydrocarbons instead of sulfur oxides. Then do it for a simultaneous and equal change for both sulfur oxides and hydrocarbons in the opposite direction from particulates.

h. Letting θ denote the percentage increase in all the policy standards given in the first table, use a parameter analysis report to systematically find an optimal solution and the total cost for the revised linear programming problem for each $\theta = 10, 20, 30, 40, 50$. Considering the tax incentive offered by the city, use these results to determine which value of θ (including the option of $\theta = 0$) should be chosen by the company to minimize its total cost of both pollution abatement and taxes.

i. For the value of θ chosen in part *h*, generate the sensitivity report and repeat parts *f* and *g* so that the decision makers can make a final decision on the relative values of the policy standards for the three pollutants.

Case 5-3

Farm Management

The **Ploughman family** owns and operates a 640-acre farm that has been in the family for several generations. The Ploughmans always have had to work hard to make a decent living from the farm and have had to endure some occasional difficult years. Stories about earlier generations overcoming hardships due to droughts, floods, and so forth, are an important part of the family history. However, the Ploughmans enjoy their self-reliant lifestyle and gain considerable satisfaction from continuing the family tradition of successfully living off the land during an era when many family farms are being abandoned or taken over by large agricultural corporations.

John Ploughman is the current manager of the farm, while his wife Eunice runs the house and manages the farm's finances. John's father, Grandpa Ploughman, lives with them and still puts in many hours working on the farm. John and Eunice's older children, Frank, Phyllis, and Carl, also are given heavy chores before and after school.

The entire family can produce a total of 4,000 person-hours' worth of labor during the winter and spring months and 4,500 person-hours during the summer and fall. If any of these person-hours are not needed, Frank, Phyllis, and Carl will use them to work on a neighboring farm for $5/hour during the winter and spring months and $5.50/hour during the summer and fall.

The farm supports two types of livestock, dairy cows and laying hens, as well as three crops: soybeans, corn, and wheat. (All three are cash crops, but the corn also is a feed crop for the cows and the wheat also is used for chicken feed.) The crops are harvested during the late summer and fall. During the winter months, John, Eunice, and Grandpa make a decision about the mix of livestock and crops for the coming year.

Currently, the family has just completed a particularly successful harvest that has provided an investment fund of $20,000 that can be used to purchase more livestock. (Other money is available for ongoing expenses, including the next planting of crops.) The family currently has 30 cows valued at $35,000 and 2,000 hens valued at $5,000. They wish to keep all this livestock and perhaps purchase more. Each new cow would cost $1,500, and each new hen would cost $3.

Over a year's time, the value of a herd of cows will decrease by about 10 percent and the value of a flock of hens will decrease by about 25 percent due to aging.

Each cow will require two acres of land for grazing and 10 person-hours of work per month, while producing a net annual cash income of $850 for the family. The corresponding figures for each hen are no significant acreage, 0.05 person-hours per month, and an annual net cash income of $4.25. The chicken house can accommodate a maximum of 5,000 hens, and the size of the barn limits the herd to a maximum of 42 cows.

For each acre planted in each of the three crops, the next table gives the number of person-hours of work that will be required during the first and second halves of the year, as well as a rough estimate of the crop's net value (in either income or savings in purchasing feed for the livestock).

To provide much of the feed for the livestock, John wants to plant at least one acre of corn for each cow in the coming year's herd and at least 0.05 acre of wheat for each hen in the coming year's flock.

John, Eunice, and Grandpa now are discussing how much acreage should be planted in each of the crops and how many cows and hens to have for the coming year. Their objective is to maximize the family's monetary worth at the end of the coming year (the *sum* of the net income from the livestock for the coming year *plus* the net value of the crops for the coming year *plus* what remains from the investment fund *plus* the value of the livestock at the end of the coming year *plus* income from working on a neighboring farm *minus* living expenses of $40,000 for the year).

Data per Acre Planted

	Soybeans	Corn	Wheat
Winter and spring, person-hours	1.0	0.9	0.6
Summer and fall, person-hours	1.4	1.2	0.7
Net value	$70	$60	$40

a. Identify verbally the components of a linear programming model for this problem.

b. Display the model on a spreadsheet.

c. Obtain an optimal solution and generate the sensitivity report. What does the model predict regarding the family's monetary worth at the end of the coming year?

d. Find the allowable range for the net value per acre planted for each of the three crops.

The above estimates of the net value per acre planted in each of the three crops assumes good weather conditions. Adverse weather conditions would harm the crops and greatly reduce the resulting value. The scenarios particularly feared by the family are a drought, a flood, an early frost, *both* a drought and an early frost, and *both* a flood and an early frost. The estimated net values for the year under these scenarios are shown next.

	Net Value per Acre Planted		
Scenario	Soybeans	Corn	Wheat
Drought	−$10	−$15	0
Flood	15	20	$10
Early frost	50	40	30
Drought and early frost	−15	−20	−10
Flood and early frost	10	10	5

e. Find an optimal solution under each scenario after making the necessary adjustments to the linear programming model formulated in part b. In each case, what is the prediction regarding the family's monetary worth at the end of the year?

f. For the optimal solution obtained under each of the six scenarios (including the good weather scenario considered in parts a-d), calculate what the family's monetary worth would be at the end of the year if each of the other five scenarios occurs instead. In your judgment, which solution provides the best balance between yielding a large monetary worth under good weather conditions and avoiding an overly small monetary worth under adverse weather conditions?

Grandpa has researched what the weather conditions were in past years as far back as weather records have been kept and obtained the data shown on the next page. With these data, the family has decided to use the following approach to making its planting and livestock decisions. Rather than the optimistic approach of assuming that good weather conditions will prevail (as done in parts a-d), the *average* net value under all weather conditions will be used for each crop (weighting the net values under the various scenarios by the frequencies in the above table).

Scenario	Frequency
Good weather	40%
Drought	20
Flood	10
Early frost	15
Drought and early frost	10
Flood and early frost	5

g. Modify the linear programming model formulated in part b to fit this new approach.

h. Repeat part c for this modified model.

i. Use a shadow price obtained in part h to analyze whether it would be worthwhile for the family to obtain a bank loan with a 10 percent interest rate to purchase more livestock now beyond what can be obtained with the $20,000 from the investment fund.

j. For each of the three crops, use the sensitivity report obtained in part h to identify how much latitude for error is available in estimating the net value per acre planted for that crop without changing the optimal solution. Which two net values need to be estimated most carefully? If both estimates are incorrect simultaneously, how close do the estimates need to be to guarantee that the optimal solution will not change? Use a two way parameter analysis report to systematically generate the optimal monetary worth as these two net values are varied simultaneously over ranges that go up to twice as far from the estimates as needed to guarantee that the optimal solution will not change.

This problem illustrates a kind of situation that is frequently faced by various kinds of organizations. To describe the situation in general terms, an organization faces an uncertain future where any one of a number of scenarios may unfold. Which one will occur depends on conditions that are outside the control of the organization. The organization needs to choose the levels of various activities, but the unit contribution of each activity to the overall measure of performance is greatly affected by which scenario unfolds. Under these circumstances, what is the best mix of activities?

k. Think about specific situations outside of farm management that fit this description. Describe one.

Case 5-4

Assigning Students to Schools (Revisited)

Reconsider Case 3-5. The **Springfield School Board** still has the policy of providing busing for all middle school students who must travel more than approximately a mile. Another current policy is to allow splitting residential areas among multiple schools if this will reduce the total busing cost. (This latter policy will be reversed in Case 7-3.) However, before adopting a busing plan based on part *a* of Case 3-5, the school board now wants to conduct some what-if analysis.

a. If you have not already done so for part *a* of Case 3-5, formulate and solve a linear programming model for this problem on a spreadsheet.

b. Use Solver to generate the sensitivity report.

One concern of the school board is the ongoing road construction in area 6. These construction projects have been delaying traffic considerably and are likely to affect the cost of busing students from area 6, perhaps increasing costs as much as 10 percent.

c. Use the sensitivity report to check how much the busing cost from area 6 to school 1 can increase (assuming no change in the costs for the other schools) before the current optimal solution would no longer be optimal. If the allowable increase is less than 10 percent, use Solver to find the new optimal solution with a 10 percent increase.

d. Repeat part *c* for school 2 (assuming no change in the costs for the other schools).

e. Now assume that the busing cost from area 6 would increase by the same percentage for all the schools. Use the sensitivity report to determine how large this percentage can be before the current optimal solution might no longer be optimal. If the allowable increase is less than 10 percent, use Solver to find the new optimal solution with a 10 percent increase.

The school board has the option of adding portable classrooms to increase the capacity of one or more of the middle schools for a few years. However, this is a costly move that the board would only consider if it would significantly decrease

busing costs. Each portable classroom holds 20 students and has a leasing cost of $2,500 per year. To analyze this option, the school board decides to assume that the road construction in area 6 will wind down without significantly increasing the busing costs from that area.

f. For each school, use the corresponding shadow price from the sensitivity report to determine whether it would be worthwhile to add any portable classrooms.

g. For each school where it is worthwhile to add any portable classrooms, use the sensitivity report to determine how many could be added before the shadow price would no longer be valid (assuming this is the only school receiving portable classrooms).

h. If it would be worthwhile to add portable classrooms to more than one school, use the sensitivity report to determine the combinations of the number to add for which the shadow prices definitely would still be valid. Then use the shadow prices to determine which of these combinations is best in terms of minimizing the total cost of busing students and leasing portable classrooms. Use Solver for finding the corresponding optimal solution for assigning students to schools.

i. If part *h* was applicable, modify the best combination of portable classrooms found there by adding one more to the school with the most favorable shadow price. Use Solver to find the corresponding optimal solution for assigning students to schools and to generate the corresponding sensitivity report. Use this information to assess whether the plan developed in part *h* is the best one available for minimizing the total cost of busing students and leasing portables. If not, find the best plan.

Additional Cases

Additional cases for this chapter also are available at the University of Western Ontario Ivey School of Business website, **cases .ivey.uwo.ca/cases**, in the segment of the CaseMate area designated for this book.

Chapter **Six**

Network Optimization Problems

Learning Objectives

After completing this chapter, you should be able to

1. Formulate network models for various types of network optimization problems.
2. Describe the characteristics of minimum-cost flow problems, maximum flow problems, and shortest path problems.
3. Identify some areas of application for these types of problems.
4. Identify several categories of network optimization problems that are special types of minimum-cost flow problems.
5. Formulate and solve a spreadsheet model for a minimum-cost flow problem, a maximum flow problem, or a shortest path problem from a description of the problem.

Networks arise in numerous settings and in a variety of guises. Transportation, electrical, and communication networks pervade our daily lives. Network representations also are widely used for problems in such diverse areas as production, distribution, project planning, facilities location, resource management, and financial planning—to name just a few examples. In fact, a network representation provides such a powerful visual and conceptual aid for portraying the relationships between the components of systems that it is used in virtually every field of scientific, social, and economic endeavor.

One of the most exciting developments in management science in recent decades has been the unusually rapid advance in both the methodology and application of network optimization problems. A number of algorithmic breakthroughs have had a major impact, as have ideas from computer science concerning data structures and efficient data manipulation. Consequently, algorithms and software now are available and are being used to solve huge problems on a routine basis that would have been completely intractable a few decades ago.

This chapter presents the network optimization problems that have been particularly helpful in dealing with managerial issues. We focus on the nature of these problems and their applications rather than on the technical details and the algorithms used to solve the problems.

You already have seen some examples of network optimization problems in Chapter 3. In particular, transportation problems (described in Section 3.5) have a network representation, as illustrated in Figure 3.9, and assignment problems (Section 3.6) have a similar network representation (as described in Chapter 15 on the CD-ROM). Therefore, both transportation problems and assignment problems are simple types of network optimization problems.

Like transportation problems and assignment problems, many other network optimization problems (including all the types considered in this chapter) also are special types of *linear programming* problems. Consequently, after formulating a spreadsheet model for these problems, they can be readily solved by Solver.

Section 6.1 discusses an especially important type of network optimization problem called a *minimum-cost flow problem*. A typical application involves minimizing the cost of shipping goods through a distribution network.

Section 6.3 presents *maximum flow problems,* which are concerned with such issues as how to maximize the flow of goods through a distribution network. Section 6.2 lays the groundwork by introducing a case study of a maximum flow problem.

Section 6.4 considers *shortest path problems.* In their simplest form, the objective is to find the shortest route between two locations.

A supplement to this chapter on the CD-ROM discusses *minimum spanning-tree problems,* which are concerned with minimizing the cost of providing connections between all users of a system. This is the only network optimization problem considered in this book that is not, in fact, a special type of linear programming problem.

6.1   MINIMUM-COST FLOW PROBLEMS

Before describing the general characteristics of minimum-cost flow problems, let us first look at a typical example.

An Example: The Distribution Unlimited Co. Problem

The **Distribution Unlimited Co.** has two factories producing a product that needs to be shipped to two warehouses. Here are some details.

Factory 1 is producing 80 units.

Factory 2 is producing 70 units.

Warehouse 1 needs 60 units.

Warehouse 2 needs 90 units.

(Each unit corresponds to a full truckload of the product.)

Figure 6.1 shows the distribution network available for shipping this product, where F1 and F2 are the two factories, W1 and W2 are the two warehouses, and DC is a distribution center. The arrows show feasible shipping lanes. In particular, there is a rail link from Factory 1 to Warehouse 1 and another from Factory 2 to Warehouse 2. (Any amounts can be shipped along these rail links.) In addition, independent truckers are available to ship up to 50 units from each factory to the distribution center, and then to ship up to 50 units from the distribution center to each warehouse. (Whatever is shipped to the distribution center must subsequently be shipped on to the warehouses.) Management's objective is to determine the shipping plan (how many units to ship along each shipping lane) that will minimize the total shipping cost.

The objective is to minimize the total shipping cost through the distribution network.

The shipping costs differ considerably among these shipping lanes. The cost per unit shipped through each lane is shown above the corresponding arrow in the *network* in Figure 6.2.

To make the network less crowded, the problem usually is presented even more compactly, as shown in Figure 6.3. The number in square brackets next to the location of each

FIGURE 6.1

The distribution network for the Distribution Unlimited Co. problem, where each feasible shipping lane is represented by an arrow.

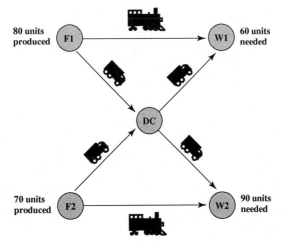

FIGURE 6.2
The data for the distribution network for the Distribution Unlimited Co. problem.

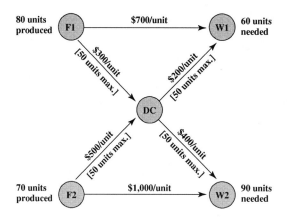

facility indicates the net number of units (outflow minus inflow) generated there. Thus, the number of units terminating at each warehouse is shown as a negative number. The number at the distribution center is 0 since the number of units leaving *minus* the number of units arriving must equal 0. The number on top of each arrow shows the unit shipping cost along that shipping lane. Any number in square brackets underneath an arrow gives the maximum number of units that can be shipped along that shipping lane. (The absence of a number in square brackets underneath an arrow implies that there is no limit on the shipping amount there.) This network provides a complete representation of the problem, including all the necessary data, so it constitutes a *network model* for this minimum-cost flow problem.

Figure 6.3 illustrates how a minimum-cost flow problem can be completely depicted by a network.

Since this is such a tiny problem, you probably can see what the optimal solution must be. (Try it.) This solution is shown in Figure 6.4, where the shipping amount along each shipping lane is given in parentheses. (To avoid confusion, we delete the unit shipping costs and shipping capacities in this figure.) Combining these shipping amounts with the unit shipping costs given in Figures 6.2 and 6.3, the total shipping cost for this solution (when starting by listing the costs from F1, then from F2, and then from DC) is

$$\text{Total shipping cost} = 30(\$700) + 50(\$300) + 30(\$500) + 40(\$1,000)$$
$$+ 30(\$200) + 50(\$400)$$
$$= \$117,000$$

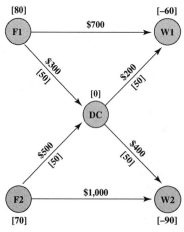

FIGURE 6.3
A network model for the Distribution Unlimited Co. problem as a minimum-cost flow problem.

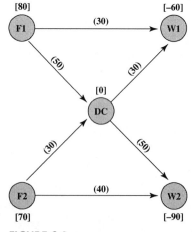

FIGURE 6.4
The optimal solution for the Distribution Unlimited Co. problem, where the shipping amounts are shown in parentheses over the arrows.

An Application Vignette

Hewlett-Packard (HP) offers many innovative products to meet the diverse needs of more than 1 billion customers. The breadth of its product offering has helped the company achieve unparalleled market reach. However, offering multiple similar products also can cause serious problems—including confusing sales representatives and customers—that can adversely affect the revenue and costs for any particular product. Therefore, it is important to find the right balance between too much product variety and too little.

With this in mind, HP top management made managing product variety a strategic business priority. HP has been a leader in applying management science to its important business problems for decades, so it was only natural that many of the company's top management scientists were called on to address this problem as well.

The heart of the methodology that was developed to address this problem involved formulating and applying a network optimization model. After excluding proposed products that do not have a sufficiently high return on investment, the remaining proposed products can be envisioned as flows through a network that can help fill some of the projected orders on the right-hand side of the network. The resulting model is a special type of *minimum cost flow problem* (related to the special type discussed in the next two sections).

Following its implementation by the beginning of 2005, this application of a minimum cost flow problem had a dramatic impact in enabling HP businesses to increase operational focus on their most critical products. This yielded companywide *profit improvements of over* **$500 million** between 2005 and 2008, and then about **$180 million** *annually* thereafter. It also yielded a variety of important qualitative benefits for HP.

These dramatic results led to HP winning the prestigious first prize in the 2009 Franz Edelman Award for Achievement in Operations Research and the Management Sciences.

Source: J. Ward and 20 co-authors, "HP Transforms Product Portfolio Management with Operations Research," *Interfaces* 40, no. 1 (January–February 2010), pp. 17–32. (A link to this article is provided on our website, **www.mhhe.com/hillier5e.**)

General Characteristics

This example possesses all the general characteristics of any minimum-cost flow problem. Before summarizing these characteristics, here is the terminology you will need.

Terminology

1. The model for any minimum-cost flow problem is represented by a *network* with flow passing through it.
2. The circles in the network are called **nodes.**

A supply node has net flow going out whereas a demand node has net flow coming in.

3. Each node where the net amount of flow generated (outflow minus inflow) is a fixed *positive* number is a **supply node.** (Thus, F1 and F2 are the supply nodes in Figure 6.3.)
4. Each node where the net amount of flow generated is a fixed *negative* number is a **demand node.** (Consequently, W1 and W2 are the demand nodes in the example.)
5. Any node where the net amount of flow generated is fixed at *zero* is a **transshipment node.** (Thus, DC is the transshipment node in the example.) Having the amount of flow out of the node equal the amount of flow into the node is referred to as **conservation of flow.**
6. The arrows in the network are called **arcs.**
7. The maximum amount of flow allowed through an arc is referred to as the **capacity** of that arc.

Using this terminology, the general characteristics of minimum-cost flow problems (the model for this type of problem) can be described in terms of the following assumptions.

Assumptions of a Minimum-Cost Flow Problem

1. *At least one* of the nodes is a *supply node.*
2. *At least one* of the other nodes is a *demand node.*
3. All the remaining nodes are *transshipment nodes.*

Since the arrowhead on an arc indicates the direction in which flow is allowed, a pair of arcs pointing in opposite directions is used if flow can occur in both directions.

4. Flow through an arc is only allowed in the direction indicated by the arrowhead, where the maximum amount of flow is given by the *capacity* of that arc. (If flow can occur in both directions, this would be represented by a pair of arcs pointing in opposite directions.)
5. The network has enough arcs with sufficient capacity to enable all the flow generated at the *supply nodes* to reach all the *demand nodes.*

6. The cost of the flow through each arc is *proportional* to the amount of that flow, where the cost per unit flow is known.

7. The objective is to minimize the total cost of sending the available supply through the network to satisfy the given demand. (An alternative objective is to maximize the total profit from doing this.)

The objective is to minimize the total cost of supplying the demand nodes.

A *solution* for this kind of problem needs to specify how much flow is going through each arc. To be a *feasible* solution, the amount of flow through each arc cannot exceed the capacity of that arc and the net amount of flow generated at each node must equal the specified amount for that node. The following property indicates when the problem will have feasible solutions.

> **Feasible Solutions Property:** Under the above assumptions, a minimum-cost flow problem will have feasible solutions if and only if the sum of the supplies from its supply nodes *equals* the sum of the demands at its demand nodes.

Note that this property holds for the Distribution Unlimited Co. problem, because the sum of its supplies is $80 + 70 = 150$ and the sum of its demands is $60 + 90 = 150$.

For many applications of minimum-cost flow problems, management desires a solution with *integer* values for all the flow quantities (e.g., integer numbers of *full* truckloads along each shipping lane). The model does not include any constraints that require this for feasible solutions. Fortunately, such constraints are not needed because of the following property.

> **Integer Solutions Property:** As long as all its supplies, demands, and arc capacities have integer values, any minimum-cost flow problem with feasible solutions is guaranteed to have an optimal solution with integer values for all its flow quantities.

See in Figure 6.3 that all the assumptions needed for this property to holds are satisfied for the Distribution Unlimited Co. problem. In particular, all the supplies (80 and 70), demands (60 and 90), and arc capacities (50) have integer values. Therefore, all the flow quantities in the optimal solution given in Figure 6.4 (30 three times, 50 two times, and 40) have integer values. This ensures that only full truckloads will be shipped into and out of the distribution center. (Remember that each unit corresponds to a full truckload of the product.)

Now let us see how to obtain an optimal solution for the Distribution Unlimited Co. problem by formulating a spreadsheet model and then applying Solver.

Using Excel to Formulate and Solve Minimum-Cost Flow Problems

Figure 6.5 shows a spreadsheet model that is based directly on the network representation of the problem in Figure 6.3. The arcs are listed in columns B and C, along with their capacities (unless unlimited) in column F and their costs per unit flow in column G. The changing cells Ship (D4:D9) show the flow amounts through these arcs and the objective cell TotalCost (D11) provides the total cost of this flow by using the equation

$$D11 = \text{SUMPRODUCT(Ship, UnitCost)}$$

Capacity constraints like these are needed in any minimum-cost flow problem that has any arcs with limited capacity.

The first set of constraints in the Solver Parameters box, D5:D8 $\leq$ Capacity (F5:F8), ensures that the arc capacities are not exceeded.

Any minimum-cost flow problem needs net flow constraints like this for every node.

Similarly, Column I lists the nodes, column J calculates the actual net flow generated at each node (given the flows in the changing cells), and column L specifies the net amount of flow that needs to be generated at each node. Thus, the second set of constraints in the Solver Parameters box is NetFlow (J4:J8) = SupplyDemand (L4:L8), requiring that the actual net amount of flow generated at each node must equal the specified amount.

Excel Tip: SUMIF(A, B, C) adds up each entry in the range C for which the corresponding entry in range A equals B. This function is especially useful in network problems for calculating the net flow generated at a node.

The equations entered into NetFlow (J4:J8) use the difference of two SUMIF functions to calculate the net flow (outflow minus inflow) generated at each node. In each case, the first SUMIF function calculates the flow leaving the node and the second one calculates the flow entering the node. For example, consider the F1 node (I4). SUMIF(From,I4,Ship) sums each individual entry in Ship (D4:D9) if that entry is in a row where the entry in From (B4:B9) is the same as in I4. Since I4 = F1 and the only rows that have F1 in the From column are rows 4 and 5, the sum in the Ship column is only over these same rows, so this sum is D4 + D5. Similarly, SUMIF(To,I4,Ship) sums each individual entry in Ship (D4:D9) if

FIGURE 6.5

A spreadsheet model for the Distribution Unlimited Co. minimum-cost flow problem, including the objective cell TotalCost (D11) and the other output cells NetFlow (J4:J8), as well as the equations entered into these cells and the other specifications needed to set up the model. The changing cells Ship (D4:D9) show the optimal shipping quantities through the distribution network obtained by Solver.

	A	B	C	D	E	F	G	H	I	J	K	L
1		**Distribution Unlimited Co. Minimum Cost Flow Problem**										
2												
3		**From**	**To**	**Ship**		**Capacity**	**Unit Cost**		**Nodes**	**Net Flow**		**Supply/Demand**
4		F1	W1	30			$700		F1	80	=	80
5		F1	DC	50	≤	50	$300		F2	70	=	70
6		DC	W1	30	≤	50	$200		DC	0	=	0
7		DC	W2	50	≤	50	$400		W1	-60	=	-60
8		F2	DC	30	≤	50	$500		W2	-90	=	-90
9		F2	W2	40			$1,000					
10												
11			**Total Cost**	$117,000								

Set Objective Cell: TotalCost
To: Min
By Changing Variable Cells:
   Ship
Subject to the Constraints:
   D5:D8 <= Capacity
   NetFlow = SupplyDemand

Solver Options:
   Make Variables Nonnegative
   Solving Method: Simplex LP

Range Name	Cells
Capacity	F5:F8
From	B4:B9
NetFlow	J4:J8
Nodes	I4:I8
Ship	D4:D9
SupplyDemand	L4:L8
To	C4:C9
TotalCost	D11
UnitCost	G4:G9

	J
3	**Net Flow**
4	=SUMIF(From,I4,Ship)-SUMIF(To,I4,Ship)
5	=SUMIF(From,I5,Ship)-SUMIF(To,I5,Ship)
6	=SUMIF(From,I6,Ship)-SUMIF(To,I6,Ship)
7	=SUMIF(From,I7,Ship)-SUMIF(To,I7,Ship)
8	=SUMIF(From,I8,Ship)-SUMIF(To,I8,Ship)

	C	D
11	**Total Cost**	=SUMPRODUCT(Ship,UnitCost)

that entry is in a row where the entry in To (C4:C9) is the same as in I4. However, F1 never appears in the To column, so this sum is 0. Therefore, the overall equation for J4 yields J4 = D4 + D5 = 30 + 50 = 80, which is the net flow generated at the F1 node.

While it appears more complicated to use the SUMIF function rather than just entering J4 = D4 + D5, J5 = D8 + D9, J6 = D6 + D7 − D5 − D8, and so on, it is actually simpler. The SUMIF formula only needs to be entered once (in cell J4). It can then be copied down into the remaining cells in NetFlow (J5:J8). For a problem with many nodes, this is much quicker and (perhaps more significantly) less prone to error. In a large problem, it is all too easy to miss an arc when determining which cells in the Ship column to add and subtract to calculate the net flow for a given node.

The first Solver option specifies that the flow amounts cannot be negative. The second acknowledges that this is still a linear programming problem.

Running Solver gives the optimal solution shown in Ship (D4:D9). This is the same solution as displayed in Figure 6.4.

Solving Large Minimum-Cost Flow Problems More Efficiently

Because minimum-cost flow problems are a special type of linear programming problem, and the *simplex method* can solve any linear programming problem, it also can solve any minimum-cost flow problem in the standard way. For example, Solver uses the simplex method to solve this type (or any other type) of linear programming problem. This works fine for small problems, like the Distribution Unlimited Co. problem, and for considerably larger ones as well. Therefore, the approach illustrated in Figure 6.5 will serve you well for any minimum-cost flow problem encountered in this book and for many that you will encounter subsequently.

However, we should mention that a different approach is sometimes needed in practice to solve really big problems. Because of the special form of minimum-cost flow problems, it is possible to greatly *streamline* the simplex method to solve them far more quickly. In particular, rather than going through all the algebra of the simplex method, it is possible to execute the same steps far more quickly by working directly with the network for the problem.

network simplex method

The network simplex method can solve much larger minimum-cost flow problems (sometimes with millions of nodes and arcs) than can the simplex method used by Solver.

This streamlined version of the simplex method is called the **network simplex method.** The network simplex method can solve some huge problems that are much too large for the simplex method.

Like the simplex method, the network simplex method not only finds an optimal solution but also can be a valuable aid to managers in conducting the kinds of what-if analyses described in Chapter 5.

Many companies now use the network simplex method to solve their minimum-cost flow problems. Some of these problems are huge, with many tens of thousands of nodes and arcs. Occasionally, the number of arcs will even be far larger, perhaps into the millions.

Although Solver does not, other commercial software packages for linear programming commonly include the network simplex method.

An important advance in recent years has been the development of excellent *graphical interfaces* for modeling minimum-cost flow problems. These interfaces make the design of the model and the interpretation of the output of the network simplex method completely visual and intuitive with no mathematics involved. This is very helpful for managerial decision making.

Some Applications

Probably the most important kind of application of minimum-cost flow problems is to the operation of a distribution network, such as the one depicted in Figures 6.1–6.4 for the Distribution Unlimited Co. problem. As summarized in the first row of Table 6.1, this kind of application involves determining a plan for shipping goods from their *sources* (factories, etc.) to *intermediate storage facilities* (as needed) and then on to the *customers.*

For some applications of minimum-cost flow problems, all the transshipment nodes are *processing facilities* rather than intermediate storage facilities. This is the case for *solid waste management,* as indicated in Table 6.1. Here, the flow of materials through the network begins at the sources of the solid waste, then goes to the facilities for processing these waste materials into a form suitable for landfill, and then sends them on to the various landfill locations. However, the objective still is to determine the flow plan that minimizes the total cost, where the cost now is for both shipping and processing.

In other applications, the *demand nodes* might be processing facilities. For example, in the third row of Table 6.1, the objective is to find the minimum-cost plan for obtaining supplies from various possible vendors, storing these goods in warehouses (as needed), and then shipping the supplies to the company's processing facilities (factories, etc.).

The next kind of application in Table 6.1 (coordinating product mixes at plants) illustrates that arcs can represent something other than a shipping lane for a physical flow of materials.

TABLE 6.1   Typical Kinds of Applications of Minimum-Cost Flow Problems

Kind of Application	Supply Nodes	Transshipment Nodes	Demand Nodes
Operation of a distribution network	Sources of goods	Intermediate storage facilities	Customers
Solid waste management	Sources of solid waste	Processing facilities	Landfill locations
Operation of a supply network	Vendors	Intermediate warehouses	Processing facilities
Coordinating product mixes at plants	Plants	Production of a specific product	Market for a specific product
Cash flow management	Sources of cash at a specific time	Short-term investment options	Needs for cash at a specific time

This application involves a company with several plants (the supply nodes) that can produce the same products but at different costs. Each arc from a supply node represents the production of one of the possible products at that plant, where this arc leads to the transshipment node that corresponds to this product. Thus, this transshipment node has an arc coming in from each plant capable of producing this product, and then the arcs leading out of this node go to the respective customers (the demand nodes) for this product. The objective is to determine how to divide each plant's production capacity among the products so as to minimize the total cost of meeting the demand for the various products.

The last application in Table 6.1 (cash flow management) illustrates that different nodes can represent some event that occurs at different times. In this case, each supply node represents a specific time (or time period) when some cash will become available to the company (through maturing accounts, notes receivable, sales of securities, borrowing, etc.). The supply at each of these nodes is the amount of cash that will become available then. Similarly, each demand node represents a specific time (or time period) when the company will need to draw on its cash reserves. The demand at each such node is the amount of cash that will be needed then. The objective is to maximize the company's income from investing the cash between each time it becomes available and when it will be used. Therefore, each transshipment node represents the choice of a specific short-term investment option (e.g., purchasing a certificate of deposit from a bank) over a specific time interval. The resulting network will have a succession of flows representing a schedule for cash becoming available, being invested, and then being used after the maturing of the investment.

Special Types of Minimum-Cost Flow Problems

There are five important categories of network problems that turn out to be special types of minimum-cost flow problems.

One is the **transportation problems** discussed in Section 3.5. Figure 3.9 shows the network representation of a typical transportation problem. In our current terminology, the sources and destinations of a transportation problem are the supply nodes and demand nodes, respectively. Thus, a transportation problem is just a minimum-cost flow problem without any transshipment nodes and without any capacity constraints on the arcs (all of which go directly from a supply node to a demand node).

A second category is the **assignment problems** discussed in Section 3.6. Recall that this kind of problem involves assigning a group of people (or other operational units) to a group of tasks where each person is to perform a single task. An assignment problem can be viewed as a special type of transportation problem whose sources are the assignees and whose destinations are the tasks. This then makes the assignment problem also a special type of minimum-cost flow problem with the characteristics described in the preceding paragraph. In addition, each person is a supply node with a supply of 1 and each task is a demand node with a demand of 1.

transshipment problem
A transshipment problem is just a minimum-cost flow problem that has unlimited capacities for all its arcs.

A third special type of minimum-cost flow problem is **transshipment problems.** This kind of problem is just like a transportation problem except for the additional feature that the shipments from the sources (supply nodes) to the destinations (demand nodes) might also pass through intermediate transfer points (transshipment nodes) such as distribution centers. Like a transportation problem, there are no capacity constraints on the arcs. Consequently, any minimum-cost flow problem where each arc can carry any desired amount of flow is a transshipment problem. For example, if the data in Figure 6.2 were altered so that any amounts (within the ranges of the supplies and demands) could be shipped into and out of the distribution center, the Distribution Unlimited Co. would become just a transshipment problem.[1]

Because of their close relationship to a general minimum-cost flow problem, we will not discuss transshipment problems further.

The other two important special types of minimum-cost flow problems are **maximum flow problems** and **shortest path problems,** which will be described in Sections 6.3 and 6.4 after presenting a case study of a maximum flow problem in the next section.

---

[1] Be aware that a minimum-cost flow problem that does have capacity constraints on the arcs is sometimes referred to as a *capacitated transshipment problem.* We will not use this terminology.

In case you are wondering why we are bothering to point out that these five kinds of problems are special types of minimum-cost flow problems, here is one very important reason. It means that the *network simplex method* can be used to solve large problems of any of these types that might be difficult or impossible for the simplex method to solve. It is true that other efficient *special-purpose algorithms* also are available for each of these kinds of problems. However, recent implementations of the network simplex method have become so powerful that it now provides an excellent alternative to these other algorithms in most cases. This is especially valuable when the available software package includes the network simplex method but not another relevant special-purpose algorithm. Furthermore, even after finding an optimal solution, the network simplex method can continue to be helpful in aiding managerial what-if sessions along the lines discussed in Chapter 5.

The network simplex method can be used to solve huge problems of any of these five special types.

Review Questions

1. Name and describe the three kinds of nodes in a minimum-cost flow problem.
2. What is meant by the *capacity* of an arc?
3. What is the usual objective for a minimum-cost flow problem?
4. What property is necessary for a minimum-cost flow problem to have feasible solutions?
5. What is the integer solutions property for minimum-cost flow problems?
6. What is the name of the streamlined version of the simplex method that is designed to solve minimum-cost flow problems very efficiently?
7. What are a few typical kinds of applications of minimum-cost flow problems?
8. Name five important categories of network optimization problems that turn out to be special types of minimum-cost flow problems.

6.2 A CASE STUDY: THE BMZ CO. MAXIMUM FLOW PROBLEM

What a day! First being called into his boss's office and then receiving an urgent telephone call from the company president himself. Fortunately, he was able to reassure them that he has the situation under control.

Although his official title is Supply Chain Manager for the BMZ Company, Karl Schmidt often tells his friends that he really is the company's *crisis manager*. One crisis after another. The supplies needed to keep the production lines going haven't arrived yet. Or the supplies have arrived but are unusable because they are the wrong size. Or an urgent shipment to a key customer has been delayed. This current crisis is typical. One of the company's most important distribution centers—the one in Los Angeles—urgently needs an increased flow of shipments from the company.

Karl was chosen for this key position because he is considered a rising young star. Having just received his MBA degree from a top American business school four years ago, he is the youngest member of upper-level management in the entire company. His business school training in the latest management science techniques has proven invaluable in improving supply chain management throughout the company. The crises still occur, but the frequent chaos of past years has been eliminated.

Karl has a plan for dealing with the current crisis. This will mean calling on management science once again.

Background

The **BMZ Company** is a European manufacturer of luxury automobiles. Although its cars sell well in all the developed countries, its exports to the United States are particularly important to the company.

BMZ has a well-deserved reputation for providing excellent service. One key to maintaining this reputation is having a plentiful supply of automobile replacement parts readily available to the company's numerous dealerships and authorized repair shops. These parts are mainly stored in the company's distribution centers and then delivered promptly when needed. One of Karl Schmidt's top priorities is avoiding shortages at these distribution centers.

The company has several distribution centers in the United States. However, the closest one to the Los Angeles center is over 1,000 miles away in Seattle. Since BMZ cars are becoming especially popular in California, it is particularly important to keep the Los Angeles center well supplied. Therefore, the fact that supplies there are currently dwindling is a matter of real concern to BMZ top management—as Karl learned forcefully today.

Most of the automobile replacement parts are produced at the company's main factory in Stuttgart, Germany, along with the production of new cars. It is this factory that has been supplying the Los Angeles center with spare parts. Some of these parts are bulky, and very large numbers of certain parts are needed, so the total volume of the supplies has been relatively massive—over 300,000 cubic feet of goods arriving monthly. Now a much larger amount will be needed over the next month to replenish the dwindling inventory.

The Problem

Karl needs to execute a plan quickly for shipping as much as possible from the main factory to the distribution center in Los Angeles over the next month. He already has recognized that this is a *maximum flow problem*—a problem of maximizing the flow of replacement parts from the factory to this distribution center.

The problem is to maximize the flow of automobile replacement parts from the factory in Stuttgart, Germany, to the distribution center in Los Angeles.

The factory is producing far more than can be shipped to this one distribution center. Therefore, the limiting factor on how much can be shipped is the limited capacity of the company's distribution network.

This distribution network is depicted in Figure 6.6, where the nodes labeled ST and LA are the factory in Stuttgart and the distribution center in Los Angeles, respectively. There is a rail head at the factory, so shipments first go by rail to one of three European ports: Rotterdam (node RO), Bordeaux (node BO), and Lisbon (node LI). They then go by ship to ports in the United States, either New York (node NY) or New Orleans (node NO). Finally, they are shipped by truck from these ports to the distribution center in Los Angeles.

The organizations operating these railroads, ships, and trucks are independently owned companies that ship goods for numerous firms. Because of prior commitments to their regular customers, these companies are unable to drastically increase the allocation of space to any single customer on short notice. Therefore, the BMZ Co. is only able to secure a limited amount of shipping space along each shipping lane over the next month. The amounts available are given in Figure 6.6, using units of *hundreds of cubic meters*. (Since each unit of 100 cubic meters is a little over 3,500 cubic feet, these are large volumes of goods that need to be moved.)

FIGURE 6.6

The BMZ Co. distribution network from its main factory in Stuttgart, Germany, to a distribution center in Los Angeles.

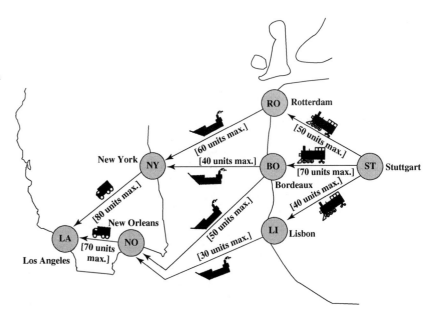

204   Chapter Six   *Network Optimization Problems*

FIGURE 6.7

A network model for the
BMZ Co. problem as a
maximum flow problem,
where the number in
square brackets below
each arc is the capacity of
that arc.

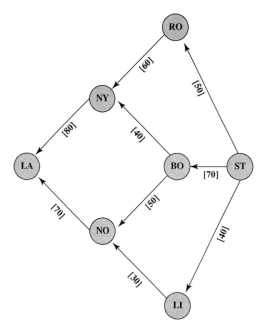

Model Formulation

Figure 6.7 shows the *network model* for this maximum flow problem. Rather than showing the geographical layout of the distribution network, this network simply lines up the nodes (representing the cities) in evenly spaced columns. The arcs represent the shipping lanes, where the capacity of each arc (given in square brackets under the arc) is the amount of shipping space available along that shipping lane. The objective is to determine how much flow to send through each arc (how many units to ship through each shipping lane) to maximize the total number of units flowing from the factory in Stuttgart to the distribution center in Los Angeles.

Figure 6.8 shows the corresponding spreadsheet model for this problem when using the format introduced in Figure 6.5. The main difference from the model in Figure 6.5 is the change in the objective. Since we are no longer minimizing the total cost of the flow through the network, column G in Figure 6.5 can be deleted in Figure 6.8. The objective cell MaxFlow (D14) in Figure 6.8 now needs to give the total number of units flowing from Stuttgart to Los Angeles. Thus, the equations at the bottom of the figure include D14 = I4, where I4 gives the net flow leaving Stuttgart to go to Los Angeles. As in Figure 6.5, the equations in Figure 6.8 entered into NetFlow (I4:I10) again use the difference of two SUMIF functions to calculate the net flow generated at each node. Since the objective is to maximize the flow shown in MaxFlow (D14), the Solver Parameters box specifies that this objective cell is to be maximized. After running Solver, the optimal solution shown in the changing cells Ship (D4:D12) is obtained for the amount that BMZ should ship through each shipping lane.

In contrast to the spreadsheet model in Figure 6.5,
which *minimizes* TotalCost
(D11), the spreadsheet
model in Figure 6.8 *maximizes* the objective cell
MaxFlow (D14).

However, Karl is not completely satisfied with this solution. He has an idea for doing even better. This will require formulating and solving another maximum flow problem. (This story continues in the middle of the next section.)

Review
Questions

1. What is the current crisis facing the BMZ Co.?
2. When formulating this problem in network terms, what is flowing through BMZ's distribution network? From where to where?
3. What is the objective of the resulting maximum flow problem?

FIGURE 6.8

A spreadsheet model for the BMZ Co. maximum flow problem, including the equations entered into the objective cell MaxFlow (D14) and the other output cells NetFlow (I4:I10), as well as the other specifications needed to set up the model. The changing cells Ship (D4:D12) show the optimal shipping quantities through the distribution network obtained by Solver.

	A	B	C	D	E	F	G	H	I	J	K
1		BMZ Co. Maximum Flow Problem									
2											
3		**From**	**To**	**Ship**		**Capacity**		**Nodes**	**Net Flow**		**Supply/Demand**
4		Stuttgart	Rotterdam	50	≤	50		Stuttgart	150		
5		Stuttgart	Bordeaux	70	≤	70		Rotterdam	0	=	0
6		Stuttgart	Lisbon	30	≤	40		Bordeaux	0	=	0
7		Rotterdam	New York	50	≤	60		Lisbon	0	=	0
8		Bordeaux	New York	30	≤	40		New York	0	=	0
9		Bordeaux	New Orleans	40	≤	50		New Orleans	0	=	0
10		Lisbon	New Orleans	30	≤	30		Los Angeles	-150		
11		New York	Los Angeles	80	≤	80					
12		New Orleans	Los Angeles	70	≤	70					
13											
14			**Maximum Flow**	150							

Set Objective Cell: MaxFlow
To: Max
By Changing Variable Cells:
  Ship
Subject to the Constraints:
  I5:I9 = SupplyDemand
  Ship <= Capacity

Solver Options:
  Make Variables Nonnegative
  Solving Method: Simplex LP

Range Name	Cells
Capacity	F4:F12
From	B4:B12
MaxFlow	D14
NetFlow	I4:I10
Nodes	H4:H10
Ship	D4:D12
SupplyDemand	K5:K9
To	C4:C12

	I
3	**Net Flow**
4	=SUMIF(From,H4,Ship)-SUMIF(To,H4,Ship)
5	=SUMIF(From,H5,Ship)-SUMIF(To,H5,Ship)
6	=SUMIF(From,H6,Ship)-SUMIF(To,H6,Ship)
7	=SUMIF(From,H7,Ship)-SUMIF(To,H7,Ship)
8	=SUMIF(From,H8,Ship)-SUMIF(To,H8,Ship)
9	=SUMIF(From,H9,Ship)-SUMIF(To,H9,Ship)
10	=SUMIF(From,H10,Ship)-SUMIF(To,H10,Ship)

	C	D
14	Maximum Flow	=I4

6.3 MAXIMUM FLOW PROBLEMS

Like a minimum-cost flow problem, a maximum flow problem is concerned with *flow through a network*. However, the objective now is different. Rather than minimizing the cost of the flow, the objective now is to find a flow plan that maximizes the amount flowing through the network. This is how Karl Schmidt was able to find a flow plan that maximizes the number of units of automobile replacement parts flowing through BMZ's distribution network from its factory in Stuttgart to the distribution center in Los Angeles.

General Characteristics

Except for the difference in objective (maximize flow versus minimize cost), the characteristics of the maximum flow problem are quite similar to those for the minimum-cost flow problem. However, there are some minor differences, as we will discuss after summarizing the assumptions.

Assumptions of a Maximum Flow Problem

1. All flow through the network originates at one node, called the **source,** and terminates at one other node, called the **sink.** (The source and sink in the BMZ problem are the factory and the distribution center, respectively.)

An Application Vignette

The network for transport of natural gas on the Norwegian Continental Shelf, with approximately 5,000 miles of subsea pipelines, is the world's largest offshore pipeline network. **Gassco** is a company entirely owned by the Norwegian state, which operates this network. Another company that is largely state owned, **StatoilHydro,** is the main Norwegian supplier of natural gas to markets throughout Europe and elsewhere.

Gassco and StatoilHydro together use management science techniques to optimize both the configuration of the network and the routing of the natural gas. The main model used for this routing is a multicommodity network-flow model in which the different hydrocarbons and contaminants in natural gas constitute the commodities. The objective function for the model is to *maximize the total flow* of the natural gas from the supply points (the offshore drilling platforms) to the demand points (typically

import terminals). However, in addition to the usual supply-and-demand constraints, the model also includes constraints involving pressure-flow relationships, maximum delivery pressures, and technical pressure bounds on pipelines. Therefore, this model is a generalization of the model for the maximum flow problem described in this section.

This key application of management science, along with a few others, has had a dramatic impact on the efficiency of the operation of this offshore pipeline network. The resulting *accumulated savings* were estimated to be approximately **$2 billion** in the period 1995–2008.

Source: F. Rømo, A. Tomasgard, L. Hellemo, M. Fodstad, B. H. Eidesen, and B. Pedersen, "Optimizing the Norwegian Natural Gas Production and Transport," *Interfaces* 39, no. 1 (January–February 2009), pp. 46–56. (A link to this article is provided on our website, **www.mhhe.com/hillier5e.**)

2. All the remaining nodes are *transshipment nodes.* (These are nodes RO, BO, LI, NY, and NO in the BMZ problem.)

3. Flow through an arc is only allowed in the direction indicated by the arrowhead, where the maximum amount of flow is given by the *capacity* of that arc. At the *source,* all arcs point away from the node. At the *sink,* all arcs point into the node.

4. The objective is to maximize the total amount of flow from the source to the sink. This amount is measured in either of two equivalent ways, namely, either the amount *leaving the source* or the amount *entering the sink.* (Cells D14 and I4 in Figure 6.8 use the amount leaving the source.)

The objective is to find a flow plan that maximizes the flow from the source to the sink.

The source and sink of a maximum flow problem are analogous to the supply nodes and demand nodes of a minimum-cost flow problem. These are the only nodes in both problems that do not have conservation of flow (flow out equals flow in). Like the supply nodes, the source *generates flow.* Like the demand nodes, the sink *absorbs flow.*

However, there are two differences between these nodes in a minimum-cost flow problem and the corresponding nodes in a maximum flow problem.

One difference is that, whereas supply nodes have fixed supplies and demand nodes have fixed demands, the source and sink do not. The reason is that the objective is to maximize the flow leaving the source and entering the sink rather than fixing this amount.

Although a maximum flow problem has only a single source and a single sink, variants with multiple sources and sinks also can be solved, as illustrated in the next subsection.

The second difference is that, whereas the number of supply nodes and the number of demand nodes in a minimum-cost flow problem may be *more than one,* there can be *only one* source and *only one* sink in a maximum flow problem. However, variants of maximum flow problems that have multiple sources and sinks can still be solved by Solver, as you now will see illustrated by the BMZ case study introduced in the preceding section.

Continuing the Case Study with Multiple Supply Points and Multiple Demand Points

Here is Karl Schmidt's idea for how to improve upon the flow plan obtained at the end of Section 6.2 (as given in column D of Figure 6.8).

The company has a second, smaller factory in Berlin, north of its Stuttgart factory, for producing automobile parts. Although this factory normally is used to help supply distribution centers in northern Europe, Canada, and the northern United States (including one in Seattle), it also is able to ship to the distribution center in Los Angeles. Furthermore, the distribution center in Seattle has the capability of supplying parts to the customers of the distribution center in Los Angeles when shortages occur at the latter center.

FIGURE 6.9

A network model for the expanded BMZ Co. problem as a variant of a maximum flow problem, where the number in square brackets below each arc is the capacity of that arc.

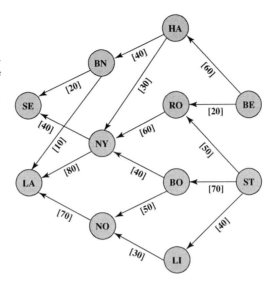

In this light, Karl now has developed a better plan for addressing the current inventory shortages in Los Angeles. Rather than simply maximizing shipments from the Stuttgart factory to Los Angeles, he has decided to maximize the total shipments from both factories to the distribution centers in both Los Angeles and Seattle.

Figure 6.9 shows the network model representing the expanded distribution network that encompasses both factories and both distribution centers. In addition to the nodes shown in Figures 6.6 and 6.7, node BE is the second, smaller factory in Berlin; nodes HA and BN are additional ports used by this factory in Hamburg and Boston, respectively; and node SE is the distribution center in Seattle. As before, the arcs represent the shipping lanes, where the number in square brackets below each arc is the capacity of that arc, that is, the maximum number of units that can be shipped through that shipping lane over the next month.

The corresponding spreadsheet model is displayed in Figure 6.10. The format is the same as in Figure 6.8. However, the objective cell MaxFlow (D21) now gives the total flow from Stuttgart and Berlin, so D21 = I4 + I5 (as shown by the equation for this objective cell given at the bottom of the figure).

The changing cells Ship (D4:D19) in this figure show the optimal solution obtained for the number of units to ship through each shipping lane over the next month. Comparing this solution with the one in Figure 6.8 shows the impact of Karl Schmidt's decision to expand the distribution network to include the second factory and the distribution center in Seattle. As indicated in column I of the two figures, the number of units going to Los Angeles directly has been increased from 150 to 160, in addition to the 60 units going to Seattle as a backup for the inventory shortage in Los Angeles. This plan solved the crisis in Los Angeles and won Karl commendations from top management.

Some Applications

The applications of maximum flow problems and their variants are somewhat similar to those for minimum-cost flow problems described in the preceding section when management's objective is to *maximize flow* rather than to *minimize cost*. Here are some typical kinds of applications.

1. Maximize the flow through a distribution network, as for the BMZ Co. problem.
2. Maximize the flow through a company's supply network from its vendors to its processing facilities.
3. Maximize the flow of oil through a system of pipelines.
4. Maximize the flow of water through a system of aqueducts.
5. Maximize the flow of vehicles through a transportation network.

FIGURE 6.10

A spreadsheet model for the expanded BMZ Co. problem as a variant of a maximum flow problem with sources in both Stuttgart and Berlin and sinks in both Los Angeles and Seattle. Using the objective cell MaxFlow (D21) to maximize the total flow from the two sources to the two sinks, Solver yields the optimal shipping plan shown in the changing cells Ship (D4:D19).

	A	B	C	D	E	F	G	H	I	J	K
1		**BMZ Co. Expanded Maximum Flow Problem**									
2											
3		**From**	**To**	**Ship**		**Capacity**		**Nodes**	**Net Flow**		**Supply/Demand**
4		Stuttgart	Rotterdam	40	≤	50		Stuttgart	140		
5		Stuttgart	Bordeaux	70	≤	70		Berlin	80		
6		Stuttgart	Lisbon	30	≤	40		Hamburg	0	=	0
7		Berlin	Rotterdam	20	≤	20		Rotterdam	0	=	0
8		Berlin	Hamburg	60	≤	60		Bordeaux	0	=	0
9		Rotterdam	New York	60	≤	60		Lisbon	0	=	0
10		Bordeaux	New York	30	≤	40		Boston	0	=	0
11		Bordeaux	New Orleans	40	≤	50		New York	0	=	0
12		Lisbon	New Orleans	30	≤	30		New Orleans	0	=	0
13		Hamburg	New York	30	≤	30		Los Angeles	-160		
14		Hamburg	Boston	30	≤	40		Seattle	-60		
15		New Orleans	Los Angeles	70	≤	70					
16		New York	Los Angeles	80	≤	80					
17		New York	Seattle	40	≤	40					
18		Boston	Los Angeles	10	≤	10					
19		Boston	Seattle	20	≤	20					
20											
21			**Maximum Flow**	220							

Solver Parameters

Set Objective Cell: MaxFlow
To: Max
By Changing Variable Cells:
  Ship
Subject to the Constraints:
  I6:I12 = SupplyDemand
  Ship <= Capacity

Solver Options:
  Make Variables Nonnegative
  Solving Method: Simplex LP

Range Name	Cells
Capacity	F4:F19
From	B4:B19
MaxFlow	D21
NetFlow	I4:I14
Nodes	H4:H14
Ship	D4:D19
SupplyDemand	K6:K12
To	C4:C19

	I
3	**Net Flow**
4	=SUMIF(From,H4,Ship)-SUMIF(To,H4,Ship)
5	=SUMIF(From,H5,Ship)-SUMIF(To,H5,Ship)
6	=SUMIF(From,H6,Ship)-SUMIF(To,H6,Ship)
7	=SUMIF(From,H7,Ship)-SUMIF(To,H7,Ship)
8	=SUMIF(From,H8,Ship)-SUMIF(To,H8,Ship)
9	=SUMIF(From,H9,Ship)-SUMIF(To,H9,Ship)
10	=SUMIF(From,H10,Ship)-SUMIF(To,H10,Ship)
11	=SUMIF(From,H11,Ship)-SUMIF(To,H11,Ship)
12	=SUMIF(From,H12,Ship)-SUMIF(To,H12,Ship)
13	=SUMIF(From,H13,Ship)-SUMIF(To,H13,Ship)
14	=SUMIF(From,H14,Ship)-SUMIF(To,H14,Ship)

	C	D
21	**Maximum Flow**	=I4+I5

Solving Very Large Problems

The expanded BMZ network in Figure 6.9 has 11 nodes and 16 arcs. However, the networks for most real applications are considerably larger, and occasionally vastly larger. As the number of nodes and arcs grows into the hundreds or thousands, the formulation and solution approach illustrated in Figures 6.8 and 6.10 quickly becomes impractical.

Fortunately, management scientists have other techniques available for formulating and solving huge problems with many tens of thousands of nodes and arcs. One technique is to reformulate a variant of a maximum flow problem so that an extremely efficient special-purpose algorithm for maximum flow problems still can be applied. Another is to reformulate the problem to fit the format for a minimum-cost flow problem so that the network simplex method can be applied. These special algorithms are available in some software packages, but not in Solver. Thus, if you should ever encounter a maximum flow problem or a variant that is beyond the scope of Solver (which won't happen in this book), rest assured that it probably can be formulated and solved in another way.

Review *Questions*

1. How does the objective of a maximum flow problem differ from that for a minimum-cost flow problem?
2. What are the *source* and the *sink* for a maximum flow problem? For each, in what direction do all their arcs point?
3. What are the two equivalent ways in which the total amount of flow from the source to the sink can be measured?
4. The source and sink of a maximum flow problem are different from the supply nodes and demand nodes of a minimum-cost flow problem in what two ways?
5. What are a few typical kinds of applications of maximum flow problems?

6.4   SHORTEST PATH PROBLEMS

The most common applications of shortest path problems are for what the name suggests—finding the *shortest path* between two points. Here is an example.

An Example: The Littletown Fire Department Problem

Littletown is a small town in a rural area. Its fire department serves a relatively large geographical area that includes many farming communities. Since there are numerous roads throughout the area, many possible routes may be available for traveling to any given farming community from the fire station. Since time is of the essence in reaching a fire, the fire chief wishes to determine in advance the *shortest path* from the fire station to each of the farming communities.

The objective is to find the shortest route from the fire station to the farming community.

Figure 6.11 shows the road system connecting the fire station to one of the farming communities, including the mileage along each road. Can you find which route from the fire station to the farming community minimizes the total number of miles?

Model Formulation for the Littletown Problem

Figure 6.12 gives the network representation of this problem, which ignores the geographical layout and the curves in the roads. This network model is the usual way of representing a shortest path problem. The junctions now are nodes of the network, where the fire station and farming community are two additional nodes labeled as O (for *origin*) and T (for *destination*), respectively. Since travel (flow) can go in either direction between the nodes, the lines

FIGURE 6.11

The road system between the Littletown Fire Station and a certain farming community, where A, B, . . . , H are junctions and the number next to each road shows its distance in miles.

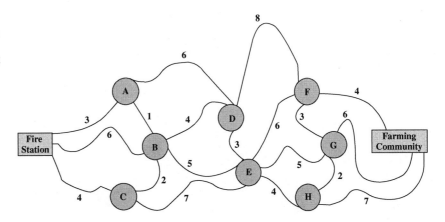

An Application Vignette

Incorporated in 1881, **Canadian Pacific Railway (CPR)** was North America's first transcontinental railway. CPR transports rail freight over a 14,000-mile network extending from Montreal to Vancouver and throughout the U.S. Northwest and Midwest. Alliances with other carriers extend CPR's market reach into the major business centers of Mexico as well.

Every day CPR receives approximately 7,000 new shipments from its customers going to destinations across North America and for export. It must route and move these shipments in railcars over the network of track, where a railcar may be switched a number of times from one locomotive engine to another before reaching its destination. CPR must coordinate the shipments with its operational plans for 1,600 locomotives, 65,000 railcars, over 5,000 train crew members, and 250 train yards.

CPR management turned to a management science consulting firm, MultiModal Applied Systems, to work with CPR employees in developing a management science approach to this problem. A variety of management science techniques were used to create a new operating strategy. However, the foundation of the approach was to represent the flow of blocks of railcars as flow through a network where each node corresponds to both a location and a point in time. This representation then enabled the application of network optimization techniques. For example, numerous *shortest path problems* are solved each day as part of the overall approach.

This application of management science is *saving CPR roughly* **US$100 million** *per year*. Labor productivity, locomotive productivity, fuel consumption, and railcar velocity have improved very substantially. In addition, CPR now provides its customers with reliable delivery times and has received many awards for its improvement in service. This application of network optimization techniques also led to CPR winning the prestigious First Prize in the 2003 international competition for the Franz Edelman Award for Achievement in Operations Research and the Management Sciences.

Source: P. Ireland, R. Case, J. Fallis, C. Van Dyke, J. Kuehn, and M. Meketon, "The Canadian Pacific Railway Transforms Operations by Using Models to Develop Its Operating Plans," *Interfaces* 34, no. 1 (January–February 2004), pp. 5–14. (A link to this article is provided on our website, www.mhhe.com/hillier5e.)

links

In a shortest path problem, travel goes from the origin to the destination through a series of links (such as roads) that connect pairs of nodes (junctions) in the network.

connecting the nodes now are referred to as **links**[2] instead of *arcs*. A link between a pair of nodes allows travel in either direction, whereas an arc allows travel in only the direction indicated by an arrowhead, so the lines in Figure 6.12 need to be links instead of arcs. (Notice that the links do not have an arrowhead at either end.)

Have you found the shortest path from the origin to the destination yet? (Try it now before reading further.) It is

$$O \rightarrow A \rightarrow B \rightarrow E \rightarrow F \rightarrow T$$

with a total distance of 19 miles.

This problem (like any shortest path problem) can be thought of as a special kind of minimum-cost flow problem (Section 6.1) where the *miles traveled* now are interpreted to be the *cost* of flow through the network. A trip from the fire station to the farming community is interpreted to be a flow of 1 on the chosen path through the network, so minimizing the cost of this flow is equivalent to minimizing the number of miles traveled. The fire station is considered to be the one supply node, with a supply of 1 to represent the start of this trip. The farming community is the one demand node, with a demand of 1 to represent the completion of this trip. All the other nodes in Figure 6.12 are transshipment nodes, so the net flow generated at each is 0.

Figure 6.13 shows the spreadsheet model that results from this interpretation. The format is basically the same as for the minimum-cost flow problem formulated in Figure 6.5, except

FIGURE 6.12

The network representation of Figure 6.11 as a shortest path problem.

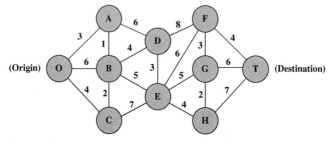

[2] Another name sometimes used is *undirected arc,* but we will not use this terminology.

FIGURE 6.13

A spreadsheet model for the Littletown Fire Department shortest path problem, including the equations entered into the objective cell TotalDistance (D29) and the other output cells SupplyDemand (K4:K13). The values of 1 in the changing cells OnRoute (D4:D27) reveal the optimal solution obtained by Solver for the shortest path (19 miles) from the fire station to the farming community.

	A	B	C	D	E	F	G	H	I	J	K
1		**Littletown Fire Department Shortest Path Problem**									
2											
3		**From**	**To**	**On Route**		**Distance**		**Nodes**	**Net Flow**		**Supply/Demand**
4		Fire St.	A	1		3		Fire St.	1	=	1
5		Fire St.	B	0		6		A	0	=	0
6		Fire St.	C	0		4		B	0	=	0
7		A	B	1		1		C	0	=	0
8		A	D	0		6		D	0	=	0
9		B	A	0		1		E	0	=	0
10		B	C	0		2		F	0	=	0
11		B	D	0		4		G	0	=	0
12		B	E	1		5		H	0	=	0
13		C	B	0		2		Farm Comm.	−1	=	−1
14		C	E	0		7					
15		D	E	0		3					
16		D	F	0		8					
17		E	D	0		3					
18		E	F	1		6					
19		E	G	0		5					
20		E	H	0		4					
21		F	G	0		3					
22		F	Farm Comm.	1		4					
23		G	F	0		3					
24		G	H	0		2					
25		G	Farm Comm.	0		6					
26		H	G	0		2					
27		H	Farm Comm.	0		7					
28											
29			**Total Distance**	19							

Solver Parameters

Set Objective Cell: TotalDistance
To: Min
By Changing Variable Cells:
  OnRoute
Subject to the Constraints:
  NetFlow = SupplyDemand

Solver Options:
  Make Variables Nonnegative
  Solving Method: Simplex LP

Range Name	Cells
Distance	F4:F27
From	B4:B27
NetFlow	I4:I13
Nodes	H4:H13
OnRoute	D4:D27
SupplyDemand	K4:K13
To	C4:C27
TotalDistance	D29

	I
3	**Net Flow**
4	=SUMIF(From,H4,OnRoute)-SUMIF(To,H4,OnRoute)
5	=SUMIF(From,H5,OnRoute)-SUMIF(To,H5,OnRoute)
6	=SUMIF(From,H6,OnRoute)-SUMIF(To,H6,OnRoute)
7	=SUMIF(From,H7,OnRoute)-SUMIF(To,H7,OnRoute)
8	=SUMIF(From,H8,OnRoute)-SUMIF(To,H8,OnRoute)
9	=SUMIF(From,H9,OnRoute)-SUMIF(To,H9,OnRoute)
10	=SUMIF(From,H10,OnRoute)-SUMIF(To,H10,OnRoute)
11	=SUMIF(From,H11,OnRoute)-SUMIF(To,H11,OnRoute)
12	=SUMIF(From,H12,OnRoute)-SUMIF(To,H12,OnRoute)
13	=SUMIF(From,H13,OnRoute)-SUMIF(To,H13,OnRoute)

	C	D
29	**Total Distance**	=SUMPRODUCT(OnRoute,Distance)

now there are no arc capacity constraints and the unit cost column is replaced by a column of distances in miles. The flow quantities given by the changing cells OnRoute (D4:D27) are 1 for each arc that is on the chosen path from the fire station to the farming community and 0 otherwise. The objective cell TotalDistance (D29) gives the total distance of this path in miles. (See the equation for this cell at the bottom of the figure.) Columns B and C together list all the vertical links in Figure 6.12 twice, once as a downward arc and once as an upward arc, since either direction might be on the chosen path. The other links are only listed as left-to-right arcs, since this is the only direction of interest for choosing a shortest path from the origin to the destination.

Column K shows the net flow that needs to be generated at each of the nodes. Using the equations at the bottom of the figure, each column I cell then calculates the *actual* net flow at that node by adding the flow out and subtracting the flow in. The corresponding constraints, Nodes (H4:H13) = SupplyDemand (K4:K13), are specified in the Solver Parameters box.

The solution shown in OnRoute (D4:D27) is the optimal solution obtained after running Solver. It is exactly the same as the shortest path given earlier.

Just as for minimum-cost flow problems and maximum flow problems, special algorithms are available for solving large shortest path problems very efficiently, but these algorithms are not included in Solver. Using a spreadsheet formulation and Solver is fine for problems of the size of the Littletown problem and somewhat larger, but you should be aware that vastly larger problems can still be solved by other means.

> This spreadsheet model is like one for a minimum-cost flow problem with no arc capacity constraints except that distances replace unit costs and travel on a chosen path is interpreted as a flow of 1 through this path.

General Characteristics

Except for more complicated variations beyond the scope of this book, all shortest path problems share the characteristics illustrated by the Littletown problem. Here are the basic assumptions.

Assumptions of a Shortest Path Problem

1. You need to choose a path through the network that starts at a certain node, called the **origin,** and ends at another certain node, called the **destination.**
2. The lines connecting certain pairs of nodes commonly are *links* (which allow travel in either direction), although arcs (which only permit travel in one direction) also are allowed.
3. Associated with each link (or arc) is a nonnegative number called its **length.** (Be aware that the drawing of each link in the network typically makes no effort to show its true length other than giving the correct number next to the link.)
4. The objective is to find the shortest path (the path with the minimum total length) from the origin to the destination.

> The objective is to find the shortest path from the origin to the destination.

Some Applications

Not all applications of shortest path problems involve minimizing the distance traveled from the origin to the destination. In fact, they might not even involve travel at all. The links (or arcs) might instead represent activities of some other kind, so choosing a path through the network corresponds to selecting the best sequence of activities. The numbers giving the "lengths" of the links might then be, for example, the costs of the activities, in which case the objective would be to determine which sequence of activities minimizes the total cost.

Here are three categories of applications.

1. Minimize the total *distance* traveled, as in the Littletown example.
2. Minimize the total *cost* of a sequence of activities, as in the example that follows in the subsection below.
3. Minimize the total *time* of a sequence of activities, as in the example involving the Quick Company at the end of this section.

An Example of Minimizing Total Cost

Sarah has just graduated from high school. As a graduation present, her parents have given her a car fund of $21,000 to help purchase and maintain a certain three-year-old used car for college. Since operating and maintenance costs go up rapidly as the car ages, Sarah's parents tell her that she will be welcome to trade in her car on another three-year-old car one or more times during the next three summers if she determines that this would minimize her total net cost. They also inform her that they will give her a new car in four years as a college graduation present, so she should definitely plan to trade in her car then. (These are pretty nice parents!)

Table 6.2 gives the relevant data for *each* time Sarah purchases a three-year-old car. For example, if she trades in her car after two years, the next car will be in ownership year 1 during her junior year, and so forth.

Sarah needs a schedule for trading in her car that will minimize her total net cost.

When should Sarah trade in her car (if at all) during the next three summers to minimize her total net cost of purchasing, operating, and maintaining the car(s) over her four years of college?

Figure 6.14 shows the network formulation of this problem as a shortest path problem. Nodes 1, 2, 3, and 4 are the end of Sarah's first, second, third, and fourth years of college, respectively. Node 0 is now, before starting college. Each arc from one node to a second node corresponds to the activity of purchasing a car at the time indicated by the first of these two nodes and then trading it in at the time indicated by the second node. Sarah begins by purchasing a car now, and she ends by trading in a car at the end of year 4, so node 0 is the *origin* and node 4 is the *destination*.

The number of arcs on the path chosen from the origin to the destination indicates how many times Sarah will purchase and trade in a car. For example, consider the path

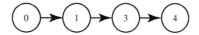

This corresponds to purchasing a car now, then trading it in at the end of year 1 to purchase a second car, then trading in the second car at the end of year 3 to purchase a third car, and then trading in this third car at the end of year 4.

Since Sarah wants to minimize her total net cost from now (node 0) to the end of year 4 (node 4), each arc length needs to measure the net cost of that arc's cycle of purchasing, maintaining, and trading in a car. Therefore,

Arc length = Purchase price + Operating and maintenance costs − Trade-in value

For example, consider the arc from node 1 to node 3. This arc corresponds to purchasing a car at the end of year 1, operating and maintaining it during ownership years 1 and 2, and then trading it in at the end of ownership year 2. Consequently,

Length of arc from ① to ③ = 12,000 + 2,000 + 3,000 − 6,500
= 10,500   (in dollars)

TABLE 6.2
Sarah's Data Each Time She Purchases a Three-Year-Old Car

Purchase Price	Operating and Maintenance Costs for Ownership Year				Trade-in Value at End of Ownership Year			
	1	2	3	4	1	2	3	4
$12,000	$2,000	$3,000	$4,500	$6,500	$8,500	$6,500	$4,500	$3,000

FIGURE 6.14
Formulation of the problem of when Sarah should trade in her car as a shortest path problem. The node labels measure the number of years from now. Each arc represents purchasing a car and then trading it in later.

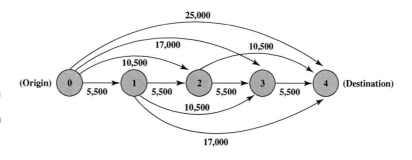

The sum of the arc lengths on any path through this network gives the total net cost of the corresponding plan for trading in cars.

The objective cell now is TotalCost instead of TotalDistance.

The arc lengths calculated in this way are shown next to the arcs in Figure 6.14. Adding up the lengths of the arcs on any path from node 0 to node 4 then gives the total net cost for that particular plan for trading in cars over the next four years. Therefore, finding the shortest path from the origin to the destination identifies the plan that will minimize Sarah's total net cost.

Figure 6.15 shows the corresponding spreadsheet model, formulated in just the same way as for Figure 6.13 except that distances are now costs. Thus, the objective cell TotalCost (D23) now gives the total cost that is to be minimized. The changing cells OnRoute (D12:D21) in the figure display the optimal solution obtained after running Solver. Since values of 1 indicate the path being followed, the shortest path turns out to be

Trade in the first car at the end of year 2.

Trade in the second car at the end of year 4.

The length of this path is 10,500 + 10,500 = 21,000, so Sarah's total net cost is $21,000, as given by the objective cell. Recall that this is exactly the amount in Sarah's car fund provided by her parents. (These are *really* nice parents!)

An Example of Minimizing Total Time

The **Quick Company** has learned that a competitor is planning to come out with a new kind of product with great sales potential. Quick has been working on a similar product that had been scheduled to come to market in 20 months. However, research is nearly complete and Quick's management now wishes to rush the product out to meet the competition.

There are four nonoverlapping phases left to be accomplished, including the remaining research (the first phase) that currently is being conducted at a normal pace. However, each phase can instead be conducted at a priority or crash level to expedite completion. These are the only levels that will be considered for the last three phases, whereas both the normal level and these two levels will be considered for the first phase. The times required at these levels are shown in Table 6.3.

Management now has allocated $30 million for these four phases. The cost of each phase at the levels under consideration is shown in Table 6.4.

The objective is to minimize the total time for the project.

Management wishes to determine at which level to conduct each of the four phases to minimize the total time until the product can be marketed, subject to the budget restriction of $30 million.

Figure 6.16 shows the network formulation of this problem as a shortest path problem. Each node indicates the situation at that point in time. Except for the destination, a node is identified by two numbers:

1. The number of phases completed.
2. The number of millions of dollars left for the remaining phases.

The sum of the arc lengths on any path through this network gives the total time of the corresponding plan for preparing the new product.

The origin is *now,* when 0 phases have been completed and the entire budget of $30 million is left. Each arc represents the choice of a particular level of effort (identified in parentheses below the arc) for that phase. [There are no crash arcs emanating from the (2, 12) and (3, 3) nodes because this level of effort would require exceeding the budget of $30 million for the four phases.] The *time* (in months) required to perform the phase with this level of effort then is the *length* of the arc (shown above the arc). Time is chosen as the measure of arc length because the objective is to minimize the total time for all four phases. Summing the arc lengths for any particular path through the network gives the total time for the plan corresponding to that path. Therefore, the shortest path through the network identifies the plan that minimizes total time.

FIGURE 6.15

A spreadsheet model that formulates Sarah's problem as a shortest path problem where the objective is to minimize the total cost instead of the total distance. The bottom of the figure shows the equations entered in the objective cell TotalCost (D23) and the other output cells Cost (E12:E21) and NetFlow (H12:H16). After applying Solver, the values of 1 in the changing cells OnRoute (D12:D21) identify the shortest (least expensive) path for scheduling trade-ins.

	A	B	C	D	E	F	G	H	I	J
1		**Sarah's Car Purchasing Problem**								
2										
3			Operating &	Trade-in Value at End	Purchase					
4			Maint. Cost	of Year	Price					
5		Year 1	$2,000	$8,500	$12,000					
6		Year 2	$3,000	$6,500						
7		Year 3	$4,500	$4,500						
8		Year 4	$6,500	$3,000						
9										
10										
11		**From**	**To**	**On Route**	**Cost**		**Nodes**	**Net Flow**		**Supply/Demand**
12		Year 0	Year 1	0	$5,500		Year 0	1	=	1
13		Year 0	Year 2	1	$10,500		Year 1	0	=	0
14		Year 0	Year 3	0	$17,000		Year 2	0	=	0
15		Year 0	Year 4	0	$25,000		Year 3	0	=	0
16		Year 1	Year 2	0	$5,500		Year 4	-1	=	-1
17		Year 1	Year 3	0	$10,500					
18		Year 1	Year 4	0	$17,000					
19		Year 2	Year 3	0	$5,500					
20		Year 2	Year 4	1	$10,500					
21		Year 3	Year 4	0	$5,500					
22										
23			**Total Cost**	$21,000						

Range Name	Cells
Cost	E12:E21
From	B12:B21
NetFlow	H12:H16
Nodes	G12:G16
OnRoute	D12:D21
OpMaint1	C5
OpMaint2	C6
OpMaint3	C7
OpMaint4	C8
PurchasePrice	E5
SupplyDemand	J12:J16
To	C12:C21
TotalCost	D23
TradeIn1	D5
TradeIn2	D6
TradeIn3	D7
TradeIn4	D8

Solver Parameters

Set Objective Cell: TotalCost
To: Min
By Changing Variable Cells:
   OnRoute
Subject to the Constraints:
   NetFlow = SupplyDemand

Solver Options:
   Make Variables Nonnegative
   Solving Method: Simplex LP

	E
11	**Cost**
12	=PurchasePrice+OpMaint1-TradeIn1
13	=PurchasePrice+OpMaint1+OpMaint2-TradeIn2
14	=PurchasePrice+OpMaint1+OpMaint2+OpMaint3-TradeIn3
15	=PurchasePrice+OpMaint1+OpMaint2+OpMaint3+OpMaint4-TradeIn4
16	=PurchasePrice+OpMaint1-TradeIn1
17	=PurchasePrice+OpMaint1+OpMaint2-TradeIn2
18	=PurchasePrice+OpMaint1+OpMaint2+OpMaint3-TradeIn3
19	=PurchasePrice+OpMaint1-TradeIn1
20	=PurchasePrice+OpMaint1+OpMaint2-TradeIn2
21	=PurchasePrice+OpMaint1-TradeIn1

	H
11	**Net Flow**
12	=SUMIF(From,G12,OnRoute)-SUMIF(To,G12,OnRoute)
13	=SUMIF(From,G13,OnRoute)-SUMIF(To,G13,OnRoute)
14	=SUMIF(From,G14,OnRoute)-SUMIF(To,G14,OnRoute)
15	=SUMIF(From,G15,OnRoute)-SUMIF(To,G15,OnRoute)
16	=SUMIF(From,G16,OnRoute)-SUMIF(To,G16,OnRoute)

	C	D
23	**Total Cost**	=SUMPRODUCT(OnRoute,Cost)

All four phases have been completed as soon as any one of the four nodes with a first label of 4 has been reached. So why doesn't the network just end with these four nodes rather than having an arc coming out of each one? The reason is that a shortest path problem is required to have only a single destination. Consequently, a **dummy destination** is added at the right-hand side.

216   Chapter Six   *Network Optimization Problems*

TABLE 6.3
Time Required for the Phases of Preparing Quick Co.'s New Product

Level	Remaining Research	Development	Design of Manufacturing System	Initiate Production and Distribution
Normal	5 months	—	—	—
Priority	4 months	3 months	5 months	2 months
Crash	2 months	2 months	3 months	1 month

TABLE 6.4
Cost for the Phases of Preparing Quick Co.'s New Product

Level	Remaining Research	Development	Design of Manufacturing System	Initiate Production and Distribution
Normal	$3 million	—	—	—
Priority	6 million	$6 million	$ 9 million	$3 million
Crash	9 million	9 million	12 million	6 million

FIGURE 6.16
Formulation of the Quick Co. problem as a shortest path problem. Except for the dummy destination, the arc labels indicate, first, the number of phases completed and, second, the amount of money left (in millions of dollars) for the remaining phases. Each arc length gives the time (in months) to perform that phase.

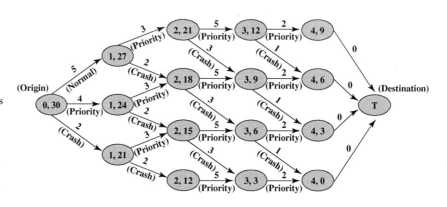

When real travel through a network can end at more than one node, an arc with length 0 is inserted from each of these nodes to a **dummy destination** so that the network will have just a single destination.

Since each of the arcs into the dummy destination has length 0, this addition to the network does not affect the total length of a path from the origin to its ending point.

Figure 6.17 displays the spreadsheet model for this problem. Once again, the format is the same as in Figures 6.13 and 6.15, except now the quantity of concern in column F and the objective cell TotalTime (D32) is time rather than distance or cost. Since Solver has already been run, the changing cells OnRoute (D4:D30) indicate which arcs lie on the path that minimizes the total time. Thus, the shortest path is

The objective cell now is TotalTime instead of TotalDistance.

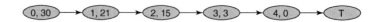

with a total length of $2 + 3 + 3 + 2 + 0 = 10$ months, as given by TotalTime (D32). The resulting plan for the four phases is shown in Table 6.5. Although this plan does consume the

TABLE 6.5
The Optimal Solution Obtained by Solver for Quick Co.'s Shortest Path Problem

Phase	Level	Time	Cost
Remaining research	Crash	2 months	$ 9 million
Development	Priority	3 months	6 million
Design of manufacturing system	Crash	3 months	12 million
Initiate production and distribution	Priority	2 months	3 million
Total		10 months	$30 million

entire budget of $30 million, it reduces the time until the product can be brought to market from the originally planned 20 months down to just 10 months.

Given this information, Quick's management now must decide whether this plan provides the best trade-off between time and cost. What would be the effect on total time of spending a few million more dollars? What would be the effect of reducing the spending somewhat instead? It is easy to provide management with this information as well by quickly solving some shortest path problems that correspond to budgets different from $30 million. The ultimate decision regarding which plan provides the best time–cost trade-off then is a judgment decision that only management can make.

FIGURE 6.17

A spreadsheet model that formulates the Quick Co. problem as a shortest path problem where the objective is to minimize the total time instead of the total distance, so the objective cell is TotalTime (D32). The other output cells are NetFlow (I4:I20). The values of 1 in the changing cells OnRoute (D4:D30) reveal the shortest (quickest) path obtained by Solver.

	A	B	C	D	E	F	G	H	I	J	K
1		**Quick Co. Product Development Scheduling Problem**									
2											
3		**From**	**To**	**On Route**		**Time**		**Nodes**	**Net Flow**		**Supply/Demand**
4		(0, 30)	(1, 27)	0		5		(0, 30)	1	=	1
5		(0, 30)	(1, 24)	0		4		(1, 27)	0	=	0
6		(0, 30)	(1, 21)	1		2		(1, 24)	0	=	0
7		(1, 27)	(2, 21)	0		3		(1, 21)	0	=	0
8		(1, 27)	(2, 18)	0		2		(2, 21)	0	=	0
9		(1, 24)	(2, 18)	0		3		(2, 18)	0	=	0
10		(1, 24)	(2, 15)	0		2		(2, 15)	0	=	0
11		(1, 21)	(2, 15)	1		3		(2, 12)	0	=	0
12		(1, 21)	(2, 12)	0		2		(3, 12)	0	=	0
13		(2, 21)	(3, 12)	0		5		(3, 9)	0	=	0
14		(2, 21)	(3, 9)	0		3		(3, 6)	0	=	0
15		(2, 18)	(3, 9)	0		5		(3, 3)	0	=	0
16		(2, 18)	(3, 6)	0		3		(4, 9)	0	=	0
17		(2, 15)	(3, 6)	0		5		(4, 6)	0	=	0
18		(2, 15)	(3, 3)	1		3		(4, 3)	0	=	0
19		(2, 12)	(3, 3)	0		5		(4, 0)	0	=	0
20		(3, 12)	(4, 9)	0		2		(T)	-1	=	-1
21		(3, 12)	(4, 6)	0		1					
22		(3, 9)	(4, 6)	0		2					
23		(3, 9)	(4, 3)	0		1					
24		(3, 6)	(4, 3)	0		2					
25		(3, 6)	(4, 0)	0		1					
26		(3, 3)	(4, 0)	1		2					
27		(4, 9)	(T)	0		0					
28		(4, 6)	(T)	0		0					
29		(4, 3)	(T)	0		0					
30		(4, 0)	(T)	1		0					
31											
32			**Total Time**	10							

(continued)

218 Chapter Six *Network Optimization Problems*

FIGURE 6.17
(continued)

Range Name	Cells
From	B4:B30
NetFlow	I4:I20
Nodes	H4:H20
OnRoute	D4:D30
SupplyDemand	K4:K20
Time	F4:F30
To	C4:C30
TotalTime	D32

Solver Parameters

Set Objective Cell: TotalTime
To: Min
By Changing Variable Cells:
    OnRoute
Subject to the Constraints:
    NetFlow = SupplyDemand

Solver Options:
    Make Variables Nonnegative
    Solving Method: Simplex LP

	I
3	**Net Flow**
4	=SUMIF(From,H4,OnRoute)-SUMIF(To,H4,OnRoute)
5	=SUMIF(From,H5,OnRoute)-SUMIF(To,H5,OnRoute)
6	=SUMIF(From,H6,OnRoute)-SUMIF(To,H6,OnRoute)
7	=SUMIF(From,H7, OnRoute)-SUMIF(To,H7,OnRoute)
8	=SUMIF(From,H8,OnRoute)-SUMIF(To,H8,OnRoute)
9	=SUMIF(From,H9,OnRoute)-SUMIF(To,H9,OnRoute)
10	=SUMIF(From,H10,OnRoute)-SUMIF(To,H10,OnRoute)
11	=SUMIF(From,H11,OnRoute)-SUMIF(To,H11,OnRoute)
12	=SUMIF(From,H12,OnRoute)-SUMIF(To,H12,OnRoute)
13	=SUMIF(From,H13,OnRoute)-SUMIF(To,H13,OnRoute)
14	=SUMIF(From,H14,OnRoute)-SUMIF(To,H14,OnRoute)
15	=SUMIF(From,H15,OnRoute)-SUMIF(To,H15,OnRoute)
16	=SUMIF(From,H16,OnRoute)-SUMIF(To,H16,OnRoute)
17	=SUMIF(From,H17,OnRoute)-SUMIF(To,H17,OnRoute)
18	=SUMIF(From,H18,OnRoute)-SUMIF(To,H18,OnRoute)
19	=SUMIF(From,H19,OnRoute)-SUMIF(To,H19,OnRoute)
20	=SUMIF(From,H20,OnRoute)-SUMIF(To,H20,OnRoute)

	C	D
32	**Total Time**	=SUMPRODUCT(OnRoute,Time)

Review Questions

1. What are the origin and the destination in the Littletown Fire Department example?
2. What is the distinction between an arc and a link?
3. What are the supply node and the demand node when a shortest path problem is interpreted as a minimum-cost flow problem? With what supply and demand?
4. What are three measures of the length of a link (or arc) that lead to three categories of applications of shortest path problems?
5. What is the objective for Sarah's shortest path problem?
6. When does a dummy destination need to be added to the formulation of a shortest path problem?
7. What kind of trade-off does the management of the Quick Co. need to consider in making its final decision about how to expedite its new product to market?

6.5 Summary

Networks of some type arise in a wide variety of contexts. Network representations are very useful for portraying the relationships and connections between the components of systems. Each component is represented by a point in the network called a *node,* and then the connections between components (nodes) are represented by lines called *arcs* (for one-way travel) or *links* (for two-way travel).

Frequently, a flow of some type must be sent through a network, so a decision needs to be made about the best way to do this. The kinds of network optimization models introduced in this chapter provide a powerful tool for making such decisions.

The model for minimum-cost flow problems plays a central role among these network optimization models, both because it is so broadly applicable and because it can be readily solved. Solver solves spreadsheet formulations of reasonable size, and the network simplex method can be used to solve larger problems, including huge problems with tens of thousands of nodes and arcs. A minimum-cost flow problem typically is concerned with optimizing the flow of goods through a network from their points of origin (the *supply nodes*) to where they are needed (the *demand nodes*). The objective is to minimize the total cost of sending the available supply through the network to satisfy the given demand. One typical application (among several) is to optimize the operation of a distribution network.

Special types of minimum-cost flow problems include transportation problems and assignment problems (discussed in Chapter 3) as well as two prominent types introduced in this chapter: maximum flow problems and shortest path problems.

Given the limited capacities of the arcs in the network, the objective of a maximum flow problem is to maximize the total amount of flow from a particular point of origin (the *source*) to a particular terminal point (the *sink*). For example, this might involve maximizing the flow of goods through a company's supply network from its vendors to its processing facilities.

A shortest path problem also has a beginning point (the *origin*) and an ending point (the *destination*), but now the objective is to find a path from the origin to the destination that has the minimum total *length*. For some applications, length refers to distance, so the objective is to minimize the total distance traveled. However, some applications instead involve minimizing either the total cost or the total time of a sequence of activities.

Glossary

arc A channel through which flow may occur from one node to another, shown as an arrow between the nodes pointing in the direction in which flow is allowed. (Section 6.1), 197

capacity of an arc The maximum amount of flow allowed through the arc. (Section 6.1), 197

conservation of flow Having the amount of flow out of a node equal the amount of flow into that node. (Section 6.1), 197

demand node A node where the net amount of flow generated (outflow minus inflow) is a fixed negative number, so that flow is absorbed there. (Section 6.1), 197

destination The node at which travel through the network is assumed to end for a shortest path problem. (Section 6.4), 212

dummy destination A fictitious destination introduced into the formulation of a shortest path problem with multiple possible termination points to satisfy the requirement that there be just a single destination. (Section 6.4), 216

length of a link or arc The number (typically a distance, a cost, or a time) associated with including the link or arc in the selected path for a shortest path problem. (Section 6.4), 212

link A channel through which flow may occur in either direction between a pair of nodes, shown as a line between the nodes. (Section 6.4), 210

network simplex method A streamlined version of the simplex method for solving minimum-cost flow problems very efficiently. (Section 6.1), 200

node A junction point of a network, shown as a labeled circle. (Section 6.1), 197

origin The node at which travel through the network is assumed to start for a shortest path problem. (Section 6.4), 212

sink The node for a maximum flow problem at which all flow through the network terminates. (Section 6.3), 205

source The node for a maximum flow problem at which all flow through the network originates. (Section 6.3), 205

supply node A node where the net amount of flow generated (outflow minus inflow) is a fixed positive number. (Section 6.1), 197

transshipment node A node where the amount of flow out equals the amount of flow in. (Section 6.1), 197

transshipment problem A special type of minimum-cost flow problem where there are no capacity constraints on the arcs. (Section 6.1), 201

Learning Aids for This Chapter in Your MS Courseware

Chapter 6 Excel Files:
Distribution Unlimited Example
BMZ Example
Expanded BMZ Example
Littletown Fire Department Example

Sarah Example
Quick Example

Supplement to Chapter 6 on the CD-ROM:
Minimum Spanning-Tree Problems

Solved Problems (See the CD-ROM or Website for the Solutions)

6.S1. Distribution at Heart Beats

Heart Beats is a manufacturer of medical equipment. The company's primary product is a device used to monitor the heart during medical procedures. This device is produced in two factories and shipped to two warehouses. The product is then shipped on demand to four third-party wholesalers. All shipping is done by truck. The product distribution network is shown below. The annual production capacity at factories 1 and

220   Chapter Six *Network Optimization Problems*

2 is 400 and 250, respectively. The annual demand at wholesalers 1, 2, 3, and 4 is 200, 100, 150, and 200, respectively. The cost of shipping one unit in each shipping lane is shown on the arcs. Because of limited truck capacity, at most 250 units can be shipped from Factory 1 to Warehouse 1 each year. Formulate and solve a network optimization model in a spreadsheet to determine how to distribute the product at the lowest possible annual cost.

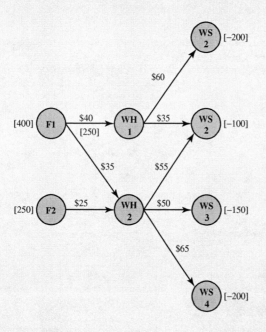

6.S2. Assessing the Capacity of a Pipeline Network

Exxo 76 is an oil company that operates the pipeline network shown below, where each pipeline is labeled with its maximum flow rate in million cubic feet (MMcf) per day. A new oil well has been constructed near A. They would like to transport oil from the well near A to their refinery at G. Formulate and solve a network optimization model to determine the maximum flow rate from A to G.

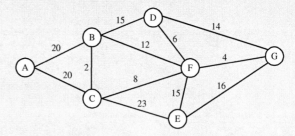

6.S3. Driving to the Mile-High City

Sarah and Jennifer have just graduated from college at the University of Washington in Seattle and want to go on a road trip. They have always wanted to see the mile-high city of Denver. Their road atlas shows the driving time (in hours) between various city pairs, as shown below. Formulate and solve a network optimization model to find the quickest route from Seattle to Denver.

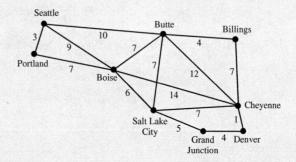

Problems

We have inserted the symbol E* to the left of each problem (or its parts) where Excel should be used (unless your instructor gives you contrary instructions). An asterisk on the problem number indicates that at least a partial answer is given in the back of the book.

6.1.   Read the referenced article that fully describes the management science study summarized in the application vignette presented in Section 6.1. Briefly describe how the model for a special type of minimum-cost flow problem was applied in this study. Then list the various financial and nonfinancial benefits that resulted from this study.

6.2.*   Consider the transportation problem having the following data.

	Destination			
	1	**2**	**3**	**Supply**
Source				
1	6	7	4	40
2	5	8	6	60
Demand	30	40	30	

a. Formulate a network model for this problem as a minimum-cost flow problem by drawing a network similar to Figure 6.3.

E*   *b.* Formulate and solve a spreadsheet model for this problem.

6.3. The Makonsel Company is a fully integrated company that both produces goods and sells them at its retail outlets. After production, the goods are stored in the company's two warehouses until needed by the retail outlets. Trucks are used to transport the goods from the two plants to the warehouses, and then from the warehouses to the three retail outlets.

Using units of full truckloads, the first table below shows each plant's monthly output, its shipping cost per truckload sent to each warehouse, and the maximum amount that it can ship per month to each warehouse.

For each retail outlet (RO), the second table below shows its monthly demand, its shipping cost per truckload from each warehouse, and the maximum amount that can be shipped per month from each warehouse.

Management now wants to determine a distribution plan (number of truckloads shipped per month from each plant to each warehouse and from each warehouse to each retail outlet) that will minimize the total shipping cost.

    a. Draw a network that depicts the company's distribution network. Identify the supply nodes, transshipment nodes, and demand nodes in this network.

    b. Formulate a network model for this problem as a minimum-cost flow problem by inserting all the necessary data into the network drawn in part *a*. (Use the format depicted in Figure 6.3 to display these data.)

E*   *c.* Formulate and solve a spreadsheet model for this problem.

6.4. The Audiofile Company produces boomboxes. However, management has decided to subcontract out the production of the speakers needed for the boomboxes. Three vendors are available to supply the speakers. Their price for each shipment of 1,000 speakers is shown below.

Vendor	Price
1	$22,500
2	22,700
3	22,300

Each shipment would go to one of the company's two warehouses. In addition to the price for each shipment, each vendor would charge a shipping cost for which it has its own formula based on the mileage to the warehouse. These formulas and the mileage data are shown below.

Vendor	Charge per Shipment	Warehouse 1	Warehouse 2
1	$300 + 40¢/mile	1,600 miles	400 miles
2	$200 + 50¢/mile	500 miles	600 miles
3	$500 + 20¢/mile	2,000 miles	1,000 miles

Whenever one of the company's two factories needs a shipment of speakers to assemble into the boomboxes, the company hires a trucker to bring the shipment in from one of the warehouses. The cost per shipment is given next, along with the number of shipments needed per month at each factory.

	Unit Shipping Cost	
	Factory 1	Factory 2
Warehouse 1	$200	$700
Warehouse 2	400	500
Monthly demand	10	6

Each vendor is able to supply as many as 10 shipments per month. However, because of shipping limitations, each vendor is only able to send a maximum of six shipments per month to each warehouse. Similarly, each warehouse is only able to send a maximum of six shipments per month to each factory.

Management now wants to develop a plan for each month regarding how many shipments (if any) to order from each vendor, how many of those shipments should go to each warehouse, and then how many shipments each warehouse should send to each factory. The objective is to minimize the sum of the purchase costs (including the shipping charge) and the shipping costs from the warehouses to the factories.

    a. Draw a network that depicts the company's supply network. Identify the supply nodes, transshipment nodes, and demand nodes in this network.

    b. This problem is only a *variant* of a minimum-cost flow problem because the supply from each vendor is a *maximum* of 10 rather than a fixed amount of 10. However, it can be converted to a full-fledged minimum-cost flow problem by adding a dummy demand node that receives (at zero cost) all the

From \ To	Unit Shipping Cost		Shipping Capacity		
	Warehouse 1	Warehouse 2	Warehouse 1	Warehouse 2	Output
Plant 1	$425	$560	125	150	200
Plant 2	510	600	175	200	300

From \ To	Unit Shipping Cost			Shipping Capacity		
	RO1	RO2	RO3	RO1	RO2	RO3
Warehouse 1	$470	$505	$490	100	150	100
Warehouse 2	390	410	440	125	150	75
Demand	150	200	150	150	200	150

222   Chapter Six   *Network Optimization Problems*

unused supply capacity at the vendors. Formulate a network model for this minimum-cost flow problem by inserting all the necessary data into the network drawn in part *a* supplemented by this dummy demand node. (Use the format depicted in Figure 6.3 to display these data.)

E*   *c.* Formulate and solve a spreadsheet model for the company's problem.

6.5.*   Consider Figure 6.9 (in Section 6.3), which depicts the BMZ Co. distribution network from its factories in Stuttgart and Berlin to the distribution centers in both Los Angeles and Seattle. This figure also gives in brackets the maximum amount that can be shipped through each shipping lane.

In the weeks following the crisis described in Section 6.2, the distribution center in Los Angeles has successfully replenished its inventory. Therefore, Karl Schmidt (the supply chain manager for the BMZ Co.) has concluded that it will be sufficient hereafter to ship 130 units per month to Los Angeles and 50 units per month to Seattle. (One unit is a hundred cubic meters of automobile replacement parts.) The Stuttgart factory (node ST in the figure) will allocate 130 units per month and the Berlin factory (node BE) will allocate 50 units per month out of their total production to cover these shipments. However, rather than resuming the past practice of supplying the Los Angeles distribution center from only the Stuttgart factory and supplying the Seattle distribution center from only the Berlin factory, Karl has decided to allow either factory to supply either distribution center. He feels that this additional flexibility is likely to reduce the total shipping cost.

The following table gives the shipping cost per unit through each of these shipping lanes.

6.6.   Reconsider Problem 6.5. Suppose now that, for administrative convenience, management has decided that all 130 units per month needed at the distribution center in Los Angeles must come from the Stuttgart factory (node ST) and all 50 units per month needed at the distribution center in Seattle must come from the Berlin factory (node BE). For each of these distribution centers, Karl Schmidt wants to determine the shipping plan that will minimize the total shipping cost.

a. For the distribution center in Los Angeles, formulate a network model for this problem as a minimum-cost flow problem by inserting all the necessary data into the distribution network shown in Figure 6.6. (Use the format depicted in Figure 6.3 to display these data.)

E*   *b.* Formulate and solve a spreadsheet model for the problem formulated in part *a.*

c. For the distribution center in Seattle, draw its distribution network emanating from the Berlin factory at node BE.

d. Repeat part *a* for the distribution center in Seattle by using the network drawn in part *c.*

E*   *e.* Formulate and solve a spreadsheet model for the problem formulated in part *d.*

f. Add the total shipping costs obtained in parts *b* and *e.* Compare this sum with the total shipping cost obtained in part *c* of Problem 6.5 (as given in the back of the book).

6.7.   Consider the maximum flow problem formulated in Figures 6.7 and 6.8 for the BMZ case study. Redraw Figure 6.7 and insert the optimal shipping quantities (cells

From \ To	LI	BO	RO	HA	NO	NY	BN	LA	SE
Unit Shipping Cost to Node									
Node									
ST	$3,200	$2,500	$2,900	—	—	—	—	—	—
BE	—	—	$2,400	$2,000	—	—	—	—	—
LI	—	—	—	—	$6,100	—	—	—	—
BO	—	—	—	—	$6,800	$5,400	—	—	—
RO	—	—	—	—	—	$5,900	—	—	—
HA	—	—	—	—	—	$6,300	$5,700	—	—
NO	—	—	—	—	—	—	—	$3,100	—
NY	—	—	—	—	—	—	—	$4,200	$4,000
BN	—	—	—	—	—	—	—	$3,400	$3,000

Karl wants to determine the shipping plan that will minimize the total shipping cost.

a. Formulate a network model for this problem as a minimum-cost flow problem by inserting all the necessary data into the distribution network shown in Figure 6.9. (Use the format depicted in Figure 6.3 to display these data.)

E*   *b.* Formulate and solve a spreadsheet model for this problem.

c. What is the total shipping cost for this optimal solution?

D4:D12 in Figure 6.8) in parentheses above the respective arcs. Examine the capacities of these arcs. Explain why these arc capacities ensure that the shipping quantities in parentheses must be an optimal solution because the maximum flow cannot exceed 150.

6.8.   Read the referenced article that fully describes the management science study summarized in the application vignette presented in Section 6.3. Briefly describe how a generalization of the model for the maximum flow problem was applied in this study. Then list the various financial and nonfinancial benefits that resulted from this study.

E*6.9. Formulate and solve a spreadsheet model for the maximum flow problem shown at the top of the next column, where node A is the source, node F is the sink, and the arc capacities are the numbers in square brackets shown next to the arcs.

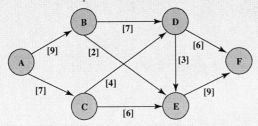

6.10. The diagram depicts a system of aqueducts that originate at three rivers (nodes R1, R2, and R3) and terminate at a major city (node T), where the other nodes are junction points in the system.

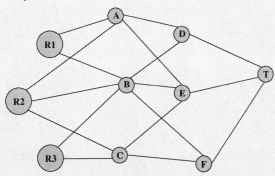

Using units of thousands of acre feet, the following tables show the maximum amount of water that can be pumped through each aqueduct per day.

To From	A	B	C
R1	75	65	—
R2	40	50	60
R3	—	80	70

To From	D	E	F
A	60	45	—
B	70	55	45
C	—	70	90

To From	T
D	120
E	190
F	130

The city water manager wants to determine a flow plan that will maximize the flow of water to the city.

    a. Formulate this problem as a maximum flow problem by identifying a source, a sink, and the transshipment nodes, and then drawing the complete network that shows the capacity of each arc.

E*   *b.* Formulate and solve a spreadsheet model for this problem.

6.11. The Texago Corporation has four oil fields, four refineries, and four distribution centers in the locations identified in the next tables. A major strike involving the transportation

industries now has sharply curtailed Texago's capacity to ship oil from the four oil fields to the four refineries and to ship petroleum products from the refineries to the distribution centers. Using units of thousands of barrels of crude oil (and its equivalent in refined products), the following tables show the maximum number of units that can be shipped per day from each oil field to each refinery and from each refinery to each distribution center.

	Refinery			
Oil Field	New Orleans	Charleston	Seattle	St. Louis
Texas	11	7	2	8
California	5	4	8	7
Alaska	7	3	12	6
Middle East	8	9	4	15

	Distribution Center			
Refinery	Pittsburgh	Atlanta	Kansas City	San Francisco
New Orleans	5	9	6	4
Charleston	8	7	9	5
Seattle	4	6	7	8
St. Louis	12	11	9	7

The Texago management now wants to determine a plan for how many units to ship from each oil field to each refinery and from each refinery to each distribution center that will maximize the total number of units reaching the distribution centers.

    a. Draw a rough map that shows the location of Texago's oil fields, refineries, and distribution centers. Add arrows to show the flow of crude oil and then petroleum products through this distribution network.

    b. Redraw this distribution network by lining up all the nodes representing oil fields in one column, all the nodes representing refineries in a second column, and all the nodes representing distribution centers in a third column. Then add arcs to show the possible flow.

    c. Use the distribution network from part *b* to formulate a network model for Texago's problem as a variant of a maximum flow problem.

E*   *d.* Formulate and solve a spreadsheet model for this problem.

6.12. Read the referenced article that fully describes the management science study summarized in the application vignette presented in Section 6.4. Briefly describe how network optimization models (including for shortest path problems) were applied in this study. Then list the various financial and nonfinancial benefits that resulted from this study.

E*6.13. Reconsider the Littletown Fire Department problem presented in Section 6.4 and depicted in Figure 6.11. Due to maintenance work on the one-mile road between nodes A and B, a detour currently must be taken that extends the trip between these nodes to four miles.

Formulate and solve a spreadsheet model for this revised problem to find the new shortest path from the fire station to the farming community.

6.14. You need to take a trip by car to another town that you have never visited before. Therefore, you are studying a map to determine the shortest route to your destination. Depending on which route you choose, there are five other towns (call them A, B, C, D, E) through which you might pass on the way. The map shows the mileage along each road that directly connects two towns without any intervening towns. These numbers are summarized in the following table, where a dash indicates that there is no road directly connecting these two towns without going through any other towns.

Town	A	B	C	D	E	Destination
	Miles between Adjacent Towns					
Origin	40	60	50	—	—	—
A		10	—	70	—	—
B			20	55	40	—
C				—	50	—
D					10	60
E						80

 a. Formulate a network model for this problem as a shortest path problem by drawing a network where nodes represent towns, links represent roads, and numbers indicate the length of each link in miles.

E* *b.* Formulate and solve a spreadsheet model for this problem.

 c. Use part *b* to identify your shortest route.

 d. If each number in the table represented your *cost* (in dollars) for driving your car from one town to the next, would the answer in part *c* now give your minimum-cost route?

 e. If each number in the table represented your *time* (in minutes) for driving your car from one town to the next, would the answer in part *c* now give your minimum-time route?

6.15.* At a small but growing airport, the local airline company is purchasing a new tractor for a tractor-trailer train to bring luggage to and from the airplanes. A new mechanized luggage system will be installed in three years, so the tractor will not be needed after that. However, because it will receive heavy use, so that the running and maintenance costs will increase rapidly as it ages, it may still be more economical to replace the tractor after one or two years. The next table gives the total net discounted cost associated with purchasing a tractor (purchase price minus trade-in allowance, plus running and maintenance costs) at the end of year *i* and trading it in at the end of year *j* (where year 0 is now).

	j		
	1	**2**	**3**
i			
0	$8,000	$18,000	$31,000
1		10,000	21,000
2			12,000

Management wishes to determine at what times (if any) the tractor should be replaced to minimize the total cost for the tractor(s) over three years.

 a. Formulate a network model for this problem as a shortest path problem.

E* *b.* Formulate and solve a spreadsheet model for this problem.

6.16. One of Speedy Airlines's flights is about to take off from Seattle for a nonstop flight to London. There is some flexibility in choosing the precise route to be taken, depending upon weather conditions. The following network depicts the possible routes under consideration, where SE and LN are Seattle and London, respectively, and the other nodes represent various intermediate locations.

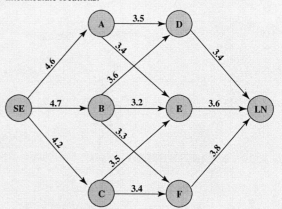

The winds along each arc greatly affect the flying time (and so the fuel consumption). Based on current meteorological reports, the flying times (in hours) for this particular flight are shown next to the arcs. Because the fuel consumed is so expensive, the management of Speedy Airlines has established a policy of choosing the route that minimizes the total flight time.

 a. What plays the role of distances in interpreting this problem to be a shortest path problem?

E* *b.* Formulate and solve a spreadsheet model for this problem.

Case 6-2

Money in Motion

Jake Nguyen runs a nervous hand through his once finely combed hair. He loosens his once perfectly knotted silk tie. And he rubs his sweaty hands across his once immaculately pressed trousers. Today has certainly not been a good day.

Over the past few months, Jake had heard whispers circulating from Wall Street—whispers from the lips of investment bankers and stockbrokers famous for their outspokenness. They had whispered about a coming Japanese economic collapse— whispered because they had believed that publicly vocalizing their fears would hasten the collapse.

And, today, their very fears have come true. Jake and his colleagues gather around a small television dedicated exclusively to the Bloomberg channel. Jake stares in disbelief as he listens to the horrors taking place in the Japanese market. And the Japanese market is taking the financial markets in all other East Asian countries with it on its tailspin. He goes numb. As manager of Asian foreign investment for **Grant Hill Associates,** a small West Coast investment boutique specializing in currency trading, Jake bears personal responsibility for any negative impacts of the collapse. And Grant Hill Associates will experience negative impacts.

Jake had not heeded the whispered warnings of a Japanese collapse. Instead, he had greatly increased the stake Grant Hill

Associates held in the Japanese market. Because the Japanese market had performed better than expected over the past year, Jake had increased investments in Japan from $2.5 million to $15 million only one month ago. At that time, one dollar was worth 80 yen.

No longer. Jake realizes that today's devaluation of the yen means that one dollar is worth 125 yen. He will be able to liquidate these investments without any loss in yen, but now the dollar loss when converting back into U.S. currency would be huge. He takes a deep breath, closes his eyes, and mentally prepares himself for serious damage control.

Jake's meditation is interrupted by a booming voice calling for him from a large, corner office. Grant Hill, the president of Grant Hill Associates, yells, "Nguyen, get the hell in here!"

Jake jumps and looks reluctantly toward the corner office hiding the furious Grant Hill. He smooths his hair, tightens his tie, and walks briskly into the office.

Grant Hill meets Jake's eyes upon his entrance and continues yelling, "I don't want one word out of you, Nguyen! No excuses; just fix this debacle! Get all of our money out of Japan! My gut tells me this is only the beginning! Get the money into safe U.S. bonds! NOW! And don't forget to get our cash positions out of Indonesia and Malaysia ASAP with it!"

Jake has enough common sense to say nothing. He nods his head, turns on his heels, and practically runs out of the office.

Safely back at his desk, Jake begins formulating a plan to move the investments out of Japan, Indonesia, and Malaysia. His experiences investing in foreign markets have taught him that when playing with millions of dollars, *how* he gets money out of a foreign market is almost as important as *when* he gets money out of the market. The banking partners of Grant Hill Associates charge different transaction fees for converting one currency into another one and wiring large sums of money around the globe.

And now, to make matters worse, the governments in East Asia have imposed very tight limits on the amount of money an individual or a company can exchange from the domestic currency into a particular foreign currency and withdraw it from the country. The goal of this dramatic measure is to reduce the outflow of foreign investments out of those countries to prevent a complete collapse of the economies in the region. Because of Grant Hill Associates' cash holdings of 10.5 billion Indonesian rupiahs and 28 million Malaysian ringgits, along with the holdings in yen, it is not clear how these holdings should be converted back into dollars.

Jake wants to find the most cost-effective method to convert these holdings into dollars. On his company's website, he

always can find on-the-minute exchange rates for most currencies in the world (see Table 1).

The table states that, for example, 1 Japanese yen equals 0.008 U.S. dollars. By making a few phone calls, he discovers the transaction costs his company must pay for large currency transactions during these critical times (see Table 2).

Jake notes that exchanging one currency for another one results in the same transaction cost as a reverse conversion. Finally, Jake finds out the maximum amounts of domestic currencies his company is allowed to convert into other currencies in Japan, Indonesia, and Malaysia (see Table 3).

a. Formulate Jake's problem as a minimum-cost flow problem, and draw the network for his problem. Identify the supply and demand nodes for the network.

b. Which currency transactions must Jake perform to convert the investments from yens, rupiahs, and ringgits into U.S. dollars to ensure that Grant Hill Associates has the maximum dollar amount after all transactions have occurred? How much money does Jake have to invest in U.S. bonds?

c. The World Trade Organization forbids transaction limits because they promote protectionism. If no transaction limits

TABLE 1
Currency Exchange Rates

From \ To	Yen	Rupiah	Ringgit	U.S. Dollar	Canadian Dollar	Euro	Pound	Peso
Japanese yen	1	50	0.04	0.008	0.01	0.0064	0.0048	0.0768
Indonesian rupiah		1	0.0008	0.00016	0.0002	0.000128	0.000096	0.001536
Malaysian ringgit			1	0.2	0.25	0.16	0.12	1.92
U.S. dollar				1	1.25	0.8	0.6	9.6
Canadian dollar					1	0.64	0.48	7.68
European euro						1	0.75	12
English pound							1	16
Mexican peso								1

TABLE 2
Transaction Cost (Percent)

From \ To	Yen	Rupiah	Ringgit	U.S. Dollar	Canadian Dollar	Euro	Pound	Peso
Yen	—	0.5	0.5	0.4	0.4	0.4	0.25	0.5
Rupiah		—	0.7	0.5	0.3	0.3	0.75	0.75
Ringgit			—	0.7	0.7	0.4	0.45	0.5
U.S. dollar				—	0.05	0.1	0.1	0.1
Canadian dollar					—	0.2	0.1	0.1
Euro						—	0.05	0.5
Pound							—	0.5
Peso								—

TABLE 3
Transaction Limits in Equivalent of 1,000 Dollars

From \ To	Yen	Rupiah	Ringgit	U.S. Dollar	Canadian Dollar	Euro	Pound	Peso
Yen	—	5,000	5,000	2,000	2,000	2,000	2,000	4,000
Rupiah	5,000	—	2,000	200	200	1,000	500	200
Ringgit	3,000	4,500	—	1,500	1,500	2,500	1,000	1,000

exist, what method should Jake use to convert the Asian holdings from the respective currencies into dollars?

d. In response to the World Trade Organization's mandate forbidding transaction limits, the Indonesian government introduces a new tax to protect its currency that leads to a 500 percent increase in transaction costs for transactions of rupiahs. Given these new transaction costs but no transaction limits, what currency transactions should Jake perform to convert the Asian holdings from the respective currencies into dollars?

e. Jake realizes that his analysis is incomplete because he has not included all aspects that might influence his planned currency exchanges. Describe other factors that Jake should examine before he makes his final decision.

Case 6-3

Airline Scheduling

Richard Cook is very concerned. Until recently, he has always had the golden touch, having successfully launched two start-up companies that made him a very wealthy man. However, the timing could not have been worse for his latest start-up—a regional airline called Northwest Commuter that operates on the west coast of the United States. All had been well at the beginning. Four airplanes had been leased and the company had become fairly well established as a no-frills airline providing low-cost commuter flights between the west coast cities of

(including some new ones) for the coming year that could feasibly be flown by the four airplanes.

A little over a decade ago, Richard had been an honor graduate of a leading MBA program. He had enjoyed the management science course he took then and he has decided to apply spreadsheet modeling to analyze his problem.

The leasing cost for each airplane is $30,000 per day. At the end of the day, an airplane might remain in the city where it landed on its last flight. Another option is to fly empty overnight

Flight Number	From	To	Depart	Arrive	Expected Revenue ($000)
1257	Seattle	San Francisco	8:00 AM	10:00 AM	37
2576	Seattle	Portland	9:30 AM	10:30 AM	20
8312	Seattle	San Francisco	9:30 AM	11:30 AM	25
1109	Seattle	San Francisco	12:00 PM	2:00 PM	27
3752	Seattle	San Francisco	2:30 PM	4:30 PM	23
2498	Seattle	Portland	3:00 PM	4:00 PM	18
8787	Seattle	San Francisco	5:00 PM	7:00 PM	29
8423	Seattle	Portland	6:30 PM	7:30 PM	27
7922	Portland	Seattle	9:00 AM	10:00 AM	20
5623	Portland	San Francisco	9:30 AM	11:00 AM	23
2448	Portland	San Francisco	11:00 AM	12:30 PM	19
1842	Portland	Seattle	12:00 PM	1:00 PM	21
3487	Portland	Seattle	2:00 PM	3:00 PM	22
4361	Portland	San Francisco	4:00 PM	5:30 PM	29
4299	Portland	Seattle	6:00 PM	7:00 PM	27
1288	San Francisco	Seattle	8:00 AM	10:00 AM	32
3335	San Francisco	Portland	8:30 AM	10:00 AM	26
9348	San Francisco	Seattle	10:30 AM	12:30 PM	24
7400	San Francisco	Seattle	12:00 PM	2:00 PM	27
7328	San Francisco	Portland	12:00 PM	1:30 PM	24
6386	San Francisco	Portland	4:00 PM	5:30 PM	28
6923	San Francisco	Seattle	5:00 PM	7:00 PM	32

Seattle, Portland, and San Francisco. Achieving fast turnaround times between flights had given Northwest Commuter an important competitive advantage. Then the cost of jet fuel began spiraling upward and the company began going heavily into the red (like so many other airlines at the time). Although some of the flights were still profitable, others were losing a lot of money. Fortunately, jet fuel costs now are starting to come down, but it has become clear to Richard that he needs to find new ways for Northwest Commuter to become a more efficient airline. In particular, he wants to start by dropping unprofitable flights and then identifying the most profitable combination of flights

to another city to be ready to start a flight from there the next morning. The cost of this latter option is $5,000.

The table above shows the 22 possible flights that are being considered for the coming year. The last column gives the estimated net revenue (in thousands of dollars) for each flight, given the average number of passengers anticipated for that flight.

a. To simplify the analysis, assume for now that there is virtually no turnaround time between flights so the next flight can begin as soon as the current flight ends. (If an immediate next flight is not available, the airplane would wait until the

230 **Chapter Six** *Network Optimization Problems*

next scheduled flight from that city.) Develop a network that displays some of the feasible routings of the flights. (*Hint*: Include separate nodes for each half hour between 8:00 AM and 7:30 PM in each city.) Then develop and apply the corresponding spreadsheet model that finds the feasible combination of flights that maximizes the total profit.

b. Richard is considering leasing additional airplanes to achieve economies of scale. The leasing cost of each one again would be $30,000 per day. Perform what-if analysis to determine whether it would be worthwhile to have 5, 6, or 7 airplanes instead of 4.

c. Now repeat part *a* under the more realistic assumption that there is a minimum turnaround time of 30 minutes on the ground for unloading and loading passengers between the arrival of a flight and the departure of the next flight by the same airplane. (Most airlines use a considerably longer turnaround time.) Does this change the number of flights that can be flown?

d. Richard now is considering having each of the four airplanes carry freight instead of flying empty if it flies overnight to another city. Instead of a cost of $5,000, this would result in net revenue of $5,000. Adapt the spreadsheet model used in part *c* to find the feasible combination of flights that maximizes the total profit. Does this change the number of airplanes that fly overnight to another city?

Case 6-4

Broadcasting the Olympic Games

The management of the WBC television network has been celebrating for days. What a coup! After several unsuccessful attempts in recent decades, they finally have hit the big jackpot. They have won the bidding war to gain the rights to broadcast the next Summer Olympic Games!

The price was enormous. However, the advertising income also will be huge. Even if the network loses some money in the process, the gain in prestige should make it all worthwhile. After all, the entire world follows these games closely every four years. Now the entire world receiving the feed of the broadcast from the WBC network will learn what a preeminent network it is.

each link in the network is shown in the diagram below (in GB/s). WBC can divide the transmission and route it through multiple paths of the network from A to G, so long as the total bandwidth required on each link does not exceed the capacity of that link.

a. By utilizing the entire computer network, what is the maximum bandwidth available (in GB/s) for transmission from the general site of the Olympic Games (node A) to the home studios (node G)? Set up and solve a linear programming spreadsheet model.

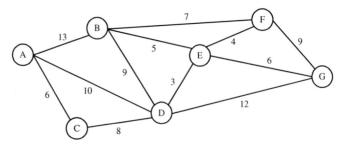

However, reality also is setting in for WBC management. Telecasting the entire Olympic Games will be an enormously complex task. Many different sporting events will be occurring simultaneously in far-flung venues. An unprecedented amount of live television and live-on-the-Internet coverage of the various sporting events needs to be planned.

Due to the high amount of bandwidth that will be required to transmit the coverage of the games back to its home studios, WBC needs to upgrade its computer network. It operates a private computer network as shown in the network diagram in the right-hand column. The games will be held near node A. WBC's home studios are located at node G. At peak times, coverage of the games will require 35 GB/s (GB per second) to be sent through the network from node A to node G. The capacity of

b. WBC would like to expand the capacity of the network so it can handle the peak requirement of 35 GB/s from the Olympics site (A) to the home studios (G). WBC can increase the capacity of each link of the computer network by installing additional fiber optic cables. The table on the next page shows the existing capacity of each network segment (in GB/s), the maximum additional capacity that can be added (in GB/s), and the cost to increase the capacity (in millions of dollars per unit GB/s added). Make a copy of the spreadsheet model used to solve part *a* and make any revisions necessary to solve this new problem.

Note: This case will be continued in the next chapter (Case 7-4), so we suggest that you save your spreadsheet model from part *b*.

Network Segment		Existing Capacity (GB/s)	Maximum Additional Capacity (GB/s)	Cost per GB/s of Additional Capacity ($million)
From	To			
A	B	13	6	2.8
A	C	6	4	2.5
A	D	10	3	2.8
B	D	9	4	2.5
B	E	5	5	3.1
B	F	7	3	1.6
C	D	8	5	3.9
D	E	3	2	2.8
D	G	12	5	1.6
E	F	4	2	4.6
E	G	6	4	2.9
F	G	9	5	1.8

Additional Cases

Additional cases for this chapter also are available at the University of Western Ontario Ivey School of Business website, **cases.ivey.uwo.ca/cases**, in the segment of the CaseMate area designated for this book.

224   **Chapter Six**   *Network Optimization Problems*

Case 6-1

Aiding Allies

Commander Votachev steps into the cold October night and deeply inhales the smoke from his cigarette, savoring its warmth. He surveys the destruction surrounding him— shattered windows, burning buildings, torn roads—and smiles. His two years of work training revolutionaries east of the Ural Mountains has proven successful; his troops now occupy seven strategically important cities in the Russian Federation: Kazan, Perm, Yekaterinburg, Ufa, Samara, Saratov, and

Orenburg. His siege is not yet over, however. He looks to the west. Given the political and economic confusion in the Russian Federation at this time, he knows that his troops will be able to conquer Saint Petersburg and Moscow shortly. Commander Votachev will then be able to rule with the wisdom and control exhibited by his communist predecessors Lenin and Stalin.

Across the Pacific Ocean, a meeting of the top security and foreign policy advisors of the **United States** is in progress at the White House. The president has recently been briefed about the communist revolution masterminded by Commander Votachev and is determining a plan of action. The president reflects upon a similar October long ago in 1917, and he fears the possibility of a new age of radical Communist rule accompanied by chaos, bloodshed, escalating tensions, and possibly nuclear war. He therefore decides that the United States needs to respond and to respond quickly. Moscow has requested assistance from the United States military, and the president plans to send troops and supplies immediately.

The president turns to General Lankletter and asks him to describe the preparations being taken in the United States to send the necessary troops and supplies to the Russian Federation.

General Lankletter informs the president that along with troops, weapons, ammunition, fuel, and supplies, aircraft, ships, and vehicles are being assembled at two port cities and airfields: Boston and Jacksonville. The aircraft and ships will transfer all troops and cargo across the Atlantic Ocean to the Eurasian continent. The general hands the president a list of the types of aircraft, ships, and vehicles being assembled along with a description of each type. The list is shown next.

launch a counter attack against Votachev to recapture the cities he currently occupies. (The map is shown at the end of the case.)

The president also explains that all Starlifters and transports leave Boston or Jacksonville. All transports that have traveled across the Atlantic must dock at one of the NATO ports to unload. Palletized load system trucks brought over in the transports will then carry all troops and materials unloaded from the ships at the NATO ports to the three strategic Russian cities not yet seized by Votachev. All Starlifters that have traveled across the Atlantic must land at one of the NATO airfields for refueling. The planes will then carry all troops and cargo from the NATO airfields to the three Russian cities.

a. Draw a network showing the different routes troops and supplies may take to reach the Russian Federation from the United States.

b. Moscow and Washington do not know when Commander Votachev will launch his next attack. Leaders from the two countries therefore have agreed that troops should reach each of the three strategic Russian cities as quickly as possible. The president has determined that the situation is so dire that cost is no object—as many Starlifters, transports, and trucks as are necessary will be used to transfer troops and cargo from the United States to Saint Petersburg, Moscow, and Rostov. Therefore, no limitations exist on the number of troops and amount of cargo that can be transferred between any cities.

The president has been given the information in the next table about the length of the available routes between cities.

Given the distance and the speed of the transportation used between each pair of cities, how can the president most

Transportation Type	Name	Capacity	Speed
Aircraft	C-141 Starlifter	150 tons	400 miles per hour
Ship	Transport	240 tons	35 miles per hour
Vehicle	Palletized Load System Truck	16,000 kilograms	60 miles per hour

All aircraft, ships, and vehicles are able to carry both troops and cargo. Once an aircraft or ship arrives in Europe, it stays there to support the armed forces.

The president then turns to Tabitha Neal, who has been negotiating with the NATO countries for the last several hours to use their ports and airfields as stops to refuel and resupply before heading to the Russian Federation. She informs the president that the following ports and airfields in the NATO countries will be made available to the U.S. military.

Ports	Airfields
Napoli	London
Hamburg	Berlin
Rotterdam	Istanbul

The president stands and walks to the map of the world projected on a large screen in the middle of the room. He maps the progress of troops and cargo from the United States to three strategic cities in the Russian Federation that have not yet been seized by Commander Votachev. The three cities are Saint Petersburg, Moscow, and Rostov. He explains that the troops and cargo will be used both to defend the Russian cities and to

quickly move troops from the United States to each of the three strategic Russian cities? Highlight the path(s) on the network. How long will it take troops and supplies to reach Saint Petersburg? Moscow? Rostov?

c. The president encounters only one problem with his first plan: He has to sell the military deployment to Congress. Under the War Powers Act, the president is required to consult with Congress before introducing troops into hostilities or situations where hostilities will occur. If Congress does not give authorization to the president for such use of troops, the president must withdraw troops after 60 days. Congress also has the power to decrease the 60-day time period by passing a concurrent resolution.

The president knows that Congress will not authorize significant spending for another country's war, especially when voters have paid so much attention to decreasing the national debt. He therefore decides that he needs to find a way to get the needed troops and supplies to Saint Petersburg, Moscow, and Rostov at the minimum cost.

Each Russian city has contacted Washington to communicate the number of troops and supplies the city needs at

From	To	(Kilometers)
Boston	Berlin	7,250 km
Boston	Hamburg	8,250
Boston	Istanbul	8,300
Boston	London	6,200
Boston	Rotterdam	6,900
Boston	Napoli	7,950
Jacksonville	Berlin	9,200
Jacksonville	Hamburg	9,800
Jacksonville	Istanbul	10,100
Jacksonville	London	7,900
Jacksonville	Rotterdam	8,900
Jacksonville	Napoli	9,400
Berlin	Saint Petersburg	1,280
Hamburg	Saint Petersburg	1,880
Istanbul	Saint Petersburg	2,040
London	Saint Petersburg	1,980
Rotterdam	Saint Petersburg	2,200
Napoli	Saint Petersburg	2,970
Berlin	Moscow	1,600
Hamburg	Moscow	2,120
Istanbul	Moscow	1,700
London	Moscow	2,300
Rotterdam	Moscow	2,450
Napoli	Moscow	2,890
Berlin	Rostov	1,730
Hamburg	Rostov	2,470
Istanbul	Rostov	990
London	Rostov	2,860
Rotterdam	Rostov	2,760
Napoli	Rostov	2,800

From	To	Cost
Boston	Berlin	$50,000 per Starlifter
Boston	Hamburg	$30,000 per transport
Boston	Istanbul	$55,000 per Starlifter
Boston	London	$45,000 per Starlifter
Boston	Rotterdam	$30,000 per transport
Boston	Napoli	$32,000 per transport
Jacksonville	Berlin	$57,000 per Starlifter
Jacksonville	Hamburg	$48,000 per transport
Jacksonville	Istanbul	$61,000 per Starlifter
Jacksonville	London	$49,000 per Starlifter
Jacksonville	Rotterdam	$44,000 per transport
Jacksonville	Napoli	$56,000 per transport
Berlin	Saint Petersburg	$24,000 per Starlifter
Hamburg	Saint Petersburg	$3,000 per truck
Istanbul	Saint Petersburg	$28,000 per Starlifter
London	Saint Petersburg	$22,000 per Starlifter
Rotterdam	Saint Petersburg	$3,000 per truck
Napoli	Saint Petersburg	$5,000 per truck
Berlin	Moscow	$22,000 per Starlifter
Hamburg	Moscow	$4,000 per truck
Istanbul	Moscow	$25,000 per Starlifter
London	Moscow	$19,000 per Starlifter
Rotterdam	Moscow	$5,000 per truck
Napoli	Moscow	$5,000 per truck
Berlin	Rostov	$23,000 per Starlifter
Hamburg	Rostov	$7,000 per truck
Istanbul	Rostov	$2,000 per Starlifter
London	Rostov	$4,000 per Starlifter
Rotterdam	Rostov	$8,000 per truck
Napoli	Rostov	$9,000 per truck

a minimum for reinforcement. After analyzing the requests, General Lankletter has converted the requests from numbers of troops, gallons of gasoline, and so on, to tons of cargo for easier planning. The requirements are listed below.

City	Requirements
Saint Petersburg	320,000 tons
Moscow	440,000 tons
Rostov	240,000 tons

Both in Boston and Jacksonville, there are 500,000 tons of the necessary cargo available. When the United States decides to send a plane, ship, or truck between two cities, several costs occur: fuel costs, labor costs, maintenance costs, and appropriate port or airfield taxes and tariffs. These costs are listed next.

The president faces a number of restrictions when trying to satisfy the requirements. Early winter weather in northern Russia has brought a deep freeze with much snow. Therefore, General Lankletter is opposed to sending truck convoys in the area. He convinces the president to supply Saint Petersburg only through the air. Moreover, the truck routes into Rostov are quite limited, so that from each port, at most 2,500 trucks can be sent to Rostov. The Ukrainian government is very sensitive about American airplanes flying through its air space. It restricts the U.S. military to at most 200 flights from Berlin to Rostov and to at most 200 flights from London to Rostov. (The U.S. military does not want to fly around the Ukraine and is thus restricted by the Ukrainian limitations.)

How does the president satisfy each Russian city's military requirements at minimum cost? Highlight the path to be used between the United States and the Russian Federation on the network.

d. Once the president releases the number of planes, ships, and trucks that will travel between the United States and the Russian Federation, Tabitha Neal contacts each of the American cities and NATO countries to indicate the number of planes to expect at the airfields, the number of ships to expect at the docks, and the number of trucks to expect traveling across the roads. Unfortunately, Tabitha learns that several additional restrictions exist that cannot be immediately eliminated. Because of airfield congestion and unalterable flight schedules, only a limited number of planes may be sent between any two cities. These plane limitations are given below.

From	To	Maximum Number of Airplanes
Boston	Berlin	300
Boston	Istanbul	500
Boston	London	500
Jacksonville	Berlin	500
Jacksonville	Istanbul	700
Jacksonville	London	600
Berlin	Saint Petersburg	500
Istanbul	Saint Petersburg	0
London	Saint Petersburg	1,000
Berlin	Moscow	300
Istanbul	Moscow	100
London	Moscow	200
Berlin	Rostov	0
Istanbul	Rostov	900
London	Rostov	100

In addition, because some countries fear that citizens will become alarmed if too many military trucks travel the public highways, they object to a large number of trucks traveling through their countries. These objections mean that a limited number of trucks are able to travel between certain ports and Russian cities. These limitations are listed below.

From	To	Maximum Number of Trucks
Rotterdam	Moscow	600
Rotterdam	Rostov	750
Hamburg	Moscow	700
Hamburg	Rostov	500
Napoli	Moscow	1,500
Napoli	Rostov	1,400

Tabitha learns that all shipping lanes have no capacity limits due to the American control of the Atlantic Ocean.

The president realizes that due to all the restrictions, he will not be able to satisfy all the reinforcement requirements of the three Russian cities. He decides to disregard the cost issue and instead to maximize the total amount of cargo he can get to the Russian cities. How does the president maximize the total amount of cargo that reaches the Russian Federation? Highlight the path(s) used between the United States and the Russian Federation on the network.

Chapter **Seven**

Using Binary Integer Programming to Deal with Yes-or-No Decisions

Learning Objectives

After completing this chapter, you should be able to

1. Describe how binary decision variables are used to represent yes-or-no decisions.
2. Use binary decision variables to formulate constraints for mutually exclusive alternatives and contingent decisions.
3. Formulate a binary integer programming model for the selection of projects.
4. Formulate a binary integer programming model for the selection of sites for facilities.
5. Formulate a binary integer programming model for crew scheduling in the travel industry.
6. Formulate other basic binary integer programming models from a description of the problems.
7. Use mixed binary integer programming to deal with setup costs for initiating the production of a product.

The preceding chapters have considered various kinds of problems where decisions need to be made about *how much to do* of various activities. Thus, the decision variables in the resulting model represent the *level* of the corresponding activities.

We turn now to a common type of problem where, instead of *how-much decisions,* the decisions to be made are **yes-or-no decisions.** A yes-or-no decision arises when a particular option is being considered and the only possible choices are yes, go ahead with this option, or no, decline this option.

The natural choice of a decision variable for a yes-or-no decision is a *binary variable.* **Binary variables** are variables whose only possible values are 0 and 1. Thus, when representing a yes-or-no decision, a **binary decision variable** is assigned a value of 1 for choosing yes and a value of 0 for choosing no.

Models that fit linear programming except that they use binary decision variables are called **binary integer programming (BIP)** models. (We hereafter will use the **BIP** abbreviation.) A **pure BIP model** is one where all the variables are binary variables, whereas a **mixed BIP model** is one where only some of the variables are binary variables.

A BIP model can be considered to be a special type of *integer programming model.* A general integer programming model is simply a linear programming model except for also having constraints that some or all of the decision variables must have integer values $(0, 1, 2, \ldots)$. A BIP model further restricts these integer values to be *only* 0 or 1.

However, BIP problems are quite different from general integer programming problems because of the difference in the nature of the decisions involved. Like linear programming problems, general integer programming problems involve how-much decisions, but where these decisions make sense only if they have integer values. For example, the TBA Airlines problem presented in Section 3.2 is a general integer programming problem because it is essentially a linear programming problem except that its how-much decisions (how many small airplanes and how many large airplanes to purchase) only make sense if they have integer values. By contrast, BIP problems involve yes-or-no decisions instead of how-much decisions.

The preceding chapters already have focused on problems involving how-much decisions and how such techniques as linear programming or integer programming can be used to analyze these problems. Therefore, this chapter will be devoted instead to problems involving yes-or-no decisions and how BIP models can be used to analyze this special category of problems.

BIP problems arise with considerable frequency in a wide variety of applications. To illustrate this, we begin with a case study and then present some more examples in the subsequent sections. One of the supplements to this chapter on the CD-ROM also provides additional formulation examples for BIP problems.

You will see throughout this chapter that BIP problems can be formulated on a spreadsheet just as readily as linear programming problems. The Solver also can solve BIP problems of modest size. You normally will have no problem solving the small BIP problems found in this book, but Solver may fail on somewhat larger problems. To provide some perspective on this issue, we include another supplement on the CD-ROM that is entitled Some Perspectives on Solving Binary Integer Programming Problems. The algorithms available for solving BIP problems (including the one used by Solver) are not nearly as efficient as those for linear programming, so this supplement discusses some of the difficulties and pitfalls involved in solving large BIP problems. One option with any large problem that fits linear programming except that it has decision variables that are restricted to integer values (but not necessarily just 0 and 1) is to ignore the integer constraints and then to round the solution obtained to integer values. This is a reasonable option in some cases but not in others. The supplement emphasizes that this is a particularly dangerous shortcut with BIP problems.

7.1   A CASE STUDY: THE CALIFORNIA MANUFACTURING CO. PROBLEM

The top management of the California Manufacturing Company wants to develop a plan for the expansion of the company. Therefore, a management science study will be conducted to help guide the decisions that need to be made. The president of the company, Armando Ortega, is about to meet with the company's top management scientist, Steve Chan, to discuss the study that management wants done. Let's eavesdrop on this meeting.

Armando Ortega (president):   OK, Steve, here is the situation. With our growing business, we are strongly considering building a new factory. Maybe even two. The factory needs to be close to a large, skilled labor force, so we are looking at Los Angeles and San Francisco as the potential sites. We also are considering building one new warehouse. Not more than one. This warehouse would make sense in saving shipping costs only if it is in the same city as a new factory. Either Los Angeles or San Francisco. If we decide not to build a new factory at all, we definitely don't want the warehouse either. Is this clear, so far?

Steve Chan (management scientist):   Yes, Armando, I understand, What are your criteria for making these decisions?

Armando Ortega: Well, all the other members of top management have joined me in addressing this issue. We have concluded that these two potential sites are very comparable on nonfinancial grounds. Therefore, we feel that these decisions should be based mainly on financial considerations. We have $10 million of capital available for this expansion and we want it to go as far as possible in improving our bottom line. Which feasible combination of investments in factories and warehouses in which locations will be most profitable for the company in the long run? In your language, we want to maximize the total net present value of these investments.

What is the most profitable combination of investments?

Steve Chan: That's very clear. It sounds like a classical management science problem.

Armando Ortega: That's why I called you in, Steve. I would like you to conduct a quick management science study to determine the most profitable combination of investments. I also would like you to take a look at the amount of capital being made available and its

An Application Vignette

With headquarters in Houston, Texas, **Waste Management, Inc.** (a Fortune 100 company), is the leading provider of comprehensive waste-management services in North America. Its network of operations includes 293 active landfill disposal sites, 16 waste-to-energy plants, 72 landfill gas-to-energy facilities, 146 recycling plants, 346 transfer stations, and 435 collection operations (depots) to provide services to nearly 20 million residential customers and 2 million commercial customers throughout the United States and Canada.

The company's collection-and-transfer vehicles need to follow nearly 20,000 daily routes. With an annual operating cost of nearly $120,000 per vehicle, management wanted to have a comprehensive route-management system that would make every route as profitable and efficient as possible. Therefore, a management science team that included a number of consultants was formed to attack this problem.

The heart of the route-management system developed by this team is a *huge mixed BIP model* that optimizes the routes assigned to the respective collection-and-transfer vehicles. Although the objective function takes several factors into account, the primary goal is the minimization of total travel time. The main decision variables are binary variables that equal 1 if the route assigned to a particular vehicle includes a particular possible leg and that equal 0 otherwise. A geographical information system (GIS) provides the data about the distance and time required to go between any two points. All of this is imbedded within a Web-based Java application that is integrated with the company's other systems.

It is estimated that the recent implementation of this comprehensive route-management system will *increase the company's cash flow by* **$648 million** *over a five-year period,* largely because of *savings of* **$498 million** in operational expenses over this same period. It also is providing better customer service.

Source: S. Sahoo, S. Kim, B.-I. Kim, B. Krass, and A. Popov, Jr., "Routing Optimization for Waste Management," *Interfaces* 35, no. 1 (January–February 2005), pp. 24–36. (A link to this article is provided on our website, **www.mhhe.com/hillier5e.**)

effect on how much profit we can get from these investments. The decision to make $10 million available is only a tentative one. That amount is stretching us, because we now are investigating some other interesting project proposals that would require quite a bit of capital, so we would prefer to use less than $10 million on these particular investments if the last few million don't buy us much. On the other hand, this expansion into either Los Angeles or San Francisco, or maybe both of these key cities, is our number one priority. It will have a real positive impact on the future of this company. So we are willing to go out and raise some more capital if it would give us a lot of bang for the buck. Therefore, we would like you to do some what-if analysis to tell us what the effect would be if we were to change the amount of capital being made available to anything between $5 million and $15 million.

Steve Chan: Sure, Armando, we do that kind of what-if analysis all the time. We refer to it as sensitivity analysis because it involves checking how sensitive the outcome is to the amount of capital being made available.

Armando Ortega: Good. Now, Steve, I need your input within the next couple weeks. Can you do it?

Steve Chan: Well, Armando, as usual, the one question is whether we can gather all the necessary data that quickly. We'll need to get good estimates of the net present value of each of the possible investments. I'll need a lot of help in digging out that information.

Armando Ortega: I thought you would say that. I already have my staff working hard on developing those estimates. I can get you together with them this afternoon.

Steve Chan: Great. I'll get right on it.

Background

The **California Manufacturing Company** is a diversified company with several factories and warehouses throughout California, but none yet in Los Angeles or San Francisco. Because the company is enjoying increasing sales and earnings, management feels that the time may be ripe to expand into one or both of those prime locations. A basic issue is whether to build a new factory in either Los Angeles or San Francisco, or perhaps even in both cities. Management also is considering building at most one new warehouse, but will restrict the choice of location to a city where a new factory is being built.

The decisions to be made are listed in the second column of Table 7.1 in the form of yes-or-no questions. In each case, giving an answer of yes to the question corresponds to the decision to make the investment to build the indicated facility (a factory or a warehouse) in

TABLE 7.1
Data for the California Manufacturing Co. Problem

Decision Number	Yes-or-No Question	Decision Variable	Net Present Value (Millions)	Capital Required (Millions)
1	Build a factory in Los Angeles?	x_1	$8	$6
2	Build a factory in San Francisco?	x_2	5	3
3	Build a warehouse in Los Angeles?	x_3	6	5
4	Build a warehouse in San Francisco?	x_4	4	2
				Capital available: $10 million

the indicated location (Los Angeles or San Francisco). The capital required for the investment is given in the rightmost column, where management has made the tentative decision that the total amount of capital being made available for all the investments is $10 million. (Note that this amount is inadequate for some of the combinations of investments.) The fourth column shows the estimated *net present value* (net long-run profit considering the time value of money) if the corresponding investment is made. (The net present value is 0 if the investment is not made.) Much of the work of Steve Chan's management science study (with substantial help from the president's staff) goes into developing these estimates of the net present values. As specified by the company's president, Armando Ortega, the objective now is to find the feasible combination of investments that maximizes the total net present value.

Introducing Binary Decision Variables for the Yes-or-No Decisions

As summarized in the second column of Table 7.1, the problem facing management is to make four interrelated *yes-or-no decisions.* To formulate a mathematical model for this problem, Steve Chan needs to introduce a decision variable for each of these decisions. Since each decision has just two alternatives, choose yes or choose no, the corresponding decision variable only needs to have two values (one for each alternative). Therefore, Steve uses a *binary variable,* whose only possible values are 0 and 1, where 1 corresponds to the decision to choose yes and 0 corresponds to choosing no.

These decision variables are shown in the second column of Table 7.2. The final two columns give the interpretation of a value of 1 and 0, respectively.

Dealing with Interrelationships between the Decisions

Recall that management wants no more than one new warehouse to be built. In terms of the corresponding decision variables, x_3 and x_4, this means that no more than one of these variables is allowed to have the value 1. Therefore, these variables must satisfy the constraint

$$x_3 + x_4 \leq 1$$

as part of the mathematical model for the problem.

With a group of mutually exclusive alternatives, only one of the corresponding binary decision variables can equal 1.

These two alternatives (build a warehouse in Los Angeles or build a warehouse in San Francisco) are referred to as **mutually exclusive alternatives** because choosing one of these alternatives excludes choosing the other. Groups of two or more mutually exclusive alternatives arise commonly in BIP problems. For each such group where at most one of the alternatives can be chosen, the constraint on the corresponding binary decision variables has the form shown above, namely, the sum of these variables must be *less than or equal to* 1. For some groups of mutually exclusive alternatives, management will exclude the possibility

TABLE 7.2
Binary Decision Variables for the California Manufacturing Co. Problem

Decision Number	Decision Variable	Possible Value	Interpretation of a Value of 1	Interpretation of a Value of 0
1	x_1	0 or 1	Build a factory in Los Angeles	Do not build this factory
2	x_2	0 or 1	Build a factory in San Francisco	Do not build this factory
3	x_3	0 or 1	Build a warehouse in Los Angeles	Do not build this warehouse
4	x_4	0 or 1	Build a warehouse in San Francisco	Do not build this warehouse

of choosing *none* of the alternatives, in which case the constraint will set the sum of the corresponding binary decision variables *equal* to 1.

The California Manufacturing Co. problem also has another important kind of restriction. Management will allow a warehouse to be built in a particular city only if a factory also is being built in that city. For example, consider the situation for Los Angeles (LA).

If decide no, do not build a factory in LA (i.e., if choose $x_1 = 0$),
    then cannot build a warehouse in LA (i.e., must choose $x_3 = 0$).

If decide yes, do build a factory in LA (i.e., if choose $x_1 = 1$),
    then can either build a warehouse in LA or not (i.e., can choose either $x_3 = 1$ or 0).

How can these interrelationships between the factory and warehouse decisions for LA be expressed in a constraint for a mathematical model? The key is to note that, for either value of x_1, the permissible value or values of x_3 are less than or equal to x_1. Since x_1 and x_3 are binary variables, the constraint

$$x_3 \leq x_1$$

forces x_3 to take on a permissible value given the value of x_1.

Exactly the same reasoning leads to

$$x_4 \leq x_2$$

as the corresponding constraint for San Francisco. Just as for Los Angeles, this constraint forces having no warehouse in San Francisco ($x_4 = 0$) if a factory will not be built there ($x_2 = 0$), whereas going ahead with the factory there ($x_2 = 1$) leaves open the decision to build the warehouse there ($x_4 = 0$ or 1).

> One yes-or-no decision is contingent on another yes-or-no decision if the first one is allowed to be yes only if the other one is yes.

For either city, the warehouse decision is referred to as a **contingent decision,** because the decision depends on a prior decision regarding whether to build a factory there. In general, one yes-or-no decision is said to be contingent on another yes-or-no decision if it is allowed to be yes *only if* the other is yes. As above, the mathematical constraint expressing this relationship requires that the binary variable for the former decision must be less than or equal to the binary variable for the latter decision.

The rightmost column of Table 7.1 reveals one more interrelationship between the four decisions, namely, that the amount of capital expended on the four facilities under consideration cannot exceed the amount available ($10 million). Therefore, the model needs to include a constraint that requires

$$\text{Capital expended} \leq \$10 \text{ million}$$

How can the amount of capital expended be expressed in terms of the four binary decision variables? To start this process, consider the first yes-or-no decision (build a factory in Los Angeles?). Combining the information in the rightmost column of Table 7.1 and the first row of Table 7.2,

$$\text{Capital expended on factory in Los Angeles} = \begin{cases} \$6 \text{ million} & \text{if } x_1 = 1 \\ 0 & \text{if } x_1 = 0 \end{cases}$$

$$= \$6 \text{ million } \textit{times } x_1$$

By the same reasoning, the amount of capital expended on the other three investment opportunities (in units of millions of dollars) is $3x_2$, $5x_3$, and $2x_4$, respectively. Consequently,

$$\text{Capital expended} = 6x_1 + 3x_2 + 5x_3 + 2x_4 \qquad \text{(in millions of dollars)}$$

Therefore, the constraint becomes

$$6x_1 + 3x_2 + 5x_3 + 2x_4 \leq 10$$

The BIP Model

> **Excel Tip:** Beware that rounding errors can occur with Excel. Therefore, even when you add a constraint that a changing cell has to be binary, Excel occasionally will return a noninteger value very close to an integer (e.g., 1.23E-10, meaning 0.000000000123). When this happens, you can replace the noninteger value with the proper integer value.

As indicated by Armando Ortega in his conversation with Steve Chan, management's objective is to find the feasible combination of investments that *maximizes* the total net present value of these investments. Thus, the value of the objective function should be

$$\text{NPV} = \text{Total net present value}$$

FIGURE 7.1

A spreadsheet formulation of the BIP model for the California Manufacturing Co. case study where the changing cells BuildFactory? (C18:D18) and BuildWarehouse? (C16:D16) give the optimal solution obtained by Solver.

	A	B	C	D	E	F	G
1		**California Manufacturing Co. Facility Location Problem**					
2							
3		**NPV ($millions)**	LA	SF			
4		Warehouse	6	4			
5							
6		Factory	8	5			
7							
8		**Capital Required**					
9		**($millions)**	LA	SF			
10		Warehouse	5	2	Capital		Capital
11					Spent		Available
12		Factory	6	3	9	?	10
13							
14					Total		Maximum
15		**Build?**	LA	SF	Warehouses		Warehouses
16		Warehouse	0	0	0	?	1
17			?	?			
18		Factory	1	1			
19							
20		Total NPV ($millions)		$13			

Solver Parameters

Set Objective Cell: TotalNPV
To: Max
By Changing Variable Cells:
  BuildWarehouse?, BuildFactory?
Subject to the Constraints:
  BuildFactory? = binary
  BuildWarehouse? = binary
  BuildWarehouse? <= BuildFactory?
  CapitalSpent <= CapitalAvailable
  TotalWarehouses <= MaxWarehouses

Solver Options:
  Make Variables Nonnegative
  Solving Method: Simplex LP

	E
10	Capital
11	Spent
12	= SUMPRODUCT(CapitalRequired,Build?)
13	
14	Total
15	Warehouses
16	= SUM(BuildWarehouse?)

Range Name	Cells
Build?	C16:D18
BuildWarehouse?	C16:D16
BuildFactory?	C18:D18
CapitalAvailable	G12
CapitalRequired	C10:D12
CapitalSpent	E12
MaxWarehouses	G16
NPV	C4:D6
TotalNPV	D20
TotalWarehouses	E16

	C	D
20	Total NPV ($millions)	=SUMPRODUCT(NPV,Build?)

Excel Tip: In the Solver Options, the *Integer Optimality (%)* setting (1 percent by default) causes Solver to stop solving an integer programming problem when it finds a feasible solution whose objective function value is within the specified percentage of being optimal. (In RSPE, this option is called *Integer Tolerance* and is found in the Engine tab of the Model pane.) This is useful for very large BIP problems since it may enable finding a near-optimal solution when finding an optimal solution in a reasonable period of time is not possible. For smaller problems (e.g., all the problems in this book), this option should be set to 0 to guarantee finding an optimal solution.

If the investment is made to build a particular facility (so that the corresponding decision variable has a value of 1), the estimated net present value from that investment is given in the fourth column of Table 7.1. If the investment is not made (so the decision variable equals 0), the net present value is 0. Therefore, continuing to use units of millions of dollars,

$$NPV = 8x_1 + 5x_2 + 6x_3 + 4x_4$$

is the quantity to enter into the objective cell to be maximized.

Incorporating the constraints developed in the preceding subsection, the complete BIP model then is shown in Figure 7.1. The format is basically the same as for linear programming models.

The one key difference arises when using Solver. Each of the decision variables (cells C18:D18 and C16:D16) is constrained to be binary. In Excel's Solver, this is accomplished in the Add Constraint dialog box by choosing each range of changing cells as the left-hand side and then choosing bin from the pop-up menu. In RSPE, this is accomplished by selecting each range of changing cells, and then under the Constraints menu on the RSPE ribbon, choose Binary in the Variable Type/Bound submenu. The other constraints shown in Solver (see the lower left-hand side of Figure 7.1) have been made quite intuitive by using the suggestive range names given in the lower right-hand side of the figure. For convenience, the equations entered into the output cells in E12 and D20 use a SUMPRODUCT function that includes C17:D17 and either C11:D11 or C5:D5 because the blanks or ≤ signs in these rows are interpreted as zeroes by Solver.

Note how helpful the range names are for interpreting this BIP spreadsheet model.

Solver gives the optimal solution shown in C18:D18 and C16:D16 of the spreadsheet, namely, build factories in *both* Los Angeles and San Francisco, but do not build any warehouses. The objective cell (D20) indicates that the total net present value from building these two factories is estimated to be $13 million.

Performing Sensitivity Analysis

Now that Steve Chan has used the BIP model to determine what should be done when the amount of capital being made available to these investments is $10 million, his next task is to perform *what-if analysis* on this amount. Recall that Armando Ortega wants him to determine *what* the effect would be *if* this amount were changed to anything else between $5 million and $15 million.

Solver's sensitivity report is not available for integer programming problems.

In Chapter 5, we described three different methods of performing what-if analysis on a linear programming spreadsheet model when there is a change in a constraint: using trial and error with the spreadsheet, generating a parameter analysis report, or referring to Solver's sensitivity report. The first two of these can be used on integer programming problems in exactly the same way as for linear programming problems. The third method, however, does not work. The sensitivity report is not available for integer programming problems. This is because the concept of a shadow price and allowable range no longer applies. In contrast to linear programming, the objective function values for an integer programming problem do not change in a predictable manner when the right-hand side of a constraint is changed.

Trial-and-error and/or a parameter analysis report can be used to perform sensitivity analysis for integer programming problems.

It is straightforward to determine the impact of changing the amount of available capital by trial and error. Simply try different values in the data cell CapitalAvailable (G12) and re-solve with Solver. However, a more systematic way to perform this analysis is to generate a parameter analysis report using RSPE. The parameter analysis report works for integer programming models in exactly the same way as it does for linear programming models (as described in Section 5.3 in the subsection entitled *Using a Parameter Analysis Report (RSPE) to Do Sensitivity Analysis Systematically*).

After defining CapitalAvailable (G12) as a parameter cell with values ranging from 5 to 15 ($millions), the parameter analysis report shown in Figure 7.2 was generated by executing the series of steps outlined in Section 5.3. Note how Figure 7.2 shows the effect on the optimal solution and the resulting total net present value of varying the amount of capital being made available.

What-if analysis also could be performed on any of the other data cells—NPV (C4:D6), CapitalRequired (C10:D12), and MaxWarehouses (G16)—in a similar way with a parameter analysis report (or by using trial and error with the spreadsheet). However, a careful job was done in developing good estimates of the net present value of each of the possible investments, and there is little uncertainty in the values entered in the other data cells, so Steve Chan decides that further what-if analysis is not needed.

Management's Conclusion

Steve Chan's report is delivered to Armando Ortega within the two-week deadline. The report recommends the plan presented in Figure 7.1 (build a factory in both Los Angeles and San Francisco but no warehouses) if management decides to stick with its tentative decision to make $10 million of capital available for these investments. One advantage of this plan is that it only uses $9 million of this capital, which frees up $1 million of capital for other project proposals currently being investigated. The report also highlights the results shown in Figure 7.2 while emphasizing two points. One is that a heavy penalty would be paid (a reduction

FIGURE 7.2

The parameter analysis report generated by RSPE that shows the effect on the optimal solution and the resulting total net present value of systematically varying the amount of capital being made available for these investments.

	A	B	C	D	E	F
1	CapitalAvailable	BuildWarehouseLA?	BuildWarehouseSF?	BuildFactoryLA?	BuildFactorySF?	TotalINPV
2	5	0	1	0	1	9
3	6	0	1	0	1	9
4	7	0	1	0	1	9
5	8	0	1	0	1	9
6	9	0	0	1	1	13
7	10	0	0	1	1	13
8	11	0	1	1	1	17
9	12	0	1	1	1	17
10	13	0	1	1	1	17
11	14	1	0	1	1	19
12	15	1	0	1	1	19

in the total net present value from $13 million to $9 million) if the amount of capital being made available were to be reduced below $9 million. The other is that *increasing* the amount of capital being made available by just $1 million (from $10 million to $11 million) would enable a substantial increase of $4 million in the total net present value (from $13 million to $17 million). However, a much larger further increase in the amount of capital being made available (from $11 million to $14 million) would be needed to enable a considerably smaller further increase in the total net present value (from $17 million to $19 million).

Armando Ortega deliberates with other members of top management before making a decision. It is quickly concluded that increasing the amount of capital being made available all the way up to $14 million would be stretching the company's financial resources too dangerously to justify the relatively small payoff. However, there is considerable discussion of the pros and cons of the two options of using either $9 million or $11 million of capital. Because of the large payoff from the latter option (an additional $4 million in total present value), management finally decides to adopt the plan presented in row 8 of Figure 7.2. Thus, the company will build new factories in both Los Angeles and San Francisco as well as a new warehouse in San Francisco, with an estimated total net present value of $17 million. However, because of the large capital requirements of this plan, management also decides to defer building the warehouse until the two factories are completed so that their profits can help finance the construction of the warehouse.

Review Questions

1. What are the four interrelated decisions that need to be made by the management of the California Manufacturing Co.?
2. Why are binary decision variables appropriate to represent these decisions?
3. What is the objective specified by management for this problem?
4. What are the mutually exclusive alternatives in this problem? What is the form of the resulting constraint in the BIP model?
5. What are the contingent decisions in this problem? For each one, what is the form of the resulting constraint in the BIP model?
6. What is the tentative managerial decision on which sensitivity analysis needs to be performed?

7.2   USING BIP FOR PROJECT SELECTION: THE TAZER CORP. PROBLEM

The California Manufacturing Co. case study focused on four proposed projects: (1) build a factory in Los Angeles, (2) build a factory in San Francisco, (3) build a warehouse in Los Angeles, and (4) build a warehouse in San Francisco. Management needed to make yes-or-no decisions about which of these projects to select. This is typical of many applications of BIP. However, the nature of the projects may vary considerably from one application to the next. Instead of the proposed construction projects in the case study, our next example involves the selection of research and development projects.

This example is adapted from both Case 3-7 and its continuation in the supplement to Chapter 13, but all the relevant information is repeated below.

The Tazer Corp. Problem

Tazer Corp., a pharmaceutical manufacturing company, is beginning the search for a new breakthrough drug. The following five potential research and development projects have been identified for attempting to develop such a drug.

Project Up:	Develop a more effective antidepressant that does not cause serious mood swings.
Project Stable:	Develop a drug that addresses manic depression.
Project Choice:	Develop a less intrusive birth control method for women.
Project Hope:	Develop a vaccine to prevent HIV infection.
Project Release:	Develop a more effective drug to lower blood pressure.

In contrast to Case 3-7, Tazer management now has concluded that the company cannot devote enough money to research and development to undertake all of these projects. Only $1.2 billion is available, which will be enough for only two or three of the projects. The first row of Table 7.3 shows the amount needed (in millions of dollars) for each of these projects. The second row estimates each project's probability of being successful. If a project is successful, it is estimated that the resulting drug would generate the revenue shown in the third row. Thus, the *expected revenue* (in the statistical sense) from a potential drug is the product of its numbers in the second and third rows, whereas its *expected profit* is this expected revenue minus the investment given in the first row. These expected profits are shown in the bottom row of Table 7.3.

> The objective is to choose the projects that will maximize the expected profit while satisfying the budget constraint.

Tazer management now wants to determine which of these projects should be undertaken to maximize their expected total profit.

Formulation with Binary Variables

Because the decision for each of the five proposed research and development projects is a yes-or-no decision, the corresponding decision variables are binary variables. Thus, the decision variable for each project has the following interpretation.

$$\text{Decision Variable} = \begin{cases} 1, & \text{if approve the project} \\ 0, & \text{if reject the project} \end{cases}$$

Let $x_1, x_2, x_3, x_4,$ and x_5 denote the decision variables for the respective projects in the order in which they are listed in Table 7.3.

If a project is rejected, there is neither any profit nor any loss, whereas the expected profit if a project is approved is given in the bottom row of Table 7.3. Therefore, when using units of millions of dollars, the expected total profit is

$$P = 300x_1 + 120x_2 + 170x_3 + 100x_4 + 70x_5$$

The objective is to select the projects to approve that will maximize this expected total profit while satisfying the budget constraint.

Other than requiring the decision variables to be binary, the budget constraint limiting the total investment to no more than $1.2 billion is the only constraint that has been imposed by Tazer management on the selection of these research and development projects.

TABLE 7.3
Data for the Tazer Project Selection Problem

	Project				
	1 (Up)	**2 (Stable)**	**3 (Choice)**	**4 (Hope)**	**5 (Release)**
R&D investment ($million)	400	300	600	500	200
Success rate	50%	35%	35%	20%	45%
Revenue if successful ($million)	1,400	1,200	2,200	3,000	600
Expected profit ($million)	300	120	170	100	70

An Application Vignette

The **Midwest Independent Transmission Operator, Inc. (MISO)** is a nonprofit organization formed in 1998 to administer the generation and transmission of electricity throughout the midwestern United States. It serves over 40 million customers (both individuals and businesses) through its control of nearly 60,000 miles of high-voltage transmission lines and more than 1,000 power plants capable of generating 146,000 megawatts of electricity. This infrastructure spans 13 midwestern states plus the Canadian province of Manitoba.

The key mission of any regional transmission organization is to reliably and efficiently provide the electricity needed by its customers. MISO transformed the way this was done by using *mixed binary integer programming* to minimize the total cost of providing the needed electricity. Each main binary variable in the model represents a yes-or-no decision about whether a particular power plant should be on during a particular time period. After solving this model, the results are then fed into a linear programming

model to set electricity output levels and establish prices for electricity trades.

The mixed BIP model is a massive one with about 3,300,000 continuous variables, 450,000 binary variables, and 3,900,000 functional constraints. A special technique (Lagrangian relaxation) is used to solve such a huge model.

This innovative application of management science yielded *savings* of approximately **$2.5 billion** over the four years from 2007 to 2010, with an additional savings of about **$7 billion** expected through 2020. These dramatic results led to MISO winning the prestigious first prize in the 2011 international competition for the Franz Edelman Award for Achievement in Operations Research and the Management Sciences.

Source: B. Carlson and 12 co-authors, "MISO Unlocks Billions in Savings through the Application of Operations Research for Energy and Ancillary Services Markets," *Interfaces* 42, no. 1 (January–February 2012), pp. 58–73. (A link to this article is provided on our website, **www.mhhe.com/hillier5e.**)

Referring to the first row of Table 7.3, this constraint can be expressed in terms of the decision variables as

$$400x_1 + 300x_2 + 600x_3 + 500x_4 + 200x_5 \leq 1{,}200$$

With this background, the stage now is set for formulating a BIP spreadsheet model for this problem.

A BIP Spreadsheet Model for the Tazer Problem

Figure 7.3 shows a BIP spreadsheet model for this problem. The data in Table 7.3 have been transferred into cells C5:G8. The changing cells are DoProject? (C10:G10) and the objective cell is TotalExpectedProfit (H8). The one functional constraint is depicted in cells H5:J5. In addition, the changing cells DoProject? are constrained to be binary, as shown in the Solver Parameters box.

The changing cells DoProject? (C10:G10) in Figure 7.3 show the optimal solution that has been obtained by Solver, namely,

Choose Project Up, Project Choice, and Project Release.

The objective cell indicates that the resulting total expected profit is $540 million.

Review Questions

1. How are binary variables used to represent managerial decisions on which projects from a group of proposed projects should be selected for approval?
2. What types of projects are under consideration in the Tazer Corp. problem?
3. What is the objective for this problem?

7.3 USING BIP FOR THE SELECTION OF SITES FOR EMERGENCY SERVICES FACILITIES: THE CALIENTE CITY PROBLEM

Although the problem encountered in the California Manufacturing Co. case study can be described as a *project selection* problem (as was done at the beginning of the preceding section), it could just as well have been called a *site selection* problem. Recall that the company's management needed to select a site (Los Angeles or San Francisco) for its new factory as

242   Chapter Seven   *Using Binary Integer Programming to Deal with Yes-or-No Decisions*

FIGURE 7.3

A spreadsheet formulation of the BIP model for the Tazer Corp. project selection problem where the changing cells DoProject? (C10:G10) give the optimal solution obtained by Solver.

	A	B	C	D	E	F	G	H	I	J
1		**Tazer Corp. Project Selection Problem**								
2										
3										
4			Up	Stable	Choice	Hope	Release	Total		Budget
5		R&D Investment ($million)	400	300	600	500	200	1,200	<=	1,200
6		Success Rate	50%	35%	35%	20%	45%			
7		Revenue If Successful ($million)	1,400	1,200	2,200	3,000	600			
8		Expected Profit ($million)	300	120	170	100	70	540		
9										
10		Do Project?	1	0	1	0	1			

	B	C	D	E	F	G
8	Expected Profit ($million)	=C7*C6-C5	=D7*D6-D5	=E7*E6-E5	=F7*F6-F5	=G7*G6-G5

Range Name	Cells
Budget	J5
DoProject?	C10:G10
ExpectedProfit	C8:G8
RandDInvestment	C5:G5
Revenue	C7:G7
SuccessRate	C6:G6
TotalExpectedProfit	H8
TotalRandD	H5

	H
4	Total
5	=SUMPRODUCT(RandDInvestment,DoProject?)
6	
7	
8	=SUMPRODUCT(ExpectedProfit,DoProject?)

Solver Parameters
Set Objective Cell: TotalExpectedProfit
To: Max
By Changing Variable Cells:
   DoProject?
Subject to the Constraints:
   DoProject? = binary
   TotalRandD <= Budget

Solver Options:
   Make Variables Nonnegative
   Solving Method: Simplex LP

well as for its possible new warehouse. For either of the possible sites for the new factory (or the warehouse), there is a *yes-or-no decision* for whether that site should be selected, so it becomes natural to represent each such decision by a binary decision variable.

Various kinds of site selection problems are one of the most common types of applications of BIP. The kinds of facilities for which sites need to be selected can be of any type. In some cases, several sites are to be selected for several facilities of a particular type, whereas only a single site is to be selected in other cases.

We will focus here on the selection of sites for emergency services facilities. These facilities might be fire stations, police stations, ambulance centers, and so forth. In any of these cases, the overriding concern commonly is to provide facilities close enough to each part of the area being served that the response time to an emergency anywhere in the area will be sufficiently small. The form of the BIP model then will be basically the same regardless of the specific type of emergency services being considered.

To illustrate, let us consider an example where sites are being selected for fire stations. For simplicity, this example will divide the area being served into only eight tracts instead of the many dozens or hundreds that would be typical in real applications.

The Caliente City Problem

Caliente City is located in a particularly warm and arid part of the United States, so it is especially prone to the occurrence of fires. The city has become a popular place for senior citizens to move to after retirement, so it has been growing rapidly and spreading well beyond its original borders. However, the city still has only one fire station, located in the congested center of the original town site. The result has been some long delays in fire trucks reaching fires in the outer parts of the city, causing much more damage than would have occurred with a prompt response. The city's residents are very unhappy about this, so the city council has directed the city manager to develop a plan for locating multiple fire stations throughout the city (including perhaps moving the current fire station) that would greatly reduce the response time to any fire. In particular, the city council has adopted the following policy about the maximum acceptable response time for fire trucks to reach a fire anywhere in the city after being notified about the fire.

Response time ≤ 10 minutes

Having had a management science course in college, the city manager recognizes that BIP provides her with a powerful tool for analyzing this problem. To get started, she divides the city into eight tracts and then gathers data on the estimated response time for a fire in each tract from a potential fire station in each of the eight tracts. These data are shown in Table 7.4. For example, if a decision were to be made to locate a fire station in tract 1 and if that fire station were to be used to respond to a fire in any of the tracts, the second column of Table 7.4 shows what the (estimated) response time would be. (Since the response time would exceed 10 minutes for a fire in tracts 3, 5, 6, 7, or 8, a fire station actually would need to be located nearer to each of these tracts to satisfy the city council's new policy.) The bottom row of Table 7.4 shows what the cost would be of acquiring the land and constructing a fire station in any of the eight tracts. (The cost is far less for tract 5 because the current fire station already is there so only a modest renovation is needed if the decision is made to retain a fire station there.)

The objective is to minimize the total cost of ensuring a response time of no more than 10 minutes.

The objective now is to determine which tracts should receive a fire station to minimize the total cost of the stations while ensuring that each tract has at least one station close enough to respond to a fire in no more than 10 minutes.

Formulation with Binary Variables

For each of the eight tracts, there is a yes-or-no decision as to whether that tract should receive a fire station. Therefore, we let $x_1, x_2, \ldots, x_8$ denote the corresponding binary decision variables, where

$$x_j = \begin{cases} 1, & \text{if tract } j \text{ is selected to receive a fire station} \\ 0, & \text{if not} \end{cases}$$

for $j = 1, 2, \ldots, 8$.

TABLE 7.4 **Response Time and Cost Data for the Caliente City Problem**

		Fire Station in Tract							
		1	2	3	4	5	6	7	8
	1	2	8	18	9	23	22	16	28
Response	2	9	3	10	12	16	14	21	25
times	3	17	8	4	20	21	8	22	17
(minutes)	4	10	13	19	2	18	21	6	12
for a fire	5	21	12	16	13	5	11	9	12
in tract	6	25	15	7	21	15	3	14	8
	7	14	22	18	7	13	15	2	9
	8	30	24	15	14	17	9	8	3
Cost of station ($thousands)		350	250	450	300	50	400	300	200

Since the objective is to minimize the total cost of the fire stations that will satisfy the city council's new policy on response times, the total cost needs to be expressed in terms of these decision variables. Using units of thousands of dollars while referring to the bottom row of Table 7.4, the total cost is

$$C = 350x_1 + 250x_2 + 450x_3 + 300x_4 + 50x_5 + 400x_6 + 300x_7 + 200x_8$$

We also need to formulate constraints in terms of these decision variables that will ensure that no response times exceed 10 minutes. For example, consider tract 1. When a fire occurs there, the row for tract 1 in Table 7.4 indicates that the only tracts close enough that a fire station would provide a response time not exceeding 10 minutes are tract 1 itself, tract 2, and tract 4. Thus, at least one of these three tracts needs to have a fire station. This requirement is expressed in the constraint

$$x_1 + x_2 + x_4 \geq 1$$

This constraint ensures that the response time for a fire in tract 1 will be no more than 10 minutes.

Incidentally, this constraint is called a **set covering constraint** because it *covers* the requirement of having a fire station located in at least one member of the *set* of tracts (tracts 1, 2, and 4) that are within 10 minutes of tract 1. In general, any constraint where a sum of binary variables is required to be greater-than-or-equal-to one is referred to as a set covering constraint.

Applying the above reasoning for tract 1 to all the tracts leads to the following constraints.

Tract 1:	x_1	$+x_2$		$+x_4$				≥ 1
Tract 2:	x_1	$+x_2$	$+x_3$					≥ 1
Tract 3:		x_2	$+x_3$			$+x_6$		≥ 1
Tract 4:	x_1			$+x_4$			$+x_7$	≥ 1
Tract 5:					$+x_5$		$+x_7$	≥ 1
Tract 6:			x_3			$+x_6$		$+x_8$ ≥ 1
Tract 7:				x_4			$+x_7$	$+x_8$ ≥ 1
Tract 8:						x_6	$+x_7$	$+x_8$ ≥ 1

These *set covering constraints* (along with requiring the variables to be binary) are all that is needed to ensure that each tract has at least one fire station close enough to respond to a fire in no more than 10 minutes.

This type of BIP model (minimizing total cost where all the functional constraints are set covering constraints) is called a **set covering problem.** Such problems arise fairly frequently. In fact, you will see another example of a set covering problem in Section 7.4.

Having identified the nature of the constraints for the Caliente City problem, it now is fairly straightforward to formulate its BIP spreadsheet model.

A BIP Spreadsheet Model for the Caliente City Problem

Figure 7.4 shows a BIP spreadsheet model for this problem. The data cells ResponseTime (D5:K12) show all the response times given in Table 7.4 and CostOfStation (D14:K14) provides the cost data from the bottom row of this table. There is a yes-or-no decision for each tract as to whether a fire station should be located there, so the changing cells are StationInTract? (D29:K29). The objective is to minimize total cost, so the objective cell is TotalCost (N29). The set covering constraints are displayed in cells L17:N24. The Station-InTract? changing cells have been constrained to be binary, as can be seen in the Solver Parameters box.

After running Solver, the optimal solution shown in the changing cells StationInTract? (D29:K29) in Figure 7.4 is obtained, namely,

Select tracts 2, 7, and 8 as the sites for fire stations.

The objective cell TotalCost (N29) indicates that the resulting total cost is $750,000.

FIGURE 7.4

A spreadsheet formulation of the BIP model for the Caliente City site selection problem where the changing cells StationInTract? (D29:K29) show the optimal solution obtained by Solver.

	A	B	C	D	E	F	G	H	I	J	K	L	M	N
1		**Caliente City Fire Station Location Problem**												
2														
3						Fire Station in Tract								
4				1	2	3	4	5	6	7	8			
5			1	2	8	18	9	23	22	16	28			
6		Response	2	9	3	10	12	16	14	21	25			
7		Times	3	17	8	4	20	21	8	22	17			
8		(minutes)	4	10	13	19	2	18	21	6	12			
9		for a Fire	5	21	12	16	13	5	11	9	12			
10		in Tract	6	25	15	7	21	15	3	14	8			
11			7	14	22	18	7	13	15	2	9			
12			8	30	24	15	14	17	9	8	3			
13														
14		Cost of Station		350	250	450	300	50	400	300	200			
15		($thousands)										Number		
16												Covering		
17			1	1	1	0	1	0	0	0	0	1	>=	1
18		Response	2	1	1	1	0	0	0	0	0	1	>=	1
19		Time	3	0	1	1	0	0	1	0	0	1	>=	1
20		<=	4	1	0	0	1	0	0	1	0	1	>=	1
21		10	5	0	0	0	0	1	0	1	0	1	>=	1
22		Minutes?	6	0	0	1	0	0	1	0	1	1	>=	1
23			7	0	0	0	1	0	0	1	1	2	>=	1
24			8	0	0	0	0	0	1	1	1	2	>=	1
25														
26														Total
27						Fire Station in Tract								Cost
28				1	2	3	4	5	6	7	8			($thousands)
29		Station in Tract?		0	1	0	0	0	0	1	1			750

	J	K	L
15			Number
16			Covering
17	=IF(J5<=MaxResponseTime,1,0)	=IF(K5<=MaxResponseTime,1,0)	=SUMPRODUCT(D17:K17,StationInTract?)
18	=IF(J6<=MaxResponseTime,1,0)	=IF(K6<=MaxResponseTime,1,0)	=SUMPRODUCT(D18:K18,StationInTract?)
19	=IF(J7<=MaxResponseTime,1,0)	=IF(K7<=MaxResponseTime,1,0)	=SUMPRODUCT(D19:K19,StationInTract?)

Solver Parameters

Set Objective Cell: TotalCost
To: Min
By Changing Variable Cells:
   StationInTract?
Subject to the Constraints:
   StationInTract? = binary
   NumberCovering >= One

Solver Options:
   Make Variables Nonnegative
   Solving Method: Simplex LP

Range Name	Cells
CostOfStation	D14:K14
MaxResponseTime	B21
NumberCovering	L17:L24
One	N17:N24
ResponseTime	D5:K12
StationInTract?	D29:K29
TotalCost	N29

	N
26	Total
27	Cost
28	($thousands)
29	=SUMPRODUCT(CostOfStation,StationInTract?)

246   Chapter Seven   *Using Binary Integer Programming to Deal with Yes-or-No Decisions*

Review
Questions

1. How are binary variables used to represent managerial decisions regarding which site or sites should be selected for new facilities?
2. What are some types of emergency services facilities for which sites may need to be selected?
3. What was the objective for the Caliente City problem?
4. What is a set covering constraint and what is a set covering problem?

7.4   USING BIP FOR CREW SCHEDULING: THE SOUTHWESTERN AIRWAYS PROBLEM

Throughout the travel industry (airlines, rail travel, cruise ships, tour companies, etc.), one of the most challenging problems in maintaining an efficient operation is the scheduling of its crews who serve customers during their travels. Given many feasible overlapping sequences of trips for a crew, to which ones should a crew be assigned so as to cover all the trips at a minimum cost? Thus, for each feasible sequence of trips, there is a *yes-or-no decision* as to whether a crew should be assigned to that sequence, so a binary decision variable can be used to represent that decision.

For many years, airline companies have been using BIP models to determine how to do their crew scheduling in the most cost-efficient way. Some airlines have saved many millions of dollars annually through this application of BIP. Consequently, other segments of the travel industry now are also using BIP in this way. For example, the application vignette in this section describes how Netherlands Railways achieved a dramatic increase in profits by applying BIP (and related techniques) in a variety of ways, including crew scheduling.

To illustrate the approach, consider the following miniature example of airline crew scheduling.

The Southwestern Airways Problem

Southwestern Airways needs to assign its crews to cover all its upcoming flights. We will focus on the problem of assigning three crews based in San Francisco (SFO) to the 11 flights shown in Figure 7.5. These same flights are listed in the first column of Table 7.5. The other 12 columns show the 12 feasible sequences of flights for a crew. (The numbers in each column indicate the order of the flights.) At most, three of the sequences need to be chosen (one per crew) in such a way that every flight is covered. (It is permissible to have more than one crew on a flight, where the extra crews would fly as passengers, but union contracts require that the extra crews still be paid for their time as if they were working.) The cost of assigning a crew to a particular sequence of flights is given (in thousands of dollars) in the bottom row of the table. The objective is to minimize the total cost of the crew assignments that cover all the flights.

FIGURE 7.5

The arrows show the 11 Southwestern Airways flights that need to be covered by the three crews based in San Francisco.

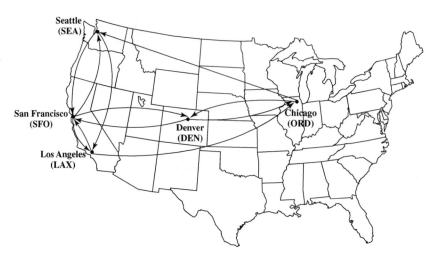

An Application Vignette

Netherlands Railways (Nederlandse Spoorwegen Reizigers) is the main Dutch railway operator of passenger trains. In this densely populated country, about 5,500 passenger trains currently transport approximately 1.1 million passengers on an average workday. The company's operating revenues are approximately 1.5 billion euros (approximately $2 billion) per year.

The amount of passenger transport on the Dutch railway network has steadily increased over the years, so a national study in 2002 concluded that three major infrastructure extensions should be undertaken. As a result, a new national timetable for the Dutch railway system, specifying the planned departure and arrival times of every train at every station, would need to be developed. Therefore, the management of Netherlands Railways directed that an extensive management science study should be conducted over the next few years to develop an optimal overall plan for both the new timetable and the usage of the available resources (rolling-stock units and train crews) for meeting this timetable. A task force consisting of several members of the company's Department of Logistics and several prominent management science scholars from European universities or a software company was formed to conduct this study.

The new timetable was launched in December 2006, along with a new system for scheduling the allocation of rolling-stock units (various kinds of passenger cars and other train units) to the trains meeting this timetable. A new system also was implemented for scheduling the assignment of crews (with a driver and a number of conductors in each crew) to the trains. *Binary integer programming* and related techniques were used to do all of this. For example, the BIP model used for crew scheduling closely resembles (except for its vastly larger size) the one shown in this section for the Southwestern Airlines problem.

This application of management science immediately resulted in *an additional annual profit of approximately $60 million* for the company and this additional profit is expected to increase to **$105 million** annually in the coming years. These dramatic results led to Netherlands Railways winning the prestigious First Prize in the 2008 international competition for the Franz Edelman Award for Achievement in Operations Research and the Management Sciences.

Source: L. Kroon, D. Huisman, E. Abbink, P.-J. Fioole, M. Fischetti, G. Maróti, A. Schrijver, A. Steenbeck, and R. Ybema, "The New Dutch Timetable: The OR Revolution," *Interfaces* 39, no. 1 (January–February 2009), pp. 6–17. (A link to this article is provided on our website, **www.mhhe.com/hillier5e.**)

TABLE 7.5 Data for the Southwestern Airways Problem

Flight	Feasible Sequence of Flights											
	1	2	3	4	5	6	7	8	9	10	11	12
1. San Francisco to Los Angeles (SFO–LAX)	1			1			1			1		
2. San Francisco to Denver (SFO–DEN)		1			1			1			1	
3. San Francisco to Seattle (SFO–SEA)			1			1			1			1
4. Los Angeles to Chicago (LAX–ORD)				2			2		3	2		3
5. Los Angeles to San Francisco (LAX–SFO)	2					3				5	5	
6. Chicago to Denver (ORD–DEN)			3	3				4				
7. Chicago to Seattle (ORD–SEA)							3	3		3	3	4
8. Denver to San Francisco (DEN–SFO)		2		4	4				5			
9. Denver to Chicago (DEN–ORD)					2			2			2	
10. Seattle to San Francisco (SEA–SFO)			2				4	4				5
11. Seattle to Los Angeles (SEA–LAX)						2			2	4	4	2
Cost, $1,000s	2	3	4	6	7	5	7	8	9	9	8	9

Formulation with Binary Variables

With 12 feasible sequences of flights, we have 12 yes-or-no decisions:

Should sequence j be assigned to a crew? $\quad (j = 1, 2, \ldots, 12)$

Therefore, we use 12 binary variables to represent these respective decisions:

$$x_j = \begin{cases} 1, & \text{if sequence } j \text{ is assigned to a crew} \\ 0, & \text{otherwise} \end{cases}$$

Since the objective is to minimize the total cost of the three crew assignments, we now need to express the total cost in terms of these binary decision variables. Referring to the bottom row of Table 7.5, this total cost (in units of thousands of dollars) is

$$C = 2x_1 + 3x_2 + 4x_3 + 6x_4 + 7x_5 + 5x_6 + 7x_7 + 8x_8 + 9x_9 + 9x_{10} + 8x_{11} + 9x_{12}$$

With only three crews available to cover the flights, we also need the constraint

$$x_1 + x_2 + \cdots + x_{12} \le 3$$

The most interesting part of this formulation is the nature of each constraint that ensures that a corresponding flight is covered. For example, consider the last flight in Table 7.5 (Seattle to Los Angeles). Five sequences (namely, sequences 6, 9, 10, 11, and 12) include this flight. Therefore, at least one of these five sequences must be chosen. The resulting constraint is

$$x_6 + x_9 + x_{10} + x_{11} + x_{12} \ge 1$$

For each of the 11 flights, the constraint that ensures that the flight is covered is constructed in the same way from Table 7.5 by requiring that at least one of the flight sequences that includes that flight is assigned to a crew. Thus, 11 constraints of the following form are needed.

These are set covering constraints, just like the constraints in the Caliente City problem in Section 7.3.

Flight 1: $x_1 + x_4 + x_7 + x_{10} \ge 1$

Flight 2: $x_2 + x_5 + x_8 + x_{11} \ge 1$

.

.

.

Flight 11: $x_6 + x_9 + x_{10} + x_{11} + x_{12} \ge 1$

Note that these constraints have the same form as the constraints for the Caliente City problem in Section 7.3 (a sum of certain binary variables ≥ 1), so these too are *set covering constraints*. Therefore, this crew scheduling problem is another example of a *set covering problem* (where this particular set covering problem also includes the side constraint that $x_1 + x_2 + \cdots + x_{12} \le 3$).

Having identified the nature of the constraints, the stage now is set for formulating a BIP spreadsheet model for this problem.

A BIP Spreadsheet Model for the Southwestern Airways Problem

Figure 7.6 shows a spreadsheet formulation of the complete BIP model for this problem. The changing cells FlySequence? (C22:N22) contain the values of the 12 binary decision variables. The data in IncludesSegment? (C8:N18) and Cost (C5:N5) come directly from Table 7.5. The last three columns of the spreadsheet are used to show the set covering constraints, Total $\ge$ AtLeastOne, and the side constraint, TotalSequences $\le$ NumberOfCrews. Finally, the changing cells FlySequence? have been constrained to be binary, as shown in the Solver Parameters box.

Solver provides the optimal solution shown in FlySequence? (C22:N22). In terms of the x_j variables, this solution is

$x_3 = 1$ (assign sequence 3 to a crew)

$x_4 = 1$ (assign sequence 4 to a crew)

$x_{11} = 1$ (assign sequence 11 to a crew)

and all other $x_j = 0$, for a total cost of \$18,000 as given by TotalCost (Q24). (Another optimal solution is $x_1 = 1$, $x_5 = 1$, $x_{12} = 1$, and all other $x_j = 0$.)

FIGURE 7.6

A spreadsheet formulation of the BIP model for the Southwestern Airways crew scheduling problem, where FlySequence (C22:N22) shows the optimal solution obtained by Solver. The list of flight sequences under consideration is given in cells A25:D37.

	A	B	C	D	E	F	G	H	I	J	K	L	M	N	O	P	Q
1		Southwestern Airways Crew Scheduling Problem															
2																	
3							Flight Sequence										
4			1	2	3	4	5	6	7	8	9	10	11	12			
5		Cost ($thousands)	2	3	4	6	7	5	7	8	9	9	8	9			At
6																	Least
7		**Includes Segment?**													Total		One
8		SFO–LAX	1	0	0	1	0	0	1	0	0	1	0	0	1	≥	1
9		SFO–DEN	0	1	0	0	1	0	0	1	0	0	1	0	1	≥	1
10		SFO–SEA	0	0	1	0	0	1	0	0	1	0	0	1	1	≥	1
11		LAX–ORD	0	0	0	1	0	0	1	0	1	1	0	1	1	≥	1
12		LAX–SFO	1	0	0	0	0	1	0	0	0	1	1	0	1	≥	1
13		ORD–DEN	0	0	0	1	1	0	0	0	1	0	0	0	1	≥	1
14		ORD–SEA	0	0	0	0	0	0	1	1	0	1	1	1	1	≥	1
15		DEN–SFO	0	1	0	1	1	0	0	0	1	0	0	0	1	≥	1
16		DEN–ORD	0	0	0	0	1	0	0	1	0	0	1	0	1	≥	1
17		SEA–SFO	0	0	1	0	0	0	1	1	0	0	0	1	1	≥	1
18		SEA–LAX	0	0	0	0	0	1	0	0	1	1	1	1	1	≥	1
19																	
20															Total		Number
21			1	2	3	4	5	6	7	8	9	10	11	12	Sequences		of Crews
22		Fly Sequence?	0	0	1	1	0	0	0	0	0	0	1	0	3	≤	3
23																	
24														Total Cost ($thousands)			18

	Flight Sequence Key
1	SFO-LAX
2	SFO-DEN-SFO
3	SFO-SEA-SFO
4	SFO-LAX-ORD-DEN-SFO
5	SFO-DEN-ORD-DEN-SFO
6	SFO-SEA-LAX-SFO
7	SFO-LAX-ORD-SEA-SFO
8	SFO-DEN-ORD-SEA-SFO
9	SFO-SEA-LAX-ORD-DEN-SFO
10	SFO-LAX-ORD-SEA-LAX-SFO
11	SFO-DEN-ORD-SEA-LAX-SFO
12	SFO-SEA-LAX-ORD-SEA-SFO

Solver Parameters

Set Objective Cell: TotalCost
To: Min
By Changing Variable Cells:
  FlySequence?
Subject to the Constraints:
  FlySequence? = binary
  Total >= AtLeastOne
  TotalSequences <= NumberOfCrews

Solver Options:
  Make Variables Nonnegative
  Solving Method: Simplex LP

Range Name	Cells
AtLeastOne	Q8:Q18
Cost	C5:N5
FlySequence?	C22:N22
IncludesSegment?	C8:N18
NumberOfCrews	Q22
Total	O8:O18
TotalCost	Q24
TotalSequences	O22

	O
7	Total
8	=SUMPRODUCT(C8:N8,FlySequence?)
9	=SUMPRODUCT(C9:N9,FlySequence?)
10	=SUMPRODUCT(C10:N10,FlySequence?)
11	=SUMPRODUCT(C11:N11,FlySequence?)
12	=SUMPRODUCT(C12:N12,FlySequence?)
13	=SUMPRODUCT(C13:N13,FlySequence?)
14	=SUMPRODUCT(C14:N14,FlySequence?)
15	=SUMPRODUCT(C15:N15,FlySequence?)
16	=SUMPRODUCT(C16:N16,FlySequence?)
17	=SUMPRODUCT(C17:N17,FlySequence?)
18	=SUMPRODUCT(C18:N18,FlySequence?)
19	
20	Total
21	Sequences
22	=SUM(FlySequence?)

	P	Q
24	Total Cost ($thousands)	=SUMPRODUCT(Cost,FlySequence?)

250   Chapter Seven   *Using Binary Integer Programming to Deal with Yes-or-No Decisions*

Many airlines are solving huge BIP models of this kind.

We should point out that this BIP model is a tiny one compared to the ones typically used in actual practice. Airline crew scheduling problems involving thousands of possible flight sequences now are being solved by using models similar to the one shown above but with thousands of binary variables rather than just a dozen.

Review Questions

1. What is the crew scheduling problem that is encountered by companies in the travel industry?
2. What are the yes-or-no decisions that need to be made when addressing a crew scheduling problem?
3. For the Southwestern Airways problem, there is a constraint for each flight to ensure that this flight is covered by a crew. Describe the mathematical form of this constraint. Then explain in words what this constraint is saying.

7.5   USING MIXED BIP TO DEAL WITH SETUP COSTS FOR INITIATING PRODUCTION: THE REVISED WYNDOR PROBLEM

All of the examples considered thus far in this chapter have been *pure BIP problems* (problems where all the decision variables are binary variables). However, *mixed BIP problems* (problems where only some of the decision variables are binary variables) also arise quite frequently because only some of the decisions to be made are yes-or-no decisions and the rest are how-much decisions.

One important example of this type is the *product-mix problem* introduced in Chapter 2, but now with the added complication that a setup cost must be incurred to initiate the production of each product. Therefore, in addition to the *how-much decisions* of how much to produce of each product, there also is a prior yes-or-no decision for each product of whether to perform a setup to enable initiating its production.

To illustrate this type of problem, we will consider a revised version of the Wyndor Glass Co. product-mix problem that was described in Section 2.1 and analyzed throughout most of Chapter 2.

The Revised Wyndor Problem with Setup Costs

Suppose now that the **Wyndor Glass Co.** will only devote one week each month to the production of the special doors and windows described in Section 2.1, so the question now is *how many* doors and windows to produce during each of these week-long production runs. Since the decisions to be made are no longer the *rates* of production for doors and windows, but rather *how many* doors and windows to produce in individual production runs, these quantities now are required to be *integer*.

Each time Wyndor's plants convert from the production of other products to the production of these doors and windows for a week, the following setup costs would be incurred to initiate this production.

Setup cost to produce doors = $700

Setup cost to produce windows = $1,300

Otherwise, all the original data given in Table 2.2 still apply, including a unit profit of $300 for doors and $500 for windows when disregarding these setup costs.

Table 7.6 shows the resulting net profit from producing any feasible quantity for either product. Note that the large setup cost for either product makes it unprofitable to produce less than three units of that product.

The dots in Figure 7.7 show the feasible solutions for this problem. By adding the appropriate entries in Table 7.6, the figure also shows the calculation of the total net profit P for each of the corner points. The optimal solution turns out to be

$$(D, W) = (0, 6) \qquad \text{with} \qquad P = 1,700$$

By contrast, the original solution

$$(D, W) = (2, 6) \qquad \text{with} \qquad P = 1,600$$

TABLE 7.6
Net Profit ($) for the Revised Wyndor Problem

Number of Units Produced	Net Profit ($)	
	Doors	**Windows**
0	0 (300) − 0 = 0	0 (500) − 0 = 0
1	1 (300) − 700 = −400	1 (500) − 1,300 = −800
2	2 (300) − 700 = −100	2 (500) − 1,300 = −300
3	3 (300) − 700 = 200	3 (500) − 1,300 = 200
4	4 (300) − 700 = 500	4 (500) − 1,300 = 700
5	Not feasible	5 (500) − 1,300 = 1,200
6	Not feasible	6 (500) − 1,300 = 1,700

FIGURE 7.7

The dots are the feasible solutions for the revised Wyndor problem. Also shown is the calculation of the total net profit *P* (in dollars) for each corner point from the net profits given in Table 7.6.

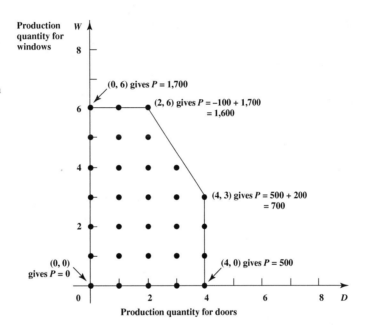

now gives a smaller value of *P*. The reason that this original solution (which gave *P* = 3,600 for the original problem) is no longer optimal is that the setup costs reduce the total net profit so much:

$$P = 3{,}600 - 700 - 1{,}300 = 1{,}600$$

Therefore, the graphical method for linear programming can no longer be used to find the optimal solution for this new problem with setup costs.

How can we formulate a model for this problem so that it fits a standard kind of model that can be solved by Solver? Table 7.6 shows that the net profit for either product is no longer *directly proportional* to the number of units produced. Therefore, as it stands, the problem no longer fits either linear programming or BIP. Before, for the original problem without setup costs, the objective function was simply $P = 300D + 500W$. Now we need to subtract from this expression each setup cost *if* the corresponding product will be produced, but we should not subtract the setup cost if the product will not be produced. This is where *binary variables* come to the rescue.

Formulation with Binary Variables

For each product, there is a *yes-or-no decision* regarding whether to perform the setup that would enable initiating the production of the product, so the setup cost is incurred only if the decision is *yes*. Therefore, we can introduce a *binary variable* for each setup cost and

An Application Vignette

Prior to its merger with United Airlines in 2010, **Continental Airlines** was a major United States air carrier that transported passengers, cargo, and mail. It operated more than 2,000 daily departures to well over 100 domestic destinations and nearly 100 foreign destinations.

Airlines like Continental face schedule disruptions daily because of unexpected events, including inclement weather, aircraft mechanical problems, and crew unavailability. Another consequence of such disruptions is that crews may not be in positions to service their remaining scheduled flights. Airlines must reassign crews quickly to cover open flights and to return them to their original schedules in a cost-effective manner while honoring all government regulations, contractual obligations, and quality-of-life requirements.

To address such problems, a management science team at Continental Airlines developed a detailed *mixed BIP model* for reassigning crews to flights as soon as such emergencies arise. Because the airline has thousands of crews and daily flights, the model needed to be huge to consider all possible pairings of crews with flights. Therefore, the model has *millions of decision variables* and *many thousands of constraints*. (Most of these decision variables

are *binary variables* and the rest are general integer variables). In its first year of use (mainly in 2001), the model was applied four times to recover from major schedule disruptions (two snowstorms, a flood, and the September 11 terrorist attacks). This led to *savings of approximately $40 million.* Subsequent applications extended to many daily minor disruptions as well.

Although other airlines subsequently scrambled to apply management science in a similar way, this initial advantage over other airlines in being able to recover more quickly from schedule disruptions with fewer delays and cancelled flights left Continental Airlines in a relatively strong position as the airline industry struggled through a difficult period during the initial years of the 21st century. This initiative led to Continental winning the prestigious First Prize in the 2002 international competition for the Franz Edelman Award for Achievement in Operations Research and the Management Sciences.

Source: G. Yu, M. Argüello, C. Song, S. M. McGowan, and A. White, "A New Era for Crew Recovery at Continental Airlines," *Interfaces* 33, no. 1 (January–February 2003), pp. 5–22. (A link to this article is provided on our website, **www.mhhe.com/hillier5e.**)

associate each value of the binary variable with one of the two possibilities for the setup cost. In particular, let

These binary variables enable subtracting each setup cost only if the setup is performed.

$$y_1 = \begin{cases} 1, & \text{if perform the setup to produce doors} \\ 0, & \text{if not} \end{cases}$$

$$y_2 = \begin{cases} 1, & \text{if perform the setup to produce windows} \\ 0, & \text{if not} \end{cases}$$

Therefore, the objective function now can be written as

$$P = 300D + 500W - 700y_1 - 1{,}300y_2$$

which fits the format for mixed BIP.

Since a setup is required to produce the corresponding product, these binary variables can be related directly to the production quantities as follows:

$$y_1 = \begin{cases} 1, & \text{if } D > 0 \text{ can hold (can produce doors)} \\ 0, & \text{if } D = 0 \text{ must hold (cannot produce doors)} \end{cases}$$

$$y_2 = \begin{cases} 1, & \text{if } W > 0 \text{ can hold (can produce windows)} \\ 0, & \text{if } W = 0 \text{ must hold (cannot produce windows)} \end{cases}$$

We need to include constraints in the model that will ensure that these relationships will hold. (An algorithm solving the model only recognizes the objective function and the constraints, not the definitions of the variables.)

So what are the constraints of the model? We still need all the constraints of the original model. We also need constraints that D and W are integers, and that y_1 and y_2 are binary. In addition, we need some ordinary linear programming constraints that will ensure the following relationships:

If $y_1 = 0$,   then D = 0.

If $y_2 = 0$,   then W = 0.

(If $y_1 = 1$, no restrictions are placed on D other than those already imposed by the other constraints, and the same thing applies to W if $y_2 = 0$.)

It is possible with Excel to use the IF function to represent this relationship between y_1 and D and between y_2 and W. Unfortunately, the IF function does not fit the assumptions of linear programming. Consequently, Solver has difficulty solving spreadsheet models that use this function. This is why another formulation with ordinary linear programming constraints is needed instead to express these relationships.

Since the other constraints impose bounds on D and W of $0 \leq D \leq 4$ and $0 \leq W \leq 6$, here are some ordinary linear programming constraints that ensure these relationships:

$$D \leq 4y_1$$
$$W \leq 6y_2$$

These constraints force the model to refuse production if the corresponding setup is not performed.

Note that setting $y_1 = 0$ gives $D \leq 0$, which forces the nonnegative D to be $D = 0$, whereas setting $y_1 = 1$ gives $D \leq 4$, which allows all the values of D already allowed by the other constraints. Then check that the same conclusions apply for W when setting $y_2 = 0$ and $y_2 = 1$.

It was not necessary to choose 4 and 6 for the respective coefficients of y_1 and y_2 in these two constraints. Any coefficients *larger* than 4 and 6 would have the same effect. You just need to avoid *smaller* coefficients, since this would impose undesired restrictions on D and W when $y_1 = 1$ and $y_2 = 1$.

If a *how-much* decision x can only be done (i.e., $x > 0$) if a corresponding *yes-no* decision y is done (i.e., $y = 1$), this can be enforced with a big-number constraint such as $x \leq 99y$. If $y = 0$, this becomes $x \leq 0$. If $y = 1$, then this becomes $x \leq 99$. The big number (99 in this example) is chosen to be big enough so that it is safely larger than x could ever become.

On larger problems, it is sometimes difficult to determine the smallest acceptable coefficients for these binary variables. Therefore, it is common to formulate the model by just using a reasonably large number (say, 99 in this case) that is safely larger than the smallest acceptable coefficient.

With this background, we now are ready to formulate a mixed BIP spreadsheet model for this problem that uses the number 99 in these constraints.

A Mixed BIP Spreadsheet Model for the Revised Wyndor Problem

Figure 7.8 shows one way of formulating this model. The format for the first 14 rows is the same as for the original Wyndor problem, so the difference arises in rows 15–17 of the spreadsheet. The values of the binary variables, y_1 and y_2, appear in the new changing cells, Setup? (C17:D17). The bottom of the figure identifies the equations entered into the output cells in row 16, C16 = 99*C17 and D16 = 99*D17. Consequently, the constraints, UnitsProduced (C14:D14) $\leq$ OnlyIfSetup (C16:D16), impose the relationships that $D \leq 99y_1$ and $W \leq 99y_2$.

The changing cells in this spreadsheet show the optimal solution obtained after applying Solver. Thus, this solution is to not produce any doors ($y_1 = 0$ and $D = 0$) but to perform the setup to enable producing 6 windows ($y_2 = 1$ and $W = 6$) to obtain a net profit of $1,700.

Note that this optimal solution does indeed satisfy the requirements that $D = 0$ must hold when $y_1 = 0$ and that $W > 0$ can hold when $y_2 = 1$. The constraints do permit performing a setup to produce a product and then not producing any units ($y_1 = 1$ with $D = 0$ or $y_2 = 1$ with $W = 0$), but the objective function causes an optimal solution automatically to avoid this foolish option of incurring the setup cost for no purpose.

Review Questions

1. How does a mixed BIP problem differ from a pure BIP problem?
2. Why is a linear programming formulation no longer valid for a product-mix problem when there are setup costs for initiating production?
3. How can a binary variable be defined in terms of whether a setup is performed to initiate the production of a certain product?
4. What caused the optimal solution for the revised Wyndor problem to differ from that for the original Wyndor problem?

254 Chapter Seven *Using Binary Integer Programming to Deal with Yes-or-No Decisions*

FIGURE 7.8

A spreadsheet model for the revised Wyndor problem, where Solver gives the optimal solution shown in the changing cells, UnitsProduced (C14:D14) and Setup? (C17:D17).

	A	B	C	D	E	F	G	H
1		**Wyndor Glass Co. Product-Mix with Setup Costs**						
2								
3			Doors	Windows				
4		Unit Profit	$300	$500				
5		Setup Cost	$700	$1,300				
6								
7					Hours		Hours	
8			Hours Used per Unit Produced		Used		Available	
9		Plant 1	1	0	0	≤	4	
10		Plant 2	0	2	12	≤	12	
11		Plant 3	3	2	12	≤	18	
12								
13			Doors	Windows				
14		Units Prod'd	0	6				
15			≤	≤			Production Profit	$3,000
16		Only if Set Up	0	99			−Total Setup Cost	$1,300
17		Setup?	0	1			Total Profit	$1,700

Solver Parameters

Set Objective Cell: TotalProfit
To: Max
By Changing Variable Cells:
    UnitsProduced, Setup?
Subject to the Constraints:
    Setup? = binary
    UnitsProduced = integer
    HoursUsed <= HoursAvailable
    UnitsProduced <= OnlyIfSetup

Solver Options:
    Make Variables Nonnegative
    Solving Method: Simplex LP

Range Name	Cells
HoursAvailable	G9:G11
HoursUsed	E9:E11
HoursUsedPerUnitProduced	C9:D11
OnlyIfSetup	C16:D16
ProductionProfit	H15
Setup?	C17:D17
SetupCost	C5:D5
TotalProfit	H17
TotalSetupCost	H16
UnitProfit	C4:D4
UnitsProduced	C14:D14

	E
7	Hours
8	Used
9	=SUMPRODUCT(C9:D9,UnitsProduced)
10	=SUMPRODUCT(C10:D10,UnitsProduced)
11	=SUMPRODUCT(C11:D11,UnitsProduced)

	B	C	D
16	Only if Set Up	=99*C17	=99*D17

	G	H
15	Production Profit	=SUMPRODUCT(UnitProfit,UnitsProduced)
16	−Total Setup Cost	=SUMPRODUCT(SetupCost,Setup?)
17	Total Profit	=ProductionProfit − TotalSetupCost

7.6 Summary

Managers frequently must make yes-or-no decisions, where the only two possible choices are yes, go ahead with a particular option, or no, decline this option. A binary integer programming (BIP) model considers many options simultaneously, with a binary decision variable for each option. Mixed BIP models include some continuous decision variables as well.

The California Manufacturing Co. case study involves yes-or-no decisions on whether a new factory should be built in certain cities and then whether a new warehouse also should be built in certain cities. This case study also introduced the modeling of mutually exclusive alternatives and contingent decisions, as well as the performance of sensitivity analysis for BIP models.

Many companies have saved millions of dollars by formulating and solving BIP models for a wide variety of applications. We have described and illustrated some of the most important types, including the selection of projects (e.g., research and development projects), the selection of sites for facilities (e.g., emergency services facilities such as fire stations), and crew scheduling in the travel industry (e.g., airlines). We also have discussed how to use mixed BIP to deal with setup costs for initiating production when addressing product-mix problems.

Glossary

binary decision variable   A binary variable that represents a yes-or-no decision by assigning a value of 1 for choosing yes and a value of 0 for choosing no. (Introduction), 232

binary integer programming   A type of problem or model that fits linear programming except that it uses binary decision variables. (Introduction), 232

binary variable   A variable whose only possible values are 0 and 1. (Introduction), 232

BIP   Abbreviation for binary integer programming. (Introduction), 232

contingent decision   A yes-or-no decision is a contingent decision if it can be yes only if a certain other yes-or-no decision is yes. (Section 7.1), 236

mixed BIP model   A BIP model where only some of the variables are restricted to be binary variables. (Introduction), 232

mutually exclusive alternatives   A group of alternatives where choosing any one alternative excludes choosing any of the others. (Section 7.1), 235

pure BIP model   A BIP model where all the variables are restricted to be binary variables. (Introduction), 232

set covering constraint   A constraint that requires the sum of certain binary variables to be greater than or equal to 1. (Section 7.3), 244

set covering problem   A type of BIP model where the objective is to minimize some quantity such as total cost and all the functional constraints are set covering constraints. (Section 7.3), 244

yes-or-no decision   A decision whose only possible choices are (1) yes, go ahead with a certain option or (2) no, decline this option. (Introduction), 232

Learning Aids for This Chapter in Your MS Courseware

Chapter 7 Excel Files:

California Mfg. Case Study

Tazer Corp. Example

Caliente City Example

Southwestern Airways Example

Revised Wyndor Example

Excel Add-in:

Risk Solver Platform for Education (RSPE)

Supplements to This Chapter on the CD-ROM:

Advanced Formulation Techniques for Binary Integer Programming

Some Perspectives on Solving Binary Integer Programming Problems

Solved Problems (See the CD-ROM or Website for the Solutions)

7.S1. Capital Budgeting with Contingency Constraints

A company is planning its capital budget over the next several years. There are eight potential projects under consideration. A calculation has been made of the expected net present value of each project, along with the cash outflow that would be required over the next four years. These data, along with the cash that is available each year, are shown in the next table. There also are the following contingency constraints: (a) at least one of project 1, 2, or 3 must be done, (b) projects 6 and 7 cannot both be done, and (c) project 5 can only be done if project 6 is done.

Formulate and solve a BIP model in a spreadsheet to determine which projects should be pursued to maximize the total expected net present value.

7.S2. Locating Search-and-Rescue Teams

The Washington State legislature is trying to decide on locations at which to base search-and-rescue teams. The teams are expensive, so the legislature would like as few as possible while still providing the desired level of service. In particular, since response time is critical, the legislature would like every county to either have a team located in that county or in an adjacent

	Cash Outflow Required ($million)								Cash Available ($million)
	Project								
	1	2	3	4	5	6	7	8	
Year 1	1	3	0	3	3	7	2	5	20
Year 2	2	2	2	2	2	3	3	4	20
Year 3	2	3	4	2	3	3	6	2	20
Year 4	2	1	0	5	4	2	1	2	20
NPV ($mil)	10	12	11	15	24	17	16	18	

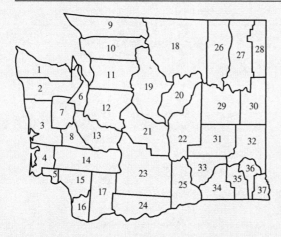

Counties

1. Clallum
2. Jefferson
3. Grays Harbor
4. Pacific
5. Wahkiakum
6. Kitsap
7. Mason
8. Thurston
9. Whatcom
10. Skagit
11. Snohomish
12. King
13. Pierce
14. Lewis
15. Cowlitz
16. Clark
17. Skamania
18. Okanogan
19. Chelan
20. Douglas
21. Kittitas
22. Grant
23. Yakima
24. Klickitat
25. Benton
26. Ferry
27. Stevens
28. Pend Oreille
29. Lincoln
30. Spokane
31. Adams
32. Whitman
33. Franklin
34. Walla Walla
35. Columbia
36. Garfield
37. Asotin

county. (The locations and names of the counties are shown above.) Formulate and solve a BIP model in a spreadsheet to determine where the teams should be located.

7.S3. Warehouse Site Selection

Consider a small company that produces a single product in two plants and serves customers in five different regions.

The company has been using a make-to-order policy of producing the product only in the quantities needed to fill the orders that have come in from the various regions. However, because of the problems caused by the sporatic production schedule, management has decided to smooth out the production rate and ship the product to one or more storage warehouses, which then will use inventory to fill the incoming regional orders. Management now needs to decide where to locate the company's new warehouse(s). There are three locations under consideration. For each location, there is a fixed monthly cost associated with leasing and operating the warehouse there. Furthermore, each potential warehouse location has a maximum capacity for monthly shipments restricted primarily by the number of trucking docks

at the site. The product costs $400 to produce at Plant 1 and $300 to produce at Plant 2. The shipping cost from each plant to each potential warehouse location is shown in the first table below. The fixed leasing and operating cost (if open), the shipping costs, and the capacity (maximum monthly shipments) of each potential warehouse location are shown in the second table below. The monthly demand in each of the customer regions is expected to be 200, 225, 100, 150, and 175 units, respectively. Formulate and solve a BIP model in a spreadsheet to determine which warehouse(s) should be used and how the product should be distributed from plant to warehouse(s) to customer.

Shipping Costs and Capacity of the Plants

	Shipping Cost (per unit)			Capacity (units/month)
	WH 1	WH 2	WH 3	
Plant 1	$25	$50	$75	500
Plant 2	$50	$75	$25	400

Fixed Cost, Shipping Costs, and Capacity of the Warehouses

	Fixed Cost (per month)	Shipping Cost (per unit)					Capacity (units/month)
		Region 1	Region 2	Region 3	Region 4	Region 5	
WH 1	$50,000	$30	$70	$75	$55	$40	700
WH 2	$30,000	$55	$30	$45	$45	$70	500
WH 3	$70,000	$70	$30	$50	$60	$55	1,000

Problems

To the left of the problems (or their parts), we have inserted an E* whenever Excel should be used (unless your instructor gives you contrary instructions). An asterisk on the problem number indicates that at least a partial answer is given in the back of the book.

7.1.   Read the referenced article that fully describes the management science study summarized in the application vignette presented in Section 7.1. Briefly describe how mixed BIP was applied in this study. Then list the various financial and nonfinancial benefits that resulted from this study.

7.2.   Reconsider the California Manufacturing Co. case study presented in Section 7.1. The mayor of San Diego now has contacted the company's president, Armando Ortega, to try to persuade him to build a factory and perhaps a warehouse in that city. With the tax incentives being offered the company, Armando's staff estimates that the net present value of building a factory in San Diego would be $7 million and the amount of capital required to do this would be $4 million. The net present value of building a warehouse there would be $5 million and the capital required would be $3 million. (This option will only be considered if a factory also is being built there.)

Armando has asked Steve Chan to revise his previous management science study to incorporate these new alternatives into the overall problem. The objective still is to find the feasible combination of investments that maximizes the total net present value, given that the amount of capital available for these investments is $10 million.

    a. Formulate a BIP model in algebraic form for this problem.

E* *b.* Formulate and solve this model on a spreadsheet.

7.3.*   A young couple, Eve and Steven, want to divide their main household chores (marketing, cooking, dishwashing, and laundering) between them so that each has two tasks but the total time they spend on household duties is kept to a minimum. Their efficiencies on these tasks differ, where the time each would need to perform the task is given by the following table.

	Time Needed per Week (Hours)			
	Marketing	Cooking	Dish Washing	Laundry
Eve	4.5	7.8	3.6	2.9
Steven	4.9	7.2	4.3	3.1

    a. Formulate a BIP model in algebraic form for this problem.

E* *b.* Formulate and solve this model on a spreadsheet.

7.4.   Read the referenced article that fully describes the management science study summarized in the application vignette presented in Section 7.2. Briefly describe how mixed binary integer programming was applied in this study. Then list the various financial and nonfinancial benefits that resulted from this study.

7.5.   A real-estate development firm, Peterson and Johnson, is considering five possible development projects. Using units of millions of dollars, the following table shows the estimated long-run profit (net present value) that each project would generate,

as well as the amount of investment required to undertake the project.

	Development Project				
	1	**2**	**3**	**4**	**5**
Estimated profit (millions)	$1	$1.8	$1.6	$0.8	$1.4
Capital required (millions)	6	12	10	4	8

The owners of the firm, Dave Peterson and Ron Johnson, have raised $20 million of investment capital for these projects. Dave and Ron now want to select the combination of projects that will maximize their total estimated long-run profit (net present value) without investing more than $20 million.

    a. Formulate a BIP model in algebraic form for this problem.

E* *b.* Formulate and solve this model on a spreadsheet.

E* *c.* Perform sensitivity analysis on the amount of investment capital made available for the development projects by generating a parameter analysis report with RSPE to solve the model with the following amounts of investment capital (in millions of dollars): 16, 18, 20, 22, 24, 26, 28, and 30. Include both the changing cells and the objective cell as output cells in the parameter analysis report.

E*7.6.   The board of directors of General Wheels Co. is considering seven large capital investments. Each investment can be made only once. These investments differ in the estimated long-run profit (net present value) that they will generate as well as in the amount of capital required, as shown by the following table.

Investment Opportunity	Estimated Profit (millions)	Capital Required (millions)
1	$17	$43
2	10	28
3	15	34
4	19	48
5	7	17
6	13	32
7	9	23

The total amount of capital available for these investments is $100 million. Investment opportunities 1 and 2 are mutually exclusive, and so are 3 and 4. Furthermore, neither 3 nor 4 can be undertaken unless one of the first two opportunities is undertaken. There are no such restrictions on investment opportunities 5, 6, and 7. The objective is to select the combination of capital investments that will maximize the total estimated long-run profit (net present value).

    a. Formulate and solve a BIP model on a spreadsheet for this problem.

    b. Perform sensitivity analysis on the amount of capital made available for the investment opportunities by generating a parameter analysis report

258 Chapter Seven *Using Binary Integer Programming to Deal with Yes-or-No Decisions*

with RSPE to solve the model with the following amounts of capital (in millions of dollars): 80, 90, 100, 110, . . . , and 200. Include both the changing cells and the objective cell as output cells in the parameter analysis report.

E*7.7. The Fly-Right Airplane Company builds small jet airplanes to sell to corporations for use by their executives. To meet the needs of these executives, the company's customers sometimes order a custom design of the airplanes being purchased. When this occurs, a substantial start-up cost is incurred to initiate the production of these airplanes.

Fly-Right has recently received purchase requests from three customers with short deadlines. However, because the company's production facilities already are almost completely tied up filling previous orders, it will not be able to accept all three orders. Therefore, a decision now needs to be made on the number of airplanes the company will agree to produce (if any) for each of the three customers.

The relevant data are given in the next table. The first row gives the start-up cost required to initiate the production of the airplanes for each customer. Once production is under way, the marginal net revenue (which is the purchase price minus the marginal production cost) from each airplane produced is shown in the second row. The third row gives the percentage of the available production capacity that would be used for each airplane produced. The last row indicates the maximum number of airplanes requested by each customer (but less will be accepted).

	Customer		
	1	**2**	**3**
Start-up cost	$3 million	$2 million	0
Marginal net revenue	$2 million	$3 million	$0.8 million
Capacity used per plane	20%	40%	20%
Maximum order	3 planes	2 planes	5 planes

Fly-Right now wants to determine how many airplanes to produce for each customer (if any) to maximize the company's total profit (total net revenue minus start-up costs). Formulate and solve a spreadsheet model with both integer variables and binary variables for this problem.

E*7.8. Consider the following special type of shortest path problem (discussed in Section 6.4) where the nodes are in columns and the only paths considered always move forward one column at a time.

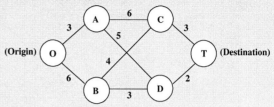

The numbers along the links represent distances (in miles), and the objective is to find the shortest path from the origin to the destination.

This problem also can be formulated as a BIP model involving both mutually exclusive alternatives and contingent decisions. Formulate and solve this BIP model on a spreadsheet. Identify the constraints for (1) mutually exclusive alternatives and (2) contingent decisions.

7.9. Read the referenced article that fully describes the management science study summarized in the application vignette presented in Section 7.4. Briefly describe how BIP and related techniques were applied in this study. Then list the various financial and nonfinancial benefits that resulted from this study.

7.10. Speedy Delivery provides two-day delivery service of large parcels across the United States. Each morning at each collection center, the parcels that have arrived overnight are loaded onto several trucks for delivery throughout the area. Since the competitive battlefield in this business is speed of delivery, the parcels are divided among the trucks according to their geographical destinations to minimize the average time needed to make the deliveries.

On this particular morning, the dispatcher for the Blue River Valley Collection Center, Sharon Lofton, is hard at work. Her three drivers will be arriving in less than an hour to make the day's deliveries. There are nine parcels to be delivered, all at locations many miles apart. As usual, Sharon has loaded these locations into her computer. She is using her company's special software package, a decision support system called Dispatcher. The first thing Dispatcher does is use these locations to generate a considerable number of attractive possible routes for the individual delivery trucks. These routes are shown in the table below (where the numbers in each column indicate the order of the deliveries), along with the estimated time required to traverse the route.

Dispatcher is an interactive system that shows these routes to Sharon for her approval or modification. (For example, the

Delivery Location	**Attractive Possible Route**									
	1	**2**	**3**	**4**	**5**	**6**	**7**	**8**	**9**	**10**
A	1				1				1	
B		2		1		2			2	2
C			3	3			3		3	
D	2					1		1		
E				2	2	3				
F		1			2					
G	3						1	2		3
H				1	3					1
I		3		4			2			
Time (in hours)	6	4	7	5	4	6	5	3	7	6

computer may not know that flooding has made a particular route infeasible.) After Sharon approves these routes as attractive possibilities with reasonable time estimates, Dispatcher next formulates and solves a BIP model for selecting three routes that minimize their total time while including each delivery location on exactly one route.

E*   *a.* Using the data in the table, demonstrate how Dispatcher can formulate and solve this BIP model on a spreadsheet.

   b. Describe how the problem addressed in part *a* is analogous to the crew scheduling problem described in Section 7.4.

E*7.11. An increasing number of Americans are moving to a warmer climate when they retire. To take advantage of this trend, Sunny Skies Unlimited is undertaking a major real-estate development project. The project is to develop a completely new retirement community (to be called Pilgrim Haven) that will cover several square miles. One of the decisions to be made is where to locate the two paramedic stations that have been allocated to the community to respond to medical emergencies. For planning purposes, Pilgrim Haven has been divided into five tracts, with no more than one paramedic station to be located in any given tract. Each station is to respond to *all* the medical emergencies that occur in the tract in which it is located as well as in the other tracts that are assigned to this station. Thus, the decisions to be made consist of (1) the tracts to receive a paramedic station and (2) the assignment of each of the other tracts to one of the paramedic stations. The objective is to minimize the overall average of the *response times* to medical emergencies.

The following table gives the average response time to a medical emergency in each tract (the rows) if that tract is served by a station in a given tract (the columns). The last column gives the forecasted average number of medical emergencies that will occur in each of the tracts per day.

station to minimize the total cost of stations while ensuring that each tract has at least one station close enough to respond to a medical emergency in no more than 15 minutes. In contrast to the original problem, note that the total number of paramedic stations is no longer fixed. Furthermore, if a tract without a station has more than one station within 15 minutes, it is no longer necessary to assign this tract to just one of these stations.

   a. Formulate the algebraic form of a pure BIP model with five binary variables for this problem.

E*   *b.* Display and solve this model on a spreadsheet.

7.13.   Reconsider the Southwestern Airways crew scheduling problem presented in Section 7.4. Because of a blizzard in the Chicago area, all the flights into and out of Chicago (including flights 4, 6, 7, and 9 in Table 7.5) have been canceled for the time being, so a new crew scheduling plan needs to be developed to cover the seven remaining flights in Table 7.5.

The 12 feasible sequences of flights still are the ones shown in Table 7.5 after deleting the canceled flights. When flights into and out of Chicago had originally been part of a sequence, a crew now would fly as passengers on a Southwestern Airways flight to the next city in the sequence to cover the remaining flights in the sequence. For example, flight sequence 4 now would be San Francisco to Los Angeles to Denver to San Francisco, where a crew would fly as passengers on a flight from Los Angeles to Denver (not shown in the table) to enable serving as the crew from Denver to San Francisco. (Since the original sequence 5 included a round-trip from Denver to Chicago and back, a crew assigned to this sequence now would simply lay over in Denver to await the flight from Denver to San Francisco.) The cost of assigning a crew to any sequence still would be the same as shown in the bottom row of Table 7.5.

The objective still is to minimize the total cost of the crew assignments that cover all the flights. The fact that only 7 flights

		Fire Station in Tract					Average Frequency of Medical Emergencies per Day
		1	**2**	**3**	**4**	**5**	
Response	**1**	5	20	15	25	10	2
times (min.)	**2**	12	4	20	15	25	1
to a medical	**3**	30	15	6	25	15	3
emergency	**4**	20	10	15	4	12	1
in tract	**5**	15	25	12	10	5	3

Formulate and solve a BIP model on a spreadsheet for this problem. Identify any constraints that correspond to mutually exclusive alternatives or contingent decisions.

7.12.   Reconsider Problem 7.11. The management of Sunny Skies Unlimited now has decided that the decision regarding the locations of the paramedic stations should be based mainly on costs.

The cost of locating a paramedic station in a tract is $200,000 for tract 1, $250,000 for tract 2, $400,000 for tract 3, $300,000 for tract 4, and $500,000 for tract 5. Management's objective now is to determine which tracts should receive a

now need to be covered instead of 11 increases the chance that fewer than three crews will need to be assigned to a flight sequence this time. (The flights where these crews fly as passengers do not need to be covered since they already are assigned to crews that are not based in San Francisco.)

   a. Formulate a BIP model in algebraic form for this problem.

E*   *b.* Formulate and solve this problem on a spreadsheet.

7.14.   Yakima Construction Corporation (YCC) is considering a number of different development projects. The cash outflows that would be required to complete each project are indicated in the table below, along with the expected net present value of each project (all values in millions of dollars).

	Project				
	1	**2**	**3**	**4**	**5**
Year 1	$ 8	$10	$12	$4	$14
Year 2	6	8	6	3	6
Year 3	3	7	6	2	5
Year 4	0	5	6	0	7
NPV	$12	$15	$20	$9	$23

Each project must be done in full (with the corresponding cash flows for all four years) or not done at all. Furthermore, there are the following additional considerations. Project 1 cannot be done unless Project 2 is also undertaken, and projects 3 and 4 would compete with each other, so they should not both be chosen. YCC expects to have the following cash available to invest in these projects: $40 million for year 1, $25 million for year 2, $16 million for year 3, and $12 million for year 4. Any available money not spent in a given year is then available to spend the following year. YCC's policy is to choose their projects so as to maximize their total expected NPV.

    a. Formulate a BIP model in algebraic form for this problem.

E*   *b.* Formulate and solve this model on a spreadsheet.

7.15.   Read the referenced article that fully describes the management science study summarized in the application vignette presented in Section 7.5. Briefly describe how mixed BIP was applied in this study. Then list the various financial and nonfinancial benefits that resulted from this study.

7.16.   An electrical utility needs to generate 6,500 megawatts of electricity today. It has five generators. If any electricity is generated by a given generator, that generator must be started up and a fixed start-up cost is incurred. There is an additional cost for each megawatt generated by a generator. These costs, as well as the maximum capacity of each generator, are shown in the following table. The objective is to determine the minimum cost plan that meets the electrical needs for today.

    a. Formulate a BIP model in algebraic form for this problem.

E*   *b.* Formulate and solve this model on a spreadsheet.

7.17.   The school board for the Bellevue School District has made the decision to purchase 1,350 additional Macintosh computers for computer laboratories in all its schools. Based on past experience, the school board also has directed that these computers should be purchased from some combination of three companies—Educomp, Macwin, and McElectronics. In all three cases, the companies charge a discounted variable cost per computer and a fixed delivery and installation cost for these large sales to school districts. The table below shows these charges as well as the capacity (the maximum number of computers that can be sold from the limited inventory) for each of the companies.

	Educomp	**Macwin**	**McElectronics**
Capacity	700	700	1,000
Fixed cost	$45,000	$35,000	$50,000
Variable cost	$750	$775	$700

    The school board wants to determine the minimum-cost plan for meeting its computer needs.

    a. Formulate a BIP model in algebraic form for this problem.

E*   *b.* Formulate and solve this model on a spreadsheet.

E*   *c.* Now suppose that Macwin has not submitted its final bid yet, so the per computer cost is not known with certainty. Generate a parameter analysis report with RSPE to show the optimal order quantities and total cost of the optimal solution when the cost per computer for Macwin is $680, $690, $700, $710, . . . , $790, or $800.

E*7.18.   Noble Amazon sells books online. Management is trying to determine the best sites for the company's warehouses. The five potential sites under consideration are listed in the first column of the table at the bottom of the page. Most of the sales come from customers in the United States. The average weekly demand from each region of the country, the average shipping

	Generator				
	A	**B**	**C**	**D**	**E**
Fixed start-up cost	$3,000	$2,000	$2,500	$1,500	$1,000
Cost per megawatt/day generated	$5	$4	$6	$6	$7
Maximum capacity (MW/day)	2,100	1,800	2,500	1,500	3,000

Warehouse Site	Average Shipping Cost ($/book)					Fixed Cost (per week)	Warehouse Capacity (books/week)
	Northwest	**Southwest**	**Midwest**	**Southeast**	**Northeast**		
Spokane, WA	$2.40	$3.50	$4.80	$6.80	$5.75	$40,000	20,000
Reno, NV	$3.25	$2.30	$3.40	$5.25	$6.00	$30,000	20,000
Omaha, NE	$4.05	$3.25	$2.85	$4.30	$4.75	$25,000	15,000
Harrisburg, PA	$5.25	$6.05	$4.30	$3.25	$2.75	$40,000	25,000
Jacksonville, FL	$6.95	$5.85	$4.80	$2.10	$3.50	$30,000	15,000
Customer demand (per week)	8,000	12,000	9,000	14,000	17,000		

cost from each warehouse site to each region of the country, the fixed cost per week of each warehouse if it is operated, and the maximum capacity of each warehouse (if it is operated) are shown in the table. Formulate and solve a mixed BIP model in a spreadsheet to determine which warehouse sites Noble Amazon should operate and how books should be distributed from each warehouse to each region of the country to minimize total cost.

E*7.19. Aberdeen Computer Corp. (ACC) is located in Aberdeen, Washington. The company has developed the WebSurfer, a low-cost e-mail and Web-surfing appliance. This product is manufactured at four plants, located in Atlanta, Kansas City, Aberdeen, and Austin. After production, the WebSurfers are shipped to three warehouses, located in Nashville, San Jose, and Houston. ACC sells the WebSurfers through the retail channel. In particular, five different retailers currently sell the WebSurfer—Sears, Best Buy, Fry's, Comp USA, and Office Max. ACC makes weekly shipments to the main warehouses of these five retailers. The shipping cost from each plant to each warehouse, along with the production cost and weekly production capacity at each plant, are given in the table below.

production and distribution of the WebSurfer from the various plants, through the warehouses, to the customers that will minimize total costs.

Plant	Fixed Cost ($/week)
Atlanta	$8,000
Kansas City	$9,000
Aberdeen	$9,000
Austin	$10,000

Warehouse	Fixed Cost ($/week)
Nashville	$4,000
San Jose	$5,000
Houston	$5,000

b. Now suppose that ACC is considering saving money by closing some of its production facilities

	Shipping Cost ($/unit)			Production	Capacity
Plant	Nashville	San Jose	Houston	Cost ($/unit)	(units/week)
Atlanta	$30	$40	$50	$208	200
Kansas City	$25	$45	$40	$214	300
Aberdeen	$45	$30	$55	$215	300
Austin	$30	$50	$30	$210	400

The shipping cost from each warehouse to each customer, the variable cost (cost per unit moved through the warehouse), the capacity (maximum number of units that can be moved through the warehouse per week) for each warehouse, and the weekly demand for each customer are given in the table below.

and/or warehouses. Suppose there is a fixed cost to operate each plant and each warehouse as indicated in the tables above. Add binary variables to your model in part *a* to incorporate the decision of which plants and warehouses to keep open so as to

	Shipping Cost ($/unit)					Variable	
Warehouse	Sears	Best Buy	Fry's	Comp USA	Office Max	Cost ($/unit)	Capacity (units/week)
Nashville	$40	$45	$30	$25	$20	$4	300
San Jose	$15	$50	$25	$15	$40	$5	500
Houston	$50	$35	$15	$40	$50	$5	500
Customer demand (per week)	100	50	75	300	150		

a. Formulate and solve a linear programming model in a spreadsheet to determine the plan for weekly

minimize total cost (including the fixed costs for any plant or warehouse that is operated).

CD S7-1-1

SUPPLEMENT 1 TO CHAPTER 7
ADVANCED FORMULATION TECHNIQUES FOR
BINARY INTEGER PROGRAMMING

Chapter 7 gives various examples of how yes-or-no decisions can arise. Each such decision is represented by a *binary decision variable* in a binary integer programming (BIP) model.

In addition to any such binary decision variables, other binary variables sometimes are introduced simply to help formulate the model. Here is the terminology to distinguish between the two kinds of binary variables.

> A **binary decision variable** is a binary variable that represents a yes-or-no decision. An **auxiliary binary variable** is an additional binary variable that is introduced into the model, not to represent a yes-or-no decision, but simply to help formulate the model as a (pure or mixed) BIP problem. Auxiliary binary variables will be denoted by $y_1, y_2, \ldots$.

This supplement to Chapter 7 illustrates some of the ways in which auxiliary binary variables can play a crucial role in being able to formulate the model to fit a standard problem so that the model can be solved. To facilitate focusing on the role of the auxiliary binary variables, the first two examples are variations of the familiar Wyndor Glass Co. problem introduced in Section 2.1 and formulated as a linear programming model on a spreadsheet in Section 2.2. To further refresh your memory, Figure 1 shows the graphical solution originally developed in Section 2.4 for this problem, where the symbol P represents the weekly profit in dollars.

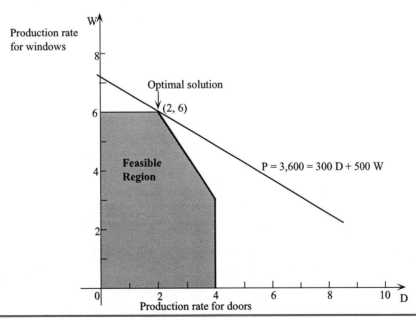

Figure 1   This graph summarizes the presentation in Section 2.4 of the application of the graphical method to the original Wyndor problem.

This original Wyndor problem has no yes-or-no decisions and so no binary decision variables. However, each of the two variations presented below introduces a complication that can be overcome by using auxiliary binary variables to formulate a model that can be readily solved. (Because the Wyndor problem has only two decision variables, we will be able to use graphical analysis to help introduce and analyze each variation before showing how auxiliary binary variables can be used with any number of decision variables.).

Example 1: The Wyndor Problem with Mutually Exclusive Products

Change for Example 1: The two potential new products (doors and windows) would compete for the same customers. Therefore, management has decided not to produce both of them together. At most one can be chosen for production, so

either $D = 0$ or $W = 0$ (or both)

Thus, we now are dealing with *mutually exclusive products*.

Figure 2 shows the feasible region for this problem, namely, the line segment from (0, 0) to (4, 0) and the line segment from (0, 0) to (0, 6). These are the only solutions from the feasible region for the original problem for which either $x_1 = 0$ or $x_2 = 0$. For this tiny problem, it can be seen from the figure that the feasible solution that maximizes P (i.e., the optimal solution) is

$$(D, W) = (0, 6) \quad \text{with} \quad P = 3,000$$

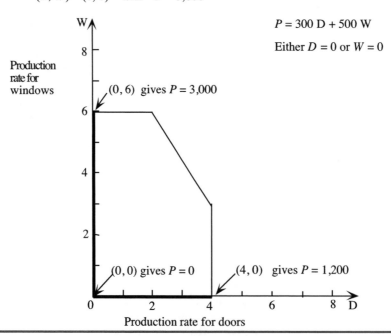

Figure 2   The dark line segments show the feasible solutions for Example 1.

Linear or integer programming models do not permit an *either-or-restriction* such as *either D = 0 or W = 0*. How can we rewrite this restriction in a standard form to fit such a model so that the model can be solved by available algorithms (including those in Solver)?

As illustrated by the case study in Section 7.1, if D and W were binary variables, we would only need to rewrite the restriction that the two products are mutually exclusive alternatives as $D + W = 1$. However, D and W represent production rates that can take on various values besides 0 and 1, so this constraint does not work.

Now watch auxiliary binary variables come to the rescue.

CD S7-1-3

Formulation with Auxiliary Binary Variables

For each product, there are just two possibilities regarding the decision of whether it can be produced. Either it can or it cannot. Therefore, we can associate each of the two values of an auxiliary binary variable with one of these possibilities. Specifically, let the auxiliary binary variables be

$$y_1 = \begin{cases} 1, & \text{if } D > 0 \text{ can hold (can produce doors)} \\ 0, & \text{if } D = 0 \text{ must hold (cannot produce doors)} \end{cases}$$

$$y_2 = \begin{cases} 1, & \text{if } W > 0 \text{ can hold (can produce windowss)} \\ 0, & \text{if } W = 0 \text{ must hold (cannot produce windows)} \end{cases}$$

The relationships between y_1 and D, as well as between y_2 and W, are identical to the ones shown in Section 7.5 for another variation of the Wyndor problem.. Therefore, proceeding as in Figure 7.8 (including using the safely large coefficient of 99). Figure 3 demonstrates that the analogous constraints involving these variables, UnitsProduced (C13:D13) ≤ OnlyIfProduce (C15:D15) and Produce? (C16:D16) = binary, can be used to ensure that these relationships hold. To make the products mutually exclusive, we now add the usual kind of constraint for mutually exclusive alternatives with regard to these two binary variables,

$$y_1 + y_2 \leq 1$$

which gives the constraint, TotalProduced (E16) ≤ MaximumToProduce (G16), in the spreadsheet model. This forces either C16 = 0 or D16 = 0 (or both).

CD S7-1-4

	A	B	C	D	E	F	G
1		**Wyndor Glass Co. with Mutually Exclusive Products**					
2							
3			Doors	Windows			
4		Unit Profit	$300	$500			
5							
6					Hours		Hours
7			Hours Used Per Unit Produced		Used		Available
8		Plant 1	1	0	0	<=	4
9		Plant 2	0	2	12	<=	12
10		Plant 3	3	2	12	<=	18
11							
12			Doors	Windows			
13		Units Produced	0	6			
14			<=	<=	Total		Maximum
15		Only If Produce	0	99	Produced		To Produce
16		Produce?	0	1	1	<=	1
17							
18							Total Profit
19							$3,000

Solver Parameters

Set Objective Cell: TotalProfit
To: Max
By Changing (Variable) Cells:
  UnitsProduced, Produce?
Subject to the Constraints:
  Produce? = binary
  HoursUsed <= HoursAvailable
  TotalProduced <= MaximumToProduce
  UnitsProduced <= OnlyIfProduce

Solver Options:
  Make Variables Nonnegative
  Solving Method: Simplex LP

Range Name	Cells
HoursAvailable	G8:G10
HoursUsed	E8:E10
HoursUsedPerUnitProduced	C8:D10
MaximumToProduce	G16
OnlyIfProduce	C15:D15
Produce?	C16:D16
TotalProduced	E16
TotalProfit	G19
UnitProfit	C4:D4
UnitsProduced	C13:D13

	E
6	Hours
7	Used
8	=SUMPRODUCT(C8:D8,UnitsProduced)
9	=SUMPRODUCT(C9:D9,UnitsProduced)
10	=SUMPRODUCT(C10:D10,UnitsProduced)

	B	C	D
15	Only If Produce	=99*C16	=99*D16

	E
14	Total
15	Produced
16	=SUM(Produce?)

	G
18	Total Profit
19	=SUMPRODUCT(UnitProfit,UnitsProduced)

Figure 3   A spreadsheet model for Example 1, where Solver provides the optimal solution shown in the changing cells, UnitsProduced (C13:D13) and Produce? (C16:D16).

CD S7-1-5

These are the only new constraints needed along with the constraints of the original model. Since D and W are *production rates*, these variables do not need to have integer values, so the model in Figure 3 is a mixed BIP model.

There are no extra costs associated with any values of y_1 and y_2. The original objective function, without y_1 and y_2, still applies, as indicated by the equation entered into the objective cell TotalProfit (G19).

Solver gives the optimal solution shown in the changing cells, namely, the windows are the product chosen to be produced, and then they are produced at the maximum rate ($W = 6$) allowed by the original constraints.

For such a small problem, we were able to find this optimal solution from Figure 3 without introducing auxiliary binary variables. However, auxiliary binary variables become necessary when dealing with larger problems. For example, if this pair of mutually exclusive products is just part of a larger group of products under consideration, then the larger model would need to add the constraints involving y_1 and y_2.

You will see this same approach included again later in Example 3 when there are *three* potential new products and *at most two* can be chosen to be produced.

Example 2: The Wyndor Problem with Either-Or Constraints

Now suppose that the only change from the original Wyndor problem is the one spelled out below.

> **Change for Example 2:** The company has just opened a new plant (plant 4) that is similar to plant 3, so the new plant can perform the same operations as plant 3 to help produce the two new products (doors and windows). However, for administrative reasons, management wants just one of the plants to be chosen to work on these products. The plant chosen should be the one that provides the most profitable product mix.

Table 1 gives the data for this problem. This table is identical to Table 2.1 for the original problem except for the addition of the data for plant 4. Although the hours of production time are different for plants 3 and 4 (because of differences in the types of production facilities being used), the costs of the operations for each product are essentially the same for the two plants. Therefore, the unit profits in the last row of the table are unaffected by the choice of which plant to use for these products.

Table 1   **Data for Example 2**

Plant	Production Time Used for Each Unit Produced (Hours)		Production Time Available per Week (Hours)
	Doors	Windows	
1	1	0	4
2	0	2	12
3	3	2	18
4	2	4	28
Unit Profit	$300	$500	

The data for plant 4 indicate that if this plant is chosen, then we must satisfy the constraint

$$2D + 4W \leq 28$$

when solving for the most profitable product mix. However, if plant 3 is chosen instead, then this constraint is irrelevant and we must instead satisfy the original constraint for plant 3,

$$3D + 2W \leq 18$$

In other words, the relevant restriction is the following pair of **either-or constraints:**

$$\text{Either} \quad 3D + 2W \leq 18$$
$$\text{Or} \quad 2D + 4W \leq 28$$

Choosing one of these two constraints as the one that must be satisfied corresponds to choosing one of the two plants to help produce the doors and windows. The choice of which plant depends on which one allows the largest total profit when considering all the constraints of the model.

Figure 4 shows the effect of these two choices. If plant 3 were chosen to help produce these two products (so $3D + 2W \leq 18$ is relevant but $2D + 4W \leq 28$ is not), then we would have the linear programming problem on the left side of the figure. Since this problem is identical to the original Wyndor problem shown in Figure 1, the best available solution would be

$$(D, W) = (2, 6) \quad \text{with} \quad P = 3{,}600$$

However, if plant 4 were chosen instead (so $2D + 4W \leq 28$ is relevant but $3D + 2W \leq 18$ is not), then we would have the linear programming problem on the right side of the figure. The best available solution for this problem would be

$$(D, W) = (4, 5) \quad \text{with} \quad P = 3{,}700$$

Since $P = 3{,}700$ is larger than $P = 3{,}600$, the largest possible weekly profit is $3,700, which is only obtainable by choosing plant 4 instead of plant 3 to help produce the two new products.

CD S7-1-7

(a) Choose Plant 3

(b) Choose Plant 4

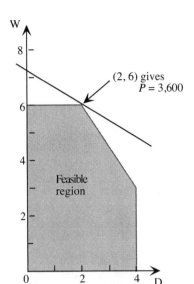

(2, 6) gives
$P = 3,600$

Feasible
region

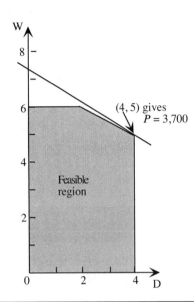

(4, 5) gives
$P = 3,700$

Feasible
region

Figure 4   These two graphs for Example 2 show the linear programming problem and its optimal solution that would result if the plant chosen to help produce the two new products were (*a*) plant 3 or (*b*) plant 4.

Despite its either-or constraints, we have just managed to solve the complete model for variation 3 by solving and comparing two linear programming problems. However, solving larger models with several pairs of either-or constraints in this way would require solving and comparing numerous linear programming problems. We would much prefer to be able to apply a standard algorithm (such as those used by Solver) just once to solve the model.

Unfortunately, the model for Example 2 is not a linear programming model, since either-or constraints are not allowed in linear or integer programming. In fact, this model does not fit the format for *any* kind of standard model. Therefore, we cannot use a standard algorithm once to find an optimal solution for this model in its current form.

How can we reformulate this model into a standard format where a standard algorithm can be used one time to find an optimal solution? Once again, auxiliary binary variables come to the rescue.

Formulation with an Auxiliary Binary Variable

There are just two possibilities: either $3D + 2W \leq 18$ must hold (due to choosing plant 3) or $2D + 4W \leq 28$ must hold (due to choosing plant 4). Therefore, we can introduce an auxiliary binary variable y to indicate which possibility is chosen by defining y as

$$y = \begin{cases} 1, & \text{if } 2D + 4W \leq 28 \text{ must hold (choose plant 4)} \\ 0, & \text{if } 3D + 2W \leq 18 \text{ must hold (choose plant 3)} \end{cases}$$

This definition is enforced by introducing an extremely large positive number (we will use 99 again) and then making the following changes in the model.

	Replace	by
Either	$3D + 2W \leq 18$	$3D + 2W \leq 18 + 99y$
Or	$2D + 4W \leq 28$	$2D + 4W \leq 28 + 99(1 - y)$
		y is binary

To see why these new constraints work, check what happens when $y = 0$.

$y = 0$ gives $3D + 2W \leq 18$

and $2D + 4W \leq 28 + 99$ (a relatively huge number)

so

$3D + 2W \leq 18$ must hold

but $2D + 4W \leq 28$ does not need to hold

Since the other constraints in the model prevent $2D + 4W$ from being much larger than 28, having $y = 0$ give $2D + 4W \leq 28 + 99$ has the same effect as eliminating this constraint from the model. Similarly,

$y = 1$ gives $3D + 2W \leq 18 + 99$ (a relatively huge number)

and $2D + 4W \leq 28$

so

$3D + 2W \leq 18$ does not need to hold

but $2D + 4W \leq 28$ must hold

Again, adding 99 to the right-hand side of $3D + 2W \leq 18$ is equivalent to eliminating the constraint.

Figure 5 shows how this approach can be incorporated into a spreadsheet model. An additional changing cell (E16) displays the value of y. As indicated in the figure by the equations entered into cells G10 and G11, these cells give the modified right-hand sides of the plants 3 and 4 constraints that result from the value of y. With the constraints included in the Solver dialog box, we now have a mixed BIP model that can be solved by Solver.

Clicking on the Solve button causes Solver to simultaneously choose the value of y and the production rates (D and W) that maximize the total profit given in the objective cell TotalProfit (H14). Since $y = 1$ in this optimal solution, plant 4 should be chosen to help produce the new products, with $D = 4$ and $W = 5$. This choice of plant provides a weekly profit of \$3,700 rather than the \$3,600 obtainable by choosing plant 3 instead.

CD S7-1-9

	A	B	C	D	E	F	G	H
1		**Wyndor Glass Co. Problem with Either-Or Constraints**						
2								
3			Doors	Windows				
4		Unit Profit	$300	$500				
5							Modified	
6					Hours		Hours	Hours
7			Hours Used Per Unit Produced		Used		Available	Available
8		Plant 1	1	0	4	<=	4	4
9		Plant 2	0	2	10	<=	12	12
10		Plant 3	3	2	22	<=	117	18
11		Plant 4	2	4	28	<=	28	28
12								
13			Doors	Windows				
14		Units Produced	4	5			Total Profit	$3,700
15								
16		Which Plant to Use? (0=Plant 3, 1=Plant 4)			1			

<table>
<tr><td colspan="2">

Solver Parameters

Set Objective Cell: TotalProfit
To: Max
By Changing Variable Cells:
    UnitsProduced, WhichPlantToUse?
Subject to the Constraints:
    WhichPlantToUse? = binary
    HoursUsed <= ModifiedHoursAvailable

Solver Options:
    Make Variables Nonnegative
    Solving Method: Simplex LP
</td></tr>
</table>

Range Name	Cells
HoursAvailable	H8:H11
HoursUsed	E8:E11
HoursUsedPerUnitProduced	C8:D11
ModifiedHoursAvailable	G8:G11
TotalProfit	H14
UnitProfit	C4:D4
UnitsProduced	C14:D14
WhichPlantToUse?	E16

	E	F	G
5			Modified
6	Hours		Hours
7	Used		Available
8	=SUMPRODUCT(C8:D8,UnitsProduced)	<=	=H8
9	=SUMPRODUCT(C9:D9,UnitsProduced)	<=	=H9
10	=SUMPRODUCT(C10:D10,UnitsProduced)	<=	=H10+99*WhichPlantToUse?
11	=SUMPRODUCT(C11:D11,UnitsProduced)	<=	=H11+99*(1-WhichPlantToUse?)

	G	H
14	Total Profit	=SUMPRODUCT(UnitProfit,UnitsProduced)

Figure 5   A spreadsheet model for Example 2, where Solver gives the optimal solution shown in the changing cells, UnitsProduced (C14:D14) and WhichPlantToUse? (E16).

Example 3: Imposing Managerial Restrictions

The Research and Development Division of the Good Products Company has developed three possible new products. However, to avoid undue diversification of the company's product line, management has imposed the following restriction:

> **Restriction 1:** From the three possible new products, *at most two* should be chosen to be produced.

Each of these products can be produced in either of two plants. For administrative reasons, management has imposed a second restriction in this regard:

> **Restriction 2:** Just one of the two plants should be chosen to be the sole producer of the new products.

The production cost per unit of each product would be essentially the same in the two plants. However, because of differences in their production facilities, the number of hours of production time needed per unit of each product might differ between the two plants. These data are given in Table 2 along with other relevant information, including marketing estimates of the number of units of each product that could be sold per week if it is produced. According to management, the objective is to choose the products, the plant, and the production rates of the chosen products so as to maximize the total profit.

Table 2 Data for Example 3 (The Good Products Co. Problem)

Plant	Production Time Used for Each Unit Produced (Hours)			Production Time Available per Week (Hours)
	Product 1	Product 2	Product 3	
1	3	4	2	30
2	4	6	2	40
Unit Profit	5	7	3	($thousands)
Sales potential	7	5	9	(units per week)

In some ways, this problem resembles a standard *product-mix problem* such as the Wyndor Glass Co. case study described in Section 2.1. In fact, if we changed the problem by dropping the two restrictions *and* by requiring each unit of a product to use the production hours given in Table 2 in *both plants* (so the two plants now perform different operations needed by the products), it would become just such a problem. In particular, let x_1, x_2, and x_3 be the production rates of the respective products. Displaying the values of these decision variables in changing cells UnitsProduced (C12:E12), the spreadsheet model then would become the one shown in rows 1–13 and 15 of Figure 6 if column H and the other rows were omitted except for TotalProfit (H21). MaximumSales (C15:E15) provides upper bounds on the production rates for the three products, so

$$x_1 \le 7, \qquad x_2 \le 5, \qquad x_3 \le 9$$

are needed as constraints in the model.

CD S7-1-11

	A	B	C	D	E	F	G	H	I
1		**Good Products Co. with Managerial Restrictions**							
2									
3			Product 1	Product 2	Product 3				
4		Unit Profit ($thousands)	5	7	3				
5								Modified	
6						Hours		Hours	Hours
7			Hours Used Per Unit Produced			Used		Available	Available
8		Plant 1	3	4	2	34.5	<=	129	30
9		Plant 2	4	6	2	40	<=	40	40
10									
11			Product 1	Product 2	Product 3				
12		Units Produced	5.5	0	9				
13			<=	<=	<=				
14		Only If Produce	7	0	9				
15		Maximum Sales	7	5	9	Total		Maximum	
16						Produced		To Produce	
17		Produce?	1	0	1	2	<=	2	
18									
19								Total Profit	
20								($thousands)	
21		Which Plant to Use? (0=Plant 1, 1=Plant 2)			1			54.5	

Set Objective Cell: TotalProfit
To: Max
By Changing Variable Cells:
    UnitsProduced, Produce?, WhichPlantToUse?
Subject to the Constraints:
    Produce? = binary
    WhichPlantToUse? = binary
    HoursUsed <= ModifiedHoursAvailable
    TotalProduced <= MaximumToProduce
    UnitsProduced <= OnlyIfProduce

Solver Options:
    Make Variables Nonnegative
    Solving Method: Simplex LP

Range Name	Cells
HoursAvailable	I8:I9
HoursUsed	F8:F9
HoursUsedPerUnitProduced	C8:E9
MaximumSales	C15:E15
MaximumToProduce	H17
ModifiedHoursAvailable	H8:H9
OnlyIfProduce	C14:E14
Produce?	C17:E17
TotalProduced	F17
TotalProfit	H21
UnitProfit	C4:E4
UnitsProduced	C12:E12
WhichPlantToUse?	E21

	F	G	H
5			Modified
6	Hours		Hours
7	Used		Available
8	=SUMPRODUCT(C8:E8,UnitsProduced)	<=	=I8+99*WhichPlantToUse?
9	=SUMPRODUCT(C9:E9,UnitsProduced)	<=	=I9+99*(1-WhichPlantToUse?)

	B	C	D	E
14	Only If Produce	=C15*C17	=D15*D17	=E15*E17

	F
15	Total
16	Produced
17	=SUM(Produce?)

	H
19	Total Profit
20	($thousands)
21	=SUMPRODUCT(UnitProfit,UnitsProduced)

Figure 6   A spreadsheet formulation of the BIP model for the Good Products Co. problem, where Solver provides the optimal solution given in the changing cells, UnitsProduced (C12:E12), Produce? (C17:E17), and WhichPlanToUse? (E21)

For the real problem, however, restriction 1 necessitates adding to the model the constraint:

No more than two of the decision variables (x_1, x_2, x_3) can have a value greater than zero.

This constraint does not fit into a linear or integer programming format, so the key question is how to convert it to such a format so that a corresponding algorithm can be used to solve the overall model. If the decision variables were binary variables, then the constraint would be expressed in this format as $x_1 + x_2 + x_3 \leq 2$. However, with *continuous* decision variables, a more complicated approach involving the introduction of auxiliary binary variables is needed.

Restriction 2 necessitates replacing the first two functional constraints ($3x_1 + 4x_2 + 2x_3 \leq 30$ and $4x_1 + 6x_2 + 2x_3 \leq 40$) by the restriction

$$\text{Either} \quad 3x_1 + 4x_2 + 2x_3 \leq 30$$

$$\text{Or} \quad 4x_1 + 6x_2 + 2x_3 \leq 40$$

must hold, where the choice of which constraint must hold corresponds to the choice of which plant will be used to produce the new products. Example 2 illustrated how such either-or constraints can be converted to a linear or integer programming format, again with the help of an auxiliary binary variable.

Formulation with Auxiliary Binary Variables

Except for involving more products and choices, restriction 1 is similar to the restriction imposed in Example 1. For Example 1, there were just *two* new products, and the restriction was that *at most one* could be chosen to be produced. Following the formulation approach used there, we can deal with restriction 1 by introducing *three* auxiliary binary variables (y_1, y_2, y_3) with the interpretation that

$$y_j = \begin{cases} 1, & \text{if } x_j > 0 \text{ can hold (can produce product } j) \\ 0, & \text{if } x_j = 0 \text{ must hold (cannot produce product } j) \end{cases}$$

for $j = 1, 2, 3$. To enforce this interpretation in the model, we replace the constraints on the maximum production rates of the three products—$x_1 \leq 7$, $x_2 \leq 5$, and $x_3 \leq 9$—by the new constraints,

$$x_1 \leq 7y_1, \qquad x_2 \leq 5y_2, \qquad x_3 \leq 9y_3$$

Therefore, $y_1 = 1$ allows any feasible value of x_1, whereas $y_1 = 0$ forces $x_1 = 0$, and both y_2 and y_3 have the same effect on x_2 and x_3, respectively. We also add the constraints,

$$y_1 + y_2 + y_3 \leq 2$$

$$y_j \text{ is binary}, \quad \text{for } j = 1, 2, 3$$

Consequently, when these constraints force choosing at most two of the y_j to equal 1, this amounts to choosing at most two of the new products as the ones that can be produced.

To deal with restriction 2, we use the same approach as for Example 2. Therefore, we introduce another auxiliary binary variable y_4 with the interpretation that

$$y_4 = \begin{cases} 1, & \text{if } 4x_1 + 6x_2 + 2x_3 \leq 40 \text{ must hold (choose plant 2)} \\ 0, & \text{if } 3x_1 + 4x_2 + 2x_3 \leq 30 \text{ must hold (choose plant 1)} \end{cases}$$

CD S7-1-13

This interpretation is enforced by adding the constraints

$$3x_1 + 4x_2 + 2x_3 \le 30 + 99y_4$$

$$4x_1 + 6x_2 + 2x_3 \le 40 + 99(1 - y_4)$$

y_4 is binary

Both column H and rows 13–21 of Figure 6 show how all of this can be incorporated into the spreadsheet model in an intuitive way. The additional changing cells, Produce? (C17:E17) and WhichPlantToUse? (E21), give the values of the four auxiliary binary variables, so all four cells are constrained to be binary. The constraint that TotalProduced (F17) ≤ MaximumToProduce (H17) forces choosing at most two of the new products to be produced. The equations entered into OnlyIfProduce (C14:E14)—as shown at the bottom of the figure—give the values of $7y_1$, $5y_2$, and $9y_3$, so the constraints that UnitsProduced (C12:E12) ≤ OnlyIfProduce (C14:E14) force the production rate of a product to be 0 in row 12 if the decision has been made in row 17 not to produce that product. With the equations that are shown for ModifiedHours Available (H8:H9), the constraints that HoursUsed (F18:F19) ≤ ModifiedHoursAvailable (H8:H9) correspond to the algebraic constraints given at the end of the preceding paragraph.

The spreadsheet model now is a mixed BIP model, with three continuous decision variables [UnitsProduced (C12:E12)] and four auxiliary binary variables [Produce? (C17:E17) and WhichPlantToUse? (E21)], so now the problem is formulated in a form that can be solved. Using Solver gives the optimal solution shown in the changing cells in Figure 6, namely, choose products 1 and 3 to produce, choose plant 2 for the production, and choose the production rates of 5½ units per week for product 1 and 9 units per week for product 3. The resulting total profit given in the objective cell TotalProfit (H21) is $54,500 per week.

Example 4: Violating Proportionality

The Supersuds Corporation is developing its marketing plans for next year's new products. For three of these products, the decision has been made to purchase a total of five TV spots for commercials on national television networks. Each spot will feature a single product. Therefore, the problem on which we will focus is how to allocate the five spots to these three products, with a maximum of three spots (and a minimum of zero) for each product.

Table 3 shows the estimated impact of allocating zero, one, two, or three spots to each product. This impact is measured in terms of the *profit* from the *additional sales* that would result from the spots, considering also the cost of producing the commercial and purchasing the spots. The objective is to allocate five spots to the products so as to maximize the total profit.

This problem is small enough that it can be solved easily by trial and error. (The optimal solution is to allocate two spots to product 1, no spots to product 2, and three spots to product 3.) However, we will show one formulation with auxiliary binary variables for illustrative purposes. Such a formulation would become necessary if this small problem needed to be incorporated into a larger model involving the allocation of resources to marketing activities for all the corporation's new products.

CD S7-1-14

Table 3   Data for Example 4 (the Supersuds Corp. Problem)

Number of TV Spots	Profit (Millions)		
	Product 1	Product 2	Product 3
0	$0	$0	$0
1	1	0	−1
2	3	2	2
3	3	3	4

A Formulation with Auxiliary Binary Variables

A natural formulation would be to let

x_1 = Number of TV spots allocated to product 1

x_2 = Number of TV spots allocated to product 2

x_3 = Number of TV spots allocated to product 3

P = Total profit (in millions of dollars)

The contribution of each of these integer decision variables (x_1, x_2, x_3) to P then would be given by the corresponding column in Table 3. However, each column indicates that profit is *not* proportional to the number of TV spots allocated to that product. Therefore, we cannot write a legitimate objective function in terms of these decision variables to fit integer programming. Using the algebraic form, the best that we can do with these decision variables is to formulate an incomplete integer programming model (not a *binary* integer programming model) that includes all the needed constraints but not an objective function.

$$\text{Maximize } P = ?$$

subject to

$$x_1 \leq 3$$
$$x_2 \leq 3$$
$$x_3 \leq 3$$
$$x_1 + x_2 + x_3 = 5$$

and

$$x_1 \geq 0 \qquad x_2 \geq 0 \qquad x_3 \geq 0$$
$$x_1, x_2, x_3 \text{ are integers}$$

Now see what happens when we introduce nine auxiliary binary variables with the following interpretations:

$$y_{11} = \begin{cases} 1, & \text{if } x_1 = 1 \\ 0, & \text{otherwise} \end{cases} \quad y_{12} = \begin{cases} 1, & \text{if } x_1 = 2 \\ 0, & \text{otherwise} \end{cases} \quad y_{13} = \begin{cases} 1, & \text{if } x_1 = 3 \\ 0, & \text{otherwise} \end{cases}$$

$$y_{21} = \begin{cases} 1, & \text{if } x_2 = 1 \\ 0, & \text{otherwise} \end{cases} \quad y_{22} = \begin{cases} 1, & \text{if } x_2 = 2 \\ 0, & \text{otherwise} \end{cases} \quad y_{23} = \begin{cases} 1, & \text{if } x_2 = 3 \\ 0, & \text{otherwise} \end{cases}$$

$$y_{31} = \begin{cases} 1, & \text{if } x_3 = 1 \\ 0, & \text{otherwise} \end{cases} \quad y_{32} = \begin{cases} 1, & \text{if } x_3 = 2 \\ 0, & \text{otherwise} \end{cases} \quad y_{33} = \begin{cases} 1, & \text{if } x_3 = 3 \\ 0, & \text{otherwise} \end{cases}$$

For example, look at the definitions of y_{11}, y_{12}, and y_{13}. These definitions imply that

$$(y_{11}, y_{12}, y_{13}) = (0, 0, 0) \quad \text{if} \quad x_1 = 0$$

$$(y_{11}, y_{12}, y_{13}) = (1, 0, 0) \quad \text{if} \quad x_1 = 1$$

$$(y_{11}, y_{12}, y_{13}) = (0, 1, 0) \quad \text{if} \quad x_1 = 2$$

$$(y_{11}, y_{12}, y_{13}) = (0, 0, 1) \quad \text{if} \quad x_1 = 3$$

These four alternative values of x_1 are the only possible values. Since these alternative values are mutually exclusive alternatives, y_1, y_2, and y_3 need to satisfy the constraints

$$y_{11} + y_{12} + y_{13} \leq 1$$

$$y_{11}, y_{12}, y_{13} \text{ are binary}$$

Selecting values of y_{11}, y_{12}, and y_{13} that satisfy these constraints is equivalent to selecting a value of x_1 that satisfies the constraints

$$x_1 \leq 3$$

$$x_1 \leq 0$$

$$x_1 \text{ is integer}$$

In just the same way, the other auxiliary binary variables need to satisfy the constraints

$$y_{21} + y_{22} + y_{23} \leq 1$$

$$y_{31} + y_{32} + y_{33} \leq 1$$

$$y_{21}, y_{22}, y_{23}, y_{31}, y_{32}, y_{33} \text{ are binary}$$

Selecting values of these variables that satisfy these constraints is equivalent to selecting values of x_2 and x_3 that satisfy the constraints

$$x_2 \leq 3$$

$$x_3 \leq 3$$

$$x_2 \geq 0, \quad x_3 \geq 0$$

$$x_2, x_3 \text{ are integers}$$

Therefore, we now can formulate a model for the Supersuds problem in terms of these auxiliary binary variables by including the above constraints on these variables. We also need to add a constraint that will ensure that the original constraint,

$$x_1 + x_2 + x_3 = 5$$

still will hold. The key here is to note that the definitions of the auxiliary binary variables imply that

$$x_1 = y_{11} + 2y_{12} + 3y_{13}$$

$$x_2 = y_{21} + 2y_{22} + 3y_{23}$$

$$x_1 = y_{31} + 2y_{32} + 3y_{33}$$

Therefore, the original constraint can be replaced by the constraint

$$y_{11} + 2y_{12} + 3y_{13} + y_{21} + 2y_{22} + 3y_{23} + y_{31} + 2y_{32} + 3y_{33} = 5$$

Finally, we come to the whole reason for bothering with all of this, namely, that the auxiliary binary variables enable us to formulate a legitimate objective function. Using monetary units of millions of dollars, the three profit columns of Table 3 respectively indicate that

$$\text{Profit from product 1} = y_{11} + 3y_{12} + 3y_{13}$$

$$\text{Profit from product 2} = 2y_{22} + 3y_{23}$$

$$\text{Profit from product 3} = -y_{31} + 2y_{32} + 4y_{33}$$

Therefore, adding these three profits, the total profit is

$$P = y_{11} + 3y_{12} + 3y_{13} + 2y_{22} + 3y_{23} - y_{31} + 2y_{32} + 4y_{33}$$

Consequently, the complete BIP model for the Supersuds problem can be formulated on a spreadsheet as shown in Figure 7, where the changing cells Solution (D11:F13) display the values of the auxiliary binary variables. Clicking on the Solve button then provides the optimal solution shown in these changing cells in the figure, namely,

$y_{11} = 0$	$y_{12} = 1$	$y_{13} = 0$	so	$x_1 = 2$	(allocate 2 TV spots to product 1)
$y_{21} = 0$	$y_{22} = 0$	$y_{23} = 0$	so	$x_2 = 0$	(allocate 0 TV spots to product 2)
$y_{31} = 0$	$y_{32} = 0$	$y_{33} = 1$	so	$x_3 = 3$	(allocate 3 TV spots to product 3)

which yields a profit of $P = 7$ ($7 million), according to the objective cell TotalProfit (I13). The number of TV spots being allocated to the respective products is shown in NumberOfSpots (D18:F18).

CD S7-1-17

	A	B	C	D	E	F	G	H	I
1		**Supersuds Corp. Marketing Plan**							
2									
3		**Profit**							
4		**($millions)**		Product 1	Product 2	Product 3			
5		Number	1	1	0	-1			
6		of	2	3	2	2			
7		Spots	3	3	3	4			
8									
9									
10		**Solution**		Product 1	Product 2	Product 3			Total
11		Number	1	0	0	0			Profit
12		of	2	1	0	0			($millions)
13		Spots	3	0	0	1			7
14			Total	1	0	1			
15				<=	<=	<=			
16		Max Of One		1	1	1	Total		Required
17							Spots		Spots
18		Number of Spots		2	0	3	5	=	5

Solver Parameters

Set Objective Cell: TotalProfit
To: Max
By Changing Variable Cells:
  Solution
Subject to the Constraints:
  Solution = binary
  Total <= MaxOfOne
  TotalSpots = RequiredSpots

Solver Options:
  Make Variables Nonnegative
  Solving Method: Simplex LP

Range Name	Cells
MaxOfOne	D16:F16
NumberOfSpots	D18:F18
Profit	D5:F7
RequiredSpots	I18
Solution	D11:F13
Total	D14:F14
TotalProfit	I13
TotalSpots	G18

	I
10	Total
11	Profit
12	($millions)
13	=SUMPRODUCT(Profit,Solution)

	C	D	E	F
14	Total	=SUM(D11:D13)	=SUM(E11:E13)	=SUM(F11:F13)

	C	D	E
18	Number of Spots	=SUMPRODUCT(C11:C13,D11:D13)	=SUMPRODUCT(C11:C13,E11:E13)

	G
16	Total
17	Spots
18	=SUM(NumberOfSpots)

Figure 7   A spreadsheet formulation of the BIP model for the Supersuds problem, where the optimal solution obtained by Solver is given in Solution (D11:F13), which yields NumberOfSpots (D18:F:18).

CD S7-1-18

REVIEW QUESTIONS

1. What is the distinction between a binary decision variable and an auxiliary binary variable?
2. What is meant by *mutually exclusive products?*
3. How can an auxiliary binary variable be defined in terms of whether to allow the production of a certain product?
4. How does an either-or constraint arise in Example 2?
5. When two individual constraints are paired together as either-or constraints, how can an auxiliary binary variable be defined in terms of which one of these individual constraints is chosen as the one that must hold?
6. How does restriction 1 for Example 3 relate to the restriction imposed in Example 1?
7. After introducing auxiliary binary variables for Example 3, what constraint on these variables forces choosing at most two of the possible new products as the ones that can be produced?
8. When using the natural (integer) decision variables (x_1, x_2, x_3) defined for Example 4, why is it not possible to write a legitimate objective function in terms of these decision variables to fit integer programming?
9. What are the groups of mutually exclusive alternatives that arise when introducing the auxiliary binary variables for Example 4?

Glossary

auxiliary binary variable A binary variable that is introduced into the model, not to represent a yes-or-no decision, but simply to help formulate the model as a (pure or mixed) BIP problem.

either-or constraints A pair of constraints such that either one can be chosen to be observed and then the other one would be ignored.

Problems

To the left of the problems (or their parts), we have inserted an E* whenever Excel should be used (unless your instructor give you contrary instructions).

E* 7s.1. The research and Development Division of the Progressing Company has been developing four possible new product lines. Management must now make a decision as to which of these four products actually will be produced and at what levels. Therefore, a management science study has been requested to find the most profitable product mix.

A substantial cost is associated with beginning the production of any product, as given in the first row of the following table. Management's objective is to find the product mix that maximizes the total profit (total net revenue minus start-up costs).

	Product			
	1	**2**	**3**	**4**
Start-up cost	$50,000	$40,000	$70,000	$60,000
Marginal revenue	70	60	90	80

Let the continuous decision variables x_1, x_2, x_3, and x_4 be the total number of units produced of products 1, 2, 3, and 4, respectively. Management has imposed the following policy constraints on these variables:

1. No more than two of the products can be produced.

2. Either product 3 or 4 can be produced only if either product 1 or 2 is produced.

3. Either $5x_1 + 3x_2 + 6x_3 + 4x_4 \leq 6,000$
   or $4x_1 + 6x_2 + 3x_3 + 5x_4 \leq 6,000$

Use auxiliary binary variables to formulate and solve a mixed BIP model on a spreadsheet for this problem.

E* 7s.2. The Toys-R-4-U Company has developed two new toys for possible inclusion in its product line for the upcoming Christmas season. Setting up the production facilities to begin production would cost $50,000 for toy 1 and $80,000 for toy 2. Once these costs are covered, the toys would generate a unit profit of $10 for toy 1 and $15 for toy 2.

The company has two factories that are capable of producing these toys. However, to avoid doubling the start-up costs, just one factory would be used, where the choice would be based on maximizing profit. For administrative reasons, the same factory would be used for both new toys if both are produced.

Toy 1 can be produced at a rate of 50 per hour in factory 1 and 40 per hour in factory 2. Toy 2 can be produced at the rate of 40 per hour in factory 1 and 25 per hour in factory 2. Factories 1 and 2, respectively, have 500 hours and 700 hours of production time available before Christmas that could be used to produce these toys.

It is not known whether these two toys would be continued after Christmas. Therefore, the problem is to determine how many units (if any) of each new toy should be produced before Christmas to maximize the total profit. Formulate and solve a mixed BIP model on a spreadsheet for this problem.

E* 7s.3. Reconsider the Fly-Right Airplane Co. problem introduced in Problem 7.7. A more detailed analysis of the various cost and revenue factors now has revealed that the potential profit from producing airplanes for each customer cannot be expressed simply in terms of a start-up cost and a fixed marginal net revenue per airplane produced. Instead, the profits are given by the following table.

Airplanes Produced	Profit (Millions)		
	Customer 1	Customer 2	Customer 3
0	0	0	0
1	−$1	$1	$1
2	2	5	3
3	4		5
4			6
5			7

Use auxiliary binary variables to formulate and solve a BIP model on a spreadsheet for this new version of the problem.

E* 7s.4. Reconsider Problem 3.6, where the management of the Omega Manufacturing Company is considering devoting excess production capacity to one or more of three products. (See the Partial Answers to Selected Problems in Appendix B in the back of the book for the optimal solution for Problem 3.6.) Management now has decided to add the restriction that no more than two of the three prospective products should be produced. Use auxiliary binary variables to formulate and solve a mixed BIP model on a spreadsheet for this new version of the problem.

E* 7s.5. Consider the following algebraic form of an integer programming model:

$$\text{Maximize Profit} = 4x_1^2 - x_1^3 + 10x_2^2 - x_2^4$$

subject to

$$x_1 + x_2 \le 3$$

and

$$x_1 \ge 0 \qquad x_2 \ge 0$$
$$x_1 \text{ and } x_2 \text{ are integers}$$

a. Reformulate this model in algebraic form as a pure BIP model with six binary variables.

E* b. Display and solve this model on a spreadsheet.

c. Reexpress the optimal solution obtained in part b in terms of the variables, x_1 and x_2, for the original model.

266 Chapter Seven *Using Binary Integer Programming to Deal with Yes-or-No Decisions*

Case 7-4

Broadcasting the Olympic Games (Revisited)

Reconsider part *b* of Case 6-4. Use the spreadsheet model developed there to incorporate the following consideration.

An additional concern not considered in Case 6-4 is that the routers at nodes C and F are each already maxed out. If any additional capacity is built into or out of node C or node F, then the routers at these stations must be upgraded. This would cost a total of $2 million at node C or a total of $3 million at node F. Which network segments should be increased in capacity and by how much so as to increase the total capacity of the network enough to transmit the peak requirement of 35 GB/s from the Olympics site (A) to the home studios (G) at the lowest possible cost?

Additional Cases

An additional case for this chapter also is available at the University of Western Ontario Ivey School of Business website, **cases.ivey.uwo.ca/cases,** in the segment of the CaseMate area designated for this book.

Case 7-3

Assigning Students to Schools (Revisited)

Reconsider Case 3-5. The **Springfield School Board** now has made the decision to prohibit the splitting of residential areas among multiple schools. Thus, each of the six areas must be assigned to a single school.

a. Formulate and solve a BIP model for this problem under the current policy of providing busing for all middle school students who must travel more than approximately a mile.

b. Referring to part *c* of Case 3-5, determine how much the total busing cost increases because of the decision to prohibit the splitting of residential areas among multiple schools.

c, d, e, f. Repeat parts *d, e, f, g* of Case 3-5 under the new school board decision to prohibit splitting of residential areas among multiple schools.

Case 7-2

Stocking Sets

Daniel Holbrook, an expediter at the local warehouse for **Furniture City,** sighed as he moved boxes and boxes of inventory to the side to reach the shelf where the particular item he needed was located. He dropped to his hands and knees and squinted at the inventory numbers lining the bottom row of the shelf. He did not find the number he needed. He worked his way up the shelf until he found the number matching the number on the order slip. Just his luck! The item was on the top row of the shelf! Daniel walked back through the warehouse to find a ladder, stumbling over boxes of inventory littering his path. When he finally climbed the ladder to reach the top shelf, his face crinkled in frustration. Not again! The item he needed was not in stock! All he saw above the inventory number was an empty space covered with dust!

Daniel trudged back through the warehouse to make the dreaded phone call. He dialed the number of Brenda Sims, the saleswoman on the kitchen showroom floor of Furniture City, and informed her that the particular light fixture the customer had requested was not in stock. He then asked her if she wanted him to look for the rest of the items in the kitchen set. Brenda told him that she would talk to the customer and call him back.

Brenda hung up the phone and frowned. Mr. Davidson, her customer, would not be happy. Ordering and receiving the correct light fixture from the regional warehouse would take at least two weeks.

Brenda then paused to reflect upon business during the last month and realized that over 80 percent of the orders for kitchen sets could not be filled because items needed to complete the sets were not in stock at the local warehouse. She also realized that Furniture City was losing customer goodwill and business because of stockouts. The furniture megastore was gaining a reputation for slow service and delayed deliveries, causing customers to turn to small competitors that sold furniture directly from the showroom floor.

Brenda decided to investigate the inventory situation at the local warehouse. She walked the short distance to the building next door and gasped when she stepped inside the warehouse. What she saw could only be described as chaos. Spaces allocated for some items were overflowing into the aisles of the warehouse while other spaces were completely bare. She walked over to one of the spaces overflowing with inventory to determine what item was overstocked. She could not believe her eyes! The warehouse had at least 30 rolls of pea-green wallpaper! No customer had ordered pea-green wallpaper since 1973!

Brenda marched over to Daniel demanding an explanation. Daniel said that the warehouse had been in such a chaotic state since his arrival one year ago. He said the inventory problems occurred because management had a policy of stocking every furniture item on the showroom floor in the local warehouse. Management only replenished inventory every three months, and when inventory was replenished, management ordered every item regardless of whether it had been sold. Daniel also said that he had tried to make management aware of the problems with overstocking unpopular items and understocking popular items, but management would not listen to him because he was simply an expediter.

Brenda understood that Furniture City required a new inventory policy. Not only was the megastore losing money by making customers unhappy with delivery delays, but it was also losing money by wasting warehouse space. By changing the inventory policy to stock only popular items and replenish them immediately when sold, Furniture City would ensure that the majority of customers would receive their furniture immediately and that the valuable warehouse space would be utilized effectively.

Brenda needed to sell her inventory policy to management. Using her extensive sales experience, she decided that the most effective sales strategy would be to use her kitchen department

264   Chapter Seven   *Using Binary Integer Programming to Deal with Yes-or-No Decisions*

as a model for the new inventory policy. She would identify all kitchen sets comprising 85 percent of customer orders. Given the fixed amount of warehouse space allocated to the kitchen department, she would identify the items Furniture City should stock to satisfy the greatest number of customer orders. She would then calculate the revenue from satisfying customer orders under the new inventory policy, using the bottom line to persuade management to accept her policy.

Brenda analyzed her records over the past three years and determined that 20 kitchen sets were responsible for 85 percent of the customer orders. These 20 kitchen sets were composed of up to eight features in a variety of styles. Brenda listed each feature and its popular styles in the tables below.

Brenda then created a table (given on the next page) showing the 20 kitchen sets and the particular features composing each set. To simplify the table, she used the codes shown in parentheses below to represent the particular feature and style. For example, kitchen set 1 consists of floor tile T2, wallpaper W2, light fixture L4, cabinet C2, countertop O2, dishwasher D2, sink S2, and range R2. Notice that sets 14 through 20 do not contain dishwashers.

a. Formulate and solve a binary integer programming problem to maximize the total number of kitchen sets (and thus the number of customer orders) Furniture City stocks in the local warehouse. Assume that when a customer orders a kitchen set, all the particular items composing that kitchen set are replenished at the local warehouse immediately.

b. How many of each feature and style should Furniture City stock in the local warehouse? How many different kitchen sets are in stock?

c. Furniture City decides to discontinue carrying nursery sets, and the warehouse space previously allocated to the nursery department is divided between the existing departments at Furniture City. The kitchen department receives enough additional space to allow it to stock both styles of dishwashers and three of the four styles of ranges. How does the optimal inventory policy for the kitchen department change with this additional warehouse space?

d. Brenda convinces management that the kitchen department should serve as a testing ground for future inventory policies. To provide adequate space for testing, management decides

Floor Tile	Wallpaper	Light Fixtures	Cabinets
(T1) White textured tile	(W1) Plain ivory paper	(L1) One large rectangular frosted fixture	(C1) Light solid wood cabinets
(T2) Ivory textured tile	(W2) Ivory paper with dark brown pinstripes	(L2) Three small square frosted fixtures	(C2) Dark solid wood cabinets
(T3) White checkered tile with blue trim	(W3) Blue paper with marble texture	(L3) One large oval frosted fixture	(C3) Light-wood cabinets with glass doors
(T4) White checkered tile with light yellow trim	(W4) Light yellow paper with marble texture	(L4) Three small frosted globe fixtures	(C4) Dark-wood cabinets with glass doors

Countertops	Dishwashers	Sinks	Ranges
(O1) Plain light-wood countertops	(D1) White energy-saving dishwasher	(S1) Sink with separate hot and cold water taps	(R1) White electric oven
(O2) Stained light-wood countertops	(D2) Ivory energy-saving dishwasher	(S2) Divided sink with separate hot and cold water taps and garbage disposal	(R2) Ivory electric oven
(O3) White lacquer-coated countertops		(S3) Sink with one hot and cold water tap	(R3) White gas oven
(O4) Ivory lacquer-coated countertops		(S4) Divided sink with one hot and cold water tap and garbage disposal	(R4) Ivory gas oven

Brenda knew she had only a limited amount of warehouse space allocated to the kitchen department. The warehouse could hold 50 square feet of tile and 12 rolls of wallpaper in the inventory bins. The inventory shelves could hold two light fixtures, two cabinets, three countertops, and two sinks. Dishwashers and ranges are similar in size, so Furniture City stored them in similar locations. The warehouse floor could hold a total of four dishwashers and ranges.

Every kitchen set always includes exactly 20 square feet of tile and exactly five rolls of wallpaper. Therefore, 20 square feet of a particular style of tile and five rolls of a particular style of wallpaper are required for the styles to be in stock.

to allocate all the space freed by the nursery department to the kitchen department. The extra space means that the kitchen department can store not only the dishwashers and ranges from part *c,* but also all sinks, all countertops, three of the four light fixtures, and three of the four cabinets. How much does the additional space help?

e. How would the inventory policy be affected if the items composing a kitchen set could not be replenished immediately? Under what conditions is the assumption of immediate replenishment nevertheless justified?

	T1	T2	T3	T4	W1	W2	W3	W4	L1	L2	L3	L4	C1	C2	C3	C4	O1	O2	O3	O4	D1	D2	S1	S2	S3	S4	R1	R2	R3	R4
Set 1		X				X						X		X						X		X		X				X		
Set 2		X							X											X		X						X		
Set 3	X		X		X					X			X			X	X								X	X			X	
Set 4			X				X								X						X	X	X		X		X			
Set 5		X					X		X		X		X			X			X		X			X			X			X
Set 6	X							X		X					X	X	X	X		X	X	X		X			X			
Set 7				X		X						X			X								X		X					X
Set 8		X					X						X				X	X		X	X	X					X			
Set 9		X			X					X	X		X		X							X	X		X			X		
Set 10					X				X				X					X	X					X					X	
Set 11			X		X										X		X				X		X			X			X	
Set 12		X			X				X					X							X	X						X		
Set 13				X		X					X				X		X	X	X			X		X	X	X				
Set 14				X				X			X						X				X		X						X	
Set 15				X			X	X		X		X	X						X						X		X			
Set 16		X	X				X		X			X	X						X										X	
Set 17	X							X							X		X		X	X				X			X			
Set 18		X					X				X	X		X					X	X			X			X		X	X	
Set 19		X						X				X	X			X	X							X						X
Set 20		X					X		X				X					X							X					X

Case 7-1

Assigning Art

It had been a dream come true for Ash Briggs, a struggling artist living in the San Francisco Bay area. He had made a trip to the corner grocery store late one Friday afternoon to buy some milk, and, on impulse, he had also purchased a California lottery ticket. One week later, he was a multimillionaire.

Ash did not want to squander his winnings on materialistic, trivial items. Instead he wanted to use his money to support his true passion: art. Ash knew all too well the difficulties of gaining recognition as an artist in this post-industrial, technological society where artistic appreciation is rare and financial support even rarer. He therefore decided to use the money to fund an exhibit of up-and-coming modern artists at the **San Francisco Museum of Modern Art.**

Ash approached the museum directors with his idea, and the directors became excited immediately after he informed them that he would fund the entire exhibit in addition to donating $1 million to the museum. Celeste McKenzie, a museum director, was assigned to work with Ash in planning the exhibit. The exhibit was slated to open one year from the time Ash met with the directors, and the exhibit pieces would remain on display for two months.

Ash began the project by combing the modern art community for potential artists and pieces. He presented a list (shown below) of artists, their pieces, and the price of displaying each piece[1] to Celeste.

Ash possesses certain requirements for the exhibit. He believes the majority of Americans lack adequate knowledge of art and artistic styles, and he wants the exhibit to educate Americans. Ash wants visitors to become aware of the collage as an art form, but he believes collages require little talent. He therefore decides to include only one collage. Additionally, Ash wants viewers to compare the delicate lines in a three-dimensional wire mesh sculpture to the delicate lines in a two-dimensional computer-generated drawing. He therefore wants at least one wire-mesh sculpture displayed if a computer-generated drawing is displayed. Alternatively, he wants at least one computer-generated drawing displayed if a wire-mesh sculpture is displayed. Furthermore, Ash wants to expose viewers to all painting styles, but he wants to limit the number of paintings displayed to achieve a balance in the exhibit between paintings and other art forms. He therefore decides to include at least one photo-realistic painting, at least one cubist painting, at least one expressionist painting, at least one watercolor painting, and at least one oil painting. At the same time, he wants the number of paintings to be no greater than twice the number of other art forms.

Ash wants all his own paintings included in the exhibit since he is sponsoring the exhibit and since his paintings celebrate the San Francisco Bay area, the home of the exhibit.

Ash possesses personal biases for and against some artists. Ash is currently having a steamy affair with Candy Tate, and he wants both of her paintings displayed. Ash counts both David Lyman and Rick Rawls as his best friends, and he does not want

Artist	Piece	Description of Piece	Price
Colin Zweibell	*Perfection*	A wire-mesh sculpture of the human body	$300,000
	Burden	A wire-mesh sculpture of a mule	250,000
	The Great Equalizer	A wire-mesh sculpture of a gun	125,000
Rita Losky	*Chaos Reigns*	A series of computer-generated drawings	400,000
	Who Has Control?	A computer-generated drawing intermeshed with lines of computer code	500,000
	Domestication	A pen-and-ink drawing of a house	400,000
	Innocence	A pen-and-ink drawing of a child	550,000
Norm Marson	*Aging Earth*	A sculpture of trash covering a larger globe	700,000
	Wasted Resources	A collage of various packaging materials	575,000
Candy Tate	*Serenity*	An all-blue watercolor painting	200,000
	Calm before the Storm	A painting with an all-blue watercolor background and a black watercolor center	225,000
Robert Bayer	*Void*	An all-black oil painting	150,000
	Sun	An all-yellow oil painting	150,000
David Lyman	*Storefront Window*	A photo-realistic painting of a jewelry store display window	850,000
	Harley	A photo-realistic painting of a Harley-Davidson motorcycle	750,000
Angie Oldman	*Consumerism*	A collage of magazine advertisements	400,000
	Reflection	A mirror (considered a sculpture)	175,000
	Trojan Victory	A wooden sculpture of a condom	450,000
Rick Rawls	*Rick*	A photo-realistic self-portrait (painting)	500,000
	Rick II	A cubist self-portrait (painting)	500,000
	Rick III	An expressionist self-portrait (painting)	500,000
Bill Reynolds	*Beyond*	A science fiction oil painting depicting Mars colonization	650,000
	Pioneers	An oil painting of three astronauts aboard the space shuttle	650,000
Bear Canton	*Wisdom*	A pen-and-ink drawing of an Apache chieftain	250,000
	Superior Powers	A pen-and-ink drawing of a traditional Native American rain dance	350,000
	Living Land	An oil painting of the Grand Canyon	450,000
Helen Row	*Study of a Violin*	A cubist painting of a violin	400,000
	Study of a Fruit Bowl	A cubist painting of a bowl of fruit	400,000
Ziggy Lite	*My Namesake*	A collage of Ziggy cartoons	300,000
	Narcissism	A collage of photographs of Ziggy Lite	300,000
Ash Briggs	*All That Glitters*	A watercolor painting of the Golden Gate Bridge	50,000*
	The Rock	A watercolor painting of Alcatraz	50,000*
	Winding Road	A watercolor painting of Lombard Street	50,000*
	Dreams Come True	A watercolor painting of the San Francisco Museum of Modern Art	50,000*

*Ash does not require personal compensation, and the cost for moving his pieces to the museum from his home in San Francisco is minimal. The cost of displaying his pieces therefore only includes the cost of constructing the display and insuring the pieces.

[1] The display price includes the cost of paying the artist for loaning the piece to the museum, transporting the piece to San Francisco, constructing the display for the piece, insuring the piece while it is on display, and transporting the piece back to its origin.

to play favorites among these two artists. He therefore decides to display as many pieces from David Lyman as from Rick Rawls and to display at least one piece from each of them. Although Ziggy Lite is very popular within art circles, Ash believes Ziggy makes a mockery of art. Ash will therefore only accept one display piece from Ziggy, if any at all.

Celeste also possesses her own agenda for the exhibit. As a museum director, she is interested in representing a diverse population of artists, appealing to a wide audience, and creating a politically correct exhibit. To advance feminism, she decides to include at least one piece from a female artist for every two pieces included from a male artist. To advance environmentalism, she decides to include either one or both of the pieces *Aging Earth* and *Wasted Resources*. To advance Native American rights, she decides to include at least one piece by Bear Canton. To advance science, she decides to include at least one of the following pieces: *Chaos Reigns, Who Has Control?, Beyond,* and *Pioneers.*

Celeste also understands that space is limited at the museum. The museum only has enough floor space for four sculptures and enough wall space for 20 paintings, collages, and drawings.

Finally, Celeste decides that if *Narcissism* is displayed, *Reflection* should also be displayed since *Reflection* also suggests narcissism.

Please explore the following questions independently except where otherwise indicated.

a. Ash decides to allocate $4 million to fund the exhibit. Given the pieces available and the specific requirements from Ash and Celeste, formulate and solve a binary integer programming problem to maximize the number of pieces displayed in the exhibit without exceeding the budget. How many pieces are displayed? Which pieces are displayed?

b. To ensure that the exhibit draws the attention of the public, Celeste decides that it must include at least 20 pieces. Formulate and solve a binary integer programming problem to minimize the cost of the exhibit while displaying at least 20 pieces and meeting the requirements set by Ash and Celeste. How much does the exhibit cost? Which pieces are displayed?

c. An influential patron of Rita Losky's work who chairs the museum's board of directors learns that Celeste requires at least 20 pieces in the exhibit. He offers to pay the minimum amount required on top of Ash's $4 million to ensure that exactly 20 pieces are displayed in the exhibit and that all of Rita's pieces are displayed. How much does the patron have to pay? Which pieces are displayed?

Chapter **Nine**

Decision Analysis

Learning Objectives

After completing this chapter, you should be able to

1. Identify the kind of decision-making environment for which decision analysis is needed.
2. Describe the logical way in which decision analysis organizes a problem.
3. Formulate a payoff table from a description of the problem.
4. Describe and evaluate several alternative criteria for making a decision based on a payoff table.
5. Apply Bayes' decision rule to solve a decision analysis problem.
6. Formulate and solve a decision tree for dealing with a sequence of decisions.
7. Use RSPE to construct and solve a decision tree.
8. Perform sensitivity analysis with Bayes' decision rule.
9. Determine whether it is worthwhile to obtain more information before making a decision.
10. Use new information to update the probabilities of the states of nature.
11. Use data tables to perform sensitivity analysis when dealing with a sequence of decisions.
12. Use utilities to better reflect the values of payoffs.
13. Describe some common features in the practical application of decision analysis.

The previous chapters have focused mainly on managerial decision making when the consequences of alternative decisions are known with a reasonable degree of certainty. This decision-making environment enabled formulating helpful mathematical models (linear programming, integer programming, nonlinear programming, etc.) with objective functions that specify the estimated consequences of any combination of decisions. Although these consequences usually cannot be predicted with complete certainty, they could at least be estimated with enough accuracy to justify using such models (along with what-if analysis, etc.).

However, managers often must make decisions in environments that are fraught with much more uncertainty. Here are a few examples.

1. A manufacturer introducing a new product into the marketplace. What will be the reaction of potential customers? How much should be produced? Should the product be test marketed in a small region before deciding upon full distribution? How much advertising is needed to launch the product successfully?
2. A financial firm investing in securities. Which are the market sectors and individual securities with the best prospects? Where is the economy headed? How about interest rates? How should these factors affect the investment decisions?
3. A government contractor bidding on a new contract. What will be the actual costs of the project? Which other companies might be bidding? What are their likely bids?
4. An agricultural firm selecting the mix of crops and livestock for the upcoming season. What will be the weather conditions? Where are prices headed? What will costs be?
5. An oil company deciding whether to drill for oil in a particular location. How likely is there to be oil in that location? How much? How deep will they need to drill? Should geologists investigate the site further before drilling?

This is the kind of decision making in the face of great uncertainty that *decision analysis* is designed to address. Decision analysis provides a framework and methodology for rational decision making when the outcomes are uncertain.

The first section introduces a case study that will be carried throughout the chapter to illustrate the various phases involved in applying decision analysis. Section 9.2 focuses on choosing an appropriate decision criterion and then the next section describes how decision trees can be used to structure and analyze a decision analysis problem. Section 9.4 discusses how sensitivity analysis can be performed efficiently with the help of decision trees. The subsequent four sections deal with whether it would be worthwhile to obtain more information and, if so, how to use this information for making a sequence of decisions. Section 9.9 then describes how to analyze the problem while calibrating the possible outcomes to reflect their true value to the decision maker. Finally, Section 9.10 discusses the practical application of decision analysis.

In addition, a supplement to this chapter on the CD-ROM presents a detailed description and evaluation of various decision criteria.

9.1 A CASE STUDY: THE GOFERBROKE COMPANY PROBLEM

Max Flyer is the founder and sole owner of the **Goferbroke Company,** which develops oil wells in unproven territory. Max's friends refer to him affectionately as a wildcatter. However, he prefers to think of himself as an entrepreneur. He has poured his life's savings into the company in the hope of making it big with a large strike of oil.

Now his chance possibly has come. His company has purchased various tracts of land that larger oil companies have spurned as unpromising even though they are near some large oil fields. Now Max has received an exciting report about one of these tracts. A consulting geologist has just informed Max that he believes there is one chance in four of oil there.

Max has learned from bitter experience to be skeptical about the chances of oil reported by consulting geologists. Drilling for oil on this tract would require an investment of about $100,000. If the land turns out to be dry (no oil), the entire investment would be lost. Since his company does not have much capital left, this loss would be quite serious.

On the other hand, if the tract does contain oil, the consulting geologist estimates that there would be enough there to generate a net revenue of approximately $800,000, leaving an approximate profit of

$$\text{Profit if find oil} = \text{Revenue if find oil} - \text{Drilling cost}$$
$$= \$800,000 - \$100,000$$
$$= \$700,000$$

Although this wouldn't be quite the big strike for which Max has been waiting, it would provide a very welcome infusion of capital into the company to keep it going until he hopefully can hit the really big gusher.

Should Max sell the land instead of drilling for oil there?

There is another option. Another oil company has gotten wind of the consulting geologist's report and so has offered to purchase the tract of land from Max for $90,000. This is very tempting. This too would provide a welcome infusion of capital into the company, but without incurring the large risk of a very substantial loss of $100,000.

Table 9.1 summarizes the decision alternatives and prospective payoffs that face Max.

So Max is in a quandary about what to do. Fortunately, help is at hand. Max's daughter Jennifer has recently earned her degree from a fine business school and now has come to

TABLE 9.1
Prospective Profits for the Goferbroke Company

	Profit	
Status of Land Alternative	Oil	Dry
Drill for oil	$700,000	−$100,000
Sell the land	90,000	90,000
Chance of status	1 in 4	3 in 4

work for her proud dad. He asks her to apply her business training to help him analyze the problem. Having studied management science in college, she recommends applying decision analysis. Having paid for her fine education, he agrees to give it a try.

Jennifer begins by interviewing her dad about the problem.

Jennifer: How much faith do you put in the consulting geologist's assessment that there is one chance in four of oil on this tract?

Max: Not too much. These guys sometimes seem to pull numbers out of the air. He has convinced me that there is some chance of oil there. But it could just as well be one chance in three, or one chance in five. They don't really know.

Jennifer: Is there a way of getting more information to pin these odds down better? This is an important option with the decision analysis approach.

Max: Yes. We could arrange for a detailed seismic survey of the land. That would pin down the odds somewhat better. But you don't really find out until you drill. Furthermore, these seismic surveys cost you an arm and a leg. I got a quote for this tract. 30,000 bucks! Then it might say oil is likely, so we drill and we might not find anything. Then I'm out another 100,000 bucks! Losing $130,000 would almost put us out of business.

Jennifer: OK. Let's put the seismic survey on the back burner for now. Here is another key consideration. It sounds like we need to go beyond dollars and cents to look at the consequences of the possible outcomes. Losing $130,000 would hurt a lot more than gaining $130,000 would help.

Max: That's for sure!

Jennifer: Well, decision analysis has a way of taking this into account by using what are called utilities. The **utility** of an outcome measures the true value to you of that outcome rather than just the monetary value.

Max: Sounds good.

Jennifer: Now this is what I suggest we do. We'll start out simple, without considering the option of the seismic survey and without getting into utilities. I'll introduce you to how decision analysis organizes our problem and to the options it provides for the criterion to use for making your decision. You'll be able to choose the criterion that feels right to you. Then we'll look at whether it might be worthwhile to do the seismic survey and, if so, how to best use its information. After that, we'll get into the nitty gritty of carefully analyzing the problem, including incorporating utilities. I think when we finish the process and you make your decision, you'll feel quite comfortable that you are making the best one.

Max: Good. Let's get started.

Here is the tutorial that Jennifer provided her dad about the logical way in which decision analysis organizes a problem.

> The utility of an outcome measures the true value to the decision maker of that outcome.

Decision Analysis Terminology

Decision analysis has a few special terms.

The **decision maker** is the individual or group responsible for making the decision (or sequence of decisions) under consideration. For the Goferbroke Co. problem, the decision maker is Max. Jennifer (the management scientist) can help perform the analyses, but the objective is to assist the decision maker in identifying the best possible decision from the decision maker's perspective.

The **alternatives** are the options for the decision to be made by the decision maker. Max's alternatives at this point are to drill for oil or to sell the tract of land.

The outcome of the decision to be made will be affected by random factors that are outside the control of the decision maker. These random factors determine the situation that will be found when the decision is executed. Each of these possible situations is referred to as a possible **state of nature**. For the Goferbroke Co. problem, the possible states of nature are that the tract contains oil or that it is dry (no oil).

The decision maker generally will have some information about the relative likelihood of the possible states of nature. This information may be in the form of just subjective estimates based on the experience or intuition of an individual, or there may be some degree of hard

TABLE 9.2

Prior Probabilities for the First Goferbroke Co. Problem

State of Nature	Prior Probability
The tract of land contains oil	0.25
The tract of land is dry (no oil)	0.75

TABLE 9.3

Payoff Table (Profit in $1,000s) for the First Goferbroke Co. Problem

	State of Nature	
Alternative	Oil	Dry
Drill for oil	700	−100
Sell the land	90	90
Prior probability	0.25	0.75

evidence involved (such as is contained in the consulting geologist's report). When these estimates are expressed in the form of probabilities, they are referred to as the **prior probabilities** of the respective states of nature. For the Goferbroke Co. problem, the consulting geologist has provided the prior probabilities given in Table 9.2. Although these are unlikely to be the true probabilities based on more information (such as through a seismic survey), they are the best available estimates of the probabilities *prior* to obtaining more information. (Later in the chapter, we will analyze whether it would be worthwhile to conduct a seismic survey, so the current problem of what to do without a seismic survey will be referred to hereafter as the *first* Goferbroke Co. problem.)

Each combination of a decision alternative and a state of nature results in some outcome. The **payoff** is a quantitative measure of the value to the decision maker of the consequences of the outcome. In most cases, the payoff is expressed as a monetary value, such as the profit. As indicated in Table 9.1, the payoff for the Goferbroke Co. at this stage is profit. (In Section 9.9, the company's payoffs will be reexpressed in terms of utilities.)

The Payoff Table

When formulating the problem, it is important to identify *all* the relevant decision alternatives and the possible states of nature. After identifying the appropriate measure for the *payoff* from the perspective of the decision maker, the next step is to estimate the payoff for each combination of a decision alternative and a state of nature. These payoffs then are displayed in a **payoff table.**

Table 9.3 shows the payoff table for the first Goferbroke Co. problem. The payoffs are given in units of thousands of dollars of profit. Note that the bottom row also shows the prior probabilities of the states of nature, as given earlier in Table 9.2.

Review Questions

1. What are the decision alternatives being considered by Max?
2. What is the consulting geologist's assessment of the chances of oil on the tract of land?
3. How much faith does Max put in the consulting geologist's assessment of the chances of oil?
4. What option is available for obtaining more information about the chances of oil?
5. What is meant by the possible *states of nature?*
6. What is meant by *prior probabilities?*
7. What do the *payoffs* represent in a payoff table?

9.2   DECISION CRITERIA

Given the payoff table for the first Goferbroke Co. problem shown in Table 9.3, what criterion should be used in deciding whether to drill for oil or sell the land? There is no single correct answer for this question that is appropriate for every decision maker. The choice of a decision criterion depends considerably on the decision maker's own temperament and attitude toward decision making, as well as the circumstances of the decision to be made. Ultimately, Max Flyer, as the owner of the Goferbroke Co., needs to decide which decision criterion is most appropriate for this situation from his personal viewpoint.

There is no single decision criterion that is best for every situation.

Over a period of many decades (and even centuries), a considerable number of criteria have been suggested for how to make a decision when given the kind of information provided by a payoff table. All these criteria consider the payoffs in some way and some also take into account the prior probabilities of the states of nature, but other criteria do not use probabilities in any way. Each criterion has some rationale as well as some drawbacks. However, in recent decades, a substantial majority of management scientists has concluded that one of these criteria (Bayes' decision rule) is a particularly appropriate criterion for most decision makers in most situations. Therefore, after describing and discussing Bayes' decision rule in this section, the rest of the chapter will focus on how to apply this particular criterion in a variety of contexts.

> Bayes' decision rule is the recommended decision criterion for most situations.

However, before turning to Bayes' decision rule, we briefly introduce three alternative decision criteria below. All of these alternative criteria are particularly simple and intuitive. At the same time, each criterion is quite superficial in the sense that it focuses on only one piece of information provided by the payoff table and ignores the rest (including the pieces considered by the other two criteria). Nevertheless, many individuals informally apply one or more of these criteria at various times in their lives. The first two make no use of prior probabilities, which can be quite reasonable when it is difficult or impossible to obtain relatively reliable values for these probabilities. Bayes' decision rule is quite different from these alternative criteria in that it makes full use of all the information in the payoff table by applying a more structured approach to decision making.

The CD-ROM includes a supplement to this chapter entitled *Decision Criteria* that provides a much more detailed discussion and critique of these three alternative decision criteria as well as three others that are somewhat more complicated. (These three others included in the supplement are the *equally likely criterion* that assigns equal probabilities to all the states of nature, the *minimax regret criterion* that minimizes the regret that can be felt afterward if the decision does not turn out well, and the *realism criterion* that uses the decision maker's pessimism–optimism index.)

Decision Making without Probabilities: The Maximax Criterion

The **maximax criterion** is the decision criterion for the eternal optimist. It says to focus only on the *best* that can happen to us. Here is how this criterion works:

1. Identify the *maximum payoff* from any state of nature for each decision alternative.
2. Find the *maximum* of these maximum payoffs and choose the corresponding decision alternative.

> The maximax criterion always chooses the decision alternative that can give the largest possible payoff.

The rationale for this criterion is that it gives an opportunity for the best possible outcome (the largest payoff in the entire payoff table) to occur. All that is needed is for the right state of nature to occur, which the eternal optimist believes is likely.

Table 9.4 shows the application of this criterion to the first Goferbroke problem. It begins with the payoff table (Table 9.3) without the prior probabilities (since these probabilities are ignored by this criterion). An extra column on the right then shows the maximum payoff for each decision alternative. Since the maximum of these maxima (700) must be the largest payoff in the entire payoff table, the corresponding decision alternative (drill for oil) is selected by this criterion.

> This criterion ignores the prior probabilities.

The biggest drawback of this criterion is that it completely ignores the prior probabilities. For example, it always would say that Goferbroke should drill for oil even if the chance of finding oil were minuscule. Another drawback is that it ignores all the payoffs except the largest one. For example, it again would say that Goferbroke should drill for oil even if the payoff from selling the land were 699 ($699,000).

Decision Making without Probabilities: The Maximin Criterion

The **maximin criterion** is the criterion for the total pessimist. In contrast to the maximax criterion, it says to focus only on the *worst* that can happen to us. Here is how this criterion works:

> The maximin criterion always chooses the decision alternative that provides the best guarantee for its minimum possible payoff.

1. Identify the *minimum payoff* from any state of nature for each decision alternative.
2. Find the *maximum* of these minimum payoffs and choose the corresponding decision alternative.

TABLE 9.4

Application of the Maximax Criterion to the First Goferbroke Co. Problem

Alternative	State of Nature		Maximum in Row
	Oil	Dry	
Drill for oil	700	−100	700 ← Maximax
Sell the land	90	90	90

TABLE 9.5

Application of the Maximin Criterion to the First Goferbroke Co. Problem

Alternative	State of Nature		Minimum in Row
	Oil	Dry	
Drill for oil	700	−100	−100
Sell the land	90	90	90 ← Maximin

The rationale for this criterion is that it provides the best possible protection against being unlucky. Even if each possible choice of a decision alternative were to lead to its worst state of nature occurring, which the total pessimist thinks is likely, the choice indicated by this criterion gives the best possible payoff under these circumstances.

The application of this criterion to the first Goferbroke problem is shown in Table 9.5. The basic difference from Table 9.4 is that the numbers in the right-hand column now are the *minimum* rather than the maximum in each row. Since 90 is the maximum of these two numbers, the alternative to be chosen is to sell the land.

The drawbacks of this criterion are similar to those for the maximax criterion. Because it completely ignores prior probabilities, it always would say that Goferbroke should sell the land even if it were almost certain to find oil if it drilled. Because it ignores all the payoffs except the maximin payoff, it again would say that Goferbroke should sell the land even if the payoff from drilling successfully for oil were 10,000 ($10 million).

This criterion also ignores the prior probabilities.

Decision Making with Probabilities: The Maximum Likelihood Criterion

The **maximum likelihood criterion** says to focus on the *most likely* state of nature as follows.

1. Identify the state of nature with the largest prior probability.
2. Choose the decision alternative that has the largest payoff for this state of nature.

The maximum likelihood criterion assumes that the most likely state of nature will occur and chooses accordingly.

The rationale for this criterion is that by basing our decision on the assumption that the most likely state of nature will occur, we are giving ourselves a better chance of a favorable outcome than by assuming any other state of nature.

Table 9.6 shows the application of this criterion to the first Goferbroke Co. problem. This table is identical to the payoff table given in Table 9.3 except for also showing step 1 (select the *dry* state of nature) and step 2 (select the *sell the land* alternative) of the criterion. Since dry is the state of nature with the larger prior probability, we only consider the payoffs in its column (−100 and 90). The larger of these two payoffs is 90, so we choose the corresponding alternative, sell the land.

This criterion ignores all the payoffs except for the most likely state of nature.

This criterion has a number of drawbacks. One is that with a considerable number of states of nature, the most likely state can have a fairly low prior probability, in which case it would make little sense to base the decision solely on this one state. Another more serious drawback is that it completely ignores all the payoffs (including any extremely large payoffs and any disastrous payoffs) throughout the payoff table except those for the single most likely state of nature. For example, no matter how large the payoff for finding oil, it automatically would say that Goferbroke should sell the land instead of drilling for oil whenever the dry state has a little larger prior probability than the oil state.

TABLE 9.6

Application of the Maximum Likelihood Criterion to the First Goferbroke Co. Problem

Alternative	State of Nature		
	Oil	Dry	
Drill for oil	700	−100	
Sell the land	90	90	← Step 2: Maximum
Prior probability	0.25	0.75	

Step 1: Maximum

Decision Making with Probabilities: Bayes' Decision Rule

Bayes' decision rule directly uses the *prior probabilities* of the possible states of nature as summarized below.

1. For each decision alternative, calculate the *weighted average* of its payoffs by multiplying each payoff by the prior probability of the corresponding state of nature and then summing these products. Using statistical terminology, refer to this weighted average as the **expected payoff (EP)** for this decision alternative.
2. Bayes' decision rule says to choose the alternative with the *largest* expected payoff.

The spreadsheet in Figure 9.1 shows the application of this criterion to the first Goferbroke Co. problem. Columns B, C, and D display the payoff table first given in Table 9.3. Cells F5 and F6 then execute step 1 of the procedure by using the equations entered into these cells, namely,

$$F5 = \text{SUMPRODUCT(PriorProbability, DrillPayoff)} = 0.25(700) + 0.75(-100) = 100$$
$$F6 = \text{SUMPRODUCT(PriorProbability, SellPayoff)} = 0.25(90) + 0.75(90) = 90$$

Since expected payoff = 100 for the drill alternative (cell F5), versus a smaller value of expected payoff = 90 for the sell the land alternative (cell F6), this criterion says to drill for oil.

Like all the others, this criterion cannot guarantee that the selected alternative will turn out to have been the best one after learning the true state of nature. However, it does provide another guarantee described below.

On the average, Bayes' decision rule provides larger payoffs in the long run than any other criterion.

The expected payoff for a particular decision alternative can be interpreted as what the *average* payoff would become if the same situation were to be repeated numerous times. Therefore, *on the average,* repeatedly using Bayes' decision rule to make decisions will lead to larger payoffs in the long run than any other criterion (assuming the prior probabilities are valid).

Thus, if the Goferbroke Co. owned many tracts of land with this same payoff table, drilling for oil on all of them would provide an average payoff of about 100 ($100,000), versus only 90 ($90,000) for selling. As the following calculations indicate, this is the average payoff from

FIGURE 9.1

This spreadsheet shows the application of Bayes' decision rule to the first Goferbroke Co. problem, where a comparison of the expected payoffs in cells F5:F6 indicates that the Drill alternative should be chosen because it has the largest expected payoff.

	A	B	C	D	E	F
1		**Bayes' Decision Rule for the Goferbroke Co.**				
2						
3		**Payoff Table**	**State of Nature**			Expected
4		Alternative	Oil	Dry		Payoff
5		Drill	700	−100		100
6		Sell	90	90		90
7						
8		Prior Probability	0.25	0.75		

Range Name	Cells
DrillPayoff	C5:D5
ExpectedPayoff	F5:F6
PriorProbability	C8:D8
SellPayoff	C6:D6

	F
3	Expected
4	Payoff
5	=SUMPRODUCT(PriorProbability,DrillPayoff)
6	=SUMPRODUCT(PriorProbability,SellPayoff)

drilling that results from having oil in an average of one tract out of every four (as indicated by the prior probabilities).

$$\text{Oil found in one tract:} \quad \text{Payoff} = 700$$
$$\text{Three tracts are dry: Payoff} = 3(-100) = -300$$
$$\text{Total payoff} = 400$$
$$\text{Average payoff} = \frac{400}{4} = 100$$

However, achieving this average payoff might require going through a long stretch of dry tracts until the "law of averages" can prevail to reach 25 percent of the tracts having oil. Surviving a long stretch of bad luck may not be feasible if the company does not have adequate financing.

This criterion also has its share of critics. Here are the main criticisms.

1. There usually is considerable uncertainty involved in assigning values to prior probabilities, so treating these values as true probabilities will not reveal the true range of possible outcomes. (Section 9.4 discusses how *sensitivity analysis* can address this concern.)

2. Prior probabilities inherently are at least largely subjective in nature, whereas sound decision making should be based on objective data and procedures. (Section 9.6 describes how new information sometimes can be obtained to improve prior probabilities and make them more objective.)

By considering only expected payoffs, Bayes' decision rule fails to give special consideration to the possibility of disastrously large losses.

3. By focusing on average outcomes, expected (monetary) payoffs ignore the effect that the amount of variability in the possible outcomes should have on the decision making. For example, since Goferbroke does not have the financing to sustain a large loss, selling the land to assure a payoff of 90 ($90,000) may be preferable to an expected payoff of 100 ($100,000) from drilling. Selling would avoid the risk of a large loss from drilling when the land is dry. (Section 9.9 will discuss how utilities can be used to better reflect the value of payoffs.)

So why is this criterion commonly referred to as Bayes' decision rule? The reason is that it is often credited to the Reverend Thomas Bayes, a nonconforming 18th century English minister who won renown as a philosopher and mathematician, although the same basic idea has even longer roots in the field of economics. Bayes' philosophy of decision making still is very influential today, and some management scientists even refer to themselves as Bayesians because of their devotion to this philosophy.

More recently, it has become somewhat popular to also call this criterion the **expected monetary value (EMV) criterion.** The reason for this alternative name is that the payoffs in the payoff table often represent monetary values (such as the number of dollars of profit), in which case the expected payoff for each decision alternative is its *expected* monetary value. However, the name is a misnomer for those cases where the measure of the payoff is something other than monetary value (as in Section 9.9). Therefore, we will consistently use the single name, Bayes' decision rule, to refer to this criterion in all situations.

Because of its popularity, the rest of the chapter focuses on procedures that are based on this criterion.

Max's Reaction

Max: So where does this leave us?

Jennifer: Well, now you need to decide which criterion seems most appropriate to you in this situation.

Max: Well, I can't say that I am very excited about any of the criteria. But it sounded like this last one is a popular one.

Jennifer: Yes, it is.

Max: Why?

Bayes' decision rule uses all the information provided by the payoff table.

Jennifer: Really, two reasons. First, this is the criterion that uses all the available information. The prior probabilities may not be as accurate as we would like, but they do give us valuable information about roughly how likely each of the possible states of nature is. Many management scientists feel that using this key information should lead to better decisions.

330   Chapter Nine   *Decision Analysis*

Max: I'm not ready to accept that yet. But what is the second reason?

Jennifer: Remember that this is the criterion that focuses on what the average payoff would be if the same situation were repeated numerous times. We called this the expected payoff. Consistently selecting the decision alternative that provides the best expected payoff would provide the most payoff to the company in the long run. Doing what is best in the long run seems like rational decision making for a manager.

Review
Questions

1. How does the maximax criterion select a decision alternative? What kind of person might find this criterion appealing?
2. What are some criticisms of the maximax criterion?
3. How does the maximin criterion select a decision alternative? What kind of person might find this criterion appealing?
4. What are some criticisms of the maximin criterion?
5. Which state of nature does the maximum likelihood criterion focus on?
6. What are some criticisms of the maximum likelihood criterion?
7. How does Bayes' decision rule select a decision alternative?
8. How is the expected payoff for a decision alternative calculated?
9. What are some criticisms of Bayes' decision rule?

9.3 DECISION TREES

FIGURE 9.2

The decision tree for the first Goferbroke Co. problem as presented in Table 9.3.

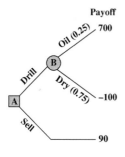

The spreadsheet in Figure 9.1 illustrates one useful way of performing decision analysis with Bayes' decision rule. Another enlightening way to apply this decision rule is to use a **decision tree** to display and analyze the problem graphically. The decision tree for the first Goferbroke Co. problem is shown in Figure 9.2. Starting on the left side and moving to the right side shows the progression of events. First, a decision is made as to whether to drill for oil or sell the land. If the decision is to drill, the next event is to learn whether the state of nature is that the land contains oil or is dry. Finally, the payoff is obtained that results from these events.

In the terminology of decision trees, the junction points are called **nodes** (or forks) and the lines emanating from the nodes are referred to as **branches.** A distinction is then made between the following two types of nodes.

> A **decision node,** represented by a *square,* indicates that a decision needs to be made at that point in the process. An **event node** (or chance node), represented by a *circle,* indicates that a random event occurs at that point.

Thus, node A in Figure 9.2 is a decision node since the decision on whether to drill or sell occurs there. Node B is an event node since a random event, the occurrence of one of the possible states of nature, takes place there. Each of the two branches emanating from this node corresponds to one of the possible random events, where the number in parentheses along the branch gives the probability that this event will occur.

A decision tree can be very helpful for visualizing and analyzing a problem. When the problem is as small as the one in Figure 9.2, using the decision tree in the analysis process is optional. However, one nice feature of decision trees is that they also can be used for more complicated problems where a sequence of decisions needs to be made. You will see this illustrated for the full Goferbroke Co. problem in Sections 9.7 and 9.9 when a decision on whether to conduct a seismic survey is made before deciding whether to drill or sell.

Spreadsheet Software for Decision Trees

We will describe and illustrate how to use Risk Solver Platform for Education (RSPE) to construct and analyze decision trees in Excel. Instructions for installing this software are on a supplementary insert included with the book and also on the book's website, **www.mhhe .com/hillier5e.** If you are a Mac user (RSPE is not compatible with Mac versions of Excel) or you or your instructor simply prefer to use different software, a supplement to this chapter on the CD-ROM and website contains instructions for TreePlan, another popular Excel add-in for constructing and analyzing decision trees in Excel.

To begin creating a decision tree using RSPE, select Add Node from the Decision Tree/ Node menu. This brings up the dialog box shown in Figure 9.3. Here you can choose the type

An Application Vignette

The **Workers' Compensation Board (WCB) of British Columbia, Canada,** is responsible for the occupational health and safety, rehabilitation, and compensation interests of the province's workers and employers. The WCB serves more than 165,000 employers who employ about 1.8 million workers in British Columbia. It spends approximately US$1 billion annually on compensation and rehabilitation.

A key factor in controlling WCB costs is to identify those short-term disability claims that pose a potentially high financial risk of converting into a *far* more expensive long-term disability claim unless there is intensive early *claim-management intervention* to provide the needed medical treatment and rehabilitation. The question was how to accurately identify these high-risk claims so as to minimize the expected total cost of claim compensation and claim-management intervention.

A management science team was formed to study this problem by *applying decision analysis.* For each of numerous categories of injury claims based on the nature of the injury, the gender and age of the worker, and so on, a *decision tree* was used to evaluate whether that category should be classified as low risk (not requiring intervention) or high risk (requiring intervention), depending on the severity of the injury. For each category, a calculation was made of the cutoff point on the critical number of short-term disability claim days paid that would trigger claim-management intervention so as to minimize the expected cost of claim payments and intervention.

This application of decision analysis with decision trees is *saving WCB approximately* **US$4 million** *per year* while also enabling some injured workers to return to work sooner.

Source: E. Urbanovich, E. E. Young, M. L. Puterman, and S. O. Fattedad, "Early Detection of High-Risk Claims at the Workers' Compensation Board of British Columbia," *Interfaces* 33, no. 4 (July–August 2003), pp. 15–26. (A link to this article is provided on our website, www.mhhe.com/hillier5e.)

RSPE Tip: The type of node, the branch names, and the values (or partial payoffs) of each branch can be entered in the RSPE Decision Tree dialog box. Alternatively, the names and values can be entered (or changed) after the fact by typing them directly into the spreadsheet.

of node (Decision or Event), give names to each of the branches, and specify a value for each branch (the partial payoff associated with that branch). The default names for the branches of a decision node in RSPE are Decision 1 and Decision 2. These can be changed (or more branches added) by double-clicking on the branch name (or in the next blank row to add a branch) and typing in a new name. The initial node in the first Goferbroke problem (node A in Figure 9.2) is a decision node with two branches: Drill and Sell. The payoff associated with drilling is –100 (the $100,000 cost of drilling) and the payoff associated with selling is 90 (the $90,000 selling price). After making all of these entries as shown in Figure 9.3, clicking OK then yields the decision tree shown in Figure 9.4.

If the decision is to drill, the next event is to learn whether or not the land contains oil. To create an event node, click on the cell containing the triangle terminal node at the end of

FIGURE 9.3

The Decision Tree dialog box used to specify that the initial node of the first Goferbroke problem is a decision node with two branches, Drill and Sell, with values (partial payoffs) of −100 and 90, respectively.

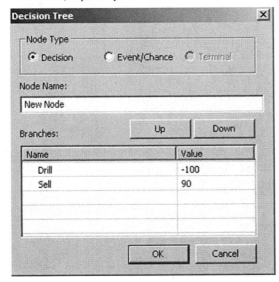

FIGURE 9.4

The initial, partial decision tree created by RSPE by selecting Add Node from the Decision Tree/Node menu on the RSPE ribbon and specifying a Decision node with two branches named Drill and Sell, with partial payoffs of −100 and 90, respectively.

	A	B	C	D	E	F	G
1							
2				Drill			
3							-100
4				-100	-100		
5			2				
6		90					
7				Sell			
8							90
9				90	90		

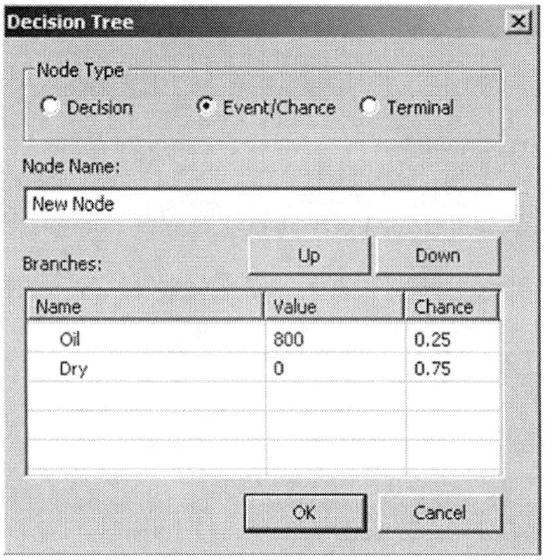

FIGURE 9.5

The Decision Tree dialog box used to specify that the second node of the first Goferbroke problem is an event node with two branches, Oil and Dry, with values (partial payoffs) of 800 and 0, and with probabilities of 0.25 and 0.75, respectively.

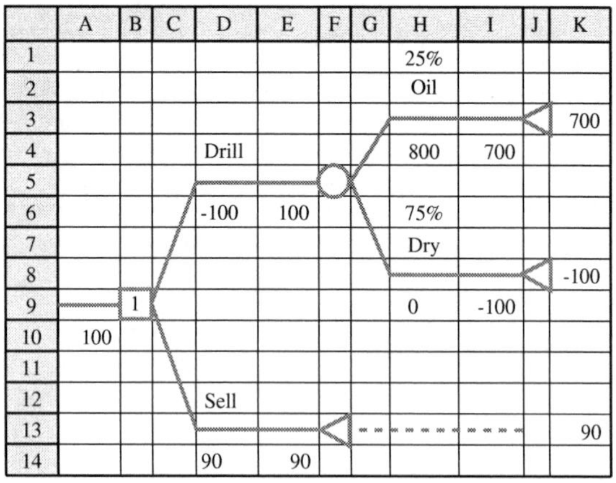

FIGURE 9.6

The decision tree constructed and solved by RSPE for the first Goferbroke Co. problem as presented in Table 9.3, where the 1 in cell B9 indicates that the top branch (the Drill alternative) should be chosen.

	A	B	C	D	E	F	G	H	I	J	K
1								25%			
2								Oil			
3											700
4				Drill				800	700		
5											
6				-100	100			75%			
7								Dry			
8											-100
9		1						0	-100		
10	100										
11											
12				Sell							
13											90
14				90	90						

the drill branch (cell F3 in Figure 9.4) and choose Add Node from the Decision Tree/Node menu on the RSPE ribbon to bring up the dialog box shown in Figure 9.5. The node is an event node with two branches, Oil and Dry, with probabilities 0.25 and 0.75, respectively, and values (partial payoffs) of 800 and 0, respectively, as entered into the dialog box in Figure 9.5. After clicking OK, the final decision tree is shown in Figure 9.6. (Note that RSPE, by default, shows all probabilities as a percentage, with 25% and 75% in H1 and H6, rather than 0.25 and 0.75.)

At any time, you also can click on any existing node and make changes using various choices under the Decision Tree menu on the RSPE ribbon. For example, under the Node submenu, you can choose Add Node, Change Node, Delete Node, Copy Node, or Paste Node. Under the Branch submenu, you can Add Branch, Change Branch, or Delete Branch.

At each stage in constructing a decision tree, RSPE automatically solves for the optimal policy with the current tree when using *Bayes' decision rule.* The number inside each decision node indicates which branch should be chosen (assuming the branches emanating from that node are numbered consecutively from top to bottom). Thus, for the final decision tree in Figure 9.6, the number 1 in cell B9 specifies that the first branch (the Drill alternative) should be chosen. The number on both sides of each terminal node is the payoff if that node is reached. The number 100 in cells A10 and E6 is the *expected payoff* (the measure of performance for Bayes' decision rule) at those stages in the process.

This description of the decision analysis tools of RSPE may seem somewhat complicated. However, we think that you will find the procedure quite intuitive when you execute it on a computer. If you spend considerable time with RSPE, you also will find that it has many helpful features that haven't been described in this brief introduction.

Max's Reaction

Max: I like this decision tree thing. It puts everything into perspective.

Jennifer: Good.

Max: But one thing still really bothers me.

Jennifer: I think I can guess.

Max: Yes. I've made it pretty plain that I don't want to make my decision based on believing the consulting geologist's numbers. One chance in four of oil. Hah! It's just an educated guess.

Jennifer: Well, let me ask this. What is the key factor in deciding whether to drill for oil or sell the land?

Max: How likely it is that there is oil there.

Jennifer: Doesn't the consulting geologist help in determining this?

Max: Definitely. I hardly ever drill without his input.

Jennifer: So shouldn't your criterion for deciding whether to drill be based directly on this input?

Max: Yes, it should.

Jennifer: But then I don't understand why you keep objecting to using the consulting geologist's numbers.

Max: I'm not objecting to using his input. This input is vital to my decision. What I object to is using his numbers, one chance in four of oil, as being the gospel truth. That is what this Bayes' decision rule seems to do. We both saw what a close decision this was, 100 versus 90. What happens if his numbers are off some, as they probably are? This is too important a decision to be based on some numbers that are largely pulled out of the air.

Jennifer: OK, I see. Now he says that there is one chance in four of oil, a 25 percent chance. Do you think that is the right ballpark at least? If not 25 percent, how much lower might it be? Or how much higher?

Max: I usually add and subtract 10 percent from whatever the consulting geologist says. So I suppose the chance of oil is likely to be somewhere between 15 percent and 35 percent.

Jennifer: Good. Now we're getting somewhere. I think I know exactly what we should do next.

Max: What's that?

Jennifer: There is a management science technique that is designed for just this kind of situation. It is called *sensitivity analysis.* It will allow us to investigate what happens if the consulting geologist's numbers are off.

Max: Great! Let's do it.

Review
Questions

1. What is a *decision tree?*
2. What is a *decision node* in a decision tree? An *event node?*
3. What symbols are used to represent decision nodes and event nodes?

9.4 SENSITIVITY ANALYSIS WITH DECISION TREES

Sensitivity analysis (an important type of *what-if analysis* introduced in Section 5.1) commonly is used with various applications of management science to study the effect if some of the numbers included in the mathematical model are not correct. In this case, the mathematical model is represented by the decision tree shown in Figure 9.6. The numbers in this tree that are most questionable are the prior probabilities in cells H1 and H6, so we will initially focus the sensitivity analysis on these numbers.

It is helpful to start this process by consolidating the data and results on the spreadsheet below the decision tree, as in Figure 9.7. As indicated by the formulas at the bottom of the figure, the cells giving the results make reference to the corresponding output cells on the decision tree. Similarly, the data cells on the decision tree now reference the corresponding data cells below the tree. Consequently, the user can experiment with various alternative values in the data cells below and the results will simultaneously change in both the decision tree and the results section below the tree to reflect the new data.

Excel Tip: Consolidating the data and results on the spreadsheet makes it easier to do sensitivity analysis and also makes the model and results easier to interpret.

Consolidating the data and results offers a couple of advantages. First, it assures that each piece of data is in only one place. Each time that piece of data is needed in the decision tree, a reference is made to the single data cell below. This greatly simplifies sensitivity analysis. To change a piece of data, it needs to be changed in only one place rather than searching through

334   Chapter Nine *Decision Analysis*

FIGURE 9.7

In preparation for performing sensitivity analysis on the first Goferbroke Co. problem, the data and results have been consolidated on the spreadsheet below the decision tree.

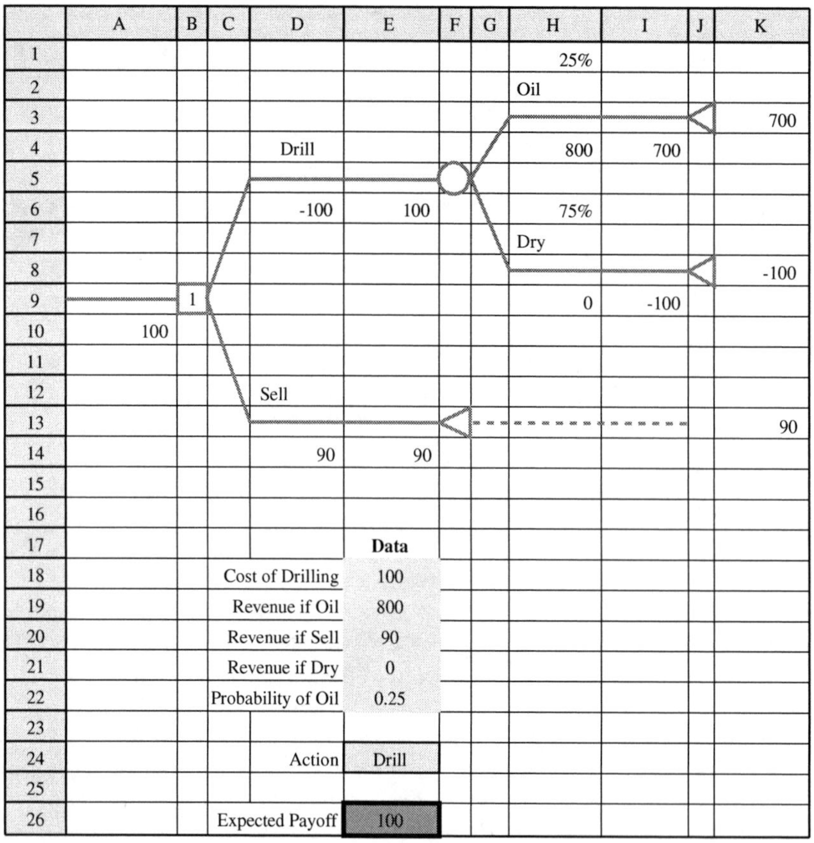

	A	B	C	D	E	F	G	H	I	J	K
1								25%			
2								Oil			
3											700
4				Drill				800	700		
5											
6				-100	100			75%			
7								Dry			
8											-100
9			1					0	-100		
10	100										
11											
12				Sell							
13											90
14				90	90						
15											
16											
17					**Data**						
18				Cost of Drilling	100						
19				Revenue if Oil	800						
20				Revenue if Sell	90						
21				Revenue if Dry	0						
22				Probability of Oil	0.25						
23											
24				Action	Drill						
25											
26				Expected Payoff	100						

	D
4	Drill
5	
6	=−CostOfDrilling

	D
12	Sell
13	
14	=RevenueIfSell

	H
1	=ProbabilityOfOil
2	Oil
3	
4	=RevenueIfOil
5	
6	=1− ProbabilityOfOil
7	Dry
8	
9	=RevenueIfDry

Range Name	Cell
Action	E24
CostOfDrilling	E18
ExpectedPayoff	E26
ProbabilityOfOil	E22
RevenueIfDry	E21
RevenueIfOil	E19
RevenueIfSell	E20

	D	E
24	Action	=IF(B9=1,"Drill","Sell")
25		
26	Expected Payoff	=A10

the entire tree to find and change all occurrences of that piece of data.[1] A second advantage of consolidating the data and results is that it makes it easy for *anyone* to interpret the model. It is not necessary to understand RSPE or how to read a decision tree in order to see what data were used in the model or what the suggested plan of action and expected payoff are.

[1] In this very simple decision tree, this advantage does not become evident since each piece of data is only used once in the tree anyway. However, in later sections, when the possibility of seismic testing is considered, some data will be repeated many times in the tree and this advantage will become more clear.

The sum of the two prior probabilities must equal one, so increasing one of these probabilities automatically decreases the other one by the same amount, and vice versa. This is enforced on the decision tree in Figure 9.7 by the equation in cell H6—the probability of a dry site = H6 = 1 − ProbabilityOfOil (E22). Max has concluded that the true chances of having oil on the tract of land are likely to lie somewhere between 15 and 35 percent. In other words, the true prior probability of having oil is likely to be in the range from 0.15 to 0.35, so the corresponding prior probability of the land being dry would range from 0.85 to 0.65.

We can begin sensitivity analysis by simply trying different trial values for the prior probability of oil. This is done in Figure 9.8, first with this probability at the lower end of the range (0.15) and next with this probability at the upper end (0.35). When the prior probability of oil is only 0.15, the decision swings over to selling the land by a wide margin (an expected payoff of 90 versus only 20 for drilling). However, when this probability is 0.35, the decision is to drill by a wide margin (expected payoff = 180 versus only 90 for selling). Thus, the decision is very *sensitive* to the prior probability of oil. This sensitivity analysis has revealed that it is important to do more, if possible, to pin down just what the true value of the probability of oil is.

Using a Data Table to Do Sensitivity Analysis Systematically

A data table displays the results of selected output cells for various trial values of a data cell.

To pin down just where the suggested course of action changes, we could continue selecting new trial values of the prior probability of oil at random. However, a better approach is to systematically consider a range of values. A feature built into Excel, called a data table, is designed to perform just this sort of analysis. Data tables are used to show the results of certain output cells for various trial values of a data cell.

To use data tables, first make a table on the spreadsheet with headings as shown in columns I, J, and K in Figure 9.9. In the first column of the table (I19:I29), list the trial values for the data cell (the prior probability of oil), except leave the first row blank. The headings of the next columns specify which output will be evaluated. For each of these columns, use the first row of the table (cells J18:K18) to write an equation that refers to the relevant output cell. In this case, the cells of interest are Action (E24) and ExpectedPayoff (E26), so the equations for J18:K18 are those shown below the spreadsheet in Figure 9.9.

Next, select the entire table (I18:K29) and then choose Data Table from the What-If Analysis menu of the Data tab. In the Data Table dialog box (as shown at the bottom left of Figure 9.9), indicate the column input cell (E22), which refers to the data cell that is being changed in the first column of the table. Nothing is entered for the row input cell because no row is being used to list the trial values of a data cell in this case.

Clicking OK then generates the data table shown in Figure 9.10. For each trial value for the data cell listed in the first column of the table, the corresponding output cell values are calculated and displayed in the other columns of the table. (The entries in the first row of the table come from the original solution in the spreadsheet.)

Figure 9.10 reveals that the best course of action switches from Sell to Drill for a prior probability of oil somewhere between 0.23 and 0.25. Trial and error (or algebra) can be used to pin this number down more precisely. It turns out to be 0.2375.

For a problem with more than two possible states of nature, the most straightforward approach is to focus the sensitivity analysis on only two states at a time as described above. This again would involve investigating what happens when the prior probability of one state increases as the prior probability of the other state decreases by the same amount, holding fixed the prior probabilities of the remaining states. This procedure then can be repeated for as many other pairs of states as desired.

Max's Reaction

Max: That data table paints a pretty clear picture. I think I'm getting a much better handle on the problem.

Jennifer: Good.

Max: Less than a 23¾ percent chance of oil, I should sell. If it's more, I should drill. It confirms what I suspected all along. This is a close decision, and it all boils down to picking the right number for the chances of oil. I sure wish I had more to go on than the consulting geologist's numbers.

336   Chapter Nine   *Decision Analysis*

FIGURE 9.8
Performing sensitivity analysis for the first Goferbroke Co. problem by trying alternative values (0.15 and 0.35) of the prior probability of oil.

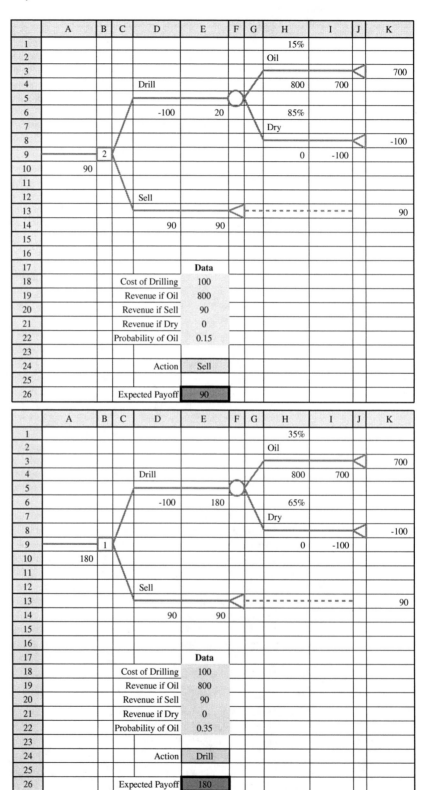

FIGURE 9.9

Expansion of the spreadsheet in Figure 9.7 to prepare for generating a data table, where the choice of E22 for the column input cell in the Data Table dialog box indicates that this is the data cell that is being changed in the first column of the data table.

	A	B	C	D	E	F	G	H	I	J	K	L	M
16									Probability		Expected		
17					**Data**				of Oil	Action	Payoff		
18				Cost of Drilling	100					Drill	100	Select these	
19				Revenue if Oil	800				15%			cells	
20				Revenue if Sell	90				17%			(I18:K29),	
21				Revenue if Dry	0				19%			before	
22				Probability of Oil	0.25				21%			choosing	
23									23%			Data Table	
24				Action	Drill				25%			from the	
25									27%			What-If	
26				Expected Payoff	100				29%			Analysis is	
27									31%			menu of the	
28									33%			Data tab	
29									35%				

Data Table

Row input cell:

Column input cell: E22

OK   Cancel

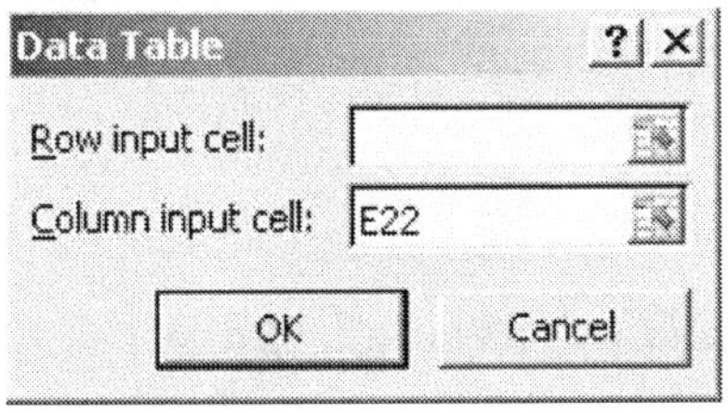

	J	K
16		Expected
17	Action	Payoff
18	=Action	=ExpectedPayoff

Range Name	Cell
Action	E24
ExpectedPayoff	E26

FIGURE 9.10

After the preparation displayed in Figure 9.9, clicking OK generates this data table that shows the optimal action and expected payoff for various trial values of the prior probability of oil.

	I	J	K
16	Probability		Expected
17	of Oil	Action	Payoff
18		Drill	100
19	15%	Sell	90
20	17%	Sell	90
21	19%	Sell	90
22	21%	Sell	90
23	23%	Sell	90
24	25%	Drill	100
25	27%	Drill	116
26	29%	Drill	132
27	31%	Drill	148
28	33%	Drill	164
29	35%	Drill	180

Jennifer: You talked earlier about the possibility of paying $30,000 to get a detailed seismic survey of the land.

Max: Yes, I might have to do that. But 30,000 bucks! I'm still not sure that it's worth that much dough.

The next section describes how to find and use the expected value of perfect information.

Jennifer: I have a quick way of checking that. It's another technique I learned in my management science course. It's called finding the **expected value of perfect information (EVPI).** The expected value of perfect information is the increase in the expected payoff you would get if the seismic survey could tell you for sure if there is oil there.

Max: But it can't tell you for sure.

Jennifer: Yes, I know. But finding out for sure if oil is there is what we refer to as perfect information. So the increase in the expected payoff if you find out for sure is the expected value of perfect information. We know that's better than you actually can do with a seismic survey.

Max: Right.

Jennifer: OK, suppose we find that the expected value of perfect information is less than $30,000. Since that is better than we can do with a seismic survey, that tells us right off the bat that it wouldn't pay to do the seismic survey.

Max: OK, I get it. But what if this expected value of perfect information is more than $30,000?

Jennifer: Then you don't know for sure whether the seismic survey is worth it until you do some more analysis. This analysis takes some time, whereas it is very quick to calculate the expected value of perfect information. So it is well worth simply checking whether the expected value of perfect information is less than $30,000 and, if so, saving a lot of additional work.

Max: OK. Let's do it.

**Review
Questions**

1. Why might it be helpful to use sensitivity analysis with Bayes' decision rule?
2. When preparing to perform sensitivity analysis, what are a couple of advantages of consolidating the data and results on the spreadsheet that contains the decision tree?
3. What is shown by a data table when it is used to perform sensitivity analysis?
4. What conclusion was drawn for the first Goferbroke Co. problem regarding how the decision should depend on the prior probability of oil?

9.5   CHECKING WHETHER TO OBTAIN MORE INFORMATION

Definitely identifying the true state of nature is referred to as *perfect information.* This represents the best outcome of seeking more information.

Prior probabilities may provide somewhat inaccurate estimates of the true probabilities of the states of nature. Might it be worthwhile for Max to spend some money for a seismic survey to obtain better estimates? The quickest way to check this is to pretend that it is possible for the same amount of money to actually determine which state is the true state of nature ("perfect information") and then determine whether obtaining this information would make this expenditure worthwhile. If having perfect information would not be worthwhile, then it definitely would not be worthwhile to spend this money just to learn more about the probabilities of the states of nature.

The key quantities for performing this analysis are

$$\text{EP (without more info)} = \text{Expected payoff from applying Bayes' decision rule}$$
$$\text{with the original prior probabilities}$$
$$= 100 \quad \text{(as given in Figure 9.7)}$$

$$\text{EP (with perfect info)} = \text{Expected payoff if the decision could be made after}$$
$$\text{learning the true state of nature}$$

$$\text{EVPI} = \text{Expected value of perfect information}$$

$$C = \text{Cost of obtaining more information}$$
$$= 30 \text{ (cost of the seismic survey in thousands of dollars)}$$

The **expected value of perfect information** is calculated as

$$\text{EVPI} = \text{EP (with perfect info)} - \text{EP (without more info)}$$

After calculating EP (with perfect info) and then EVPI, the last step is to compare EVPI with C.

If $C > \text{EVPI}$, then it is not worthwhile to obtain more information.

If $C \leq \text{EVPI}$, then it might be worthwhile to obtain more information.

To calculate EP (with perfect info), we pretend that the decision can be made *after* learning the true state of nature. Given the true state of nature, we then would automatically choose the alternative with the maximum payoff for that state. Thus, we drill if we know there is oil,

FIGURE 9.11
By starting with an event node involving the states of nature, RSPE uses this decision tree to obtain the expected payoff with perfect information for the first Goferbroke Co. problem.

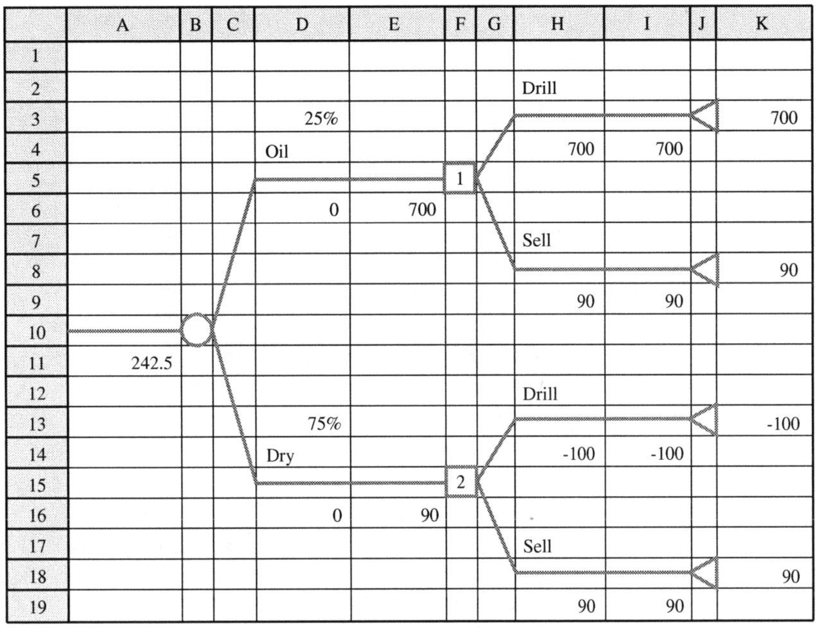

	A	B	C	D	E	F	G	H	I	J	K
1											
2								Drill			
3				25%							700
4				Oil				700	700		
5						1					
6				0	700						
7								Sell			
8											90
9								90	90		
10											
11	242.5										
12								Drill			
13				75%							-100
14				Dry				-100	-100		
15						2					
16				0	90						
17								Sell			
18											90
19								90	90		

whereas we sell if we know the site is dry. The prior probabilities still give our best estimate of the probability that each state of nature will turn out to be the true one. EP (with perfect info) is therefore the weighted average of the maximum payoff for each state, multiplying each maximum payoff by the prior probability of the corresponding state of nature. Thus,

$$\text{EP (with perfect info)} = (0.25)(700) + (0.75)(90)$$
$$= 242.5$$

RSPE also can be used to calculate EP (with perfect info) by constructing and solving the decision tree shown in Figure 9.11. The clever idea here is to *start* the decision tree with an event node whose branches are the various states of nature (oil and dry in this case). Since a decision node follows each of these branches, the decision is being made with perfect information about the true state of nature. Therefore, the expected payoff of 242.5 obtained by RSPE in cell A11 is the expected payoff with perfect information.

Starting the decision tree with an event node whose branches are the various states of nature corresponds to starting with perfect information about the true state of nature.

Since EP (with perfect info) = 242½, we now can calculate the expected value of perfect information as

$$\text{EVPI} = \text{EP (with perfect info)} - \text{EP (without more info)}$$
$$= 242.5 - 100$$
$$= 142.5$$

Conclusion: EVPI > C, since 142.5 > 30. Therefore, it might be worthwhile to do the seismic survey.

Max's Reaction

Max: So you're telling me that if the seismic survey could really be definitive in determining whether oil is there, doing the survey would increase my average payoff by about $142,500?

Jennifer: That's right.

Max: So after subtracting the $30,000 cost of the survey, I would be ahead $112,500. Well, too bad the surveys aren't that good. In fact, they're not all that reliable.

Jennifer: Tell me more. How reliable are they?

340 Chapter Nine *Decision Analysis*

Max: Well, they come back with seismic soundings. If the seismic soundings are favorable, then oil is fairly likely. If they are unfavorable, then oil is pretty unlikely. But you can't tell for sure.

Jennifer: OK. Suppose oil is there. How often would you get favorable seismic soundings?

Max: I can't give you an exact number. Maybe 60 percent.

Jennifer: OK, good. Now suppose that the land is dry. How often would you still get favorable seismic soundings?

Max: Too often! I've lost a lot of money drilling when the seismic survey said to and then nothing was there. That's why I don't like to spend the 30,000 bucks.

Jennifer: Sure. So it tells you to drill when you shouldn't close to half the time?

Max: No. It's not that bad. But fairly often.

Jennifer: Can you give me a percentage?

Max: OK. Maybe 20 percent.

Jennifer: Good. Thanks. Now I think we can do some analysis to determine whether it is really worthwhile to do the seismic survey.

Max: How do you do the analysis?

Jennifer: Well, I'll describe the process in detail pretty soon. But here is the general idea. We'll do some calculations to determine what the chances of oil would be if the seismic soundings turn out to be favorable. Then we'll calculate the chances if the soundings are unfavorable. We called the consulting geologist's numbers prior probabilities because they were prior to obtaining more information. The improved numbers are referred to as **posterior probabilities.**

Max: OK.

Posterior probabilities are the revised probabilities of the states of nature after doing a test or survey to improve the prior probabilities.

Jennifer: Then we'll use these posterior probabilities to determine the average payoff, after subtracting the $30,000 cost, if we do the seismic survey. If this payoff is better than we would do without the seismic survey, then we should do it. Otherwise, not.

Max: That makes sense.

Review Questions

1. What is meant by perfect information regarding the states of nature?
2. How can the expected payoff with perfect information be calculated from the payoff table?
3. How should a decision tree be constructed to obtain the expected payoff with perfect information by solving the tree?
4. What is the formula for calculating the expected value of perfect information?
5. What is the conclusion if the cost of obtaining more information is more than the expected value of perfect information?
6. What is the conclusion if the cost of obtaining more information is less than the expected value of perfect information?
7. Which of these two cases occurs in the Goferbroke Co. problem?

9.6 USING NEW INFORMATION TO UPDATE THE PROBABILITIES

The prior probabilities of the possible states of nature often are quite subjective in nature, so they may be only very rough estimates of the true probabilities. Fortunately, it frequently is possible to do some additional testing or surveying (at some expense) to improve these estimates. These improved estimates are called **posterior probabilities.**

In the case of the Goferbroke Co., these improved estimates can be obtained at a cost of $30,000 by conducting a detailed seismic survey of the land. The possible findings from such a survey are summarized below.

Possible Findings from a Seismic Survey

FSS: Favorable seismic soundings; oil is fairly likely.

USS: Unfavorable seismic soundings; oil is quite unlikely.

TABLE 9.7

Probabilities of the Possible Findings from the Seismic Survey, Given the State of Nature, for the Goferbroke Co. Problem

	P (finding | state)	
State of Nature	**Favorable (FSS)**	**Unfavorable (USS)**
Oil	*P*(FSS | Oil) = 0.6	*P*(USS | Oil) = 0.4
Dry	*P*(FSS | Dry) = 0.2	*P*(USS | Dry) = 0.8

To use either finding to calculate the posterior probability of oil (or of being dry), it is necessary to estimate the probability of obtaining this finding for each state of nature. During the conversation at the end of the preceding section, Jennifer elicited these estimates from Max, as summarized in Table 9.7. (Max actually only estimated the probability of favorable seismic soundings, but subtracting this number from one gives the probability of unfavorable seismic soundings.) The symbol used in the table for each of these estimated probabilities is

$$P(\text{finding} \mid \text{state}) = \text{Probability that the indicated finding will occur, given that the state of nature is the indicated one}$$

This kind of probability is referred to as a *conditional probability,* because it is conditioned on being given the state of nature.

Recall that the prior probabilities are

$$P(\text{Oil}) = 0.25$$
$$P(\text{Dry}) = 0.75$$

The next step is to use these probabilities and the probabilities in Table 9.7 to obtain a combined probability called a *joint probability.* Each combination of a state of nature and a finding from the seismic survey will have a joint probability that is determined by the following formula.

$$P(\text{state and finding}) = P(\text{state}) \, P(\text{finding} \mid \text{state})$$

For example, the joint probability that the state of nature is Oil *and* the finding from the seismic survey is favorable (FSS) is

$$P(\text{Oil and FSS}) = P(\text{Oil}) \, P(\text{FSS} \mid \text{Oil})$$
$$= 0.25(0.6)$$
$$= 0.15$$

Each joint probability in the third column of the probability tree diagram is the product of the probabilities in the first two columns.

The calculation of all these joint probabilities is shown in the third column of the **probability tree diagram** given in Figure 9.12. The case involved is identified underneath each branch of the tree and the probability is given over the branch. The first column gives the prior probabilities and then the probabilities from Table 9.7 are shown in the second column. Multiplying each probability in the first column by a probability in the second column gives the corresponding joint probability in the third column.

Having found each joint probability of both a particular state of nature and a particular finding from the seismic survey, the next step is to use these probabilities to find each probability of just a particular finding without specifying the state of nature. Since any finding can be obtained with any state of nature, the formula for calculating the probability of just a particular finding is

$$P(\text{finding}) = P(\text{Oil and finding}) + P(\text{Dry and finding})$$

The probability of a finding is the sum of the corresponding joint probabilities in the third column of the probability tree diagram.

For example, the probability of a favorable finding (FSS) is

$$P(\text{FSS}) = P(\text{Oil and FSS}) + P(\text{Dry and FSS})$$
$$= 0.15 + 0.15 = 0.3$$

where the two joint probabilities on the right-hand side of this equation are found on the first and third branches of the third column of the probability tree diagram. The calculation of both *P*(FSS) and *P*(USS) is shown underneath the diagram. (These are referred to as *unconditional* probabilities to differentiate them from the *conditional* probabilities of a finding given the state of nature, shown in the second column.)

342 Chapter Nine *Decision Analysis*

FIGURE 9.12

Probability tree diagram for the Goferbroke Co. problem showing all the probabilities leading to the calculation of each posterior probability of the state of nature given the finding of the seismic survey.

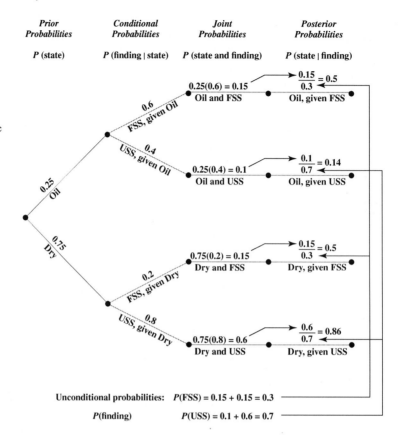

Finally, we now are ready to calculate each *posterior probability* of a particular state of nature given a particular finding from the seismic survey. The formula involves combining the joint probabilities in the third column with the unconditional probabilities underneath the diagram as follows.

$$P(\text{state} \mid \text{finding}) = \frac{P(\text{state and finding})}{P(\text{finding})}$$

For example, the posterior probability that the true state of nature is oil, given a favorable finding (FSS) from the seismic survey, is

$$P(\text{Oil} \mid \text{FSS}) = \frac{P(\text{Oil and FSS})}{P(\text{FSS})}$$

$$= \frac{0.15}{0.3} = 0.5$$

The arrows in the probability tree diagram show where the numbers come from for calculating the posterior probabilities.

The fourth column of the probability tree diagram shows the calculation of all the posterior probabilities. The arrows indicate how each numerator comes from the corresponding joint probability in the third column and the denominator comes from the corresponding unconditional probability below the diagram.

By using the formulas given earlier for the joint probabilities and unconditional probabilities, each posterior probability also can be calculated directly from the prior probabilities (first column) and the conditional probabilities (second column) as follows.

$$P(\text{state} \mid \text{finding}) = \frac{P(\text{state}) \, P(\text{finding} \mid \text{state})}{P(\text{Oil}) \, P(\text{finding} \mid \text{Oil}) + P(\text{Dry}) \, P(\text{finding} \mid \text{Dry})}$$

TABLE 9.8

Posterior Probabilities of the States of Nature, Given the Finding from the Seismic Survey, for the Goferbroke Co. Problem

	P (state | finding)	
Finding	**Oil**	**Dry**
Favorable (FSS)	*P*(Oil | FSS) = 1/2	*P*(Dry | FSS) = 1/2
Unfavorable (USS)	*P*(Oil | USS) = 1/7	*P*(Dry | USS) = 6/7

For example, the posterior probability of oil, given a favorable finding (FSS), is

$$P(\text{Oil} \mid \text{FSS}) = \frac{P(\text{Oil})\, P(\text{FSS} \mid \text{Oil})}{P(\text{Oil})\, P(\text{FSS} \mid \text{Oil}) + P(\text{Dry})\, P(\text{FSS} \mid \text{Dry})}$$

$$= \frac{0.25(0.6)}{0.25(0.6) + 0.75(0.2)}$$

$$= 0.5$$

This formula for a posterior probability is known as **Bayes' theorem,** in honor of its discovery by the Reverend Bayes. The clever Reverend Bayes found that any posterior probability can be found in this way for any decision analysis problem, regardless of how many states of nature it has. The denominator in the formula would contain one such term for each of the states of nature. Note that the probability tree diagram also is applying Bayes' theorem, but in smaller steps rather than a single long formula.

Table 9.8 summarizes all the posterior probabilities calculated in Figure 9.12.

After you learn the logic of calculating posterior probabilities, we suggest that you use the computer to perform these rather lengthy calculations. We have provided an Excel template (labeled Posterior Probabilities) for this purpose in this chapter's Excel files in your MS Courseware. Figure 9.13 illustrates the use of this template for the Goferbroke Co. problem. All you do is enter the prior probabilities and the conditional probabilities from the first two columns of Figure 9.12 into the top half of the template. The posterior probabilities then immediately appear in the bottom half. (The equations entered into the cells in columns E through H are similar to those for column D shown at the bottom of the figure.)

Max's Reaction

Max: So this is saying that even with favorable seismic soundings, I still only have one chance in two of finding oil. No wonder I've been disappointed so often in the past when I've drilled after receiving a favorable seismic survey. I thought those surveys were supposed to be more reliable than that. So now I'm even more unenthusiastic about paying 30,000 bucks to get a survey done.

Jennifer: But one chance in two of oil. Those are good odds.

Max: Yes, they are. But I'm likely to lay out 30,000 bucks and then just get an unfavorable survey back.

Jennifer: My calculations indicate that you have about a 70 percent chance of that happening.

Max: See what I mean?

Jennifer: But even an unfavorable survey tells you a lot. Just one chance in seven of oil then. That might rule out drilling. So a seismic survey really does pin down the odds of oil a lot better. Either one chance in two or one chance in seven instead of the ballpark estimate of one chance in four from the consulting geologist.

Max: Yes, I suppose that's right. I really would like to improve the consulting geologist's numbers. It sounds like you're recommending that we do the seismic survey.

Jennifer: Well, actually, I'm not quite sure yet. What we'll do is sketch out a decision tree, showing the decision on whether to do the seismic survey and then the decision on whether to drill or sell. Then we'll work out the average payoffs for these decisions on the decision tree.

Max: OK, let's do it. I want to make a decision soon.

FIGURE 9.13
The Posterior Probabilities template in your MS Courseware enables efficient calculation of posterior probabilities, as illustrated here for the Goferbroke Co. problem.

	A	B	C	D	E	F	G	H
1		**Template for Posterior Probabilities**						
2								
3		**Data:**		*P*(Finding I State)				
4		State of	Prior	Finding				
5		Nature	Probability	FSS	USS			
6		Oil	0.25	0.6	0.4			
7		Dry	0.75	0.2	0.8			
8								
9								
10								
11								
12		**Posterior**		*P*(State I Finding)				
13		**Probabilities:**		State of Nature				
14		Finding	*P*(Finding)	Oil	Dry			
15		FSS	0.3	0.5	0.5			
16		USS	0.7	0.14286	0.85714			
17								
18								
19								

	B	C	D
12	**Posterior**		*P*(State I Finding)
13	**Probabilities:**		State of Nature
14	Finding	*P*(Finding)	=B6
15	=D5	=SUMPRODUCT(C6:C10,D6:D10)	=C6*D6/SUMPRODUCT(C6:C10,D6:D10)
16	=E5	=SUMPRODUCT(C6:C10,E6:E10)	=C6*E6/SUMPRODUCT(C6:C10,E6:E10)
17	=F5	=SUMPRODUCT(C6:C10,F6:F10)	=C6*F6/SUMPRODUCT(C6:C10,F6:F10)
18	=G5	=SUMPRODUCT(C6:C10,G6:G10)	=C6*G6/SUMPRODUCT(C6:C10,G6:G10)
19	=H5	=SUMPRODUCT(C6:C10,H6:H10)	=C6*H6/SUMPRODUCT(C6:C10,H6:H10)

Review Questions

1. What are posterior probabilities of the states of nature?
2. What are the possible findings from a seismic survey for the Goferbroke Co.?
3. What probabilities need to be estimated in addition to prior probabilities in order to begin calculating posterior probabilities?
4. What five kinds of probabilities are considered in a probability tree diagram?
5. What is the formula for calculating *P*(state and finding)?
6. What is the formula for calculating *P*(finding)?
7. What is the formula for calculating a posterior probability, *P*(state | finding), from *P*(state and finding) and *P*(finding)?
8. What is the name of the famous theorem for how to calculate posterior probabilities?

9.7 USING A DECISION TREE TO ANALYZE THE PROBLEM WITH A SEQUENCE OF DECISIONS

We now turn our attention to analyzing the *full* Goferbroke Co. problem with the help of a decision tree. For the full problem, there is a sequence of two decisions to be made. First, should a seismic survey be conducted? Second, after obtaining the results of the seismic survey (if it is conducted), should the company drill for oil or sell the land?

As described in Section 9.3, a **decision tree** provides a graphical display of the progression of decisions and random events for the problem. Figure 9.2 in that section shows the decision tree for the first Goferbroke problem where the only decision under consideration is whether to drill for oil or sell the land. Figure 9.6 then shows the same decision tree as it would be constructed and solved with RSPE.

Constructing the Decision Tree

Now that a prior decision needs to be made on whether to conduct a seismic survey, this same decision tree needs to be expanded as shown in Figure 9.14 (before including any numbers). Recall that each *square* in the tree represents a *decision node,* where a decision needs to be made, and each *circle* represents an *event node,* where a random event will occur.

Thus, the first decision (should we have a seismic survey done?) is represented by decision node *a* in Figure 9.14. The two branches leading out of this node correspond to the two alternatives for this decision. Node *b* is an event node representing the random event of the outcome of the seismic survey. The two branches emanating from node *b* represent the two possible outcomes of the survey. Next comes the second decision (nodes *c, d,* and *e*) with its two possible choices. If the decision is to drill for oil, then we come to another event node (nodes *f, g,* and *h*), where its two branches correspond to the two possible states of nature.

The next step is to insert numbers into the decision tree as shown in Figure 9.15. The numbers under or over the branches that are *not* in parentheses are the cash flows (in thousands of dollars) that occur at those branches. For each path through the tree from node *a* to a final branch, these same numbers then are added to obtain the resulting total payoff shown in boldface to the right of that branch. The last set of numbers is the probabilities of random events. In particular, since each branch emanating from an event node represents a possible random event, the probability of this event occurring from this node has been inserted in parentheses along this branch. From event node *h,* the probabilities are the *prior probabilities* of these states of nature, since no seismic survey has been conducted to obtain more information in this case. However, event nodes *f* and *g* lead out of a decision to do the seismic survey (and then to drill). Therefore, the probabilities from these event nodes are the *posterior probabilities* of the states of nature, given the outcome of the seismic survey, where these numbers are obtained from Table 9.8 or from cells D15:E16 in Figure 9.13. Finally, we have the two

The numbers in parentheses are probabilities.

FIGURE 9.14

The decision tree for the full Goferbroke Co. problem (before including any numbers) when first deciding whether to conduct a seismic survey.

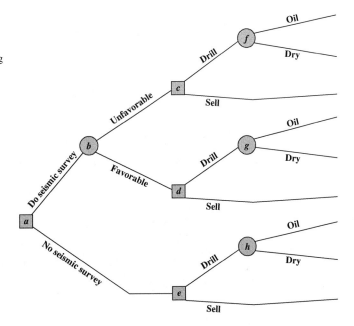

An Application Vignette

The **Westinghouse Science and Technology Center** is the Westinghouse Electric Corporation's main research and development (R&D) arm to develop new technology. The process of evaluating R&D projects to decide which ones should be initiated and then which ones should be continued as progress is made (or not made) is particularly challenging for management because of the great uncertainties and very long time horizons involved. The actual launch date for an embryonic technology may be years, even decades, removed from its inception as a modest R&D proposal to investigate the technology's potential.

As the center came under increasing pressure to reduce costs and deliver high-impact technology quickly, the center's controller funded a management science project to improve this evaluation process. The management science team developed a *decision tree approach* to analyzing any R&D proposal while considering its complete sequence of key decision points. The first decision point is whether to fund the proposed embryonic project for the first year or so. If its early technical milestones are reached, the next decision point is whether to continue funding the project for some period. This may then be repeated one or more times. If the late technical milestones are reached, the next decision point is whether to prelaunch because the innovation still meets strategic business objectives. If a strategic fit is achieved, the final decision point is whether to commercialize the innovation now or to delay its launch or to abandon it altogether. A *decision tree* with a progression of decision nodes and intervening event nodes provides a natural way of depicting and analyzing such an R&D project.

Source: R. K. Perdue, W. J. McAllister, P. V. King, and B. G. Berkey, "Valuation of R and D Projects Using Options Pricing and Decision Analysis Models," *Interfaces* 29, no. 6 (November–December 1999), pp. 57–74. (A link to this article is provided on our website, **www.mhhe.com/hillier5e**.)

branches emanating from event node b. The numbers here are the probabilities of these findings from the seismic survey, Favorable (FSS) or Unfavorable (USS), as given underneath the probability tree diagram in Figure 9.12 or in cells C15:C16 of Figure 9.13.

Performing the Analysis

Having constructed the decision tree, including its numbers, we now are ready to analyze the problem by using the following procedure.

1. Start at the right side of the decision tree and move left one column at a time. For each column, perform either step 2 or step 3 depending on whether the nodes in that column are event nodes or decision nodes.

FIGURE 9.15

The decision tree in Figure 9.14 after adding both the probabilities of random events and the payoffs.

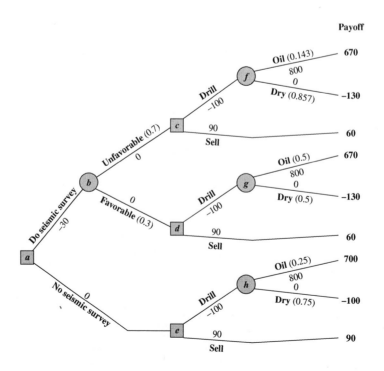

The expected payoff needs to be calculated for each event node.

2. For each event node, calculate its *expected payoff* by multiplying the expected payoff of each branch (shown in boldface to the right of the branch) by the probability of that branch and then summing these products. Record this expected payoff for each event node in boldface next to the node, and designate this quantity as also being the expected payoff for the branch leading to this node.

3. For each decision node, compare the expected payoffs of its branches and choose the alternative whose branch has the largest expected payoff. In each case, record the choice on the decision tree.

To begin the procedure, consider the rightmost column of nodes, namely, event nodes *f, g,* and *h*. Applying step 2, their expected payoffs (EP) are calculated as

$$\text{EP} = \frac{1}{7}(670) + \frac{6}{7}(-130) = -15.7 \quad \text{for node } f$$

$$\text{EP} = \frac{1}{2}(670) + \frac{1}{2}(-130) = 270 \quad \text{for node } g$$

$$\text{EP} = \frac{1}{4}(700) + \frac{3}{4}(-100) = 100 \quad \text{for node } h$$

These expected payoffs then are placed above these nodes, as shown in Figure 9.16.

Next, we move one column to the left, which consists of decision nodes *c, d,* and *e*. The expected payoff for a branch that leads to an event node now is recorded in boldface over that event node. Therefore, step 3 can be applied as follows:

Node *c:*   Drill alternative has EP = −15.7
           Sell alternative has EP = 60
           60 > −15.7, so choose the Sell alternative

Node *d:*   Drill alternative has EP = 270
           Sell alternative has EP = 60
           270 > 60, so choose the Drill alternative

FIGURE 9.16

The final decision tree that records the analysis for the full Goferbroke Co. problem when using monetary payoffs.

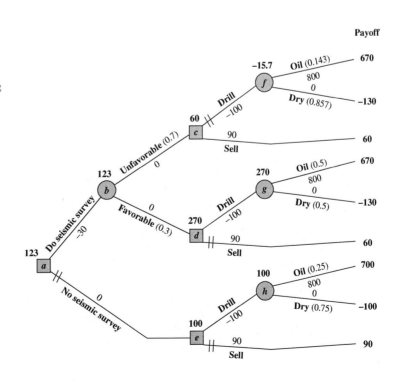

Node *e:*   Drill alternative has EP $= 100$

Sell alternative has EP $= 90$

$100 > 90$, so choose the Drill alternative

A double dash indicates a rejected decision.

The expected payoff for each chosen alternative now would be recorded in boldface over its decision node, as shown in Figure 9.16. The chosen alternative also is indicated by inserting a double dash as a barrier through each rejected branch.

Next, moving one more column to the left brings us to node *b*. Since this is an event node, step 2 of the procedure needs to be applied. The expected payoff for each of its branches is recorded over the following decision node. Therefore, the expected payoff is

$$EP = 0.7(60) + 0.3(270) = 123 \qquad \text{for node } b$$

as recorded over this node in Figure 9.16.

Finally, we move left to node *a,* a decision node. Applying step 3 yields

Node *a*:   Do seismic survey has EP $= 123$

No seismic survey has EP $= 100$

$123 > 100$, so choose Do seismic survey.

This expected payoff of 123 now would be recorded over the node, and a double dash inserted to indicate the rejected branch, as already shown in Figure 9.16.

This procedure has moved from right to left for analysis purposes. However, having completed the decision tree in this way, the decision maker now can read the tree from left to right to see the actual progression of events. The double dashes have closed off the undesirable paths. Therefore, given the payoffs for the final outcomes shown on the right side, *Bayes' decision rule* says to follow only the open paths from left to right to achieve the largest possible expected payoff.

The open paths (no double dashes) provide the optimal decision at each decision node.

Following the open paths from left to right in Figure 9.16 yields the following optimal policy, according to Bayes' decision rule.

Optimal Policy

Do the seismic survey.

If the result is unfavorable, sell the land.

If the result is favorable, drill for oil.

The expected payoff (including the cost of the seismic survey) is 123 ($123,000).

Expected Value of Sample Information

We have assumed so far that the cost of the seismic survey for the full Goferbroke Co. problem is known in advance to be $30,000. However, suppose that there is uncertainty about this cost. How would this change the analysis described above?

In this case, the analysis would begin by identifying two key quantities,

EP (with more info)   = Expected payoff (excluding the cost of the survey) when the survey is done

EP (without more info) = Expected payoff when the survey is not done

where Bayes' decision rule is applied to find both quantities. EP (with more info) is obtained by using the top half of the decision tree in Figure 9.17 *except* that the (unknown) cost of the seismic survey is not included, so all the payoffs and expected payoffs would be 30 larger than shown there. Therefore, cell E19 indicates that

$$EP \text{ (with more info)} = 123 + 30 = 153$$

EP (without more info) is described at the beginning of Section 9.5, and is obtained here from the bottom half of the decision tree in Figure 9.17 without any change, so cell E42 shows that

$$EP \text{ (without more info)} = 100$$

FIGURE 9.17

The decision tree constructed and solved by RSPE for the full Goferbroke Co. problem that also considers whether to do a seismic survey.

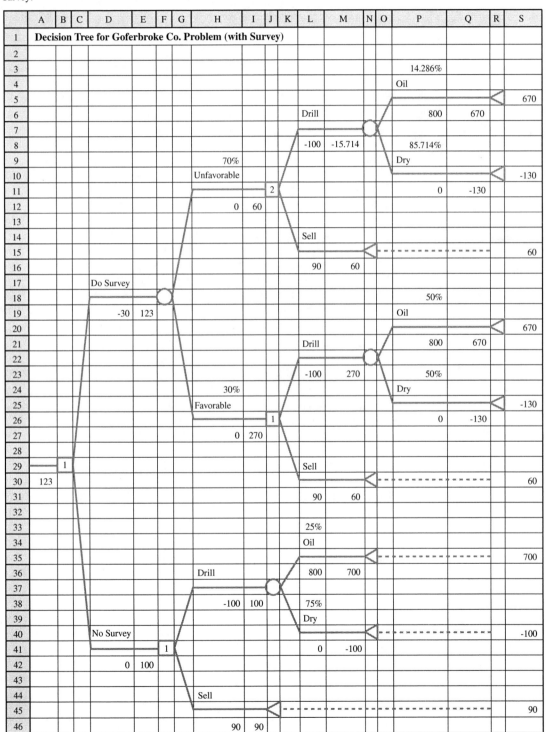

Now we can calculate the **expected value of sample information (EVSI)** (where "sample information" refers to the information from the seismic survey in this case) as

$$EVSI = EP \text{ (with more info)} - EP \text{ (without more info)}$$
$$= 153 - 100$$
$$= 53$$

Let

C = Best available estimate of the cost of the seismic survey (in thousands of dollars)

The final step in the analysis is to compare C and EVSI.

If $C <$ EVSI, then perform the seismic survey.

If $C \geq$ EVSI, then do not perform the seismic survey.

Using RSPE

Using the procedures described in Section 9.3, the Decision Tree tools of RSPE can be used to construct and solve this same decision tree on a spreadsheet. Figure 9.17 shows the decision tree obtained with RSPE. Although the form is somewhat different, note that this decision tree is completely equivalent to the one in Figure 9.16. Besides the convenience of constructing the tree directly on a spreadsheet, RSPE also provides the key advantage of automatically solving the decision tree. Rather than relying on hand calculations as in Figure 9.16, RSPE instantaneously calculates all the expected payoffs at each stage of the tree, as shown below and to the left of each node, as soon as the decision tree is constructed. Instead of using double dashes, RSPE puts a number inside each decision node indicating which branch should be chosen (assuming the branches emanating from that node are numbered consecutively from top to bottom).

Max's Reaction

Max: I see that this decision tree gives me some numbers to compare alternatives. But how reliable are those numbers?

Jennifer: Well, you have to remember that these average payoffs for the alternatives at the decision nodes are based on both the payoffs on the right and the probabilities at the event nodes. These probabilities are based in turn on the consulting geologist's numbers and the numbers you gave me on how frequently you get favorable seismic soundings when you have oil or when the land is dry.

Max: That doesn't sound so good. You know what I think about the consulting geologist's numbers. And the numbers I gave you were pretty rough estimates.

Jennifer: True. So the average payoffs shown in the decision tree are only approximations. This is when some sensitivity analysis can be helpful, like we did earlier before we considered doing the seismic survey.

Max: OK. So let's do it.

Review Questions

1. What does a decision tree display?
2. What is happening at a decision node?
3. What is happening at an event node?
4. What kinds of numbers need to be inserted into a decision tree before beginning the analysis?
5. When performing the analysis, where do you begin on the decision tree and in which direction do you move for dealing with the nodes?
6. What calculation needs to be performed at each event node?
7. What comparison needs to be made at each decision node?
8. What is meant by the expected value of sample information and how might it be used?

9.8 PERFORMING SENSITIVITY ANALYSIS ON THE PROBLEM WITH A SEQUENCE OF DECISIONS

Section 9.4 describes how the decision tree created with RSPE (Figures 9.6 and 9.7) was used to perform sensitivity analysis for the first Goferbroke problem where the only decision being made was whether to drill for oil or sell the land (without conducting the seismic survey). The focus was on one particularly critical piece of data, the prior probability of oil, so the analysis involved checking whether the decision would change if the original value of this prior probability (0.25) were changed to various other trial values. New trial values first were considered in a trial-and-error manner (Figure 9.8) and then were investigated more systematically by constructing a data table (Figure 9.10).

Since Max Flyer wants to consider whether to have a seismic survey conducted before deciding whether to drill or sell, the relevant decision tree now is the one in Figure 9.17 instead of the one in Figure 9.6. With this sequence of decisions and the resulting need to obtain and apply posterior probabilities, conducting **sensitivity analysis** becomes somewhat more involved. Let's see how it is done.

Organizing the Spreadsheet

As was done in Section 9.4, it is helpful to begin by consolidating the data and results into one section of the spreadsheet, as shown in Figure 9.18. The data cells in the decision tree now make reference to the consolidated data cells to the right of the decision tree (cells V4:V11). Similarly, the summarized results to the right of the decision tree make reference to the output cells within the decision tree (the decision nodes in cells B29, F41, J11, and J26, as well as the expected payoff in cell A30).

The probability data in the decision tree are complicated by the fact that the posterior probabilities will need to be updated any time a change is made in any of the prior probability data. Fortunately, the template for calculating posterior probabilities (as shown in Figure 9.13) can be used to do these calculations. The relevant portion of this template (B3:H19) has been copied (using the Copy and Paste commands in the Edit menu) to the spreadsheet in Figure 9.18 (now appearing in U30:AA46). The data for the template refer to the probability data in the data cells PriorProbabilityOfOil (V9), ProbFSSGivenOil (V10), and ProbUSSGivenDry (V11), as shown in the formulas for cells V33:X34 at the bottom of Figure 9.18. The template automatically calculates the probability of each finding and the posterior probabilities (in cells V42:X43) based on these data. The decision tree then refers to these calculated probabilities when they are needed, as shown in the formulas for cells P3:P11 in Figure 9.18.

While it takes some time and effort to consolidate the data and results, including all the necessary cross-referencing, this step is truly essential for performing sensitivity analysis. Many pieces of data are used in several places on the decision tree. For example, the revenue if Goferbroke finds oil appears in cells P6, P21, and L36. Performing sensitivity analysis on this piece of data now requires changing its value in only one place (cell V6) rather than three (cells P6, P21, and L36). The benefits of consolidation are even more important for the probability data. Changing any prior probability may cause *all* the posterior probabilities to change. By including the posterior probability template, the prior probability can be changed in one place and then all the other probabilities are calculated and updated appropriately.

After making any change in the cost data, revenue data, or probability data in Figure 9.18, the spreadsheet nicely summarizes the new results after the actual work to obtain these results is instantly done by the posterior probability template and the decision tree. Therefore, experimenting with alternative data values in a trial-and-error manner is one useful way of performing sensitivity analysis.

Now let's see how this sensitivity analysis can be done more systematically by using a data table.

Consolidating the data and results on the spreadsheet is important for sensitivity analysis.

Organize the spreadsheet so that any piece of data needs to be changed in only one place.

FIGURE 9.18

In preparation for performing sensitivity analysis on the full Goferbroke Co. problem, the data and results have been consolidated on the spreadsheet to the right of the decision tree.

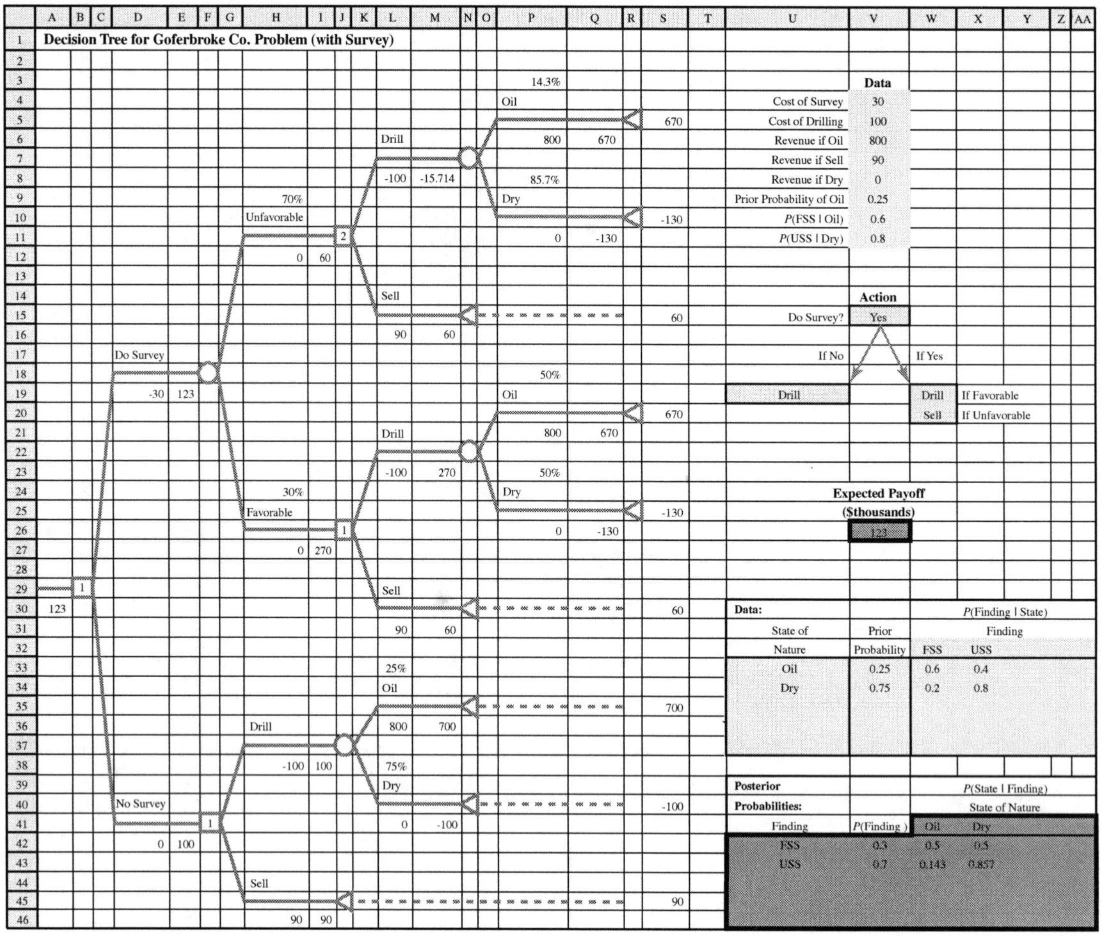

Range Name	Cell
CostOfDrilling	V5
CostOfSurvey	V4
PriorProbabilityOfOil	V9
ProbDryGivenFSS	X42
ProbDryGivenUSS	X43
ProbFSS	V42
ProbFSSGivenOil	V10
ProbOilGivenFSS	W42
ProbOilGivenUSS	W43
ProbUSS	V43
ProbUSSGivenDry	V11
RevenueIfDry	V8
RevenueIfOil	V6
RevenueIfSell	V7

	U	V	W	X
14		Action		
15	Do Survey?	=IF(B29=1,"Yes","No")		
16				
17	If No		If Yes	
18				
19	=IF(F41=1,"Drill","Sell")		=IF(J26=1,"Drill","Sell")	If Favorable
20			=IF(J11=1,"Drill","Sell")	If Unfavorable

	P
3	=ProbOilGivenUSS
4	Oil
5	
6	=RevenueIfOil
7	
8	=ProbDryGivenUSS
9	Dry
10	
11	=RevenueIfDry

	V
23	Expected
24	Payoff
25	($thousands)
26	=A30

	U	V	W	X
30	Data:		P(Finding | State)	
31	State of	Prior	Finding	
32	Nature	Probability	FSS	USS
33	Oil	=PriorProbabilityOfOil	=ProbFSSGivenOil	=1–ProbFSSGivenOil
34	Dry	=1–PriorProbabilityOfOil	=1–ProbUSSGivenDry	=ProbUSSGivenDry

Using a Data Table to Do Sensitivity Analysis Systematically

To systematically determine how the decisions and expected payoffs change as the prior probability of oil (or any other data) changes, a data table can be generated with Excel by using the same procedure described in Section 9.4. First make a table on the spreadsheet with headings as shown in columns Y through AD in Figure 9.19. In the first column of the table (Y5:Y15), list the trial values for the data cell (the prior probability of oil), except leave the first row blank. The headings of the next columns specify which output will be evaluated. For each of these columns, use the first row of the table (cells Y4:AD4) to write an equation that refers to the relevant output cell. In this case, the cells of interest are (1) the decision of whether to do the survey (V15), (2) if so, whether to drill if the survey is favorable or unfavorable (W19 and W20), (3) if not, whether to drill (U19), and (4) the value of ExpectedPayoff (V26). The equations for Y4:AD4 referring to these output cells are shown below the spreadsheet in Figure 9.19.

Next, select the entire table (Y4:AD15) and then choose Data Table from the What-If Analysis menu of the Data tab. In the Data Table dialog box (as shown at the bottom left of Figure 9.19), indicate the column input cell (V9), which refers to the data cell that is being changed in the first column of the table.

Clicking OK then generates the table shown in Figure 9.19. For each trial value for the data cell listed in the first column of the table, the corresponding output cell values are calculated and displayed in the other columns of the table. Some of the output in the data table is not relevant. For example, when the decision is to not do the survey in column Z, the results in columns AA and AB (what to do given favorable or unfavorable survey results) are not relevant. Similarly, when the decision is to do the survey in column Z, the results in column AC (what to do if you don't do the survey) are not relevant. The relevant output has been formatted in boldface to make it stand out compared to the irrelevant output.

Figure 9.19 reveals that the optimal initial decision switches from Sell without a survey to doing the survey somewhere between 0.1 and 0.2 for the prior probability of oil and then switches again to Drill without a survey somewhere between 0.3 and 0.4. Using the spreadsheet in Figure 9.18, trial-and-error analysis soon leads to the following conclusions about how the optimal policy depends on this probability.

Optimal Policy

Let p = Prior probability of oil.

If $p \leq 0.168$, then sell the land (no seismic survey).

If $0.169 \leq p \leq 0.308$, then do the survey: drill if favorable and sell if not.

If $p \geq 0.309$, then drill for oil (no seismic survey).

Max's Reaction

Max: Very interesting. I especially liked the way we were able to use that sensitivity analysis spreadsheet to see immediately what would happen when we change some of the numbers. And there was one thing that I found particularly encouraging.

Jennifer: What was that?

Max: When we changed that prior probability of oil to nearly every other plausible value, it kept coming back with the same answer. Do the seismic survey and then drill only if the survey is favorable. Otherwise, sell. So the consulting geologist's numbers can be off by quite a bit and we still would be doing the right thing.

Jennifer: Yes, that was a key finding, wasn't it? OK. Does this mean that you are comfortable now with a decision to proceed with the seismic survey and then either drill or sell depending on the outcome of the survey?

Max: Not quite. There is still one thing that bothers me.

Jennifer: What's that?

Max: Suppose the seismic survey gives us a favorable seismic sounding, so we drill. If the land turns out to be dry, then I'm out 130,000 bucks! As I said at the beginning, that would nearly put us out of business. That scares me. I currently am shorter of working capital than I normally am. Therefore, losing $130,000 now would hurt more than it normally does. It doesn't look like this approach is really taking that into account.

354 Chapter Nine *Decision Analysis*

FIGURE 9.19
The data table that shows the optimal policy and expected payoff for various trial values of the prior probability of oil.

	Y	Z	AA	AB	AC	AD
1	Prior					Expected
2	Probability	Do	If Survey	If Survey	If No	Payoff
3	of Oil	Survey?	Favorable	Unfavorable	Survey	($thousands)
4		Yes	Drill	Sell	Drill	123
5	0	No	Sell	Sell	**Sell**	90
6	0.1	No	Drill	Sell	**Sell**	90
7	0.2	**Yes**	**Drill**	**Sell**	Sell	102.8
8	0.3	**Yes**	**Drill**	**Sell**	Drill	143.2
9	0.4	No	Drill	Drill	**Drill**	220
10	0.5	No	Drill	Drill	**Drill**	300
11	0.6	No	Drill	Drill	**Drill**	380
12	0.7	No	Drill	Drill	**Drill**	460
13	0.8	No	Drill	Drill	**Drill**	540
14	0.9	No	Drill	Drill	**Drill**	620
15	1	No	Drill	Drill	**Drill**	700

	Y	Z	AA	AB	AC	AD
1	Prior					Expected
2	Probability	Do	If Survey	If Survey	If No	Payoff
3	of Oil	Survey?	Favorable	Unfavorable	Survey	($thousands)
4		=V15	=W19	=W20	=U19	=ExpectedPayoff

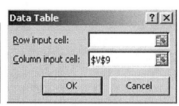

Considering average monetary values isn't good enough when uncomfortably large losses can occur.

Jennifer: No, you're right. It really doesn't. This approach just looks at average *monetary* values. That isn't good enough when you're dealing with such large amounts. You wouldn't be willing to flip a coin to determine whether you win or lose $130,000, right?

Max: No, I sure wouldn't.

Jennifer: OK, that's the tipoff. As I mentioned the first time we talked about this problem, I think the circumstances here indicate that we need to go beyond dollars and cents to look at the consequences of the possible outcomes. Fortunately, decision analysis has a way of doing this by introducing utilities. The basic idea is that the utility of an outcome measures the true value to you of that outcome rather than just the monetary value. So by expressing payoffs in terms of utilities, the decision tree analysis would find the average utility at each node instead of the average monetary value. So now the decisions would be based on giving you the highest possible average utility.

Review Questions

1. When preparing to perform sensitivity analysis, how should one begin organizing the spreadsheet that contains the decision tree?
2. Performing sensitivity analysis on a certain piece of data should require changing its value in how many places on the spreadsheet?
3. What conclusion was drawn for the full Goferbroke problem regarding how the decision should depend on the prior probability of oil?

9.9 USING UTILITIES TO BETTER REFLECT THE VALUES OF PAYOFFS

Thus far, when applying Bayes' decision rule, we have assumed that the expected payoff in *monetary terms* is the appropriate measure of the consequences of taking an action. However, in many situations where very large amounts of money are involved, this assumption is inappropriate.

For example, suppose that an individual is offered the choice of (1) accepting a 50–50 chance of winning $100,000 or (2) receiving $40,000 with certainty. Many people would prefer the $40,000 even though the expected payoff on the 50–50 chance of winning $100,000 is $50,000. A company may be unwilling to invest a large sum of money in a new product, even when the expected profit is substantial, if there is a risk of losing its investment and thereby becoming bankrupt. People buy insurance even though it is a poor investment from the viewpoint of the expected payoff.

Do these examples invalidate Bayes' decision rule? Fortunately, the answer is no, because there is a way of transforming monetary values to an appropriate scale that reflects the decision maker's preferences. This scale is called the *utility function for money.*

Utility Functions for Money

Figure 9.20 shows a typical **utility function U(M)** for money **M.** The intuitive interpretation is that it indicates that an individual having this utility function would value obtaining $30,000 twice as much as $10,000 and would value obtaining $100,000 twice as much as $30,000. This reflects the fact that the person's highest-priority needs would be met by the first $10,000. Having this decreasing slope of the function as the amount of money increases is referred to as having a *decreasing marginal utility for money.* Such an individual is referred to as being **risk averse.**

However, not all individuals have a decreasing marginal utility for money. Some people are **risk seekers** instead of *risk averse,* and they go through life looking for the "big score." The slope of their utility function *increases* as the amount of money increases, so they have an *increasing marginal utility for money.*

Figure 9.21 compares the shape of the utility function for money for risk-averse and risk-seeking individuals. Also shown is the intermediate case of a **risk-neutral individual,** who prizes money at its face value. Such an individual's utility for money is simply proportional to the amount of money involved. Although some people appear to be risk neutral when only small amounts of money are involved, it is unusual to be truly risk neutral with very large amounts.

It also is possible to exhibit a mixture of these kinds of behavior. For example, an individual might be essentially risk neutral with small amounts of money, then become a risk seeker with moderate amounts, and then turn risk averse with large amounts. In addition, one's attitude toward risk can shift over time depending on circumstances.

Managers of a business firm need to consider the company's circumstances and the collective philosophy of top management in determining the appropriate attitude toward risk when making managerial decisions.

Two different individuals can have very different utility functions for money.

FIGURE 9.20
A typical utility function for money, where U(M) is the utility of obtaining an amount of money M.

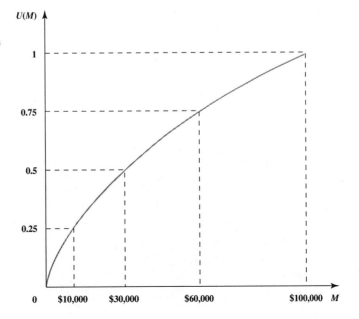

FIGURE 9.21

The shape of the utility function for money for (a) risk-averse, (b) risk-seeking, and (c) risk-neutral individuals.

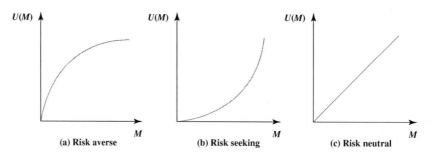

(a) Risk averse   (b) Risk seeking   (c) Risk neutral

The fact that different people have different utility functions for money has an important implication for decision making in the face of uncertainty.

> When a *utility function for money* is incorporated into a decision analysis approach to a problem, this utility function must be constructed to fit the current preferences and values of the decision maker involved. (The decision maker can be either a single individual or a group of people.)

The key to constructing the utility function for money to fit the decision maker is the following fundamental property of utility functions.

Fundamental Property: Under the assumptions of utility theory, the decision maker's *utility function for money* has the property that the decision maker is *indifferent* between two alternative courses of action if the two alternatives have the *same expected utility.*

To illustrate, suppose that the decision maker has the utility function shown in Figure 9.20. Further suppose that the decision maker is offered the following opportunity.

Offer: An opportunity to obtain either $100,000 (utility = 1) with probability p or nothing (utility = 0) with probability $(1 - p)$.

Thus, by weighting the two possible utilities (1 and 0) by their probabilities, the expected utility is

$$E(\text{utility}) = p + 0(1 - p)$$
$$= p \text{ for this offer}$$

Therefore, for *each* of the following three pairs of alternatives, the above fundamental property indicates that the decision maker is indifferent between the first and second alternatives.

1. *First alternative:* The offer with $p = 0.25$, so $E(\text{utility}) = 0.25$.
   Second alternative: Definitely obtain $10,000, so utility = 0.25.

2. *First alternative:* The offer with $p = 0.5$, so $E(\text{utility}) = 0.5$.
   Second alternative: Definitely obtain $30,000, so utility = 0.5.

3. *First alternative:* The offer with $p = 0.75$, so $E(\text{utility}) = 0.75$.
   Second alternative: Definitely obtain $60,000, so utility = 0.75.

In all three of these cases, a decision maker with the utility function in Figure 9.20 would be indifferent between the two alternatives because they have the same expected utility.

This example also illustrates one way in which the decision maker's utility function for money can be constructed in the first place. The decision maker would be made the same hypothetical offer to obtain a large amount of money (e.g., $100,000) with probability p, or nothing (utility = 0) otherwise. Then, for each of a few smaller amounts of money (e.g., $10,000, $30,000, and $60,000), the decision maker would be asked to choose a value of p that would make him or her *indifferent* between the offer and definitely obtaining that amount of money. The utility of the smaller amount of money then is p times the utility of the large amount. When the utility of the large amount has been set equal to 1, as in Figure 9.20, this conveniently makes the utility of the smaller amount simply equal to p. The utility values in Figure 9.20 imply that the decision maker has chosen $p = 0.25$ when $M = \$10,000$, $p = 0.5$ when $M = \$30,000$, and $p = 0.75$ when $M = \$60,000$. (Constructing the utility function in this way is an example of the *equivalent lottery method* described later in this section.)

The *scale* of the utility function is irrelevant. In other words, it doesn't matter whether the values of $U(M)$ at the dashed lines in Figure 9.20 are 0.25, 0.5, 0.75, 1 (as shown) or 10,000,

20,000, 30,000, 40,000, or whatever. All the utilities can be multiplied by any positive constant without affecting which decision alternative will have the largest expected utility. It also is possible to add the same constant (positive or negative) to all the utilities without affecting which decision alternative will have the largest expected utility.

For these reasons, we have the liberty to set the value of $U(M)$ arbitrarily for two values of M, so long as the higher monetary value has the higher utility. It is particularly convenient to set $U(M) = 0$ for the smallest value of M under consideration and to set $U(M) = 1$ for the largest M, as was done in Figure 9.20. By assigning a utility of 0 to the worst outcome and a utility of 1 to the best outcome, and then determining the utilities of the other outcomes accordingly, it becomes easy to see the relative utility of each outcome along the scale from worst to best.

Now we are ready to summarize the basic role of utility functions in decision analysis.

> When the decision maker's utility function for money is used to measure the relative worth of the various possible monetary outcomes, *Bayes' decision rule* replaces monetary payoffs by the corresponding utilities. Therefore, the optimal decision (or series of decisions) is the one that *maximizes the expected utility*.

The objective now is to maximize the expected utility rather than the expected payoff in monetary terms.

Only utility functions for *money* have been discussed here. However, we should mention that utility functions can sometimes still be constructed when some or all of the important consequences of the decision alternatives are *not* monetary in nature. (For example, the consequences of a doctor's decision alternatives in treating a patient involve the future health of the patient.) This is not necessarily easy, since it may require making value judgments about the relative desirability of rather intangible consequences. Nevertheless, under these circumstances, it is important to incorporate such value judgments into the decision process.

Dealing with the Goferbroke Co. Problem

Recall that the Goferbroke Co. is operating without much capital, so a loss of $100,000 would be quite serious. As the owner of the company, Max already has gone heavily into debt to keep going. The worst-case scenario would be to come up with $30,000 for a seismic survey and then still lose $100,000 by drilling when there is no oil. This scenario would not bankrupt the company at this point but definitely would leave it in a precarious financial position.

On the other hand, striking oil is an exciting prospect, since earning $700,000 finally would put the company on fairly solid financial footing.

Max is the decision maker for this problem. Therefore, to prepare for using utilities to analyze the problem, it is necessary to construct Max's utility function for money, $U(M)$, where we will express the amount of money M in units of thousands of dollars.

We start by assigning utilities of 0 and 1, respectively, to the smallest and largest possible payoffs. Since the smallest possible payoff is $M = -130$ (a loss of $130,000) and the largest is $M = 700$ (a gain of $700,000), this gives $U(-130) = 0$ and $U(700) = 1$.

To determine the utilities for other possible monetary payoffs, it is necessary to probe Max's attitude toward risk. Especially important are his feelings about the consequences of the worst possible loss ($130,000) and the best possible gain ($700,000), as well as how he compares these consequences. Let us eavesdrop as Jennifer probes these feelings with Max.

Interviewing Max

Jennifer: Well now, these utilities are intended to reflect your feelings about the true value to you of these various possible payoffs. Therefore, to pin down what your utilities are, we need to talk some about how you feel about these payoffs and their consequences for the company.

Max: Fine.

Jennifer: A good place to begin would be the best and worst possible cases. The possibility of gaining $700,000 or losing $130,000.

Max: Those are the big ones all right.

Jennifer: OK, suppose you drill without paying for a seismic survey and then you find oil, so your profit is about $700,000. What would that do for the company?

Max: A lot. That would finally give me the capital I need to become more of a major player in this business. I then could take a shot at finding a big oil field. That big strike I've talked about.

Jennifer: OK, good. Now let's talk about the consequences if you were to get that biggest possible loss instead. Suppose you pay for a seismic survey, then you drill and the land is dry. So you're out about $130,000. How bad would that be? What kind of future would the company have?

Max: Well, let me put it this way. It would put the company in a pretty uncomfortable financial position. I would need to work hard on getting some more financing. Then we would need to cautiously work our way out of the hole by forming some partnerships for some low-risk, low-gain drilling. But I think we could do it. I've been in that position a couple times before and come out of it. We'd be OK.

Jennifer: It sounds like you wouldn't be overly worried about such a loss as long as you have reasonable odds for a big payoff to justify this risk.

Max: That's right.

Jennifer: OK, now let's talk about those odds. What I'm going to do is set up a simpler hypothetical situation. Suppose these are your alternatives. One is to drill. If you find oil, you clear $700,000. If the land is dry, you're out $130,000. The only other alternative is to sell the land for $90,000. I know this isn't your actual situation since $700,000 does not include the cost of a survey whereas the loss of $130,000 does, but let's pretend that these are your alternatives.

Max: I don't understand why you want to talk about a situation that is different from what we are facing.

Jennifer: Trust me. Considering these kinds of hypothetical situations are going to enable us to determine your utilities.

Max: OK.

Jennifer: Now presumably if you had a 50–50 chance of either clearing $700,000 or losing $130,000, you would drill.

Max: Sure.

Jennifer: If you had a smaller chance, say one-in-four of gaining $700,000, versus a three-in-four chance of losing $130,000, would you choose to drill or sell the land for $90,000?

Max: Well, that's almost the original decision we were trying to make, before we considered the seismic survey. However, there is one big difference. Now you're asking me to suppose that the loss if there is no oil is $130,000 rather than $100,000. The higher loss would be quite a bit more painful. I wouldn't be willing to take this risk with just a one-in-four chance of gaining $700,000.

Jennifer: OK, so now we know that the point at which you would be indifferent between going ahead or not is somewhere between having a one-in-four chance and a 50–50 chance of gaining $700,000 rather than losing $130,000. Let's see if we can pin down just where your **point of indifference** is within this range from one-in-four and 50–50. Let's try a one-in-three chance. Would you go ahead and drill with a one-in-three chance of gaining $700,000 versus a two-in-three chance of losing $130,000, or would you choose to sell the land for $90,000?

The *point of indifference* is the point where the decision maker is indifferent between two hypothetical alternatives.

Max: Hmm. That's not so clear. What would be the average payoff in this case?

Jennifer: Almost $147,000.

Max: Not bad. Hmm, one chance in three of gaining $700,000. That's tempting. But two chances in three of losing $130,000 with all the problems involved with that. I don't know. $90,000 would be a sure thing. That's a tough one.

Jennifer: OK, let's try this. Suppose your chances of gaining $700,000 were a little better than one-in-three. Would you do it?

Max: Yes, I think so.

Jennifer: And if your chances were a little under one-in-three?

Max: Then I don't think I would do it.

Jennifer: OK. You've convinced me that your point of indifference is one-in-three. That's exactly what I needed to know.

Finding *U*(90)

Max has indeed given Jennifer just the information she needs to determine $U(90)$, Max's utility for a payoff of 90 (a gain of $90,000). Recall that $U(-130)$ already has been set at $U(-130) = 0$ and that $U(700)$ already has been set at $U(700) = 1$. Here is the procedure that Jennifer is using to find $U(90)$.

The decision maker (Max) is offered two alternatives, A_1 and A_2.

A_1: Obtain a payoff of 700 with probability p.

Obtain a payoff of -130 with probability $(1 - p)$.

A_2: Definitely obtain a payoff of 90.

Question to the decision maker: What value of p makes you *indifferent* between these two alternatives? Recall that Max has chosen $p = 1/3$.

For a given choice of p, the expected utility for A_1 is

$$E(\text{utility for } A_1) = pU(700) + (1 - p)U(-130)$$
$$= p(1) + (1 - p)(0)$$
$$= p$$

If the decision maker is indifferent between the two alternatives, the fundamental property of utility functions says that the two alternatives must have the same expected utility. Therefore, the utility for A_2 must also be p. Since Max chose a *point of indifference* of $p = 1/3$, the utility for A_2 must be 1/3, so $U(90) = 1/3$.

The Equivalent Lottery Method for Determining Utilities

The above procedure for finding $U(90)$ illustrates that the key to finding the utility for any payoff M is having the decision maker select a *point of indifference* between two alternatives, where one of them (A_1) involves a *lottery* between the largest payoff and the smallest payoff and the other alternative (A_2) is to receive a sure payoff of M. At the point of indifference, the lottery is *equivalent* to the sure payoff in the sense that they have the same expected utility, so the procedure is referred to as the **equivalent lottery method.** Here is an outline of the procedure.

Equivalent Lottery Method

1. Determine the largest potential payoff, M = maximum, and assign it a utility of 1:

$$U(\text{maximum}) = 1$$

2. Determine the smallest potential payoff, and assign it a utility of 0:

$$U(\text{minimum}) = 0$$

3. To determine the utility of another potential payoff M, the decision maker is offered the following two hypothetical alternatives:

A_1: Obtain a payoff of *maximum* with probability p.

Obtain a payoff of *minimum* with probability $1 - p$.

A_2: Definitely obtain a payoff of M.

Question to the decision maker: What value of p makes you *indifferent* between these two alternatives? Then $U(M) = p$.

Constructing Max's Utility Function for Money

We now have found utilities for three possible payoffs (-130, 90, and 700) for Goferbroke. Plotting these values on a graph of the utility function $U(M)$ versus the monetary payoff M and then drawing a smooth curve through these points gives the curve shown in Figure 9.22.

This curve is an estimate of Max's utility function for money. To find the utility values for the other possible payoffs (-100, 60, and 670), Max could repeat step 3 of the equivalent lottery method for $M = -100$, $M = 60$, and $M = 670$. However, since -100 is so close to -130, 60 is so close to 90, and 670 is so close to 700, an alternative is to estimate these utilities as the values on the curve in Figure 9.22 at $M = -100$, $M = 60$, and $M = 670$. Following the corresponding dotted lines in the figure leads to $U(-100) = 0.05$, $U(60) = 0.30$, and $U(670) = 0.97$. Table 9.9 gives the complete list of possible payoffs and their utilities.

360 Chapter Nine   *Decision Analysis*

FIGURE 9.22

Max's utility function for money as the owner of Goferbroke Co.

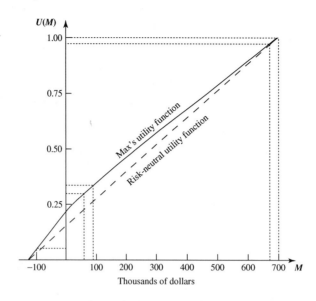

TABLE 9.9

Utilities for the Goferbroke Co. Problem

Monetary Payoff, M	Utility, U(M)
−130	0
−100	0.05
60	0.30
90	0.333
670	0.97
700	1

For comparative purposes, the dashed line in Figure 9.22 shows the utility function that would result if Max were completely *risk neutral*. By nature, Max is inclined to be a risk seeker. However, the difficult financial circumstances of his company that he badly wants to keep solvent has forced him to adopt a moderately risk-averse stance in addressing his current decisions.

Using a Decision Tree to Analyze the Problem with Utilities

Now that Max's utility function for money has been constructed in Table 9.9 (and Figure 9.22), this information can be used with a decision tree as summarized next.

> The procedure for using a decision tree to analyze the problem now is *identical* to that described in Section 9.7 *except* for substituting utilities for monetary payoffs. Therefore, the value obtained to evaluate each node of the tree now is the *expected utility* there rather than the expected (monetary) payoff. Consequently, the optimal decision selected by Bayes' decision rule maximizes the expected utility for the overall problem.

Thus, using RSPE once again, our final decision tree with utilities shown in Figure 9.23 closely resembles the one in Figure 9.17 given in Section 9.7. The nodes and branches are exactly the same, as are the probabilities for the branches emanating from the event nodes. However, the key difference from Figure 9.17 is that the monetary payoff at each terminal node now has been replaced by the corresponding utility from Table 9.9. (This was accomplished with RSPE by entering this same utility as the "cash flow" at the terminal branch and then entering "cash flows" of 0 at all the preceding branches.) It is these utilities that have been used by RSPE to compute the *expected utilities* given next to all the nodes.

At each terminal branch, enter the utility of that outcome as the "cash flow" there and then do not change the default value of 0 for the "cash flow" at the preceding branches.

These expected utilities lead to the same decisions as in Figure 9.17 at all decision nodes except the bottom one in cell F41. The decision at this node now switches to *sell* instead of *drill*. However, the solution procedure still leaves this node on a *closed* path, as indicated by the 1 in cell B29. Therefore, the overall optimal policy remains the same as that obtained in Figure 9.17 (do the seismic survey; sell if the result is unfavorable; drill if the result is favorable).

FIGURE 9.23
The final decision tree constructed and solved by RSPE for the full Goferbroke Co. problem when using Max's utility function for money to maximize expected utility.

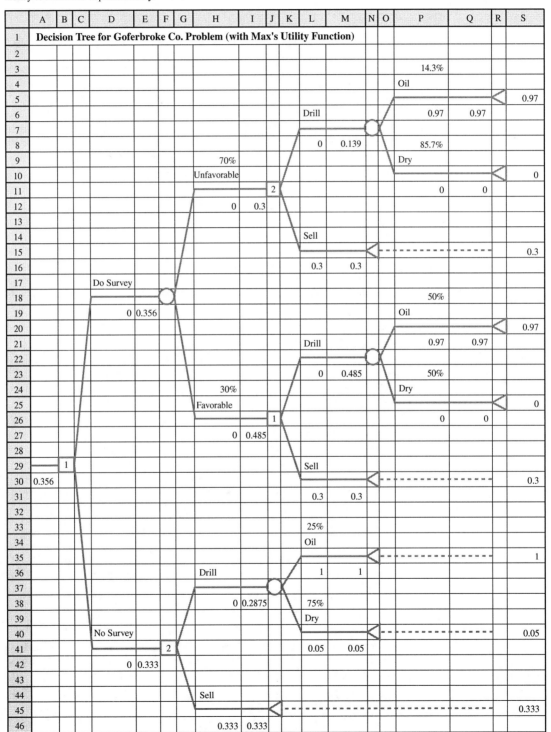

The previous approach of maximizing the expected monetary payoff assumes a risk-neutral decision maker.

The approach of maximizing the expected monetary payoff used in the preceding sections was equivalent to assuming that the decision maker is neutral toward risk. By using utility theory with an appropriate utility function, the optimal solution now reflects the decision maker's attitude about risk. Because Max adopted only a moderately risk-averse stance, the optimal policy did not change from before. For a somewhat more risk-averse decision maker, the optimal solution would switch to the more conservative approach of immediately selling the land (no seismic survey).

Jennifer and Max are to be commended for incorporating utilities into a decision analysis approach to his problem. Utilities help to provide a rational approach to decision making in the face of uncertainty. However, many managers are not sufficiently comfortable with the relatively abstract notion of utilities, or with working with probabilities to construct a utility function, to be willing to use this approach. Consequently, utilities are not used nearly as widely in practice as some of the other techniques of decision analysis described in this chapter, including Bayes' decision rule (with monetary payoffs) and decision trees.

Another Approach for Estimating U(M)

The procedure described earlier for constructing $U(M)$ asks the decision maker to repeatedly apply the equivalent lottery method, which requires him (or her) each time to make a difficult decision about which probability would make him indifferent between two alternatives. Many managers would be uncomfortable with making this kind of decision. Therefore, an alternative approach is sometimes used instead to estimate the utility function for money.

This approach assumes that the utility function has a certain mathematical form and then adjusts this form to fit the decision maker's attitude toward risk as closely as possible. For example, one particularly popular form to assume (because of its relative simplicity) is the **exponential utility function,**

$$U(M) = 1 - e^{-\frac{M}{R}}$$

where R is the decision maker's *risk tolerance*. This utility function has the kind of shape shown in Figure 9.21(*a*), so it is designed to fit a *risk-averse* individual. A great aversion to risk corresponds to a small value of R (which would cause the curve in this figure to bend sharply), whereas a small aversion to risk corresponds to a large value of R (which gives a much more gradual bend in the curve).

Since *R* measures the decision maker's *risk tolerance,* the *aversion* to risk decreases as *R* increases.

A decision maker's risk tolerance tends to vary over time as his (or her) wealth changes. He tends to have a higher risk tolerance when he is relatively wealthy than when he is not. However, given his *current* degree of wealth, the exponential utility function assumes that he has a *constant* risk tolerance over the entire range of potential outcomes that may be realized after the decision is made. This often is a reasonable assumption. Unfortunately, it is a questionable assumption in Max's situation because he is unusually risk averse about the worst possible outcome (a loss of $130,000) but has a very high risk tolerance when comparing large potential gains. This is why Jennifer never raised the possibility of using an exponential utility function.

In other situations where the consequences of the potential losses are not as severe, assuming an exponential utility function may provide a reasonable approximation. In such a case, here is an easy way of estimating the appropriate value of R. The decision maker would be asked to choose the number R that would make him indifferent between the following two alternatives.

A_1:   A 50–50 gamble where he would gain R dollars with probability 0.5 and lose $R/2$ dollars with probability 0.5.

A_2:   Neither gain nor lose anything.

For example, if the decision maker were indifferent between doing nothing or taking a 50–50 gamble where he would gain $1,000 with probability 0.5 and lose $500 with probability 0.5, then $R = 1,000$.

Using RSPE with an Exponential Utility Function

RSPE includes the option of using the exponential utility function. Clicking on the Options button on the RSPE ribbon and choosing Tree reveals the options shown in Figure 9.24. The Certainty Equivalents section gives two choices—Expected Values or Exponential Utility

An Application Vignette

Following the merger of Conoco Inc. and the Phillips Petroleum Company in 2002, **ConocoPhillips** became the third-largest integrated energy company in the United States with $160 billion in assets and 38,000 employees. Like any company in this industry, the management of ConocoPhillips must grapple continually with decisions about the allocation of limited investment capital across a set of risky petroleum exploration projects. These decisions have a great impact on the profitability of the company.

In the early 1990s, the then Phillips Petroleum Company became an industry leader in the application of sophisticated management science methodology to aid these decisions by developing a *decision analysis software package* called DISCOVERY. The user interface allows a geologist or engineer to model the uncertainties associated with a project and then the software interprets the inputs and constructs a decision tree that shows all the decision nodes

(including opportunities to obtain additional seismic information) and the intervening event nodes. A key feature of the software is the use of an *exponential utility function* to incorporate management's attitudes about financial risk. An intuitive questionnaire is used to measure corporate risk preferences in order to determine an appropriate value of the risk tolerance parameter for this utility function.

Management uses the software to (1) evaluate *petroleum exploration projects* with a consistent risk-taking policy across the company, (2) rank projects in terms of overall preference, (3) identify the firm's appropriate level of participation in these projects, and (4) stay within budget.

Source: M. R. Walls, G. T. Morahan, and J. S. Dyer, "Decision Analysis of Exploration Opportunities in the Onshore U.S. at Phillips Petroleum Company," *Interfaces* 25, no. 6 (November–December 1995), pp. 39–56. (A link to this article is provided on our website, **www.mhhe.com/hillier5e.**)

RSPE Tip: The Decision Tree section of the Platform tab on the Model pane lets you specify whether to use expected monetary values or the exponential utility function for applying Bayes' decision rule. The entry in Decision Node EV/CE (either Maximize or Minimize) also lets you specify whether the objective is to maximize the measure of performance (expected payoff or expected utility) or to minimize that measure.

Function. Choosing the latter revises the decision tree to incorporate the exponential utility function. The Decision Node EV/CE section has two choices, Maximize or Minimize, which enable you to specify whether the objective is to maximize the measure of performance (expected utility in this case) or to minimize that measure. (Maximize is the default choice, as has been used throughout the chapter.) The Risk Tolerance box is used to enter a value to be used for R when calculating the exponential utility function. (These same options are also available on the Platform tab of the Model pane in RSPE.)

To illustrate, suppose that the exponential utility function with a risk tolerance of $R = 1,000$ were to be used as a rough approximation for analyzing the full Goferbroke Co. problem. (Since this problem expresses payoffs in units of thousands of dollars, $R = 1,000$ here is equivalent to using $R = 1,000,000$ when payoffs are in units of dollars.) The resulting decision tree is shown in Figure 9.25. There are now two values calculated below and to the left of each node. The lower number represents the expected utility value at that stage in the decision tree. The upper number represents the certain payoff that is equivalent to this expected utility value. For example, cell A31 indicates that the expected value of the exponential utility

FIGURE 9.24
The Tree tab of the RSPE Options dialog box allows you to set several options for how the decision tree is solved. Here the options are set to use the exponential utility function, to maximize profit, and to use an *R* value of 1,000.

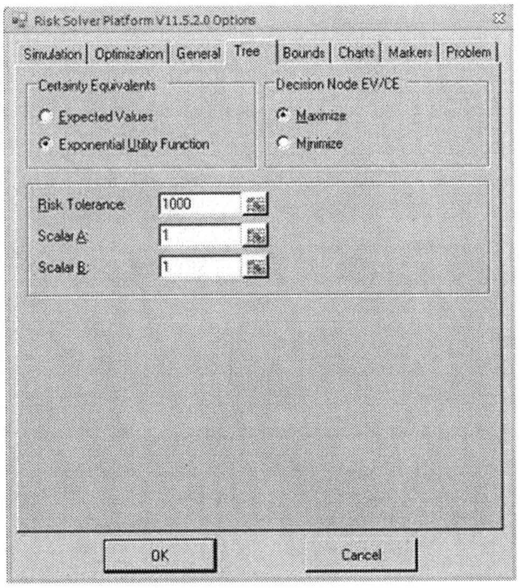

364   Chapter Nine   *Decision Analysis*

FIGURE 9.25

The final decision tree constructed and solved by RSPE for the full Goferbroke Co. problem when using an exponential utility function with R = 1,000.

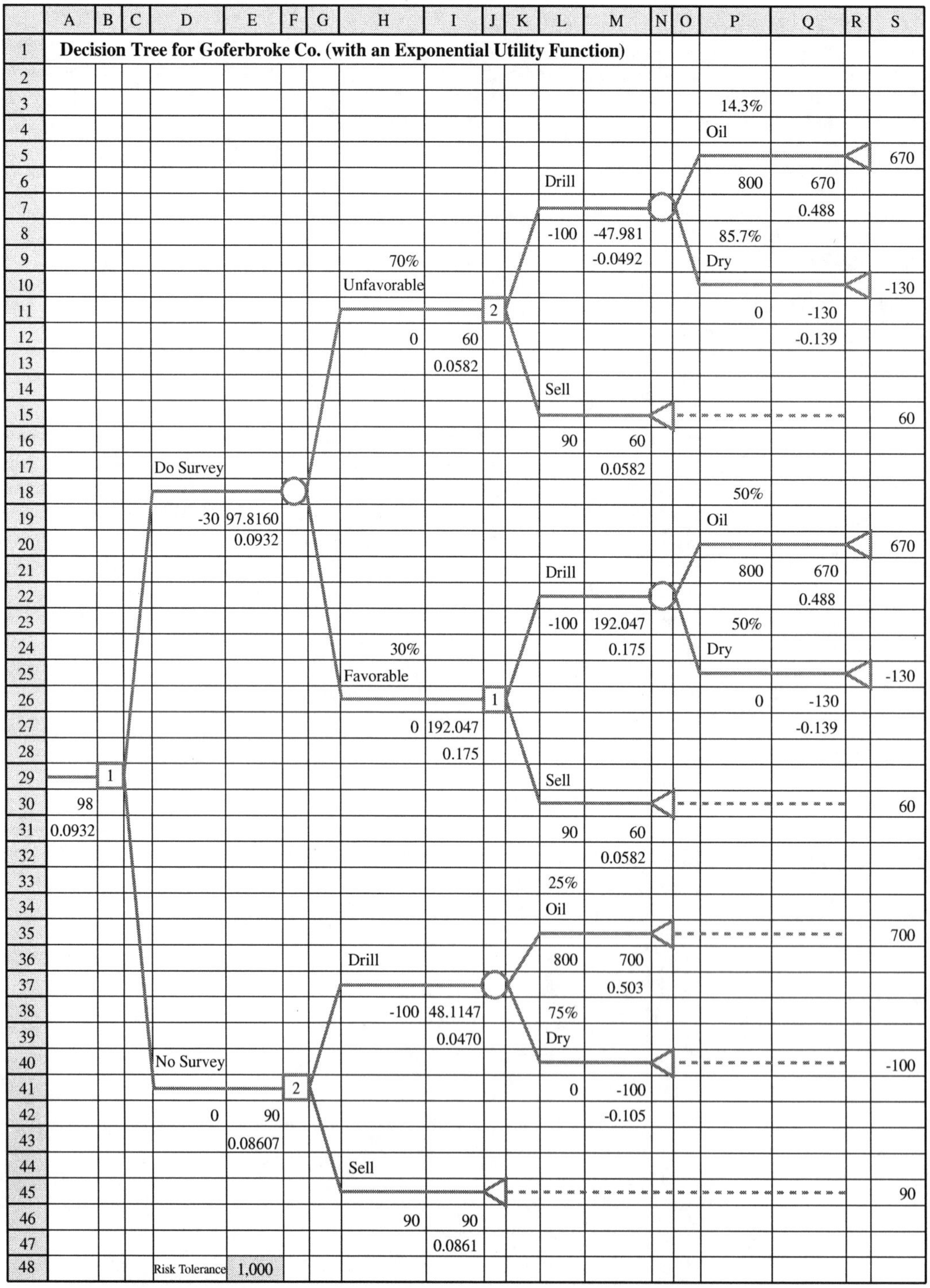

	A	B	C	D	E	F	G	H	I	J	K	L	M	N	O	P	Q	R	S
1	**Decision Tree for Goferbroke Co. (with an Exponential Utility Function)**																		
2																			
3																14.3%			
4																Oil			
5																			670
6								Drill								800	670		
7																	0.488		
8												-100	-47.981			85.7%			
9													-0.0492			Dry			
10								70%											-130
11								Unfavorable		2						0	-130		
12							0	60									-0.139		
13								0.0582											
14												Sell							
15																			60
16								90	60										
17				Do Survey									0.0582						
18																50%			
19				-30	97.8160											Oil			
20					0.0932														670
21								Drill								800	670		
22																	0.488		
23												-100	192.047			50%			
24							30%						0.175			Dry			
25							Favorable												-130
26										1						0	-130		
27							0	192.047									-0.139		
28								0.175											
29			1									Sell							
30	98																		60
31	0.0932							90	60										
32													0.0582						
33												25%							
34												Oil							
35																			700
36							Drill					800	700						
37													0.503						
38								-100	48.1147			75%							
39								0.0470				Dry							
40				No Survey															-100
41							2					0	-100						
42				0	90								-0.105						
43					0.08607														
44							Sell												
45																			90
46							90	90											
47								0.0861											
48				Risk Tolerance	1,000														

Range Name	Cells
RiskTolerance	E48

function for this decision would be 0.0932. This expected utility is equivalent to a certain payoff of $98,000, as indicated in cell A30.

The exponential utility function leads to the same decisions as in Figure 9.23. The overall optimal policy remains to do the seismic survey; sell if the result is unfavorable; drill if the result is favorable. However, the optimal policy changes when the value of R is decreased far enough. For values of R less than 728, the optimal policy switches to not doing the survey and selling the land. Thus, a more risk-averse decision maker would make the safer decision for Goferbroke—sell the land and receive $90,000 for sure.

Review
Questions

1. What are utilities intended to reflect?
2. What is the shape of the utility function for money for a risk-averse individual? A risk-seeking individual? A risk-neutral individual?
3. What is the fundamental property of utility functions?
4. What is the lottery when using the equivalent lottery method?
5. Given two hypothetical alternatives where one of them involves a probability p, what is meant by the point of indifference between these two alternatives?
6. When using utilities with a decision tree, what kind of value is obtained to evaluate each node of the tree?
7. What decisions did Max make regarding the full Goferbroke Co. problem?

9.10   THE PRACTICAL APPLICATION OF DECISION ANALYSIS

In one sense, the Goferbroke Co. problem is a very typical application of decision analysis. Like other applications, Max needed to make his decisions (Do a seismic survey? Drill for oil or sell the land?) in the face of great uncertainty. The decisions were difficult because their payoffs were so unpredictable. The outcome depended on factors that were outside Max's control (does the land contain oil or is it dry?). He needed a framework and methodology for rational decision making in this uncertain environment. These are the usual characteristics of applications of decision analysis.

However, in other ways, the Goferbroke problem is not such a typical application. It was oversimplified to include only two possible states of nature (oil and dry), whereas there actually would be a considerable number of distinct possibilities. For example, the actual state might be dry, a small amount of oil, a moderate amount, a large amount, and a huge amount, plus different possibilities concerning the depth of the oil and soil conditions that impact the cost of drilling to reach the oil. Max also was considering only two alternatives for each of two decisions. Real applications commonly involve more decisions, more alternatives to be considered for each one, and many possible states of nature.

The Goferbroke Co. problem could have included many more states of nature.

Problems as tiny as the Goferbroke problem can be readily analyzed and solved by hand. However, real applications typically involve large decision trees, whose construction and analysis require the use of a software package (such as RSPE introduced in this chapter). In some cases, the decision tree can explode in size with many thousand terminal branches. Special algebraic techniques are being developed and incorporated into the solvers for dealing with such large problems.

Other kinds of graphical techniques also are available to complement the decision tree in representing and solving decision analysis problems. One that has become quite popular is called the **influence diagram,** which provides another helpful way of showing the interrelationships among a decision maker's alternatives, uncertainties, and values.

Although the Goferbroke problem only involved a single decision maker (Max) assisted by a single analyst (Jennifer), many strategic business decisions are made collectively by management. One technique for group decision making is called **decision conferencing.** This is a process where the group comes together for discussions in a decision conference with the help of an analyst and a group facilitator. The facilitator works directly with the group to help it structure and focus discussions, think creatively about the problem, bring assumptions to the surface, and address the full range of issues involved. The analyst uses decision analysis to assist the group in exploring the implications of the various decision alternatives. With the assistance of a computerized *group decision support system,* the analyst builds and solves models on the spot, and then performs sensitivity analysis to respond to what-if questions from the group.

Applications of decision analysis commonly involve a partnership between the managerial decision maker (whether an individual or a group) and an analyst (whether an individual or a team) with training in management science. Some managers are not as fortunate as Max in having a staff member (let alone a daughter) like Jennifer who is qualified to serve as the analyst. Therefore, a considerable number of management consulting firms specializing in decision analysis have been formed to fill this role.

If you would like to do more reading about the practical application of decision analysis, a good place to begin would be the leadoff article[2] in the first issue of the journal *Decision Analysis* that was founded in 2004 to focus on applied research in decision analysis. This leadoff article provides a detailed discussion of various publications that present applications of decision analysis.

Review *Questions*

1. How does the Goferbroke Co. problem compare with typical applications of decision analysis?
2. What is the purpose of an influence diagram?
3. Who are the typical participants in a decision-conferencing process?
4. Where can a manager go for expert help in applying decision analysis if a qualified analyst is not available on staff?

[2] D. L. Keefer, C. W. Kirkwood, and J. L. Corner, "Perspective on Decision Analysis Applications," *Decision Analysis* 1 (2004), pp. 4–22.

9.11 Summary

Decision analysis is a valuable technique for decision making in the face of great uncertainty. It provides a framework and methodology for rational decision making when the outcomes are uncertain.

In a typical application, a decision maker needs to make either a single decision or a short sequence of decisions (with additional information perhaps becoming available between decisions). A number of alternatives are available for each decision. Uncontrollable random factors affect the payoff that would be obtained from a decision alternative. The possible outcomes of the random factors are referred to as the possible *states of nature.*

Which state of nature actually occurs will be learned only after making the decisions. However, prior to the decisions, it often is possible to estimate *prior probabilities* of the respective states of nature.

Various alternative decision criteria are available for making the decisions. A particularly popular one is *Bayes' decision rule,* which uses the prior probabilities to determine the expected payoff for each decision alternative and then chooses the one with the largest expected payoff. This is the criterion (accompanied by sensitivity analysis) that is mostly used in practice, so it is the focus of much of the chapter.

Sensitivity analysis is very helpful for evaluating the effect of having inaccurate estimates of the data for the problem, including the probabilities, revenues, and costs. Data tables can be used to systematically vary the data and see how it affects the optimal decisions or expected payoffs.

It sometimes is possible to pay for a test or survey to obtain additional information about the probabilities of the various states of nature. Calculating the *expected value of perfect information* provides a quick way of checking whether doing this might be worthwhile.

When more information is obtained, the updated probabilities are referred to as *posterior probabilities.* A *probability tree diagram* is helpful for calculating these new probabilities.

For problems involving a sequence of decisions (including perhaps a decision on whether to obtain more information), a decision tree commonly is used to graphically display the progression of decisions and random events. The calculations for applying Bayes' decision rule then can be performed directly on the decision tree one event node or decision node at a time. Spreadsheet packages, such as RSPE, are very helpful for constructing and solving decision trees.

When the problem involves the possibility of uncomfortably large losses, utilities provide a way of incorporating the decision maker's attitude toward risk into the analysis. Bayes' decision rule then is applied by expressing payoffs in terms of utilities rather than monetary values.

Decision analysis is widely used. Versatile software packages for personal computers have become an integral part of the practical application of decision analysis.

Glossary

alternatives   The options available to the decision maker for the decision under consideration. (Section 9.1), 324

Bayes' decision rule   A popular criterion for decision making that uses probabilities to calculate the expected payoff for each decision alternative and then chooses the one with the largest expected payoff. (Section 9.2), 328

Bayes' theorem   A formula for calculating a posterior probability of a state of nature. (Section 9.6), 343

branch   A line emanating from a node in a decision tree. (Section 9.3), 330

decision conferencing   A process used for group decision making. (Section 9.10), 365

decision maker   The individual or group responsible for making the decision under consideration. (Section 9.1), 324

decision node   A point in a decision tree where a decision needs to be made. (Section 9.3), 330

decision tree   A graphical display of the progression of decisions and random events to be considered. (Sections 9.3 and 9.7), 330, 345

equivalent lottery method   The procedure for finding the decision maker's utility for a specific amount of money by comparing two hypothetical alternatives where one involves a gamble. (Section 9.9), 359

event node   A point in a decision tree where a random event will occur. (Section 9.3), 330

expected monetary value (EMV) criterion   An alternative name for Bayes' decision rule when the payoffs have monetary values. (Section 9.2), 329

expected payoff (EP)   For a decision alternative, it is the weighted average of the payoffs, using the probabilities of the states of nature as the weights. (Section 9.2), 328

expected value of perfect information (EVPI)   The increase in the expected payoff that could be obtained if it were possible to learn the true state of nature before making the decision. (Sections 9.4 and 9.5), 337, 338

expected value of sample information (EVSI)   The increase in the expected payoff that could be obtained by performing a test to obtain more information, excluding the cost of the test. (Section 9.7), 350

exponential utility function   A utility function designed to fit some risk-averse individuals. (Section 9.9), 362

influence diagram   A diagram that complements the decision tree for representing and analyzing decision analysis problems. (Section 9.10), 365

maximax criterion   A very optimistic decision criterion that does not use prior probabilities and simply chooses the decision alternative that could give the largest possible payoff. (Section 9.2), 326

maximin criterion   A very pessimistic decision criterion that does not use prior probabilities and simply chooses the decision alternative that provides the best guarantee for its minimum possible payoff. (Section 9.2), 326

maximum likelihood criterion   A criterion for decision making with probabilities that focuses on the most likely state of nature. (Section 9.2), 327

node   A junction point in a decision tree. (Section 9.3), 330

payoff   A quantitative measure of the outcome from a decision alternative and a state of nature. (Section 9.1), 325

payoff table   A table giving the payoff for each combination of a decision alternative and a state of nature. (Section 9.1), 325

point of indifference   The point where the decision maker is indifferent between the two hypothetical alternatives in the equivalent lottery method. (Section 9.9), 358

posterior probabilities   Revised probabilities of the states of nature after doing a test or survey to improve the prior probabilities. (Sections 9.5 and 9.6), 340

prior probabilities   The estimated probabilities of the states of nature prior to obtaining additional information through a test or survey. (Section 9.1), 325

probability tree diagram   A diagram that is helpful for calculating the posterior probabilities of the states of nature. (Section 9.6), 341

risk-averse individual   An individual whose utility function for money has a decreasing slope as the amount of money increases.(Section 9.9), 355

risk-neutral individual   An individual whose utility for money is proportional to the amount of money involved. (Section 9.9), 355

risk seeker   An individual whose utility function for money has an increasing slope as the amount of money increases. (Section 9.9), 355

sensitivity analysis   The study of how other plausible values for the probabilities of the states of nature (or for the payoffs) would affect the recommended decision alternative. (Sections 9.4 and 9.8), 333, 351

states of nature   The possible outcomes of the random factors that affect the payoff that would be obtained from a decision alternative. (Section 9.1), 324

utility   The utility of an outcome measures the instrinsic value to the decision maker of that outcome. (Sections 9.1 and 9.9), 324

utility function for money, *U(M)*   A plot of utility versus the amount of money *M* being received. (Section 9.9), 355

Learning Aids for This Chapter in Your MS Courseware

Chapter 9 Excel Files:

Bayes' Decision Rule for First Goferbroke Problem

Decision Tree for First Goferbroke Problem

Data Table for First Goferbroke Problem

EP with Perfect Info for First Goferbroke Problem

Decision Tree for EVPI for First Goferbroke Problem

Template for Posterior Probabilities

Decision Tree for Full Goferbroke Problem (with Data Table)

Decision Tree for Full Goferbroke Problem with Max's Utility Function

Decision Tree for Full Goferbroke Problem with Exponential Utility Function

Excel Add-in:

Risk Solver Platform for Education (RSPE)

Supplement to This Chapter on the CD-ROM:

Decision Criteria Using TreePlan Software for Decision Trees

"Ch. 9 Supplement" Excel Files:

Template for Maximax Criterion

Template for Maximin Criterion

Template for Realism Criterion

Template for Minimax Regret Criterion

Template for Maximum Likelihood Criterion

Template for Equally Likely Criterion

Solved Problems (See the CD-ROM or Website for the Solutions)

9.S1. New Vehicle Introduction

The General Ford Motors Corporation (GFMC) is planning the introduction of a brand new SUV—the Vector., There are two options for production. One is to build the Vector at the company's existing plant in Indiana, sharing production time with its line of minivans that are currently being produced there. If sales of the Vector are just moderate, this will work out well as there is sufficient capacity to produce both types of vehicles at the same plant. However, if sales of the Vector are strong, this option would require the operation of a third shift, which would lead to significantly higher costs.

A second option is to open a new plant in Georgia. This plant would have sufficient capacity to meet even the largest projections for sales of the Vector. However, if sales are only moderate, the plant would be underutilized and therefore less efficient.

This is a new design, so sales are hard to predict. However, GFMC predicts that there would be about a 60 percent chance of strong sales (annual sales of 100,000), and a 40 percent chance of moderate sales (annual sales of 50,000). The average revenue per Vector sold is $30,000. Production costs per vehicle for the two production options depend upon sales, as indicated in the table below.

Expected Production Cost per Vehicle for the Vector ($thousands)

	Moderate Sales	Strong Sales
Shared plant in Indiana	16	24
Dedicated plant in Georgia	22	20

The amortized annual cost of plant construction and other associated fixed costs for the Georgia plant would total $400 million per year (regardless of sales volume). The fixed costs for adding Vector production to the plant in Indiana would total $200 million per year (regardless of sales volume).

a. Construct a decision tree to determine which production option maximizes the expected annual profit, considering fixed costs, production costs, and sales revenues.

b. Because of the uncertainty in expected sales for the Vector, GFMC is considering conducting a marketing survey to determine customer attitudes toward the Vector to better predict the likelihood of strong sales. The marketing survey would give one of two results—a positive attitude or a negative attitude toward the design. GFMC has used this marketing survey for other vehicles. For vehicles that eventually had strong sales, the marketing survey indicated positive attitudes toward the design 70 percent of the time and negative attitudes 30 percent of the time. For vehicles that eventually had moderate sales, the marketing survey indicated positive attitudes toward the design 20 percent of the time and negative attitudes 80 percent of the time. Assuming GFMC conducts such a survey, construct a decision tree to to determine how the company should proceed and what the expected annual profit would be (ignoring the cost of the survey).

c. What is the expected value of sample information in part *b?* What does this say about how large the cost of the marketing survey can be before it would no longer be worthwhile to conduct the survey?

9.S2. Settle or Go to Trial

Meredith Delgado owns a small firm that has developed software for organizing and playing music on a computer. Her software contains a number of unique features that she has patented, so her company's future has looked bright.

However, there now has been an ominous development. It appears that a number of her patented features were copied in similar software developed by MusicMan Software, a huge software company with annual sales revenue in excess of $1 billion. Meredith is distressed. MusicMan Software has stolen her ideas and that company's marketing power is likely to enable it to capture the market and drive Meredith out of business.

In response, Meredith has sued MusicMan Software for patent infringement. With attorney fees and other expenses, the cost of going to trial (win or lose) is expected to be $1 million. She feels that she has a 60 percent chance of winning the case, in which case she would receive $5 million in damages. If she loses the case, she gets nothing. Moreover, if she loses the case, there is a 50 percent chance that the judge would also order Meredith to pay for court expenses and lawyer fees for Music-Man (an additional $1 million cost). MusicMan Software has offered Meredith $1.5 million to settle this case out of court.

a. Construct and use a decision tree to determine whether Meredith should go to court or accept the settlement offer, assuming she wants to maximize her expected payoff.

b. To implement the equivalent lottery method to determine appropriate utility values for all the possible payoffs in this problem, what questions would need to be asked of Meredith?

c. Suppose that Meredith's attitude toward risk is such that she would be indifferent between doing nothing and a gamble where she would win $1 million with 50 percent probability and lose $500 thousand with 50 percent probability. Use the exponential utility function to re-solve the decision tree from part a.

Problems

To the left of the following problems (or their parts), we have inserted the symbol R whenever RSPE can be used. The symbol T indicates that the Excel template for posterior probabilities can be helpful. Nearly all the problems can be conveniently formulated in a spreadsheet format, so no special symbol is used to designate this. An asterisk on the problem number indicates that at least a partial answer is given in the back of the book.

9.1.   You are given the following payoff table (in units of thousands of dollars) for a decision analysis problem without probabilities.

	State of Nature		
Alternative	S_1	S_2	S_3
A_1	6	2	4
A_2	3	4	3
A_3	8	1	5

    a. Which alternative should be chosen under the maximax criterion?

    b. Which alternative should be chosen under the maximin criterion?

9.2.   Follow the instructions of Problem 9.1 with the following payoff table.

	State of Nature			
Alternative	S_1	S_2	S_3	S_4
A_1	25	30	20	24
A_2	17	14	31	21
A_3	22	22	22	22
A_4	29	21	26	27

9.3.   Jean Clark is the manager of the Midtown Saveway Grocery Store. She now needs to replenish her supply of strawberries. Her regular supplier can provide as many cases as she wants. However, because these strawberries already are very ripe, she will need to sell them tomorrow and then discard any that remain unsold. Jean estimates that she will be able to sell 10, 11, 12, or 13 cases tomorrow. She can purchase the strawberries for $3 per case and sell them for $8 per case. Jean now needs to decide how many cases to purchase.

Jean has checked the store's records on daily sales of strawberries. On this basis, she estimates that the prior probabilities are 0.2, 0.4, 0.3, and 0.1 for being able to sell 10, 11, 12, and 13 cases of strawberries tomorrow.

    a. Develop a decision analysis formulation of this problem by identifying the decision alternatives, the states of nature, and the payoff table.

    b. If Jean is dubious about the accuracy of these prior probabilities and so chooses to ignore them and use the maximax criterion, how many cases of strawberries should she purchase?

    c. How many cases should be purchased if she uses the maximin criterion?

    d. How many cases should be purchased if she uses the maximum likelihood criterion?

    e. How many cases should be purchased according to Bayes' decision rule?

    f. Jean thinks she has the prior probabilities just about right for selling 10 cases and selling 13 cases, but is uncertain about how to split the prior probabilities for 11 cases and 12 cases. Reapply Bayes' decision rule when the prior probabilities of 11 and 12 cases are (*i*) 0.2 and 0.5, (*ii*) 0.3 and 0.4, and (*iii*) 0.5 and 0.2.

9.4.*   Warren Buffy is an enormously wealthy investor who has built his fortune through his legendary investing acumen. He currently has been offered three major investments and he would like to choose one. The first one is a *conservative investment* that would perform very well in an improving economy and only suffer a small loss in a worsening economy. The second is a *speculative investment* that would perform extremely well in an improving economy but would do very badly in a worsening economy. The third is a *countercyclical investment* that would lose some money in an improving economy but would perform well in a worsening economy.

Warren believes that there are three possible scenarios over the lives of these potential investments: (1) an improving economy, (2) a stable economy, and (3) a worsening economy. He is pessimistic about where the economy is headed, and so has assigned prior probabilities of 0.1, 0.5, and 0.4, respectively, to these three scenarios. He also estimates that his profits under these respective scenarios are those given by the following table.

	Improving Economy	Stable Economy	Worsening Economy
Conservative investment	$ 30 million	$ 5 million	$−10 million
Speculative investment	40 million	10 million	−30 million
Countercyclical investment	−10 million	0	15 million
Prior probability	0.1	0.5	0.4

Which investment should Warren make under each of the following criteria?

    a. Maximax criterion.

    b. Maximin criterion.

    c. Maximum likelihood criterion.

    d. Bayes' decision rule.

9.5.   Reconsider Problem 9.4. Warren Buffy decides that Bayes' decision rule is his most reliable decision criterion. He believes that 0.1 is just about right as the prior probability of an improving economy, but is quite uncertain about how to split the remaining probabilities between a stable economy and a worsening economy. Therefore, he now wishes to do sensitivity analysis with respect to these latter two prior probabilities.

    a. Reapply Bayes' decision rule when the prior probability of a stable economy is 0.3 and the prior probability of a worsening economy is 0.6.

    b. Reapply Bayes' decision rule when the prior probability of a stable economy is 0.7 and the prior probability of a worsening economy is 0.2.

    c. Construct a decision tree by hand for this problem with the original prior probabilities.

R   *d.* Use RSPE to construct and solve a decision tree for this problem with the original prior probabilities.

R   *e.* In preparation for performing sensitivity analysis, consolidate the data and results on the same spreadsheet as the decision tree constructed in part *d* (as was done in Figure 9.7 for the case study).

R   *f.* Use the spreadsheet (including the decision tree) obtained in parts *d* and *e* to do parts *a* and *b*.

R   *g.* Expanding the spreadsheet as needed, generate a data table that shows which investment Warren should make and the resulting expected profit for the following prior probabilities of a stable economy: 0, 0.1, 0.2, 0.3, 0.4, 0.5, 0.6, 0.7, 0.8, 0.9.

    h. For each of the three investments, find the expected profit when the prior probability of a stable economy is 0 and then when it is 0.9 (with

the prior probability of an improving economy fixed at 0.1). Plot these expected profits on a single graph that has expected profit as the vertical axis and the prior probability of a stable economy as the horizontal axis. For each of the three investments, draw a line segment connecting its two points on this graph to show how its expected profit would vary with the prior probability of a stable economy. Use this graph to describe how the choice of the investment depends on the prior probability of a stable economy.

9.6.   Read the referenced article that fully describes the management science study summarized in the application vignette presented in Section 9.3. Briefly describe how decision analysis was applied in this study. Then list the various financial and nonfinancial benefits that resulted from this study.

9.7.*   Consider a decision analysis problem whose payoffs (in units of thousands of dollars) are given by the following payoff table.

Alternative	State of Nature	
	S_1	S_2
A_1	80	25
A_2	30	50
A_3	60	40
Prior probability	0.4	0.6

    a. Which alternative should be chosen under the maximax criterion?

    b. Which alternative should be chosen under the maximin criterion?

    c. Which alternative should be chosen under the maximum likelihood criterion?

    d. Which alternative should be chosen under Bayes' decision rule?

R   *e.* Use RSPE to construct and solve a decision tree for this problem.

R   *f.* Expanding the spreadsheet containing this decision tree as needed, perform sensitivity analysis with the decision tree by re-solving when the prior probability of S_1 is 0.2 and again when it is 0.6.

R   *g.* Now perform this sensitivity analysis systematically by generating a data table that shows the best alternative (according to Bayes' decision rule) and the resulting expected payoff as the prior probability of S_1 increases in increments of 0.04 from 0.2 to 0.6.

9.8. You are given the following payoff table (in units of thousands of dollars) for a decision analysis problem.

Alternative	State of Nature		
	S_1	S_2	S_3
A_1	220	170	110
A_2	200	180	150
Prior probability	0.6	0.3	0.1

    a. Which alternative should be chosen under the maximax criterion?

    b. Which alternative should be chosen under the maximin criterion?

    c. Which alternative should be chosen under the maximum likelihood criterion?

    d. Which alternative should be chosen under Bayes' decision rule?

    e. Construct a decision tree by hand for this problem.

R   *f.* Use RSPE to construct and solve a decision tree for this problem.

R   *g.* Perform sensitivity analysis with this decision tree by generating a data table that shows what happens when the prior probability of S_1 increases in increments of 0.05 from 0.3 to 0.7 while the prior probability of S_3 remains fixed at its original value. Then use trial and error to estimate the value of the prior probability of S_1 at which the best alternative changes as this prior probability increases.

R   *h.* Repeat part *g* when it is the prior probability of S_2 that remains fixed at its original value.

R   *i.* Repeat part *g* when it is the prior probability of S_1 that remains fixed at its original value while the prior probability of S_2 increases in increments of 0.05 from 0 to 0.4.

    j. If you feel that the true probabilities of the states of nature should be within 10 percent of the given prior probabilities, which alternative would you choose?

9.9. Dwight Moody is the manager of a large farm with 1,000 acres of arable land. For greater efficiency, Dwight always devotes the farm to growing one crop at a time. He now needs to make a decision on which one of four crops to grow during the upcoming growing season. For each of these crops, Dwight has obtained the following estimates of crop yields and net incomes per bushel under various weather conditions.

After referring to historical meteorological records, Dwight also has estimated the following prior probabilities for the weather during the growing season:

Dry	0.3
Moderate	0.5
Damp	0.2

    a. Develop a decision analysis formulation of this problem by identifying the decision alternatives, the states of nature, and the payoff table.

R   *b.* Construct a decision tree for this problem and use Bayes' decision rule to determine which crop to grow.

R   *c.* Using Bayes' decision rule, do sensitivity analysis with respect to the prior probabilities of moderate weather and damp weather (without changing the prior probability of dry weather) by re-solving when the prior probability of moderate weather is 0.2, 0.3, 0.4, and 0.6.

9.10. Barbara Miller makes decisions according to Bayes' decision rule. For her current problem, Barbara has constructed the following payoff table (in units of hundreds of dollars) and she now wishes to maximize the expected payoff.

Alternative	State of Nature		
	S_1	S_2	S_3
A_1	$2x$	50	10
A_2	25	40	90
A_3	35	$3x$	30
Prior probability	0.4	0.2	0.4

The value of x currently is 50, but there is an opportunity to increase x by spending some money now.

What is the maximum amount Barbara should spend to increase x to 75?

9.11. You are given the following payoff table (in units of thousands of dollars) for a decision analysis problem.

Alternative	State of Nature		
	S_1	S_2	S_3
A_1	4	0	0
A_2	0	2	0
A_3	3	0	1
Prior probability	0.2	0.5	0.3

Weather	Expected Yield, Bushels/Acre			
	Crop 1	Crop 2	Crop 3	Crop 4
Dry	20	15	30	40
Moderate	35	20	25	40
Damp	40	30	25	40
Net income per bushel	$1.00	$1.50	$1.00	$0.50

a. According to Bayes' decision rule, which alternative should be chosen?

b. Find the expected value of perfect information.

R c. Check your answer in part *b* by recalculating it with the help of a decision tree.

d. You are given the opportunity to spend $1,000 to obtain more information about which state of nature is likely to occur. Given your answer to part *b*, might it be worthwhile to spend this money?

9.12.* Betsy Pitzer makes decisions according to Bayes' decision rule. For her current problem, Betsy has constructed the following payoff table (in units of dollars).

	State of Nature		
Alternative	S_1	S_2	S_3
A_1	50	100	−100
A_2	0	10	−10
A_3	20	40	−40
Prior probability	0.5	0.3	0.2

a. Which alternative should Betsy choose?

b. Find the expected value of perfect information.

R c. Check your answer in part *b* by recalculating it with the help of a decision tree.

d. What is the most that Betsy should consider paying to obtain more information about which state of nature will occur?

9.13. Using Bayes' decision rule, consider the decision analysis problem having the following payoff table (in units of thousands of dollars).

	State of Nature		
Alternative	S_1	S_2	S_3
A_1	−100	10	100
A_2	−10	20	50
A_3	10	10	60
Prior probability	0.2	0.3	0.5

a. Which alternative should be chosen? What is the resulting expected payoff?

b. You are offered the opportunity to obtain information that will tell you with certainty whether the first state of nature S_1 will occur. What is the maximum amount you should pay for the information? Assuming you will obtain the information, how should this information be used to choose an alternative? What is the resulting expected payoff (excluding the payment)?

c. Now repeat part *b* if the information offered concerns S_2 instead of S_1.

d. Now repeat part *b* if the information offered concerns S_3 instead of S_1.

R e. Now suppose that the opportunity is offered to provide information that will tell you with certainty which state of nature will occur (perfect information). What is the maximum amount you should

pay for the information? Assuming you will obtain the information, how should this information be used to choose an alternative? What is the resulting expected payoff (excluding the payment)?

f. If you have the opportunity to do some testing that will give you partial additional information (not perfect information) about the state of nature, what is the maximum amount you should consider paying for this information?

9.14. Reconsider the Goferbroke Co. case study, including its analysis in Sections 9.6 and 9.7. With the help of the consulting geologist, Jennifer Flyer now has obtained some historical data that provides more precise information than Max could supply on the likelihood of obtaining favorable seismic soundings on similar tracts of land. Specifically, when the land contains oil, favorable seismic soundings are obtained 80 percent of the time. This percentage changes to 40 percent when the land is dry.

a. Revise Figure 9.12 to find the new posterior probabilities.

T b. Use the corresponding Excel template to check your answers in part *a*.

c. Revise Figure 9.16 to find the new decision tree. What is the resulting optimal policy?

R d. Use RSPE to construct and solve this new decision tree.

9.15. Read the referenced article that fully describes the management science study summarized in the application vignette presented in Section 9.7. Briefly describe how decision analysis was applied in this study. Then list the various financial and nonfinancial benefits that resulted from this study.

9.16.* Vincent Cuomo is the credit manager for the Fine Fabrics Mill. He is currently faced with the question of whether to extend $100,000 of credit to a potential new customer, a dress manufacturer. Vincent has three categories for the creditworthiness of a company—poor risk, average risk, and good risk—but he does not know which category fits this potential customer. Experience indicates that 20 percent of companies similar to this dress manufacturer are poor risks, 50 percent are average risks, and 30 percent are good risks. If credit is extended, the expected profit for poor risks is −$15,000, for average risks $10,000, and for good risks $20,000. If credit is not extended, the dress manufacturer will turn to another mill. Vincent is able to consult a credit-rating organization for a fee of $5,000 per company evaluated. For companies whose actual credit records with the mill turn out to fall into each of the three categories, the following table shows the percentages that were given each of the three possible credit evaluations by the credit-rating organization.

	Actual Credit Record		
Credit Evaluation	Poor	Average	Good
Poor	50%	40%	20%
Average	40	50	40
Good	10	10	40

a. Develop a decision analysis formulation of this problem by identifying the decision alternatives, the states of nature, and the payoff table when the credit-rating organization is not used.

b. Assuming the credit-rating organization is not used, use Bayes' decision rule to determine which decision alternative should be chosen.

c. Find the expected value of perfect information. Does this answer indicate that consideration should be given to using the credit-rating organization?

d. Assume now that the credit-rating organization is used. Develop a probability tree diagram to find the posterior probabilities of the respective states of nature for each of the three possible credit evaluations of this potential customer.

T   e. Use the corresponding Excel template to obtain the answers for part *d*.

f. Draw the decision tree for this entire problem by hand. Use this decision tree to determine Vincent's optimal policy.

R   g. Use RSPE to construct and solve this decision tree.

R   h. Find the expected value of sample information. If the fee for using the credit-rating organization is open to negotiation, how large can the fee be and use of this organization still be worthwhile?

9.17. You are given the following payoff table (in units of dollars).

	State of Nature	
Alternative	S_1	S_2
A_1	400	−100
A_1	0	100
Prior probability	0.4	0.6

You have the option of paying $100 to have research done to better predict which state of nature will occur. When the true state of nature is S_1, the research will accurately predict S_1 60 percent of the time (but will inaccurately predict S_2 40 percent of the time). When the true state of nature is S_2, the research will accurately predict S_2 80 percent of the time (but will inaccurately predict S_1 20 percent of the time).

a. Given that the research is not done, use Bayes' decision rule to determine which decision alternative should be chosen.

R   b. Use a decision tree to help find the expected value of perfect information. Does this answer indicate that it might be worthwhile to do the research?

c. Given that the research is done, find the joint probability of each of the following pairs of outcomes: (*i*) the state of nature is S_1 and the research predicts S_1, (*ii*) the state of nature is S_1 and the research predicts S_2, (*iii*) the state of nature is S_2 and the research predicts S_1, and (*iv*) the state of nature is S_2 and the research predicts S_2.

d. Find the unconditional probability that the research predicts S_1. Also find the unconditional probability that the research predicts S_2.

e. Given that the research is done, use your answers in parts *c* and *d* to determine the posterior probabilities of the states of nature for each of the two possible predictions of the research.

T   f. Use the corresponding Excel template to obtain the answers for part *e*.

g. Given that the research predicts S_1, use Bayes' decision rule to determine which decision alternative should be chosen and the resulting expected payoff.

h. Repeat part *g* when the research predicts S_2.

i. Given that research is done, what is the expected payoff when using Bayes' decision rule?

j. Use the preceding results to determine the optimal policy regarding whether to do the research and the choice of the decision alternative.

R   k. Construct and solve the decision tree to show the analysis for the entire problem. (Using RSPE is optional.)

9.18. An athletic league does drug testing of its athletes, 10 percent of whom use drugs. The test, however, is only 95 percent reliable. That is, a drug user will test positive with probability 0.95 and negative with probability 0.05, and a nonuser will test negative with probability 0.95 and positive with probability 0.05.

Develop a probability tree diagram to determine the posterior probability of each of the following outcomes of testing an athlete.

a. The athlete is a drug user, given that the test is positive.

b. The athlete is not a drug user, given that the test is positive.

c. The athlete is a drug user, given that the test is negative.

d. The athlete is not a drug user, given that the test is negative.

T   e. Use the corresponding Excel template to check your answers in the preceding parts.

9.19. Management of the Telemore Company is considering developing and marketing a new product. It is estimated to be twice as likely that the product would prove to be successful as unsuccessful. If it were successful, the expected profit would be $1,500,000. If unsuccessful, the expected loss would be $1,800,000. A marketing survey can be conducted at a cost of $100,000 to predict whether the product would be successful. Past experience with such surveys indicates that successful products have been predicted to be successful 80 percent of the time, whereas unsuccessful products have been predicted to be unsuccessful 70 percent of the time.

a. Develop a decision analysis formulation of this problem by identifying the decision alternatives, the states of nature, and the payoff table when the market survey is not conducted.

b. Assuming the market survey is not conducted, use Bayes' decision rule to determine which decision alternative should be chosen.

c. Find the expected value of perfect information. Does this answer indicate that consideration should be given to conducting the market survey?

T   d. Assume now that the market survey is conducted. Find the posterior probabilities of the respective states of nature for each of the two possible predictions from the market survey.

R   e. Use RSPE to construct and solve the decision tree for this entire problem.

9.20. The Hit-and-Miss Manufacturing Company produces items that have a probability p of being defective. These items are produced in lots of 150. Past experience indicates that p for an entire lot is either 0.05 or 0.25. Furthermore, in 80 percent of the lots produced, p equals 0.05 (so p equals 0.25 in 20 percent of the lots). These items are then used in an assembly, and ultimately their quality is determined before the final assembly leaves the plant. Initially the company can *either* screen each item in a lot at a cost of $10 per item and replace defective items *or* use the items directly without screening. If the latter action is chosen, the cost of rework is ultimately $100 per defective item. Because screening requires scheduling of inspectors and equipment, the decision to screen or not screen must be made two days before the screening is to take place. However, one item can be taken from the lot and sent to a laboratory for inspection, and its quality (defective or nondefective) can be reported before the screen/no-screen decision must be made. The cost of this initial inspection is $125.

    a. Develop a decision analysis formulation of this problem by identifying the decision alternatives, the states of nature, and the payoff table if the single item is not inspected in advance.

    b. Assuming the single item is not inspected in advance, use Bayes' decision rule to determine which decision alternative should be chosen.

    c. Find the expected value of perfect information. Does this answer indicate that consideration should be given to inspecting the single item in advance?

T   *d.* Assume now that the single item is inspected in advance. Find the posterior probabilities of the respective states of nature for each of the two possible outcomes of this inspection.

R   *e.* Construct and solve the decision tree for this entire problem.

R   *f.* Find the expected value of sample information. If the cost of using the laboratory to inspect the single item in advance is open to negotiation, how large can the cost of using the laboratory be and still be worthwhile?

9.21.* Silicon Dynamics has developed a new computer chip that will enable it to begin producing and marketing a personal computer if it so desires. Alternatively, it can sell the rights to the computer chip for $15 million. If the company chooses to build computers, the profitability of the venture depends on the company's ability to market the computer during the first year. It has sufficient access to retail outlets that it can guarantee sales of 10,000 computers. On the other hand, if this computer catches on, the company can sell 100,000 machines. For analysis purposes, these two levels of sales are taken to be the two possible outcomes of marketing the computer, but it is unclear what their prior probabilities are. The cost of setting up the assembly line is $6 million. The difference between the selling price and the variable cost of each computer is $600.

    a. Develop a decision analysis formulation of this problem by identifying the decision alternatives, the states of nature, and the payoff table.

    b. Construct a decision tree for this problem by hand.

R   *c.* Assuming the prior probabilities of the two levels of sales are both 0.5, use RSPE to construct and solve this decision tree. According to this analysis, which decision alternative should be chosen?

9.22.* Reconsider Problem 9.21. Management of Silicon Dynamics now is considering doing full-fledged market research at an estimated cost of $1 million to predict which of the two levels of demand is likely to occur. Previous experience indicates that such market research is correct two-thirds of the time.

    a. Find the expected value of perfect information for this problem.

    b. Does the answer in part *a* indicate that it might be worthwhile to perform this market research?

    c. Develop a probability tree diagram to obtain the posterior probabilities of the two levels of demand for each of the two possible outcomes of the market research.

T   *d.* Use the corresponding Excel template to check your answers in part *c.*

R9.23.* Reconsider Problem 9.22. The management of Silicon Dynamics now wants to see a decision tree displaying the entire problem.

    a. Use RSPE to construct and solve this decision tree.

    b. Find the expected value of sample information. How large can the cost of doing full-fledged market research be and still be worthwhile?

    c. Assume now that the estimate of $1 million for the cost of doing full-fledged market research is correct but that there is some uncertainty in the financial data ($15 million, $6 million, and $600) stated in Problem 9.20. Each could vary from its base value by as much as 10 percent. For each one, perform sensitivity analysis to find what would happen if its value were at either end of this range of variability (without any change in the other two pieces of data). Then do the same for the eight cases where all these pieces of data are at one end or the other of their ranges of variability.

9.24. You are given the following decision tree, where the numbers in parentheses are probabilities and the numbers on the right are payoffs at these terminal points.

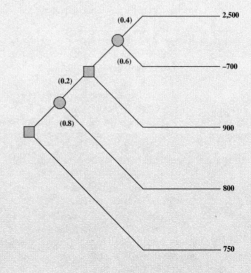

a. Analyze this decision tree to obtain the optimal policy.

R b. Use RSPE to construct and solve the same decision tree.

9.25.   You are given the following decision tree, with the probabilities at event nodes shown in parentheses and with the payoffs at terminal points shown on the right. Analyze this decision tree to obtain the optimal policy.

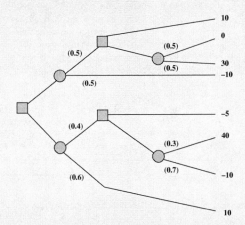

9.26.*   The Athletic Department of Leland University is considering whether to hold an extensive campaign next year to raise funds for a new athletic field. The response to the campaign depends heavily on the success of the football team this fall. In the past, the football team has had winning seasons 60 percent of the time. If the football team has a winning season (W) this fall, then many of the alumni will contribute and the campaign will raise $3 million. If the team has a losing season (L), few will contribute and the campaign will lose $2 million. If no campaign is undertaken, no costs are incurred. On September 1, just before the football season begins, the Athletic Department needs to make its decision about whether to hold the campaign next year.

   a. Develop a decision analysis formulation of this problem by identifying the decision alternatives, the states of nature, and the payoff table.

   b. According to Bayes' decision rule, should the campaign be undertaken?

   c. What is the expected value of perfect information?

   d. A famous football guru, William Walsh, has offered his services to help evaluate whether the team will have a winning season. For $100,000, he will carefully evaluate the team throughout spring practice and then throughout preseason workouts. William then will provide his prediction on September 1 regarding what kind of season, W or L, the team will have. In similar situations in the past when evaluating teams that have winning seasons 50 percent of the time, his predictions have been correct 75 percent of the time. Considering that this team has more of a winning tradition, if William predicts a winning season, what is the posterior probability that the team actually will have a winning season? What is the posterior probability of a losing season?

If William predicts a losing season instead, what is the posterior probability of a winning season? Of a losing season? Show how these answers are obtained from a probability tree diagram.

T e. Use the corresponding Excel template to obtain the answers requested in part *d*.

   f. Draw the decision tree for this entire problem by hand. Analyze this decision tree to determine the optimal policy regarding whether to hire William and whether to undertake the campaign.

R g. Use RSPE to construct and solve this decision tree.

R h. Find the expected value of sample information. If the fee for hiring William Walsh is open to negotiation, how large can William's fee be and still be worthwhile?

9.27.   The comptroller of the Macrosoft Corporation has $100 million of excess funds to invest. She has been instructed to invest the entire amount for one year in either stocks or bonds (but not both) and then to reinvest the entire fund in either stocks or bonds (but not both) for one year more. The objective is to maximize the expected monetary value of the fund at the end of the second year.

The annual rates of return on these investments depend on the economic environment, as shown in the following table.

	Rate of Return	
Economic Environment	Stocks	Bonds
Growth	20%	5%
Recession	−10	10
Depression	−50	20

The probabilities of growth, recession, and depression for the first year are 0.7, 0.3, and 0, respectively. If growth occurs in the first year, these probabilities remain the same for the second year. However, if a recession occurs in the first year, these probabilities change to 0.2, 0.7, and 0.1, respectively, for the second year.

   a. Construct by hand the decision tree for this problem and then analyze the decision tree to identify the optimal policy.

R b. Use RSPE to construct and solve the decision tree.

9.28.   On Monday, a certain stock closed at $10 per share. On Tuesday, you expect the stock to close at $9, $10, or $11 per share, with respective probabilities 0.3, 0.3, and 0.4. On Wednesday, you expect the stock to close 10 percent lower, unchanged, or 10 percent higher than Tuesday's close, with the following probabilities.

	10 Percent		10 Percent
Today's Close	Lower	Unchanged	Higher
$ 9	0.4	0.3	0.3
10	0.2	0.2	0.6
11	0.1	0.2	0.7

On Tuesday, you are directed to buy 100 shares of the stock before Thursday. All purchases are made at the end of the day, at the known closing price for that day, so your only options are to

376   Chapter Nine   *Decision Analysis*

buy at the end of Tuesday or at the end of Wednesday. You wish to determine the optimal strategy for whether to buy on Tuesday or defer the purchase until Wednesday, given the Tuesday closing price, to minimize the expected purchase price.

    a. Develop and evaluate a decision tree by hand for determining the optimal strategy.

R   *b.* Use RSPE to construct and solve the decision tree.

R9.29. Jose Morales manages a large outdoor fruit stand in one of the less affluent neighborhoods of San Jose, California. To replenish his supply, Jose buys boxes of fruit early each morning from a grower south of San Jose. About 90 percent of the boxes of fruit turn out to be of satisfactory quality, but the other 10 percent are unsatisfactory. A satisfactory box contains 80 percent excellent fruit and will earn $200 profit for Jose. An unsatisfactory box contains 30 percent excellent fruit and will produce a loss of $1,000. Before Jose decides to accept a box, he is given the opportunity to sample one piece of fruit to test whether it is excellent. Based on that sample, he then has the option of rejecting the box without paying for it. Jose wonders (1) whether he should continue buying from this grower, (2) if so, whether it is worthwhile sampling just one piece of fruit from a box, and (3) if so, whether he should be accepting or rejecting the box based on the outcome of this sampling.

Use RSPE (and the Excel template for posterior probabilities) to construct and solve the decision tree for this problem.

9.30.* The Morton Ward Company is considering the introduction of a new product that is believed to have a 50–50 chance of being successful. One option is to try out the product in a test market, at an estimated cost of $2 million, before making the introduction decision. Past experience shows that ultimately successful products are approved in the test market 80 percent of the time, whereas ultimately unsuccessful products are approved in the test market only 25 percent of the time. If the product is successful, the net profit to the company will be $40 million; if unsuccessful, the net loss will be $15 million.

    a. Discarding the test market option, develop a decision analysis formulation of the problem by identifying the decision alternatives, states of nature, and payoff table. Then apply Bayes' decision rule to determine the optimal decision alternative.

    b. Find the expected value of perfect information.

R   *c.* Now including the option of trying out the product in a test market, use RSPE (and the Excel template for posterior probabilities) to construct and solve the decision tree for this problem.

R   *d.* Find the expected value of sample information. How large can the cost of trying out the product in a test market be and still be worthwhile to do?

R   *e.* Assume now that the estimate of $2 million for the cost of trying out the product in a test market is correct. However, there is some uncertainty in the stated profit and loss figures ($40 million and $15 million). Either could vary from its base by as much as 25 percent in either direction. For each of these two financial figures, perform sensitivity analysis to check how the results in part *c* would change if the value of the financial figure were at either end of this range of variability (without any change in the value of the other financial figure).

Then do the same for the four cases where both financial figures are at one end or the other of their ranges of variability.

R9.31. Chelsea Bush is an emerging candidate for her party's nomination for president of the United States. She now is considering whether to run in the high-stakes Super Tuesday primaries. If she enters the Super Tuesday (S.T.) primaries, she and her advisers believe that she will either do well (finish first or second) or do poorly (finish third or worse) with probabilities 0.4 and 0.6, respectively. Doing well on Super Tuesday will net the candidate's campaign approximately $16 million in new contributions, whereas a poor showing will mean a loss of $10 million after numerous TV ads are paid for. Alternatively, she may choose not to run at all on Super Tuesday and incur no costs.

Chelsea's advisors realize that her chances of success on Super Tuesday may be affected by the outcome of the smaller New Hampshire (N.H.) primary occurring three weeks before Super Tuesday. Political analysts feel that the results of New Hampshire's primary are correct two-thirds of the time in predicting the results of the Super Tuesday primaries. Among Chelsea's advisers is a decision analysis expert who uses this information to calculate the following probabilities:

    P(Chelsea does well in S.T. primaries, given she does well in N.H.) = $4/7$

    P(Chelsea does well in S.T. primaries, given she does poorly in N.H.) = $1/4$

    P(Chelsea does well in N.H. primary) = $7/15$

The cost of entering and campaigning in the New Hampshire primary is estimated to be $1.6 million.

Chelsea feels that her chance of winning the nomination depends largely on having substantial funds available after the Super Tuesday primaries to carry on a vigorous campaign the rest of the way. Therefore, she wants to choose the strategy (whether to run in the New Hampshire primary and then whether to run in the Super Tuesday primaries) that will maximize her expected funds after these primaries.

    a. Construct and solve the decision tree for this problem.

    b. There is some uncertainty in the estimates of a gain of $16 million or a loss of $10 million depending on the showing on Super Tuesday. Either amount could differ from this estimate by as much as 25 percent in either direction. For each of these two financial figures, perform sensitivity analysis to check how the results in part *a* would change if the value of the financial figure were at either end of this range of variability (without any change in the value of the other financial figure). Then do the same for the four cases where both financial figures are at one end or the other of their ranges of variability.

R9.32. The executive search being conducted for Western Bank by Headhunters Inc. may finally be bearing fruit. The position to be filled is a key one—vice president for Information Processing—because this person will have responsibility for developing a state-of-the-art management information system that will link together Western's many branch banks. However, Headhunters feels it has found just the right person, Matthew

Fenton, who has an excellent record in a similar position for a midsized bank in New York.

After a round of interviews, Western's president believes that Matthew has a probability of 0.7 of designing the management information system successfully. If Matthew is successful, the company will realize a profit of $2 million (net of Matthew's salary, training, recruiting costs, and expenses). If he is not successful, the company will realize a net loss of $600,000.

For an additional fee of $40,000, Headhunters will provide a detailed investigative process (including an extensive background check, a battery of academic and psychological tests, etc.) that will further pinpoint Matthew's potential for success. This process has been found to be 90 percent reliable, that is, a candidate who would successfully design the management information system will pass the test with probability 0.9, and a candidate who would not successfully design the system will fail the test with probability 0.9.

Western's top management needs to decide whether to hire Matthew and whether to have Headhunters conduct the detailed investigative process before making this decision.

    a. Construct and solve the decision tree for this problem to identify the optimal policy.

    b. Now suppose that Headhunters's fee for administering its detailed investigative process is negotiable. What is the maximum amount that Western Bank should pay?

9.33.   Read the referenced article that fully describes the management science study summarized in the application vignette presented in Section 9.9. Briefly describe how decision analysis was applied in this study. Then list the various financial and nonfinancial benefits that resulted from this study.

9.34.   Reconsider the Goferbroke Co. case study, including the application of utilities in Section 9.9. Max Flyer now has decided that, given the company's precarious financial situation, he needs to take a much more risk-averse approach to the problem. Therefore, he has revised the utilities given in Table 9.9 as follows: $U(-130) = 0$, $U(-100) = 0.07$, $U(60) = 0.40$, $U(90) = 0.45$, $U(670) = 0.99$, and $U(700) = 1$.

    a. Analyze the revised decision tree corresponding to Figure 9.23 by hand to obtain the new optimal policy.

R   *b.* Use RSPE to construct and solve this revised decision tree.

9.35.*   You live in an area that has a possibility of incurring a massive earthquake, so you are considering buying earthquake insurance on your home at an annual cost of $180. The probability of an earthquake damaging your home during one year is 0.001. If this happens, you estimate that the cost of the damage (fully covered by earthquake insurance) will be $160,000. Your total assets (including your home) are worth $250,000.

    a. Apply Bayes' decision rule to determine which alternative (take the insurance or not) maximizes your expected assets after one year.

    b. You now have constructed a utility function that measures how much you value having total assets worth x dollars ($x \geq 0$). This utility function is $U(x) = \sqrt{x}$. Compare the utility of reducing your total assets next year by the cost of the earthquake insurance with the expected utility next year of not

taking the earthquake insurance. Should you take the insurance?

9.36.   For your graduation present from college, your parents are offering you your choice of two alternatives. The first alternative is to give you a money gift of $19,000. The second alternative is to make an investment in your name. This investment will quickly have the following two possible outcomes.

Outcome	Probability
Receive $10,000	0.3
Receive $30,000	0.7

Your utility for receiving M thousand dollars is given by the utility function $U(M) = \sqrt{M + 6}$. Which choice should you make to maximize expected utility?

9.37.   Reconsider Problem 9.36. You now are uncertain about what your true utility function for receiving money is, so you are in the process of constructing this utility function by using the equivalent lottery method and units of thousands of dollars. You have concluded that you are indifferent between the two alternatives offered to you by your parents. Use this information to find $U(19)$ after setting $U(10) = 0$ and $U(30) = 1$.

9.38.   You wish to construct your personal utility function $U(M)$ for receiving M thousand dollars. After setting $U(0) = 0$, you next set $U(10) = 1$ as your utility for receiving $10,000. You next want to find $U(1)$ and then $U(5)$.

    a. You offer yourself the following two hypothetical alternatives:

        A_1: Obtain $10,000 with probability p.
            Obtain 0 with probability $(1 - p)$.

        A_2: Definitely obtain $1,000.

    You then ask yourself the question: What value of p makes you indifferent between these two alternatives? Your answer is $p = 0.125$. Find $U(1)$ by using the equivalent lottery method.

    b. You next repeat part *a* except for changing the second alternative to definitely receiving $5,000. The value of p that makes you indifferent between these two alternatives now is $p = 0.5625$. Find $U(5)$.

    c. Repeat parts *a* and *b*, but now use *your* personal choices for p.

9.39.   You are given the following payoff table.

	State of Nature	
Alternative	S_1	S_2
A_1	25	36
A_2	100	0
A_3	0	49
Prior probability	p	$1 - p$

    a. Assume that your utility function for the payoffs is $U(x) = \sqrt{x}$. Plot the expected utility of each decision alternative versus the value of p on the same graph. For each decision alternative, find the range of values of p over which this alternative maximizes the expected utility.

378 Chapter Nine *Decision Analysis*

R   *b.* Now assume that your utility function is the exponential utility function with a risk tolerance of $R = 50$. Use RSPE to construct and solve the resulting decision tree in turn for $p = 0.25$, $p = 0.5$, and $p = 0.75$.

R9.40. Dr. Switzer has a seriously ill patient but has had trouble diagnosing the specific cause of the illness. The doctor now has narrowed the cause down to two alternatives: disease A or disease B. Based on the evidence so far, she feels that the two alternatives are equally likely.

Beyond the testing already done, there is no test available to determine if the cause is disease B. One test is available for disease A, but it has two major problems. First, it is very expensive. Second, it is somewhat unreliable, giving an accurate result only 80 percent of the time. Thus, it will give a positive result (indicating disease A) for only 80 percent of patients who have disease A, whereas it will give a positive result for 20 percent of patients who actually have disease B instead.

Disease B is a very serious disease with no known treatment. It is sometimes fatal, and those who survive remain in poor health with a poor quality of life thereafter. The prognosis is similar for victims of disease A if it is left untreated. However, there is a fairly expensive treatment available that eliminates the danger for those with disease A, and it may return them to good health. Unfortunately, it is a relatively radical treatment that always leads to death if the patient actually has disease B instead.

The probability distribution for the prognosis for this patient is given for each case in the following table, where the column headings (after the first one) indicate the disease for the patient.

9.41. Consider the following decision tree, where the probabilities for each event node are shown in parentheses.

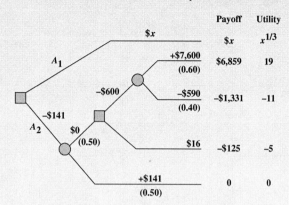

The dollar amount given next to each branch is the cash flow generated along that branch, where these intermediate cash flows add up to the total net cash flow shown to the right of each terminal branch. (The unknown amount for the top branch is represented by the variable x.) The decision maker has a utility function $U(y) = y^{1/3}$ where y is the total net cash flow after a terminal branch. The resulting utilities for the various terminal branches are shown to the right of the decision tree.

Use these utilities to analyze the decision tree. Then determine the value of x for which the decision maker is indifferent between decision alternatives A_1 and A_2.

	Outcome Probabilities			
	No Treatment		Receive Treatment for Disease A	
Outcome	A	B	A	B
Die	0.2	0.5	0	1.0
Survive with poor health	0.8	0.5	0.5	0
Return to good health	0	0	0.5	0

The patient has assigned the following utilities to the possible outcomes.

Outcome	Utility
Die	0
Survive with poor health	10
Return to good health	30

In addition, these utilities should be incremented by -2 if the patient incurs the cost of the test for disease A and by -1 if the patient (or the patient's estate) incurs the cost of the treatment for disease A.

Use decision analysis with a complete decision tree to determine if the patient should undergo the test for disease A and then how to proceed (receive the treatment for disease A?) to maximize the patient's expected utility.

R9.42. Reconsider the Goferbroke Co. case study when using utilities, as presented in Section 9.9.

a. Beginning with the decision tree shown in Figure 9.23 (available in one of this chapter's Excel files), prepare to perform sensitivity analysis by expanding and organizing the spreadsheet to (1) consolidate the data and results in one section and (2) incorporate the Excel template for posterior probabilities in another section (similar to what was done in Figure 9.18).

b. Perform sensitivity analysis by re-solving the decision tree (after using the Excel template for posterior probabilities to revise these probabilities) when the prior probability of oil is changed in turn to 0.15, 0.2, 0.3, and 0.35.

Case 9-1

Who Wants to Be a Millionaire?

You are a contestant on "Who Wants to Be a Millionaire?" You already have answered the $250,000 question correctly and now must decide if you would like to answer the $500,000 question. You can choose to walk away at this point with $250,000 in winnings or you may decide to answer the $500,000 question. If you answer the $500,000 question correctly, you can then choose to walk away with $500,000 in winnings or go on and try to answer the $1,000,000 question. If you answer the $1,000,000 question correctly, the game is over and you win $1,000,000. If you answer either the $500,000 or the $1,000,000 question incorrectly, the game is over immediately and you take home "only" $32,000.

A feature of the game "Who Wants to Be a Millionaire?" is that you have three "lifelines"—namely "50–50," "ask the audience," and "phone a friend." At this point (after answering the $250,000 question), you already have used two of these lifelines, but you have the "phone a friend" lifeline remaining. With this option, you may phone a friend to obtain advice on the correct answer to a question before giving your answer. You may use this option only once (i.e., you can use it on either the $500,000

question or the $1,000,000 question, but not both). Since some of your friends are smarter than you are, "phone a friend" significantly improves your odds for answering a question correctly. Without "phone a friend," if you choose to answer the $500,000 question you have a 65 percent chance of answering correctly, and if you choose to answer the $1,000,000 question you have a 50 percent chance of answering correctly (the questions get progressively more difficult). With "phone a friend," you have an 80 percent chance of answering the $500,000 question correctly and a 65 percent chance of answering the $1,000,000 question correctly.

a. Use RSPE to construct and solve a decision tree to decide what to do. What is the best course of action, assuming your goal is to maximize your *expected* winnings?

b. Use the equivalent lottery method to determine your personal utility function (in particular, your utility values for all of the possible payoffs in the game).

c. Re-solve the decision tree, replacing the payoffs with your utility values, to maximize your expected utility. Does the best course of action change?

Case 9-2

University Toys and the Business Professor Action Figures

University Toys has developed a brand new product line—a series of Business Professor Action Figures (BPAFs) featuring likenesses of popular professors at the local business school. Management needs to decide how to market the dolls.

One option is to immediately ramp up production and simultaneously launch an ad campaign in the university newspaper. This option would cost $1,000. Based on past experience, new action figures either take off and do well or fail miserably. Hence, the prediction is for one of two possible outcomes—total sales of 2,500 units or total sales of only 250 units. University Toys receives revenue of $2 per unit sold. Management currently thinks that there is about a 50 percent chance that the product will do well (sell 2,500 units) and a 50 percent chance that it will do poorly (sell 250 units).

Another option is to test-market the product. The company could build a few units, put up a display in the campus bookstore, and see how they sell without any further advertising. This would require less capital for the production run and no money for advertising. Again, the prediction is for one of two possible outcomes for this test market, namely, the product will either do well (sell 200 units) or do poorly (sell 20 units). The cost for this option is estimated to be $100. University Toys receives revenue of $2 per unit sold for the test market as well. The company has often test marketed toys in this manner. Products that sell well when fully marketed have also sold well in the test market 80 percent of the time. Products that sell poorly when fully marketed also sell poorly in the test market 60 percent of the time.

There is a complication with the test market option, however. A rival toy manufacturer is rumored to be considering the development of Law School Professor Action Figures (LSPAF). After doing the test marketing, if University Toys decides to go ahead and ramp up production and fully market the BPAF, the cost of doing so would still be $1,000. However, the sales prospects depend upon whether LSPAF has been introduced into the market or not. If LSPAF has not entered the market, then the sales prospects will be the same as described above (i.e., 2,500 units if BPAF does well, or 250 units if BPAF does poorly, on top of any units sold in the test market). However, if LSPAF has been introduced, the increased competition will diminish sales of BPAF. In particular, management expects in this case to sell 1,000 if BPAF does well or 100 units if it does poorly (on top of any units sold in the test market). Note that the probability of BPAF doing well or doing poorly is not affected by LSPAF, just the final sales totals of each possibility. The probability that LSPAF will enter the market *before the end* of the test market is 20 percent. On the other hand, if University Toys markets BPAF immediately, they are guaranteed to beat the LSPAF to market (thus making LSPAF a nonfactor).

a. Suppose that the test marketing is done. Use the Posterior Probabilities template to determine the likelihood that the BPAF would sell well if fully marketed, given that it sells well in the test market and then given that it sells poorly in the test market.

380   Chapter Nine   *Decision Analysis*

b. Use RSPE to develop and solve a decision tree to help University Toys decide the best course of action and the expected payoff.

c. Now suppose that University Toys is uncertain of the probability that the LSPAFs will enter the market before the test marketing would be completed (if it were done). How would you expect the expected payoff to vary as the probability that the LSPAFs will enter the market changes?

d. Generate a data table that shows how the expected payoff and the test marketing decision changes as the probability that the LSPAFs will enter the market varies from 0 percent to 100 percent (at 10 percent increments).

e. At what probability does the test marketing decision change?

Case 9-3

Brainy Business

While El Niño is pouring its rain on northern California, Charlotte Rothstein, CEO, major shareholder, and founder of **Cerebrosoft,** sits in her office, contemplating the decision she faces regarding her company's newest proposed product, Brainet. This has been a particularly difficult decision. Brainet might catch on and sell very well. However, Charlotte is concerned about the risk involved. In this competitive market, marketing Brainet also could lead to substantial losses. Should she go ahead anyway and start the marketing campaign? Or just abandon the product? Or perhaps buy additional marketing research information from a local market research company before deciding whether to launch the product? She has to make a decision very soon and so, as she slowly drinks from her glass of high-protein-power multivitamin juice, she reflects on the events of the past few years.

Cerebrosoft was founded by Charlotte and two friends after they had graduated from business school. The company is located in the heart of Silicon Valley. Charlotte and her friends managed to make money in their second year in business and have continued to do so every year since. Cerebrosoft was one of the first companies to sell software over the World Wide Web and to develop PC-based software tools for the multimedia sector. Two of the products generate 80 percent of the company's revenues: Audiatur and Videatur. Each product has sold more than 100,000 units during the past year. Business is done over the Web: Customers can download a trial version of the software, test it, and if they are satisfied with what they see, they can purchase the product (by using a password that enables them to disable the time counter in the trial version). Both products are priced at $75.95 and are sold exclusively over the Web.

Although the World Wide Web is a network of computers of different types, running different kinds of software, a standardized protocol between the computers enables them to communicate. Users can surf the Web and visit computers many thousands of miles away, accessing information available at the site. Users also can make files available on the Web, and this is how Cerebrosoft generates its sales. Selling software over the Web eliminates many of the traditional cost factors of consumer products: packaging, storage, distribution, sales force, and so on. Instead, potential customers can download a trial version, take a look at it (that is, use the product) before its trial period expires, and then decide whether to buy it. Furthermore, Cerebrosoft can always make the most recent files available to the

customer, avoiding the problem of having outdated software in the distribution pipeline.

Charlotte is interrupted in her thoughts by the arrival of Jeannie Korn. Jeannie is in charge of marketing for online products and Brainet has had her particular attention from the beginning. She is more than ready to provide the advice that Charlotte has requested. "Charlotte, I think we should really go ahead with Brainet. The software engineers have convinced me that the current version is robust and we want to be on the market with this as soon as possible! From the data for our product launches during the past two years, we can get a rather reliable estimate of how the market will respond to the new product, don't you think? And look!" She pulls out some presentation slides. "During that time period we launched 12 new products altogether and 4 of them sold more than 30,000 units during the first six months alone! Even better: The last two we launched even sold more than 40,000 copies during the first two quarters!" Charlotte knows these numbers as well as Jeannie does. After all, two of these launches have been products she herself helped to develop. But she feels uneasy about this particular product launch. The company has grown rapidly during the past three years and its financial capabilities are already rather stretched. A poor product launch for Brainet would cost the company a lot of money, something that isn't available right now due to the investments Cerebrosoft has recently made.

Later in the afternoon, Charlotte meets with Reggie Ruffin, a jack of all trades and the production manager. Reggie has a solid track record in his field and Charlotte wants his opinion on the Brainet project.

"Well, Charlotte, quite frankly, I think that there are three main factors that are relevant to the success of this project: competition, units sold, and cost—ah, and, of course, our pricing. Have you decided on the price yet?"

"I am still considering which of the three strategies would be most beneficial to us. Selling for $50.00 and trying to maximize revenues—or selling for $30.00 and trying to maximize market share. Of course, there is still your third alternative; we could sell for $40.00 and try to do both."

At this point, Reggie focuses on the sheet of paper in front of him. "And I still believe that the $40.00 alternative is the best one. Concerning the costs, I checked the records; basically we have to amortize the development costs we incurred for Brainet. So far we have spent $800,000 and we expect to spend another

$50,000 per year for support and shipping the CDs to those who want a hardcopy on top of their downloaded software." Reggie next hands a report to Charlotte. "Here we have some data on the industry. I just received that yesterday, hot off the press. Let's see what we can learn about the industry here." He shows Charlotte some of the highlights. Reggie then agrees to compile the most relevant information contained in the report and have it ready for Charlotte the following morning. It takes him long into the night to gather the data from the pages of the report, but in the end he produces three tables, one for each of the three alternative pricing strategies. Each table shows the corresponding probability of various amounts of sales given the level of competition (severe, moderate, or weak) that develops from other companies.

80 percent of the time, while 15 percent of the time they predicted moderate competition in that setting. Given that the competition turned out to be moderate, they predicted severe competition 15 percent of the time and moderate competition 80 percent of the time. Finally, for the case of weak competition, the numbers were 90 percent of the time a correct prediction, 7 percent of the time a 'moderate' prediction and 3 percent of the time a 'severe' prediction."

Charlotte feels that all these numbers are too much for her. "Don't we have a simple estimate of how the market will react?"

"Some prior probabilities, you mean? Sure, from our past experience, the likelihood of facing severe competition is 20 percent, whereas it is 70 percent for moderate competition

TABLE 1

Probability Distribution of Unit Sales, Given a High Price ($50)

Sales	Level of Competition		
	Severe	Moderate	Weak
50,000 units	0.2	0.25	0.3
30,000 units	0.25	0.3	0.35
20,000 units	0.55	0.45	0.35

TABLE 2

Probability Distribution of Unit Sales, Given a Medium Price ($40)

Sales	Level of Competition		
	Severe	Moderate	Weak
50,000 units	0.25	0.30	0.40
30,000 units	0.35	0.40	0.50
20,000 units	0.40	0.30	0.10

TABLE 3

Probability Distribution of Unit Sales, Given a Low Price ($30)

Sales	Level of Competition		
	Severe	Moderate	Weak
50,000 units	0.35	0.40	0.50
30,000 units	0.40	0.50	0.45
20,000 units	0.25	0.10	0.05

The next morning, Charlotte is sipping from another power drink. Jeannie and Reggie will be in her office any moment now and, with their help, she will have to decide what to do with Brainet. Should they launch the product? If so, at what price?

When Jeannie and Reggie enter the office, Jeannie immediately bursts out: "Guys, I just spoke to our marketing research company. They say that they could do a study for us about the competitive situation for the introduction of Brainet and deliver the results within a week."

"How much do they want for the study?"

"I knew you'd ask that, Reggie. They want $10,000, and I think it's a fair deal."

At this point, Charlotte steps into the conversation. "Do we have any data on the quality of the work of this marketing research company?"

"Yes, I do have some reports here. After analyzing them, I have come to the conclusion that the predictions of the marketing research company are pretty good: Given that the competition turned out to be severe, they predicted it correctly

and 10 percent for weak competition," says Jeannie, her numbers always ready when needed.

All that is left to do now is to sit down and make sense of all this . . .

a. For the initial analysis, ignore the opportunity of obtaining more information by hiring the marketing research company. Identify the decision alternatives and the states of nature. Construct the payoff table. Then formulate the decision problem in a decision tree. Clearly distinguish between decision and event nodes and include all the relevant data.

b. What is Charlotte's decision if she uses the maximum likelihood criterion?

c. What is Charlotte's decision if she uses Bayes' decision rule?

d. Now consider the possibility of doing the market research. Develop the corresponding decision tree. Calculate the relevant probabilities and analyze the decision tree. Should Cerebrosoft pay the $10,000 for the marketing research? What is the overall optimal policy?

Case 9-4

Smart Steering Support

On a sunny May morning, Marc Binton, CEO of **Bay Area Automobile Gadgets (BAAG),** enters the conference room on the 40th floor of the Gates building in San Francisco, where BAAG's offices are located. The other executive officers of the company have already gathered. The meeting has only one item on its agenda: planning a research and development project to develop a new driver support system (DSS). Brian Huang, manager of Research and Development, is walking around nervously. He has to inform the group about the R&D strategy he has developed for the DSS. Marc has identified DSS as the strategic new product for the company. Julie Aker, vice president of Marketing, will speak after Brian. She will give detailed information about the target segment, expected sales, and marketing costs associated with the introduction of the DSS.

BAAG builds electronic nonaudio equipment for luxury cars. Founded by a group of Stanford graduates, the company sold its first product—a car routing system relying on a technology called Global Positioning Satellites (GPS)—a few years ago. Such routing systems help drivers to find directions to their desired destinations using satellites to determine the exact position of the car. To keep up with technology and to meet the wishes of its customers, the company has added a number of new features to its router during the last few years. The DSS will be a completely new product, incorporating recent developments in GPS as well as voice recognition and display technologies. Marc strongly supports this product, as it will give BAAG a competitive advantage over its Asian and European competitors.

Driver support systems have been a field of intense research for more than a decade. These systems provide the driver with a wide range of information, such as directions, road conditions, traffic updates, and so forth. The information exchange can take place verbally or via projection of text onto the windscreen. Other features help the driver avoid obstacles that have been identified by cars ahead on the road (these cars transmit the information to the following vehicles). Marc wants to incorporate all these features and other technologies into one support system that would then be sold to BAAG's customers in the automobile industry.

After all the attendees have taken their seats, Brian starts his presentation: "Marc asked me to inform you about our efforts with the driver support system, particularly the road scanning device. We have reached a stage where we basically have to make a go or no-go decision concerning the research for this device, which, as you all know by now, is a key feature in the DSS. We have already integrated the other devices, such as the GPS-based positioning and direction system. The question with which we have to deal is whether to fund basic research into the road scanning device. If this research is successful, we then will have to decide if we want to develop a product based on these results—or if we just want to sell the technology without developing a product. If we do decide to develop the product ourselves, there is a chance that the product development process might not be successful. In that case, we could still sell the technology. In the case of successful product development, we would have to decide whether to market the product. If we decide not to market the developed product, we could at least

sell the product concept that was the result of our successful research and development efforts. Doing so would earn more than just selling the technology prematurely. If, on the other hand, we decide to market the driver support system, then we are faced with the uncertainty of how the product will be received by our customers."

"You completely lost me," snipes Marc.

Max, Julie's assistant, just shakes his head and murmurs, "those techno-nerds. . . ."

Brian starts to explain: "Sorry for the confusion. Let's just go through it again, step by step."

"Good idea—and perhaps make smaller steps!" Julie obviously dislikes Brian's style of presentation.

"OK, the first decision we are facing is whether to invest in research for the road scanning device."

"How much would that cost us?" asks Marc.

"Our estimated budget for this is $300,000. Once we invest that money, the outcome of the research effort is somewhat uncertain. Our engineers assess the probability of successful research at 80 percent."

"That's a pretty optimistic success rate, don't you think?" Julie remarks sarcastically. She still remembers the disaster with Brian's last project, the fingerprint-based car-security-system. After spending half a million dollars, the development engineers concluded that it would be impossible to produce the security system at an attractive price.

Brian senses Julie's hostility and shoots back: "In engineering, we are quite accustomed to these success rates—something we can't say about marketing. . . ."

"What would be the next step?" intervenes Marc.

"Hm, sorry. If the research is not successful, then we can only sell the DSS in its current form."

"The profit estimate for that scenario is $2 million," Julie throws in.

"If, however, the research effort is successful, then we will have to make another decision, namely, whether to go on to the development stage."

"If we wouldn't want to develop a product at that point, would that mean that we would have to sell the DSS as it is now?" asks Max.

"Yes, Max. Except that additionally we would earn some $200,000 from selling our research results to GM. Their research division is very interested in our work and they have offered that money for our findings."

"Ah, now that's good news," remarks Julie.

Brian continues, "If, however, after successfully completing the research stage, we decide to develop a new product, then we'll have to spend another $800,000 for that task, at a 35 percent chance of not being successful."

"So you are telling us we'll have to spend $800,000 for a ticket in a lottery where we have a 35 percent chance of not winning anything?" asks Julie.

"Julie, don't focus on the losses but on the potential gains! The chance of winning in this lottery, as you call it, is 65 percent. I believe that that's much more than with a normal lottery ticket," says Marc.

"Thanks, Marc," says Brian. "Once we invest that money in development, we have two possible outcomes: either we will be successful in developing the road scanning device or we won't. If we fail, then once again we'll sell the DSS in its current form and cash in the $200,000 from GM for the research results. If the development process is successful, then we have to decide whether to market the new product."

"Why wouldn't we want to market it after successfully developing it?" asks Marc.

"That's a good question. Basically what I mean is that we could decide not to sell the product ourselves but instead give the right to sell it to somebody else, to GM for example. They would pay us $1 million for it."

"I like those numbers!" remarks Julie.

"Once we decide to build the product and market it, we will face the market uncertainties and I'm sure that Julie has those numbers ready for us. Thanks."

At this point, Brian sits down and Julie comes forward to give her presentation. Immediately some colorful slides are projected on the wall behind her as Max operates the computer.

"Thanks, Brian. Well, here's the data we have been able to gather from some marketing research. The acceptance of our new product in the market can be high, medium, or low." Julie is pointing to some figures projected on the wall behind her. "Our estimates indicate that high acceptance would result in profits of $8.0 million and that medium acceptance would give us $4.0 million. In the unfortunate case of a poor reception by our customers, we still expect $2.2 million in profit. I should mention that these profits do not include the additional costs of marketing or R&D expenses."

"So, you are saying that in the worst case we'll make barely more money than with the current product?" asks Brian.

"Yes, that's what I am saying."

"What budget would you need for the marketing of our DSS with the road scanner?" asks Marc.

"For that we would need an additional $200,000 on top of what has already been included in the profit estimates," Julie replies.

"What are the chances of ending up with a high, medium, or low acceptance of the new DSS?" asks Brian.

"We can see those numbers at the bottom of the slide," says Julie, while she is turning toward the projection behind her. There is a 30 percent chance of high market acceptance and a 20 percent chance of low market acceptance.

At this point, Marc moves in his seat and asks: "Given all these numbers and bits of information, what are you suggesting that we do?"

a. Organize the available data on cost and profit estimates in a table.

b. Formulate the problem in a decision tree. Clearly distinguish between decision and event nodes.

c. Calculate the expected payoffs for each node in the decision tree.

d. What is BAAG's optimal policy according to Bayes' decision rule?

e. What would be the expected value of perfect information on the outcome of the research effort?

f. What would be the expected value of perfect information on the outcome of the development effort?

g. Marc is a risk-averse decision maker. In a number of interviews, it has been determined that he would just barely be willing to consider taking a 50-50 gamble where he either makes $1.2 million or loses $600 thousand. Based on Marc's level of risk aversion, use the exponential utility function to determine BAAG's optimal policy.

Additional Cases

Additional cases for this chapter also are available at the University of Western Ontario Ivey School of Business website, **cases.ivey.uwo.ca/cases**, in the segment of the CaseMate area designated for this book.

SUPPLEMENT 1 TO CHAPTER 9
DECISION CRITERIA

Section 9.2 briefly introduced three decision criteria — the maximax criterion, the maximin criterion, and the maximum likelihood criterion — before focusing on Bayes' decision rule as the criterion to be used in the remainder of the chapter. We now will describe these first three decision criteria, as well as three additional criteria, in greater detail. This presentation is self-contained and so will include much of what was said in Section 9.2 in this expanded coverage.

Recall that Max Flyer, the founder and sole owner of the Goferbroke Co., does not put much faith in the consulting geologist's numbers in estimating that there is one chance in four of oil on a tract of land he has purchased. Since these numbers led to the prior probabilities of the possible states of nature, Max would prefer to make his decision without relying on these prior probabilities if there is a good way of doing so. His daughter Jennifer, who has studied management science, agreed to begin by introducing him to some decision criteria which don't use these probabilities before going on to others which do use probabilities.

Now let us eavesdrop on her description.

The Maximax Criterion

The **maximax criterion** is the decision criterion for the eternal optimist. It says to focus only on the *best* that can happen to us. Here is how it works.

1. For each decision alternative, determine its *maximum payoff* from any state of nature.

2. Determine the *maximum* of these maximum payoffs.

3. Choose the alternative that can yield this maximum of the maximum payoffs.

Figure 1 shows the application of this criterion to the first Goferbroke problem when using the corresponding Excel template in one of this chapter's Excel files. It begins with the payoff table (Table 9.3) without the prior probabilities. In step 1, we find the maximum in each row (700 and 90). Step 2 identifies 700 as the maximum of these two numbers. Since 700 is the payoff that can be yielded by drilling for oil, this is the decision alternative to be chosen in step 3.

	A	B	C	D	E	F	G	H	I
1	**Maximax Criterion for the Goferbroke Co. Problem**								
2									
3					State of Nature			Maximum	
4		Alternative	Oil	Dry				in Row	
5		Drill	700	-100				700	Maximax
6		Sell	90	90				90	
7									
8									
9									

	H	I
3	Maximum	
4	in Row	
5	=MAX(C5:G5)	=IF(H5=MAX($H$5:$H$9),"Maximax","")
6	=MAX(C6:G6)	=IF(H6=MAX($H$5:$H$9),"Maximax","")
7	=MAX(C7:G7)	=IF(H7=MAX($H$5:$H$9),"Maximax","")
8	=MAX(C8:G8)	=IF(H8=MAX($H$5:$H$9),"Maximax","")
9	=MAX(C9:G9)	=IF(H9=MAX($H$5:$H$9),"Maximax","")

Figure 1   The Excel template for the maximax criterion, applied to the first Goferbroke Co. problem.

AN OBJECTION TO THIS CRITERION: Now suppose that the payoff table were the one shown in Figure 2. The maximax criterion again leads to choosing the alternative of drilling for oil. What a terrible decision! In the somewhat unlikely event that oil is there, drilling only does negligibly better than selling. In the far more likely event that the land is dry, drilling gives a disastrously large loss.

	A	B	C	D	E	F	G	H	I
1	**Maximax Criterion for a Variation of the Goferbroke Co. Problem**								
2									
3					State of Nature			Maximum	
4		Alternative	Oil	Dry				in Row	
5		Drill	91	-1000				91	Maximax
6		Sell	90	90				90	
7									
8									
9									

Figure 2   Application of the maximax criterion to a variation of the first Goferbroke Co. problem.

Max's Reaction

Max: At first, I thought this criterion might have possibilities because I view myself as something of an optimist. However, now I see that this criterion is really over the top in being totally optimistic. I need something that is more discriminating.

Jennifer: Now that you see that you need to rein in your optimistic tendencies, let us look at a more conservative criterion.

The Maximin Criterion

The **maximin criterion** is the criterion for the total pessimist. In contrast to the maximax criterion, it says to focus only on the *worst* that can happen to us. Here are the steps.

1. For each decision alternative, determine its *minimum payoff* from any state of nature.

2. Determine the *maximum* of these minimum payoffs.

3. Choose the alternative that can yield this maximum of the minimum payoffs.

Applying this criterion to the first Goferbroke problem gives Figure 3 (another Excel template). The basic difference from Figure 1 is that the numbers in column H (-100 and 90) now are the *minimum* rather than the maximum in each row. Since 90 is the maximum of these two numbers, the alternative to be chosen is to sell the land.

	A	B	C	D	E	F	G	H	I
1		**Maximin Criterion for the Goferbroke Co. Problem**							
2									
3					State of Nature			Minimum	
4		Alternative	Oil	Dry				in Row	
5		Drill	700	-100				-100	
6		Sell	90	90				90	Maximin
7									
8									
9									

	H	I
3	Minimum	
4	in Row	
5	=MIN(C5:G5)	=IF(H5=MAX($H$5:$H$9),"Maximin","")
6	=MIN(C6:G6)	=IF(H6=MAX($H$5:$H$9),"Maximin","")
7	=MIN(C7:G7)	=IF(H7=MAX($H$5:$H$9),"Maximin","")
8	=MIN(C8:G8)	=IF(H8=MAX($H$5:$H$9),"Maximin","")
9	=MIN(C9:G9)	=IF(H9=MAX($H$5:$H$9),"Maximin","")

Figure 3　The Excel template for the maximin criterion, applied to the first Goferbroke Co. problem.

AN OBJECTION TO THIS CRITERION: The fact that this criterion is overly cautious is dramatically illustrated in Figure 4. The maximin criterion still says to sell the land. However, the "Dry" state of nature now means there is a little oil there so drilling gives virtually the same payoff as selling. Furthermore, the "Oil" state of nature means that there is a huge oil field there. With roughly one chance in four that the latter state of nature is the true one, the gamble of drilling for oil instead is the obvious best decision.

	A	B	C	D	E	F	G	H	I
1		**Maximin Criterion for a Variation of the Goferbroke Co. Problem**							
2									
3					State of Nature			Minimum	
4		Alternative	Oil	Dry				in Row	
5		Drill	10,000	89				89	
6		Sell	90	90				90	Maximin
7									
8									
9									

Figure 4   Application of the maximin criterion to a variation of the first Goferbroke Co. problem.

Max's Reaction:

Max: I can see now that this criterion would never say to drill for oil unless we absolutely knew that there was some there. That is no way to run an oil prospecting company. Don't you have a criterion that strikes a happy medium between being totally optimistic and totally pessimistic?

Jennifer: Yes, that is our next one. You now have seen that you are neither a total optimist nor a total pessimist. This next criterion asks you to rate yourself as to just where you fall in between. On a scale from 0 to 1, where

> 0 = totally pessimistic,
>
> 1 = totally optimistic,
>
> 0.5 = neutral (midway between),

where would you place yourself?

Max: I definitely am a little on the optimistic side. On this scale, I would put myself at about 0.6.

Jennifer: OK, good. We call this number your **pessimism-optimism index**. So setting yours at 0.6, let's now look at how this criterion works.

The Realism Criterion

The **realism criterion** is basically a combination of the preceding two, where the pessimism-optimism index is used to combine them appropriately. The steps are given below.

1. For each decision alternative, determine both its *maximum payoff* and *minimum payoff* from any state of nature.

2. For each decision alternative, use the pessimism-optimism index to calculate its *weighted payoff* as
   Weighted payoff = index *times* maximum payoff + (1 - index) *times* minimum payoff.

3. Choose the alternative with the *largest* weighted payoff.

Figure 5 shows the application of this criterion to the first Goferbroke problem on the corresponding Excel template. Note that columns H and I are just column H of Figures 1 and 3, respectively. Column J then uses the formula in step 2, with an index of 0.6, to calculate these weighted payoffs. Since the weighted payoff for drilling (380) is larger than for selling (90), the decision is to drill for oil.

	A	B	C	D	E	F	G	H	I	J	K
1		**Realism Criterion for the Goferbroke Co. Problem**									
2											
3		Pessimism-Optimism Index =			0.6						
4											
5					State of Nature			Maximum	Minimum	Weighted	
6		Alternative	Oil	Dry				in Row	in Row	Payoff	
7		Drill	700	-100				700	-100	380	Maximum
8		Sell	90	90				90	90	90	
9											
10											
11											

	H	I	J	K
5	Maximum	Minimum	Weighted	
6	in Row	in Row	Payoff	
7	=MAX(C7:G7)	=MIN(C7:G7)	=$E$3*H7+(1-$E$3)*I7	=IF(J7=MAX($J$7:$J$11),"Maximum","")
8	=MAX(C8:G8)	=MIN(C8:G8)	=$E$3*H8+(1-$E$3)*I8	=IF(J8=MAX($J$7:$J$11),"Maximum","")
9	=MAX(C9:G9)	=MIN(C9:G9)	=$E$3*H9+(1-$E$3)*I9	=IF(J9=MAX($J$7:$J$11),"Maximum","")
10	=MAX(C10:G10)	=MIN(C10:G10)	=$E$3*H10+(1-$E$3)*I10	=IF(J10=MAX($J$7:$J$11),"Maximum","")
11	=MAX(C11:G11)	=MIN(C11:G11)	=$E$3*H11+(1-$E$3)*I11	=IF(J11=MAX($J$7:$J$11),"Maximum","")

Figure 5   The Excel template for the realism criterion, applied to the first Goferbroke Co. problem.

This criterion provides a welcome middle ground between the maximax and minimax criteria. Furthermore, selecting a value for the pessimism-optimism index enables the decision maker to choose just how aggressive or cautious to be. The criterion even gives the decision maker the flexibility to be totally optimistic (index = 1) or totally pessimistic (index = 0) if desired, so the maximax and maximin criteria actually are special cases of this one.

However, this criterion also has its flaws, as indicated below.

AN OBJECTION TO THIS CRITERION: Figure 6 gives the payoff table for another problem (unrelated to Goferbroke's problem) that has been specially designed to show an extreme case where the realism criterion performs badly. Note that alternative 2 is much better than alternative 1 for just the first state of nature, whereas the reverse is true for the other four states of nature. Assuming that the first state of nature is not particularly more likely than any of the others, alternative 1 clearly is far better than alternative 2. Nevertheless, the realism criterion with an index of 0.6 chooses alternative 2.

	A	B	C	D	E	F	G	H	I	J	K
1		**Realism Criterion**									
2											
3		Pessimism-Optimism Index =			0.6						
4											
5					State of Nature			Maximum	Minimum	Weighted	
6		Alternative	1	2	3	4	5	in Row	in Row	Payoff	
7		1	0	500	500	500	500	500	0	300	
8		2	501	1	1	1	1	501	1	301	Maximum
9											
10											
11											

Figure 6   Application of the realism criterion to another example.

In fact, this criterion would choose alternative 2 with *any* value of the pessimism-optimism index. The reason is that this alternative has the larger value in both columns H and I of Figure 6.

Max's Reaction:

Max: I rather like this criterion. It is more realistic than the first two criteria, and it even takes into account how optimistic or pessimistic I want to be. Furthermore, my problem only has two states of nature rather than the five in the example you just gave. Therefore, your objection to the criterion doesn't really apply to my problem, does it?

Jennifer: Unfortunately, it does to some extent. The reason for having five states of nature in the example was to emphasize that the payoffs for one unlikely state of nature should not dictate the decision as strongly as this criterion allows.

Max: I still don't see how this applies to my problem.

Jennifer: Well, suppose you have a tract of land that is probably dry, but there is a small possibility of a lot of oil there. This possibility is your unlikely state of nature. However, suppose the possibility is so small that it clearly is not worthwhile to drill for oil. What do you think this criterion would tell you to do?

Max: Oh oh. I suppose it would tell me to drill anywhere.

Jennifer: Yes, it would! It just doesn't differentiate between very unlikely and somewhat likely states of nature. Now you have your consulting geologist's report estimating that there is one chance in four of oil on your tract of land. Is this likely enough to make drilling worthwhile? This criterion just doesn't address this question.

Max: You're right. And this really is the key question, isn't it? I am beginning to think that I need to use the consulting geologist's numbers somehow, unless you have a better criterion that doesn't need them.

Jennifer: I do have one more that you might like better.

The Minimax Regret Criterion

The **minimax regret criterion** gets away from the focus on optimism versus pessimism. Instead, its focus is on choosing a decision that minimizes the *regret* that can be felt afterward if the decision does not turn out well.

    This is how regret is measured.

After observing what the true state of nature turns out to be, the **regret** from having chosen a particular decision alternative is

Regret = maximum payoff - actual payoff,

where *maximum payoff* is the largest payoff that could have been obtained from any decision alternative for the observed state of nature.

Table 1 shows the calculation of the regret for the first Goferbroke problem. On the left is the payoff table, with the *maximum payoff* for each state of nature given just below this table. On the right, the above formula is used with these maximum payoffs to calculate the regret for each combination of a decision alternative and a state of nature. The table on the right is called the *regret table*. Note that the regret is 0 if you drill for oil and oil is found, because this is the best alternative for this state of nature. The same holds true for selling the land if the land is dry. However, if you sell the land and it contains oil, you have given up a payoff of another 610 by not drilling. Similarly, drilling when the land is dry is 190 worse than selling.

Table 1   Calculation of the Regrets for the Goferbroke Co. Problem

Payoff Table

Alternative	State of Nature Oil	Dry	Alternative	State of Nature Oil	Dry
Drill for oil	700	-100		700	90
			Drill for oil	-700	-(-100)
Sell the land	90	90		0	190
Maximum payoff:	700	90		700	90
			Sell the land	-90	-90
				610	0

Regret Table

After obtaining the regret table, the following steps are followed.

1. For each decision alternative, determine its *maximum regret* from any state of nature by referring to the regret table.
2. Determine the *minimum* of these maximum regrets.
3. Choose the alternative that can yield this minimum of the maximum regrets.

Figure 7 illustrates the application of these three steps to the first Goferbroke problem on the Excel template for this criterion. The numbers in cells H17 and H18 are obtained in step 1. Step 2 determines that the minimum of these numbers is 190, so step 3 chooses the corresponding alternative of drilling for oil. This alternative guarantees that the regret after learning the true state cannot exceed 190, whereas the regret can be as large as 610 with the other alternative.

	A	B	C	D	E	F	G	H	I
1	**Minimax Regret Criterion for the Goferbroke Co. Problem**								
2									
3				Payoff Table					
4				State of Nature					
5		Alternative	Oil	Dry					
6		Drill	700	-100					
7		Sell	90	90					
8									
9									
10									
11		Maximum	700	90	0	0	0		
12									
13									
14				Regret Table					
15				State of Nature				Maximum	
16		Alternative	Oil	Dry				in Row	
17		Drill	0	190				190	Minimax
18		Sell	610	0				610	
19									
20									
21									

	B	C	D	E	F	G
11	Maximum	=MAX(C6:C10)	=MAX(D6:D10)	=MAX(E6:E10)	=MAX(F6:F10)	=MAX(G6:G10)

	B	C	D	E	F	G	H	I
15				tate of Natur			Maximum	
16	Alternative	=C5	=D5	=E5	=F5	=G5	in Row	
17	=B6	=C$11-C6	=D$11-D6	=E$11-E6	=F$11-F6	=G$11-G6	=MAX(C17:G17)	=IF(H17=MIN($H$17:$H$21),"M
18	=B7	=C$11-C7	=D$11-D7	=E$11-E7	=F$11-F7	=G$11-G7	=MAX(C18:G18)	=IF(H18=MIN($H$17:$H$21),"M
19	=B8	=C$11-C8	=D$11-D8	=E$11-E8	=F$11-F8	=G$11-G8	=MAX(C19:G19)	=IF(H19=MIN($H$17:$H$21),"M
20	=B9	=C$11-C9	=D$11-D9	=E$11-E9	=F$11-F9	=G$11-G9	=MAX(C20:G20)	=IF(H20=MIN($H$17:$H$21),"M
21	=B10	=C$11-C10	=D$11-D10	=E$11-E10	=F$11-F10	=G$11-G10	=MAX(C21:G21)	=IF(H21=MIN($H$17:$H$21),"M

Figure 7   The Excel template for the minimax regret criterion, applied to the first Goferbroke problem.

AN OBJECTION TO THIS CRITERION: Now let us add a third decision alternative to the problem. Based on the consulting geologist's report, an insurance company would be willing to sell the Goferbroke Co. an insurance policy to protect against the land being dry. If Goferbroke pays a massive premium and then drills for oil without finding any, the insurance company will pay an amount $700,000 larger than the premium. After deducting the cost of $100,000 for drilling, this would leave a profit of $600,000 if the land is dry. Unfortunately, the premium for this insurance policy is so exorbitant — $6.7 million—that Max could never buy the policy. Even if he finds oil for a gain of $700,000, the net loss of $6 million would put him out of business immediately.

Nevertheless, let us go ahead and apply the minimax regret criterion when the bad alternative of buying the insurance policy is included in the problem. Continuing to use units of thousands of dollars, the payoff table for this problem is shown in the top half of Figure 8.

	A	B	C	D	E	F	G	H	I
1		**Minimax Regret Criterion for Goferbroke with Insurance Option**							
2									
3				**Payoff Table**					
4				State of Nature					
5		Alternative	Oil	Dry					
6		Drill	700	-100					
7		Sell	90	90					
8		Insurance	-6000	600					
9									
10									
11		Maximum	700	600	0	0	0		
12									
13									
14				**Regret Table**					
15				State of Nature				Maximum	
16		Alternative	Oil	Dry				in Row	
17		Drill	0	700				700	
18		Sell	610	510				610	Minimax
19		Insurance	6700	0				6700	
20									
21									

Figure 8   Application of the minimax regret criterion to the first Goferbroke Co. problem when an insurance option is included.

The maximum payoff for each state of nature given in row 11 is used to calculate the regrets. This yields the regret table shown in rows 14-21. Applying the minimax regret criterion to this regret table presumably will lead either to choosing the new alternative, buy insurance, or the alternative that was chosen before, drill for oil (see Figure 7). Right? Wrong! For some reason, introducing a new alternative that is soundly rejected leads this criterion to switch its choice to the alternative that was rejected in Figure 7.

This new option of buying insurance is a completely irrelevant alternative. Not only is its maximum regret approximately ten times that for the other alternatives, but Max would never consider such exorbitantly expensive insurance. However, a reasonable criterion certainly should not make its choice between the serious alternatives depend upon which (if any) irrelevant alternatives are included in the payoff table.

Max's Reaction:

Max: That is pretty bizarre behavior for a criterion, all right. But I have two other reasons why I don't like this criterion very much.

Jennifer: What are those?

Max: First, I like to look ahead rather than worrying about past mistakes. I'm really not the kind of person who loses a lot of sleep regretting a decision which turned out badly. It seems to me that this criterion really is designed for that kind of person. Or for someone who wants to avoid getting a poor evaluation from the boss because of making a disastrous decision.

Jennifer: You're right. So what is the second reason?

Max: It seems to me that this criterion has the same problem as the realism criterion. If the possibility of a lot of oil on a tract of land is so small that it clearly is not worthwhile to drill for oil, this criterion probably would still say to drill. Or at least it would if we leave out irrelevant alternatives like buying that insurance policy.

Jennifer: Yes, you're right again. Like the realism criterion, this criterion doesn't differentiate between very unlikely and somewhat likely states of nature.

Max: OK. So where does this leave us? You really don't have a good criterion for me that doesn't need to use the consulting geologist's numbers?

Jennifer: Sorry. No. What constitutes a good criterion depends on one's philosophy of decision making. So one of these criteria might suit someone else fine. But you have concluded that none of these really work for you.

Max: Yes.

Jennifer: OK. With this conclusion, I think you are now ready to believe something I learned in my management science course. Many years ago, some eminent management scientists set down a set of rules that any reasonable criterion should satisfy. They then tried to develop a criterion that would satisfy all these rules. What they found instead is that this is impossible. There just doesn't exist a uniformly reasonable criterion that ignores whatever information you have about the relative likelihood of the various possible states of nature.

Max: A pity. OK. You have convinced me that I need a criterion that uses the information from the consulting geologist. But I don't want to make a decision that relies on having exactly one chance in four of oil as being the gospel truth, because I know those numbers can be off quite a bit.

Jennifer: You won't have to. We do have enough faith in the consulting geologist's report to believe that there is a substantial chance of oil, but a much larger chance that the land is dry. That is the information that we need to use.

Max: I agree. So tell me how we can do this.

The Maximum Likelihood Criterion

The **maximum likelihood criterion** says to focus on the most likely state of nature as follows.

1. Identify the state of nature with the largest prior probability.

2. Choose the decision alternative that has the largest payoff for this state of nature.

Your MS Courseware includes an Excel template for applying this criterion. Figure 9 shows how this would be done for the first Goferbroke problem. Since *Dry* is the state of nature with the largest prior probability, we only consider the payoffs in column D (-100 and 90). The larger of these two payoffs is 90, so we choose the corresponding alternative, sell the land.

	A	B	C	D	E	F	G	H
1		**Template for Maximum Likelihood Criterion**						
2								
3				State of Nature				
4		Alternative	Oil	Dry				
5		Drill	700	-100				
6		Sell	90	90				Maximum
7								
8								
9								
10		Prior Probability	0.25	0.75				
11				Maximum				

Figure 9   The application of the Excel template for the *maximum likelihood criterion* to the first Goferbroke Co. problem.

The rationale for this criterion is a simple one. The final payoff will depend partially on which state of nature will turn out to be the true one. Although we don't know which state of nature will occur, we do know which one probably has the maximum likelihood. By basing our decision on the assumption that this state of nature will occur, we are giving ourselves a better chance of a favorable outcome than by assuming any other state of nature.

This criterion also has received a number of criticisms outlined below.

1. This criterion chooses an alternative without considering its payoffs for states of nature other than the most likely one. What if any of these other payoffs would be disastrous? (Fortunately, this is not the case for the first Goferbroke problem, where the payoff from selling the land is the same for both states of nature.)

2. For alternatives that are not chosen, this criterion also ignores their payoffs for states of nature other than the most likely one. What if any of these payoffs would be far better than could be obtained with the chosen alternative? Shouldn't we consider the fact that Goferbroke's payoff from drilling for oil and finding it is much, much more than from selling the land?

3. If the differences in the payoffs for the most likely state of nature are much less than for another somewhat likely state of nature, then it might make more sense to focus on this latter state of nature instead. For Goferbroke, the difference between the payoffs for drilling and selling when the land is dry is only 190, whereas it is 610 when the land contains oil, so perhaps it is more crucial to choose the best alternative for this latter state of nature instead.

4. If there are many states of nature and they are nearly equally likely, then the probability that the most likely state of nature will be the true one is fairly low. In this case, would it make sense to make the decision based on just one state of nature that has a fairly low probability?

Max's Reaction:

Max: It sounds like this criterion won't fit some situations very well. But I kind of like it for my problem. It is simple for one thing. But more importantly, it doesn't require me to use the consulting geologist's number that I know are pulled somewhat out of the air. I do have enough faith in his report to believe it is more likely that the land is dry than that there is oil there. So I am pretty comfortable in providing the information the criterion needs by specifying which is more likely.

Jennifer: Sure, you can do that. But is it making the decision the way you want?

Max: What do you mean?

Jennifer: When you buy your tracts of land, is your main goal to find oil there? Or are you mostly interested in reselling the land?

Max: Finding oil, of course. That is the whole point.

Jennifer: Typically, for a tract of land you buy, will it be more likely that it is dry or that it contains oil?

Max: Dry. That's the nature of our business. You have to try a lot of sites to find that one big strike.

Jennifer: So what do you think this criterion will tell you to do on those sites?

Max: Oh, you're right! Now I see your point. Because it normally is more likely that the land is dry, it will keep telling me time after time to sell rather than drilling for oil. That is no way to run an oil prospecting business.

Jennifer: Exactly! The key is the second and third criticisms I gave earlier. You really need to take into account how large the payoff might be if you do find oil.

Max: I agree. This is not a good criterion for an oil prospector to use. I hope the next one is better.

Jennifer: You'll be the judge of that.

The Equally Likely Criterion

It usually is difficult to place a lot of faith in the prior probabilities of the possible states of nature. Therefore, the **equally likely criterion** says to not even try to assign meaningful numbers to these probabilities. In the absence of further information, simply assume instead that the states of nature are *equally likely* and proceed as follows.

1. For each decision alternative, calculate the *average* of its payoffs over all the states of nature. (With equally likely states of nature, this average is the *expected payoff* in the statistical sense.)

2. Choose the alternative with the *largest* average payoff.

Using the corresponding Excel template in your MS Courseware, Figure 10 shows the application of this criterion to the first Goferbroke problem. The average payoff for each alternative is given in column H. Since drilling for oil has an average payoff of 300, versus only 90 for selling the land, the choice is to drill.

	A	B	C	D	E	F	G	H	I
1		**Equally Likely Criterion for the Goferbroke Co. Problem**							
2									
3					State of Nature			Row	
4		Alternative	Oil	Dry				Average	
5		Drill	700	-100				300	Maximum
6		Sell	90	90				90	
7									
8									
9									

	H	I
3	Row	
4	Average	
5	=AVERAGE(C5:G5)	=IF(H5=MAX($H$5:$H$9),"Maximum","")
6	=AVERAGE(C6:G6)	=IF(H6=MAX($H$5:$H$9),"Maximum","")
7	=AVERAGE(C7:G7)	=IF(H7=MAX($H$5:$H$9),"Maximum","")
8	=AVERAGE(C8:G8)	=IF(H8=MAX($H$5:$H$9),"Maximum","")
9	=AVERAGE(C9:G9)	=IF(H9=MAX($H$5:$H$9),"Maximum","")

Figure 10   The application of the Excel template for the *equally likely criterion* to the first Goferbroke Co. problem.

This criterion is sometimes called the *Laplace Principle*, because it was first enunciated (to our knowledge) over 200 years ago by the famous French mathematician, the Marquis Pierre-Simon de Laplace. (Sometimes called the Isaac Newton of France, Laplace was a key founder of the modern theory of probability.)

Some modern decision makers agree with Laplace that decision making should be based on the reality that it is impossible to accurately predict the future. Events occur randomly. A typical random event is the occurrence of a state of nature. It is unrealistic to try to assign prior probabilities to states of nature, since this would go beyond our ability to predict the future. Nature gives us no advance information that it will do anything but randomize over its states. Therefore, to stay within the bounds of rationality, we should simply assume that the states of nature are equally likely.

Critics of this line of reasoning make three main points.

1. Treating the states of nature as equally likely amounts to assigning each one the following prior probability:

$$\text{Prior probability} = \frac{1}{\text{number of states of nature}}.$$

Assigning this value to each prior probability is just as arbitrary as assigning any other values to these probabilities.

2. In some situations, there is good evidence that certain states of nature are more likely than others. Using this information should improve the decision.

3.   There often are alternative ways of itemizing the possible states of nature. For example, the state of having oil could be broken down into several states involving different amounts of oil. Changing the number of states changes the prior probability of each one, which might then change the resulting decision. It is undesirable to have the decision depend on the arbitrary way in which the possible states of nature are itemized.

Max's Reaction:

Max: I like the fact that this criterion doesn't force me to rely on the consulting geologist's numbers.

Jennifer: You mean his estimate that there is 1 chance in 4 of having oil on this tract of land?

Max: Yes. I just don't trust his numbers.

Jennifer: Would you have any more faith in his numbers if he had said 1 chance in 2 of oil?

Max: No, not particularly. Whatever numbers he comes up with, the real chance of oil could be quite a bit lower or quite a bit higher.

Jennifer: But if 1 chance in 2 of oil is the right ballpark, would you want to drill?

Max: Certainly. Those are great odds in this business. Why?

Jennifer: Because this criterion is always giving you odds of 1 chance in 2 of oil.

Max: Really? I didn't catch that. You mean it would tell me to drill regardless of how promising or unpromising the land looked?

Jennifer: Yes, pretty automatically. I guess I didn't make clear that this equally likely criterion says to assume that the odds of having oil are the same as for being dry.

Max: Whoa. Now I get it. That won't do at all! I may not trust the consulting geologist's numbers completely, but this criterion's numbers seem completely worthless in my business. I need real odds based on solid evidence, not numbers pulled completely out of the air.

Jennifer: If 1 chance in 2 of oil is not the right ballpark, then you certainly are correct. So you prefer the consulting geologist's numbers?

Max: Definitely. But I don't want my decision to depend on his numbers being exactly correct.

Jennifer: OK. Let's look at a criterion that uses his numbers. Then we'll talk about how to analyze the situation if his numbers are off some.

Max: "Good.

Now you can return to Section 9.2 for a full description of one more decision criterion — Bayes' decision rule. You will see that Max reacts favorably to this decision criterion and so decides to adopt this one.

REVIEW QUESTIONS

1. Why might it be desirable to use a decision criterion that doesn't rely on the prior probabilities of the respective states of nature?
2. What is the *maximax criterion*?
3. What is the *maximin criterion*?
4. What is the *pessimism-optimism index*? How is it used with the realism criterion?
5. Why are the maximax and minimax criteria special cases of the realism criterion?
6. How is *regret* measured in the minimax regret criterion?
7. What is being minimized with the minimax regret criterion?
8. For each of the first four decision criteria, what type of person might find it appealing?
9. Is it possible to develop a decision criterion that doesn't use the prior probabilities and still is reasonable for every situation?
10. On which state of nature does the maximum likelihood criterion focus?
11. What are some criticisms of the maximum likelihood criterion?
12. What assumption about the states of nature is made by the equally likely criterion?
13. What are some criticisms of the equally likely criterion?

Glossary

Equally Likely criterion: A criterion for decision making that assigns equal probabilities to all the states of nature.

Maximax Criterion: A very optimistic criterion for decision making without using probabilities.

Maximin criterion: A very pessimistic criterion for decision making without using probabilities.

Maximum likelihood criterion: A criterion for decision making with probabilities that focuses on the most likely state of nature.

Minimax regret criterion: A criterion for decision making without using probabilities that instead minimizes the regret that can be felt afterward if the decision does not turn out well.

Pessimism-optimism index: An index that measures where the decision maker falls on a scale from totally pessimistic to totally optimistic.

Realism criterion: A criterion for decision making without using probabilities that instead uses the decision maker's pessimism-optimism index.

Problems

Although optional, an Excel template is available in your MS Courseware that can aid in doing each part of the following problems.

9s.1.   You are given the following payoff table (in units of thousands of dollars) for a decision analysis problem without probabilities:

	State of Nature	
Alternative	S_1	S_2
A_1	1	7
A_2	6	3
A_3	4	4

a.   Which alternative should be chosen under the maximax criterion?

b.   Which alternative should be chosen under the maximin criterion?

c.   Which alternative should be chosen under the realism criterion when the pessimism-optimism index is 0.5? When this index is 0.25? When the index is 0.75?

d.   Which alternative should be chosen under the minimax regret criterion?

9s.2.   Follow the instructions of Problem 9s.1 with the following payoff table:

	State of Nature		
Alternative	S_1	S_2	S_3
A_1	15	30	20
A_2	12	24	28
A_3	5	25	35
A_4	18	20	25

9s.3.   Silicon Dynamics has developed a new computer chip that will enable it to begin producing and marketing a personal computer if it so desires. Alternatively, it can sell the rights to the computer chip for $15 million. If the company chooses to build computers, the profitability of the venture depends upon the company's ability to market the computer during the first year. It has sufficient access to retail outlets that it can guarantee sales of 10,000 computers. On the other hand, if this computer catches on, the company can sell 100,000 machines. For analysis purposes, these two levels of sales are taken to be the two possible outcomes of marketing the computer, but it is unclear what their prior probabilities are. The cost of setting up the assembly line is $6 million. The difference between the selling price and the variable cost of each computer is $600.

After developing the payoff table, determine which decision alternative should be chosen under each of the following criteria.

a.   Maximax criterion.

b.   Maximin criterion.

c.   Realism criterion with a pessimism - optimism index of 0.5.

d.   Minimax regret criterion.

9s.4.   Refer to Problem 9.3 in Chapter 9. After developing the payoff table, determine how many cases of strawberries Jean should purchase under the following criteria.

   a.   Maximax criterion.

   b.   Maximin criterion.

   c.   Realism criterion with a pessimism - optimism index of 0.5.

   d.   Minimax regret criterion.

   e.   Maximum likelihood criterion.

   f.   Equally likely criterion.

9s.5.   You are preparing to apply the minimax regret criterion to a decision analysis problem. You have identified the two states of nature and three decision alternatives (A_1, A_2, A_3) that you definitely want to consider. A fourth decision alternative (A_4) also has occurred to you, but you consider this alternative to be a poor one that would never be chosen. However, for completeness, you include this fourth decision alternative in the problem formulation and obtain the following payoff table.

	State of Nature	
Alternative	S_1	S_2
A_1	12	17
A_2	13	15
A_3	15	12
A_4	0	20

   a.   Apply the minimax regret criterion to this payoff table to determine which decision alternative should be chosen.

   b.   Remove the irrelevant decision alternative A_4 from the payoff table to determine which decision alternative should be chosen.

   c.   What objection to this criterion is revealed by your answers to parts *a* and *b*?

9s.6.   Refer to Problem 9.4 in Chapter 9. Warren Buffy does not have great confidence in the accuracy of his prior probabilities. Therefore, he decides to try some decision criteria that do not use these probabilities, as well as two that do. Which investment should he make under each of the following criteria?

   a.   Maximax criterion.

   b.   Maximin criterion.

   c.   Realism criterion with a pessimism - optimism index of 0.5.

   d.   Minimax regret criterion.

   e.   Maximum likelihood criterion.

   f.   Equally likely criterion.

SUPPLEMENT 2 TO CHAPTER 9:
USING TREEPLAN SOFTWARE FOR DECISION TREES

We will describe and illustrate how to use TreePlan, an Excel add-in developed by Professor Michael Middleton, for constructing and analyzing decision trees on a spreadsheet. This software is compatible with both Excel for Windows (2003-2010) and Excel for Mac (2011). A free 30-day trial of this software is available from www.treeplan.com. If you want to continue to use the software longer than this period of time, you will need to register and pay. Like any Excel add-in, this add-in needs to be installed before it will show up in Excel. To install it, simply open the TreePlan Excel file.

       To demonstrate how to use TreePlan, we will re-create the first Goferbroke Co. problem introduced in Section 9.1. The decision tree for this problem is shown in Figure 9.2, which is repeated here as Figure 1. To begin creating such a decision tree using TreePlan, select Decision Tree from the Add-Ins tab (for Windows versions of Excel) or Tools menu (Excel 2011 for Mac) and click on New Tree. This creates the default decision tree shown in Figure 2, which has a single (square) decision node with two branches. It so happens that this is exactly what is needed for the first node in the first Goferbroke problem (this node corresponds to node A in Figure 1). However, even if something else were needed, it is easy to make changes to a node in TreePlan. Simply select the cell containing the node (B5 in Figure 2) and choose Decision Tree from the Add-Ins tab or Tools menu. This brings up a dialog box that allows you to change the type of node (e.g., from a decision node to an event node) or add more branches.

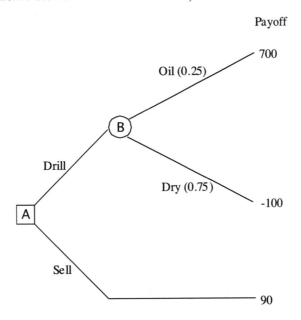

Figure 1   The decision tree for the first Goferbroke Co. problem (as first given in Figure 9.2).

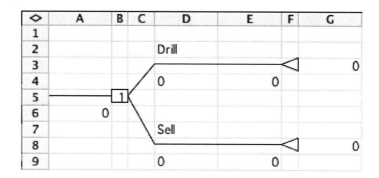

Figure 2   The default decision tree created by TreePlan by selecting Decision Tree from the Add-Ins tab (Windows versions of Excel) or Tools menu (Excel 2011 for Mac), clicking on New Tree, and then entering Drill and Sell labels for the two decision alternatives.

By default, the labels for the decisions (cells D2 and D7 in Figure 2) are "Decision 1," "Decision 2," etc. These labels are changed by clicking on them and typing a new label. In Figure 2, these labels have already been changed to "Drill" and "Sell." If the decision is to drill, the next event is to learn whether or not the land contains oil. To create an event node, click on the cell containing the triangle terminal node at the end of the drill branch (cell F3 in Figure 2), and choose Decision Tree from the Add-Ins tab or Tools menu. This brings up the TreePlan Terminal dialogue box shown in Figure 3. Choose the "Change to event node" option on the left and select the two branches option on the right, and then click OK. This results in the decision tree with the nodes and branches shown in Figure 4 (after replacing the default labels "Event 1" and "Event 2" by "Oil" and "Dry," respectively).

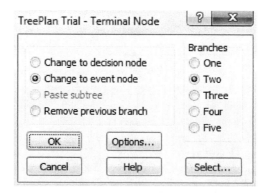

Figure 3   Selecting the cell that contains a terminal node and choosing Decision Tree from the Add-Ins tab or Tools menu brings up the TreePlan Terminal Node dialog box shown here. This dialog box allows you to change a terminal node to a different type of node. It is used here to change the terminal node in cell F3 of Figure 2 to an event node.

CD S Ch 9-3

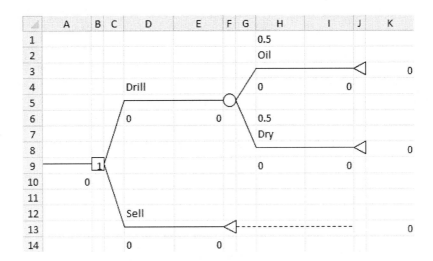

Figure 4   The decision tree created by TreePlan after changing the terminal node in cell F3 of Figure 2 into an event node and then relabeling the two branches as Oil and Dry.

At any time, you also can click on any existing decision node (a square) or event node (a circle) and choose Decision Tree from the Add-Ins tab or Tools menu to make changes to that node. Initially, each branch shows a default value of 0 for the net cash flow being generated there (the numbers appear below the branch labels: D6, D14, H4, and H9 in Figure 4). Also, each of the two branches leading from the event node displays the default values of 0.5 for their prior probabilities (the probabilities are just above the corresponding labels: H1 and H6 in Figure 4). Therefore, you next should click on these default values and replace them with the correct numbers, namely,

D6 =	-100	(the cost of drilling is $100,000)
D14 =	90	(the profit from selling is $90,000)
H1 =	0.25	(the prior probability of oil is 0.25)
H4 =	800	(the net revenue after finding oil is $800,000)
H6 =	0.75	(the prior probability of dry is 0.75)
H9 =	0	(the net revenue after finding dry is 0).

This leads to the final decision tree shown in Figure 5.

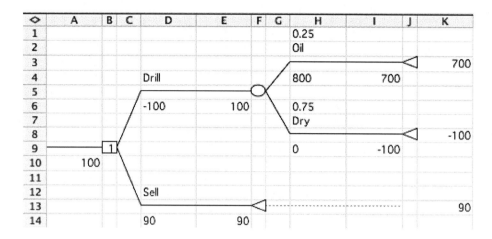

◇	A	B	C	D	E	F	G	H	I	J	K
1								0.25			
2								Oil			
3										◁	700
4				Drill				800	700		
5											
6				-100	100			0.75			
7								Dry			
8										◁	-100
9		1						0	-100		
10	100										
11											
12				Sell							
13							◁				90
14				90	90						

Figure 5   The final decision tree constructed and solved by TreePlan for the first Goferbroke Co. problem shown in Figure 1. The 1 in cell B9 indicates that the top branch (the Drill alternative) should be chosen. The 100 in cell A10 specifies that the expected payoff of this venture is $100 thousand.

At each stage in constructing a decision tree, TreePlan automatically solves for the optimal policy with the current tree when using Bayes' decision rule. The number inside each decision node indicates which branch should be chosen (assuming the branches emanating from that node are numbered consecutively from top to bottom). Thus, for the final decision tree in Figure 5, the number 1 in cell B9 specifies that the first branch (the Drill alternative) should be chosen. The number on both sides of each terminal node is the payoff if that node is reached. The number 100 in cells A10 and E6 is the expected payoff (the measure of performance for Bayes' decision rule) at those stages in the process.

This description of TreePlan may seem somewhat complicated. However, we think that you will find the procedure quite intuitive when you execute it on a computer. If you spend considerable time with TreePlan, you also will find that it has many helpful features that haven't been described in this brief introduction.

CHAPTER 15
TRANSPORTATION AND ASSIGNMENT PROBLEMS

Learning objectives

After completing this chapter, you should be able to

1. Describe the characteristics of transportation problems.
2. Formulate a spreadsheet model for a transportation problem from a description of the problem.
3. Do the same for some variants of transportation problems.
4. Give the name of two algorithms that can solve huge transportation problems that are well beyond the scope of Solver.
5. Identify several areas of application of transportation problems and their variants.
6. Describe the characteristics of assignment problems.
7. Identify the relationship between assignment problems and transportation problems.
8. Formulate a spreadsheet model for an assignment problem from a description of the problem.
9. Do the same for some variants of assignment problems.
10. Give the name of an algorithm that can solve huge assignment problems that are well beyond the scope of Solver.

Transportation problems were introduced in Section 3.5 and Section 3.6 did the same for assignment problems. Both of these similar types of problems arise quite frequently in a variety of contexts. Because of their importance, we now will elaborate much further on these kinds of problems and their applications in this self-contained chapter.

Transportation problems received this name because many of their applications involve determining how to transport goods optimally. However, you will see that some of their important applications have nothing to do with transportation.

Assignment problems are best known for applications involving assigning people to tasks. However, they have a variety of other applications as well.

Following a case study, the initial sections of this chapter describe the characteristics of transportation problems and their variants, illustrate the formulation of spreadsheet models for such problems, and survey a variety of applications. The subsequent sections then do the same for assignment problems.

15.1 A CASE STUDY: THE P&T COMPANY DISTRIBUTION PROBLEM

Douglas Whitson is concerned. Costs have been escalating and revenues have not been keeping pace. If this trend continues, shareholders are going to be very unhappy with the next earnings report. As CEO of the P & T Company, he knows that the buck stops with him. He's got to find a way to bring costs under control.

Douglas suddenly picks up the telephone and places a call to his distribution manager, Richard Powers.

Douglas (CEO): Richard. Douglas Whitson here.

Richard (distribution manager): Hello, Douglas.

Douglas: Say, Richard. I've just been looking over some cost data and one number jumped out at me.

Richard: Oh? What's that?

Douglas: The shipping costs for our peas. $178,000 last season! I remember it running under $100,000 just a few years ago. What's going on here?

Richard: Yes, you're right. Those costs have really been going up. One factor is that our shipping volume is up a little. However, the main thing is that the fees charged by the truckers we've been using have really shot up. We complained. They said something about their new contract with the union representing their drivers pushed their costs up substantially. And their insurance costs are up.

Douglas: Have you looked into changing truckers?

Richard: Yes. In fact, we've already selected new truckers for the upcoming growing season.

Douglas: Good. So your shipping costs should come down quite a bit next season?

Richard: Well, my projection is that they should run about $165,000.

Douglas: Ouch. That's still too high.

Richard: That seems to be the best we can do.

Douglas: Well, let's approach this from another angle. You're shipping the peas from our three canneries to all four of our warehouses?

Richard: That's right.

Douglas: How do you decide how much each cannery will ship to each warehouse?

Richard: We have a standard strategy that we've been using for many years.

Douglas: Does this strategy minimize your total shipping cost?

Richard: I think it does a pretty good job of that.

Douglas: But does it use an algorithm to generate a shipping plan that is guaranteed to minimize the total shipping cost?

Richard: No, I can't say it does that. Is there a way of doing that?

Douglas: Yes. I understand there is a management science technique for doing that. This is something I learned when I interviewed that new MBA graduate we hired last month, Kim Baker. Kim thought this technique could be directly applicable to our company. We hired Kim to help us incorporate some of the best techniques being taught in business schools these days. I think we should have Kim look at your shipping plan and see if she can improve upon it.

Richard: Sounds reasonable.

Douglas: OK, good. I would like you to coordinate with Kim and report back to me soon.

Richard: Will do.

The conversation ends quickly.

Background
The P & T Company is a small family-owned business. It receives raw vegetables, processes and cans them at its canneries, and then distributes the canned goods for eventual sale.

CD 15-3

One of the company's main products is canned peas. The peas are prepared at three canneries (near Bellingham, Washington; Eugene, Oregon; and Albert Lea, Minnesota) and then shipped by truck to four distributing warehouses in the western United States (Sacramento, California; Salt Lake City, Utah; Rapid City, South Dakota; and Albuquerque, New Mexico), as shown in Figure 15.1.

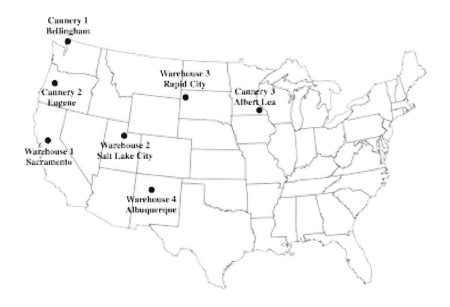

| **Figure 15.1** | Location of the canneries and warehouses for the P&T Co. problem. |

The Company's Current Approach

For many years, the company has used the following strategy for determining how much output should be shipped from each of the canneries to meet the needs of each of the warehouses.

Current Shipping Strategy

1. Since the cannery in Bellingham is furthest from the warehouses, ship its output to its nearest warehouse, namely, the one in Sacramento, with any surplus going to the warehouse in Salt Lake City.

2. Since the warehouse in Albuquerque is furthest from the canneries, have its nearest cannery (the one in Albert Lea) ship its output to Albuquerque, with any surplus going to the warehouse in Rapid City.

3. Use the cannery in Eugene to supply the remaining needs of the warehouses.

For the upcoming harvest season, an estimate has been made of the output from each cannery, and each warehouse has been allocated a certain amount from the total supply of peas. This information is given in Table 15.1.

Applying the current shipping strategy to the data in Table 15.1 gives the shipping plan shown in Table 15.2. The shipping costs per truckload for the upcoming season are shown in Table 15.3.

Table 15.1   Shipping Data for the P & T Co.

Cannery	Output	Warehouse	Allocation
Bellingham	75 truckloads	Sacramento	80 truckloads
Eugene	125 truckloads	Salt Lake City	65 truckloads
Albert Lea	100 truckloads	Rapid City	70 truckloads
Total	300 truckloads	Albuquerque	85 truckloads
		Total	300 truckloads

Table 15.2   Current Shipping Plan for the P & T Co.

	To From	Warehouse			
		Sacramento	Salt Lake City	Rapid City	Albuquerque
	Bellingham	75	0	0	0
Cannery	Eugene	5	65	55	0
	Albert Lea	0	0	15	85

Table 15.3   Shipping Costs for the P & T Co.

Shipping Cost per Truckload

	To From	Warehouse			
		Sacramento	Salt Lake City	Rapid City	Albuquerque
	Bellingham	$464	$513	$654	$867
Cannery	Eugene	$352	$416	$690	$791
	Albert Lea	$995	$682	$388	$685

Combining the data in Tables 15.2 and 15.3 yields the total shipping cost under the current plan for the upcoming season:

Total shipping cost $= 75(\$464) + 5(\$352) + 65(\$416) + 55(\$690) + 15(\$388) + 85(\$685)$

$= \$165,595$

Kim Baker now is reexamining the current shipping strategy to see if she can develop a new shipping plan that would reduce the total shipping cost to an absolute minimum.

The Management Science Approach

Kim immediately recognizes that this problem is just a classic example of a *transportation problem*. Formulating the problem in this way is straightforward. Furthermore, software is readily

CD 15-5

available for quickly finding an optimal solution on a desktop computer. This enables Kim to return to management the next day with a new shipping plan that would reduce the total shipping cost by over $13,000.

This story will unfold in the next section after we provide more background about transportation problems.

REVIEW QUESTIONS

1. What is the specific concern being raised by the CEO of the P & T Co. in this case study?
2. What is Kim Baker being asked to do?

15.2 CHARACTERISTICS OF TRANSPORTATION PROBLEMS

The Model for Transportation Problems

To describe the model for transportation problems, we need to use terms that are considerably less specific than for the P & T Co. problem. Transportation problems in general are concerned (literally or figuratively) with distributing *any* commodity from *any* group of supply centers, called **sources,** to *any* group of receiving centers, called **destinations,** in such a way as to minimize the total distribution cost. The correspondence in terminology between the specific application to the P & T Co. problem and the general model for any transportation problem is summarized in Table 15.4.

As indicated by the fourth and fifth rows of the table, each source has a certain **supply** of units to distribute to the destinations, and each destination has a certain **demand** for units to be received from the sources. The model for a transportation problem makes the following assumption about these supplies and demands.

Table 15.4 Terminology for a Transportation Problem

P & T Co. Problem	General Model
Truckloads of canned peas	Units of a commodity
Canneries	Sources
Warehouses	Destinations
Output from a cannery	Supply from a source
Allocation to a warehouse	Demand at a destination
Shipping cost per truckload from a cannery to a warehouse	Cost per unit distributed from a source to a destination

The Requirements Assumption: Each source has a fixed *supply* of units, where this entire supply must be distributed to the destinations. Similarly, each destination has a fixed *demand* for units, where this entire demand must be received from the sources.

This assumption that there is no leeway in the amounts to be sent or received means that there needs to be a balance between the total supply from all sources and the total demand at all destinations.

The Feasible Solutions Property: A transportation problem will have feasible solutions if and only if the *sum* of its supplies *equals* the *sum* of its demands.

Fortunately, these sums are equal for the P & T Co. since Table 15.1 indicates that the supplies (outputs) sum to 300 truckloads and so do the demands (allocations).

In some real problems, the supplies actually represent *maximum* amounts (rather than fixed amounts) to be distributed. Similarly, in other cases, the demands represent maximum amounts (rather than fixed amounts) to be received. Such problems do not fit the model for a transportation problem because they violate the *requirements assumption,* so they are *variants* of a transportation problem. Fortunately, it is relatively straightforward to formulate a spreadsheet model for such variants that Solver can still solve, as will be illustrated in Section 15.3.

The last row of Table 15.4 refers to a cost per unit distributed. This reference to a *unit cost* implies the following basic assumption for any transportation problem.

> **The Cost Assumption**: The cost of distributing units from any particular source to any particular destination is *directly proportional* to the number of units distributed. Therefore, this cost is just the *unit cost* of distribution *times* the *number of units distributed.*

The only data needed for a transportation problem model are the supplies, demands, and unit costs. These are the *parameters of the model.* All these parameters for the P & T Co. problem are shown in Table 15.5. This table (including the description implied by its column and row headings) summarizes the model for the problem.

> **The Model**: Any problem (whether involving transportation or not) fits the model for a transportation problem if it (1) can be described completely in terms of a table like Table 15.5 that identifies all the sources, destinations, supplies, demands, and unit costs, and (2) satisfies both the *requirements assumption* and the *cost assumption.* The objective is to minimize the total cost of distributing the units.

Table 15.5 The Data for the P & T Co. Problem Formulated as a Transportation Problem

Unit Cost

Destination (Warehouse)	Sacramento	Salt Lake City	Rapid City	Albuquerque	Supply
Source (Cannery)					
Bellingham	$464	$513	$654	$867	75
Eugene	$352	$416	$690	$791	125
Albert Lea	$995	$682	$388	$685	100
Demand	80	65	70	85	

Therefore, formulating a problem as a transportation problem only requires filling out a table in the format of Table 15.5. It is not necessary to write out a formal mathematical model (even though we will do this for demonstration purposes later).

The Big M Company problem presented in Section 3.5 is another example of a transportation problem. In this example, the company's two factories need to ship turret lathes to three customers and the objective is to determine how to do this so as to minimize the total shipping cost. Table 3.9 presents the data for this problem in the same format as Table 15.5, where the factories are the sources, their outputs are the supplies, the customers are the destinations, and their order sizes are the demands.

CD 15-7

Using Excel to Formulate and Solve Transportation Problems

Section 3.5 describes the formulation of the spreadsheet model for the Big M Company problem. We now will do the same for the P & T Co. problem.

The decisions to be made are the number of truckloads of peas to ship from each cannery to each warehouse. The constraints on these decisions are that the total amount shipped from each cannery must equal its output (the supply) and the total amount received at each warehouse must equal its allocation (the demand). The overall measure of performance is the total shipping cost, so the objective is to minimize this quantity.

This information leads to the spreadsheet model shown in Figure 15.2. All the data provided in Table 15.5 are displayed in the following data cells: UnitCost (D5:G7), Supply (J12:J14), and Demand (D17:G17). The decisions on shipping quantities are given by the changing cells, ShippingQuantity (D12:G14). The output cells are TotalShipped (H12:H14) and Total Received (D15:G15), where the SUM functions entered into these cells are shown near the bottom of Figure 15.2. The constraints, TotalShipped (H12:H14) = Supply (J12:J14) and TotalReceived (D15:G15) = Demand (D17:G17), have been specified on the spreadsheet and entered into Solver Parameters box. The objective cell is TotalCost (J17), where its SUMPRODUCT function is shown in the lower right-hand corner of Figure 15.2. The Solver Parameters box specifies that the objective is to minimize this objective cell. The Solver Options specify that all shipment quantities must be nonnegative and that this transportation problem is also a linear programming problem (as described later in this section).

	A	B	C	D	E	F	G	H	I	J
1		**P&T Co. Distribution Problem**								
2										
3		**Unit Cost**				Destination (Warehouse)				
4				Sacramento	Salt Lake City	Rapid City	Albuquerque			
5		Source	Bellingham	$464	$513	$654	$867			
6		(Cannery)	Eugene	$352	$416	$690	$791			
7			Albert Lea	$995	$682	$388	$685			
8										
9										
10		**Shipment Quantity**				Destination (Warehouse)				
11		**(Truckloads)**		Sacramento	Salt Lake City	Rapid City	Albuquerque	Total Shipped		Supply
12		Source	Bellingham	0	20	0	55	75	=	75
13		(Cannery)	Eugene	80	45	0	0	125	=	125
14			Albert Lea	0	0	70	30	100	=	100
15			Total Received	80	65	70	85			
16				=	=	=	=			Total Cost
17			Demand	80	65	70	85			$152,535

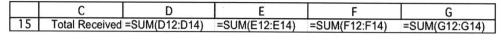

Solver Parameters

Set Objective Cell: TotalCost
To: Min
By Changing Variable Cells:
  ShipmentQuantity
Subject to the Constraints:
  TotalReceived = Demand
  TotalShipped = Supply
Solver Options:
  Make Variables Nonnegative
  Solving Method: Simplex LP

Range Name	**Cells**
Demand	D17:G17
ShipmentQuantity	D12:G14
Supply	J12:J14
TotalCost	J17
TotalReceived	D15:G15
TotalShipped	H12:H14
UnitCost	D5:G7

	H
11	Total Shipped
12	=SUM(D12:G12)
13	=SUM(D13:G13)
14	=SUM(D14:G14)

	C	D	E	F	G
15	Total Received	=SUM(D12:D14)	=SUM(E12:E14)	=SUM(F12:F14)	=SUM(G12:G14)

	J
16	Total Cost
17	=SUMPRODUCT(UnitCost,ShipmentQuantity)

Figure 15.2   A spreadsheet formulation of the P & T Co. problem as a transportation problem, including the objective cell TotalCost (J17) and the other output cells TotalShipped (H12:H14) and TotalReceived (D15:G15), as well as the specifications needed to set up the model. The changing cells ShipmentQuantity (D12:G14) show the optimal shipping plan obtained by Solver.

To begin the process of solving the problem, any value (such as 0) can be entered in each of the changing cells. Solver will use the simplex method to solve the transportation problem and determine the best value for each of the decision variables. This optimal solution is shown in ShippingQuantity (D12:G14) in Figure 15.2, along with the resulting value $152,535 in the objective cell TotalCost (J17).

CD 15-9

The Network Representation of a Transportation Problem

A nice way to visualize a transportation problem graphically is to use its *network representation*. This representation ignores the geographical layout of the sources and destinations. Instead, it simply lines up all the sources in one column on the left (where S_1 is the symbol for Source 1, etc.) and all the destinations in one column on the right (where D_1 is the symbol for Destination 1, etc.). Figure 15.3 shows the network representation of the P & T Co. problem, where the numbering of the sources (canneries) and destinations (warehouses) is that given in Figure 15.1. The arrows show the possible routes for the truckloads of canned peas, where the number next to each arrow is the shipping cost (in dollars) per truckload for that route. Since the figure also includes the supplies and demands, it includes all the data provided by Table 15.5. Therefore, this network representation provides an alternative way of summarizing the model for a transportation problem model.

Since the Big M Company problem presented in Section 3.5 also is a transportation problem, it too has a network representation like the one in Figure 15.3, as shown in Figure 3.9.

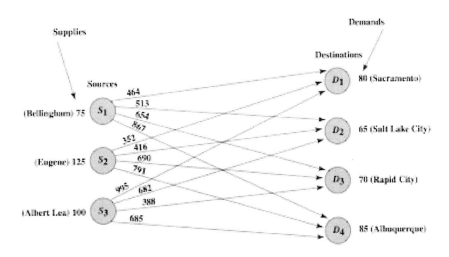

| **Figure 15.3** | The network representation of the P & T Co. transportation problem shows all the data in Table 15.5 graphically. |

For transportation problems larger than the P & T Co. problem, it is not very convenient to draw the entire network and display all the data. Consequently, the network representation is mainly a visualization device.

Recall that Section 3.5 described transportation problems as a major category of linear programming problems that often involve the distribution of goods through a distribution network. The networks in both Figure 3.9 and Figure 15.3 are a simple type of distribution network where every shipping lane goes directly from a source to a destination.

Recall that Chapter 6 presents some related kinds of network optimization problems that sometimes also involve the distribution of goods through a distribution network. In fact, Section 6.1 points out that transportation problems are a special type of minimum-cost flow problem, which commonly involves the flow of goods through a distribution network.

The Transportation Problem Is a Linear Programming Problem

To demonstrate that the P & T Co. problem (or any other transportation problem) is, in fact, a linear programming problem, let us formulate its mathematical model in algebraic form.

Using the numbering of canneries and warehouses given in Figure 15.1, let x_{ij} be the number of truckloads to be shipped from Cannery i to Warehouse j for each $i = 1, 2, 3$ and $j = 1, 2, 3, 4$. The objective is to choose the values of these 12 decision variables (the x_{ij}) so as to

$$\text{Minimize} \quad \text{Cost} = 464x_{11} + 513x_{12} + 654x_{13} + 867x_{14} + 352x_{21} + 416x_{22}$$
$$+ 690x_{23} + 791x_{24} + 995x_{31} + 682x_{32} + 388x_{33} + 685x_{34},$$

subject to the constraints

$$
\begin{array}{rcl}
x_{11} + x_{12} + x_{13} + x_{14} & = & 75 \\
x_{21} + x_{22} + x_{23} + x_{24} & = & 125 \\
x_{31} + x_{32} + x_{33} + x_{34} & = & 100 \\
x_{11} + x_{21} + x_{31} & = & 80 \\
x_{12} + x_{22} + x_{32} & = & 65 \\
x_{13} + x_{23} + x_{33} & = & 70 \\
x_{14} + x_{24} + x_{34} & = & 85 \\
\end{array}
$$

and

$$x_{ij} \geq 0 \quad (i = 1, 2, 3; j = 1, 2, 3, 4).$$

This is indeed a linear programming problem.

The P & T Co. always ships *full* truckloads of canned peas since anything less would be uneconomical. This implies that each x_{ij} should have an *integer* value (0, 1, 2, . . .). To avoid obtaining an optimal solution for our model that has *fractional* values for any of the decision variables, we could add another set of constraints specifying that each x_{ij} must have an integer value. This would convert our linear programming problem into an *integer programming* problem, which is more difficult to solve. (Recall that we discuss integer programming problems in Chapters 3 and 7.) Fortunately, this conversion is not necessary because of the following property of transportation problems.

> **Integer Solutions Property**: As long as all its supplies and demands have integer values, any transportation problem with feasible solutions is guaranteed to have an optimal solution with integer values for all its decision variables. Therefore, it is not necessary to add constraints to the model that restrict these variables to only have integer values.

When dealing with transportation problems, practitioners typically do not bother to write out the complete linear programming model in algebraic form since all the essential information can be presented much more compactly in a table like Table 15.5 or in the corresponding spreadsheet model.

CD 15-11

Before leaving this linear programming model though, take a good look at the left-hand side of the functional constraints. Note that every coefficient is either 0 (so the variable is deleted) or 1. Also note the distinctive pattern for the locations of the coefficients of 1, including the fact that each variable has a coefficient of 1 in exactly two constraints. These distinctive features of the coefficients play a key role in being able to solve transportation problems extremely efficiently.

Solving Transportation Problems

Because transportation problems are a special type of linear programming problem, they can be solved by the *simplex method* (the procedure used by Solver to solve linear programming problems). However, because of the very distinctive pattern of coefficients in its functional constraints noted above, it is possible to greatly *streamline* the simplex method to solve transportation problems far more quickly. This streamlined version of the simplex method is called the **transportation simplex method.** It sometimes can solve large transportation problems more than 100 times faster than the regular simplex method. However, it is only applicable to transportation problems.

Just like a transportation problem, other *minimum-cost flow problems* also have a similar distinctive pattern of coefficients in their functional constraints. Therefore, the simplex method can be greatly streamlined in much the same way as for the transportation simplex method to solve *any* minimum-cost flow problem (including any transportation problem) very quickly. This streamlined method is called the **network simplex method.**

Linear programming software often includes the network simplex method, and may include the transportation simplex method as well. When only the network simplex method is available, it provides an excellent alternative way of solving transportation problems. In fact, the network simplex method has become quite competitive with the transportation simplex method in recent years.

After obtaining an optimal solution, *what-if analysis* generally is done for transportation problems in much the same way as described in Chapter 5 for other linear programming problems. Either the transportation or network simplex method can readily obtain the allowable range for each coefficient in the objective function. Dealing with changes in right-hand sides (supplies and demands) is more complicated now because of the requirement that the sum of the supplies must equal the sum of the demands. Thus, each change in a supply must be accompanied by a corresponding change in a demand (or demands), and vice versa.

Because Solver is not intended to solve really large linear programming problems that often arise in practice, it simply uses the simplex method to solve transportation problems as well as other minimum-cost flow problems encountered in this book (and considerably larger ones as well), so we will continue to use Solver and thereby forgo any use of the transportation simplex method or network simplex method.

Completing the P & T Co. Case Study

We now can summarize the end of the story of how the P & T Co. was able to substantially improve on the current shipping plan shown in Table 15.2, which has a total shipping cost of $165,595.

You already have seen how Kim Baker was able to formulate this problem as a *transportation problem* simply by filling out the table shown in Table 15.5. The corresponding formulation on a spreadsheet was shown in Figure 15.2. Applying Solver then gave the optimal solution shown in ShipmentQuantity (D12:G14).

Note that this optimal solution is not an intuitive one. Of the 75 truckloads being supplied by Bellingham, 55 of them are being sent to Albuquerque, even though this is far more expensive

($867 per truckload) than to any other warehouse. However, this sacrifice for Cannery 1 enables low-cost shipments for both Canneries 2 and 3. Although it would be difficult to find this optimal solution manually, the simplex method in Solver finds it readily.

As given in the objective cell TotalCost (J17), the total shipping cost for this optimal shipping plan is

$$\text{Total shipping cost} = 20(\$513) + 55(\$867) + 80(\$352) + 45(\$416) + 70(\$388) + 30(\$685)$$
$$= \$152,535$$

a reduction of $13,060 from the current shipping plan. Richard Powers is pleased to report this reduction to his CEO, Douglas Whitson, who congratulates him and Kim Baker for achieving this significant savings.

An Award-Winning Application of a Transportation Problem

Except for its small size, the P & T Co. problem is typical of the problems faced by many corporations that must ship goods from their manufacturing plants to their customers.

For example, consider an award-winning management science study conducted at **Procter & Gamble** (as described in the January–February 1997 issue of *Interfaces*). Prior to the study, the company's supply chain consisted of hundreds of suppliers, over 50 product categories, over 60 plants, 15 distribution centers, and over 1,000 customer zones. However, as the company moved toward global brands, management realized that it needed to consolidate plants to reduce manufacturing expenses, improve speed to market, and reduce capital investment. Therefore, the study focused on redesigning the company's production and distribution system for its North American operations. The result was a reduction in the number of North American plants by almost 20 percent, saving over $200 million in pretax costs per year.

A major part of the study revolved around formulating and solving transportation problems for individual product categories. For each option regarding the plants to keep open, and so forth, solving the corresponding transportation problem for a product category shows what the distribution cost would be for shipping the product category from those plants to the distribution centers and customer zones. Numerous such transportation problems were solved in the process of identifying the best new production and distribution system.

REVIEW QUESTIONS

1. Give a one-sentence description of transportation problems.
2. What data are needed for the model of a transportation problem?
3. What needs to be done to formulate a problem as a transportation problem?
4. What is required for a transportation problem to have feasible solutions?
5. Under what circumstances will a transportation problem automatically have an optimal solution with integer values for all its decision variables?
6. Name two algorithms that can solve transportation problems much faster than the general simplex method.

CD 15-13

15.3 MODELING VARIANTS OF TRANSPORTATION PROBLEMS

The P & T Co. problem is an example of a transportation problem where everything fits immediately. Real life is seldom this easy. Linear programming problems frequently arise that are *almost* transportation problems, but one or more features do not quite fit. Here are the features that we will consider in this section.

1. The sum of the supplies *exceeds* the sum of the demands, so each supply represents a *maximum* amount (not a *fixed* amount) to be distributed from that source.

2. The sum of the supplies is *less* than the sum of the demands, so each demand represents a *maximum* amount (not a *fixed* amount) to be received at that destination.

3. A destination has both a *minimum* demand and a *maximum* demand, so any amount between these two values can be received.

4. Certain source–destination combinations cannot be used for distributing units.

5. The objective is to maximize the total profit associated with distributing units rather than to minimize the total cost.

For each of these features, it is possible to reformulate the problem in a clever way to make it fit the format for transportation problems. When this is done with a really big problem (say, one with many thousands of sources and destinations), it is extremely helpful because either the transportation simplex method or network simplex method can solve the problem in this format *much* faster (perhaps more than 100 times faster) than the simplex method can solve the general linear programming formulation.

However, when the problem is *not* really big, the simplex method still is capable of solving the general linear programming formulation in a reasonable period of time. Therefore, a basic software package (such as the Excel Solver) that includes the simplex method but not the transportation simplex method or network simplex method can be applied to such problems without trying to force them into the format for a transportation problem. This is the approach we will use. In particular, this section illustrates the formulation of spreadsheet models for *variants* of transportation problems that have some of the features listed above.

Our first example focuses on features 1 and 4. A second example will illustrate the other features.

Example 1: Assigning Plants to Products

The Better Products Company has decided to initiate the production of four new products, using three plants that currently have excess production capacity. The products require a comparable production effort per unit, so the available production capacity of the plants is measured by the number of units of any product that can be produced per day, as given in the rightmost column of Table 15.6. The bottom row gives the required production rate (number of units produced per day) to meet projected sales. Each plant can produce any of these products, *except* that Plant 2 *cannot* produce Product 3. However, the variable costs per unit of each product differ from plant to plant, as shown in the main body of the table.

Management now needs to make a decision about which plants should produce which products. *Product splitting,* where the same product is produced in more than one plant, is permitted. (We shall return to this same example in Section 15.7 to consider the option where product splitting is prohibited, which requires a different kind of formulation.)

460

Formulation of a Spreadsheet Model

This problem is almost a transportation problem. In fact, after substituting conventional terminology (supply, demand, etc.) for the column and row headings in Table 15.6, this table basically fits the formulation for a transportation problem, as shown in Table 15.7. But there are two ways in which this problem deviates from a transportation problem.

Table 15.6   Data for the Better Products Co. Problem

| Product: | Unit Cost | | | | Capacity Available |
	1	2	3	4	
Plant					
1	$41	$27	$28	$24	75
2	$40	$29	–	$23	75
3	$37	$30	$27	$21	45
Required production	20	30	30	40	

Table 15.7   The Data for the Better Products Co. Problem Formulated as a Variant of a Transportation Problem

| Destination (Product) Source (Plant) | Unit Cost | | | | Supply |
	1	2	3	4	
1	$41	$27	$28	$24	75
2	$40	$29	–	$23	75
3	$37	$30	$27	$21	45
Demand	20	30	30	40	

One (minor) deviation is that a transportation problem requires a unit cost for *every* source–destination combination, but Plant 2 cannot produce Product 3, so no unit cost is available for this particular combination. The other deviation is that the sum of the supplies (75 + 75 + 45+ 195) *exceeds* the sum of the demands (20 + 30 + 30 + 40 + 120) in Table 15.7. Thus, as the *feasible solutions property* (Section 15.2) indicates, the transportation problem represented by Table 15.7 would have no feasible solutions. The *requirements assumption* (Section 15.2) specifies that the entire supply from each source must be used.

In reality, these supplies in Table 15.7 represent production capacities that will not need to be fully used to meet the sales demand for the products. Thus, these supplies are *upper bounds* on the amounts to be used.

The spreadsheet model for this problem, shown in Figure 15.4, has the same format as the one in Figure 15.2 for the P & T Co. transportation problem with two key differences. First, because Plant 2 cannot produce Product 3, a dash is inserted into cell E5 and the constraint that E12 = 0 is included in the Solver Parameters box. Second, because the supplies are upper bounds, cells H11:H13 have ≤ signs instead of = signs and the corresponding constraints in the Solver Parameters box are ProducedAtPlant (G11:G13) ≤ Capacity (I11:I13).

CD 15-15

	A	B	C	D	E	F	G	H	I
1		**Better Products Co. Production Planning Problem**							
2									
3		**Unit Cost**	Product 1	Product 2	Product 3	Product 4			
4		Plant 1	$41	$27	$28	$24			
5		Plant 2	$40	$29	-	$23			
6		Plant 3	$37	$30	$27	$21			
7									
8									
9							Produced		
10		**Daily Production**	Product 1	Product 2	Product 3	Product 4	At Plant		Capacity
11		Plant 1	0	30	30	0	60	<=	75
12		Plant 2	0	0	0	15	15	<=	75
13		Plant 3	20	0	0	25	45	<=	45
14		Products Produced	20	30	30	40			
15			=	=	=	=			Total Cost
16		Required Production	20	30	30	40			$3,260

Solver Parameters

Set Objective Cell: TotalCost
To: Min
By Changing Variable Cells:
    DailyProduction
Subject to the Constraints:
    E12 = 0
    ProducedAtPlant <= Capacity
    ProductsProduced = RequiredProduction
Solver Options:
    Make Variables Nonnegative
    Solving Method: Simplex LP

Range Name	Cells
Capacity	I11:I13
DailyProduction	C11:F13
ProducedAtPlant	G11:G13
ProductsProduced	C14:F14
RequiredProduction	C16:F16
TotalCost	I16
UnitCost	C4:F6

	G
9	Produced
10	At Plant
11	=SUM(C11:F11)
12	=SUM(C12:F12)
13	=SUM(C13:F13)

	B	C	D	E	F
14	Products Produced	=SUM(C11:C13)	=SUM(D11:D13)	=SUM(E11:E13)	=SUM(F11:F13)

	I
15	Total Cost
16	=SUMPRODUCT(UnitCost,DailyProduction)

Figure 15.4   A spreadsheet formulation of the Better Products Co. problem as a variant of a transportation problem, including the objective cell TotalCost (I16) and the other output cells ProducedAtPlant (G11:G13) and ProductsProduced (C14:F14), as well as the specifications needed to set up the model. The changing cells DailyProduction (C11:F13) show the optimal production plan obtained by Solver.

Using Solver then gives the optimal solution shown in the changing cells DailyProduction (C11:F13) for the production rate of each product at each plant. This solution minimizes the cost of distributing 120 units of production from the total supply of 195 to meet the total demand of 120 at the four destinations (products). The total cost given in the objective cell TotalCost (I16) is $3,260 per day.

Example 2: Choosing Customers

The Nifty Company specializes in the production of a single product, which it produces in three plants. The product is doing very well, so the company currently is receiving more purchase requests than it can fill. Plans have been made to open an additional plant, but it will not be ready until next year.

For the coming month, four potential customers (wholesalers) in different parts of the country would like to make major purchases. Customer 1 is the company's best customer, so his full order will be met. Customers 2 and 3 also are valued customers, so the marketing manager has decided that, at a minimum, at least a third of their order quantities should be met. However, she does not feel that Customer 4 warrants special consideration, and so is unwilling to guarantee any minimum amount for this customer. There will be enough units produced to go somewhat above these minimum amounts.

Due largely to substantial variations in shipping costs, the net profit that would be earned on each unit sold varies greatly, depending on which plant is supplying which customer. Therefore, the final decision on how much to send to each customer (above the minimum amounts established by the marketing manager) will be based on maximizing profit.

The unit profit for each combination of a plant supplying a customer is shown in Table 15.8. The rightmost column gives the number of units that each plant will produce for the coming month (a total of 20,000). The bottom row shows the order quantities that have been requested by the customers (a total of 30,000). The next-to-last row gives the minimum amounts that will be provided (a total of 12,000), based on the marketing manager's decisions described above.

The marketing manager needs to determine how many units to sell to each customer (observing these minimum amounts) and how many units to ship from each plant to each customer to maximize profit.

Formulation of a Spreadsheet Model

This problem is almost a transportation problem, since the plants can be viewed as *sources* and the customers as *destinations,* where the production quantities are the *supplies* from the sources.

If this were fully a transportation problem, the purchase quantities would be the *demands* for the destinations. However, this does not work here because the *requirements assumption* (Section 15.2) says that the demand must be a *fixed* quantity to be received from the sources. Except for Customer 1, all we have here are *ranges* for the purchase quantities between the minimum and the maximum given in the last two rows of Table 15.8. In fact, one objective is to solve for the most desirable values of these purchase quantities.

Table 15.8   Data for the Nifty Co. Problem

Customer	Unit Profit 1	2	3	4	Production Quantity
Plant					
1	$55	$42	$46	$53	8,000
2	$37	$18	$32	$48	5,000
3	$29	$59	$51	$35	7,000
Minimum purchase	7,000	3,000	2,000	0	
Requested purchase	7,000	9,000	6,000	8,000	

CD 15-17

Figure 15.5 shows the spreadsheet model for this variant of a transportation problem. Instead of a demand row below the changing cells, we instead have both a minimum row and a maximum row. The corresponding constraints in the Solver Parameter box are TotalShipped (C17:F17) ≤ MaxPurchase (C19:F19) and TotalShipped (C17:F17) ≥ MinPurchase (C15:F15), along with the usual supply constraints. Since the objective is to maximize the total profit rather than minimize the total cost, the Solver Parameter box specifies that the objective cell TotalProfit (I17) is to be maximized.

After solving, the optimal solution shown in Figure 15.5 is obtained. Cells TotalShipped (C17:F17) indicate how many units to sell to the respective customers. The changing cells Shipment (C11:F13) show how many units to ship from each plant to each customer. The resulting total profit of $1.076 million is given in the objective cell TotalProfit (I17).

REVIEW QUESTIONS

1. What needs to be done to formulate the spreadsheet model for a variant of a transportation problem where each supply from a source represents a maximum amount rather than a fixed amount to be distributed from that source?

2. What needs to be done to formulate the spreadsheet model for a variant of a transportation problem where the demand for a destination can be anything between a specified minimum amount and a specified maximum amount?

CD 15-18

	A	B	C	D	E	F	G	H	I
1		**Nifty Co. Product-Distribution Problem**							
2									
3		**Unit Profit**	Customer 1	Customer 2	Customer 3	Customer 4			
4		Plant 1	$55	$42	$46	$53			
5		Plant 2	$37	$18	$32	$48			
6		Plant 3	$29	$59	$51	$35			
7									
8									
9							Total		Production
10		**Shipment**	Customer 1	Customer 2	Customer 3	Customer 4	Production		Quantity
11		Plant 1	7,000	0	1,000	0	8,000	=	8,000
12		Plant 2	0	0	0	5,000	5,000	=	5,000
13		Plant 3	0	6,000	1,000	0	7,000	=	7,000
14									
15		Min Purchase	7,000	3,000	2,000	0			
16			<=	<=	<=	<=			Total Profit
17		Total Shipped	7,000	6,000	2,000	5,000			$1,076,000
18			<=	<=	<=	<=			
19		Max Purchase	7,000	9,000	6,000	8,000			

Solver Parameters

Set Objective Cell: TotalProfit
To: Max
By Changing Variable Cells:
  Shipment
Subject to the Constraints:
  TotalProduction = ProductionQuantity
  TotalShipped <= MaxPurchase
  TotalShipped >= MinPurchase
Solver Options:
  Make Variables Nonnegative
  Solving Method: Simplex LP

Range Name	**Cells**
MaxPurchase	C19:F19
MinPurchase	C15:F15
ProductionQuantity	I11:I13
Shipment	C11:F13
TotalProduction	G11:G13
TotalProfit	I17
TotalShipped	C17:F17
UnitProfit	C4:F6

	G
9	Total
10	Production
11	=SUM(C11:F11)
12	=SUM(C12:F12)
13	=SUM(C13:F13)

	B	C	D	E	F
17	Total Shipped	=SUM(C11:C13)	=SUM(D11:D13)	=SUM(E11:E13)	=SUM(F11:F13)

	I
16	Total Profit
17	=SUMPRODUCT(UnitProfit,Shipment)

Figure 15.5 A spreadsheet formulation of the Nifty Co. problem as a variant of a transportation problem, including the objective cell TotalProfit (I17) and the other output cells TotalProduction (G11:G13) and TotalShipped (C17:F17), as well as the specifications needed to set up the model. The changing cells Shipment (C11:F13) show the optimal shipping plan obtained by Solver.

CD 15-19

15.4 SOME OTHER APPLICATIONS OF VARIANTS OF TRANSPORTATION PROBLEMS

You now have seen examples illustrating three areas of application of transportation problems and their variants:

1. Shipping goods (the P & T Co. problem).

2. Assigning plants to products (the Better Products Co. problem).

3. Choosing customers (the Nifty Co. problem).

You will further broaden your horizons in this section by seeing examples illustrating some (but far from all) other areas of application.

Distributing Natural Resources

Metro Water District is an agency that administers water distribution in a large geographic region. The region is fairly arid, so the district must purchase and bring in water from outside the region. The sources of this imported water are the Colombo, Sacron, and Calorie rivers. The district then resells the water to users in its region. Its main customers are the water departments of the cities of Berdoo, Los Devils, San Go, and Hollyglass.

It is possible to supply any of these cities with water brought in from any of the three rivers, with the exception that no provision has been made to supply Hollyglass with Calorie River water. However, because of the geographic layouts of the aqueducts and the cities in the region, the cost to the district of supplying water depends upon both the source of the water and the city being supplied. The variable cost per acre foot of water for each combination of river and city is given in Table 15.9.

Using units of 1 million acre feet, the bottom row of the table shows the amount of water needed by each city in the coming year (a total of 12.5). The rightmost column shows the amount available from each river (a total of 16).

Since the total amount available exceeds the total amount needed, management wants to determine how much water to take from each river, and then how much to send from each river to each city. The objective is to minimize the total cost of meeting the needs of the four cities.

Formulation and Solution

Figure 15.6 shows a spreadsheet model for this variant of a transportation problem. Because Hollyglass cannot be supplied with Calorie River water, the Solver Parameters box includes the constraint that F13 = 0. The amounts available in column I represent maximum amounts rather than fixed amounts, so ≤ signs are used for the corresponding constraints, TotalFromRiver (G11:G13) ≤ Available (I11:I13).

Solver then gives the optimal solution shown in Figure 15.6. The cells TotalFromRiver (G11:G13) indicate that the entire available supply from the Colombo and Sacron rivers should be used whereas only 1.5 million acre feet of the 5 million acre feet available from the Calorie River should be used. The changing cells WaterDistribution (C11:F13) provide the plan for how much to send from each river to each city. The total cost is given in the objective cell TotalCost (I17) as $1.975 billion.

CD 15-20

	A	B	C	D	E	F	G	H	I
1		**Metro Water District Distribution Problem**							
2									
3		Unit Cost ($millions)	Berdoo	Los Devils	San Go	Hollyglass			
4		Colombo River	160	130	220	170			
5		Sacron River	140	130	190	150			
6		Calorie River	190	200	230	-			
7									
8									
9		Water Distribution					Total		
10		(million acre-feet)	Berdoo	Los Devils	San Go	Hollyglass	From River		Available
11		Colombo River	0	5	0	0	5	<=	5
12		Sacron River	2	0	2.5	1.5	6	<=	6
13		Calorie River	0	0	1.5	0	1.5	<=	5
14		Total To City	2	5	4	1.5			
15			=	=	=	=			Total Cost
16		Needed	2	5	4	1.5			($million)
17									1,975

Solver Parameters

Set Objective Cell: TotalCost
To: Min
By Changing Variable Cells:
 WaterDistribution
Subject to the Constraints:
 F13 = 0
 TotalFromRiver <= Available
 TotalToCity = Needed
Solver Options:
 Make Variables Nonnegative
 Solving Method: Simplex LP

Range Name	Cells
Available	I11:I13
Needed	C16:F16
TotalCost	I17
TotalFromRiver	G11:G13
TotalToCity	C14:F14
UnitCost	C4:F6
WaterDistribution	C11:F13

	G
9	Total
10	From River
11	=SUM(C11:F11)
12	=SUM(C12:F12)
13	=SUM(C13:F13)

	B	C	D	E	F
14	Total To City	=SUM(C11:C13)	=SUM(D11:D13)	=SUM(E11:E13)	=SUM(F11:F13)

	I
15	Total Cost
16	($million)
17	=SUMPRODUCT(UnitCost,WaterDistribution)

Figure 15.6 A spreadsheet formulation of the Metro Water District problem as a variant of a transportation problem, including the objective cell TotalCost I17) and the other output cells TotalFromRiver (G11:G13) and TotalToCity (C14:F14), as well as the specifications needed to set up the model. The changing cells WaterDistribution (C11:F13) show the optimal solution obtained by Solver.

CD 15-21

Table 15.9   Water Resources Data for Metro Water District

| | Cost per Acre Foot | | | | |
	Berdoo	Los Devils	San Go	Hollyglass	Available
Colombo River	$160	$130	$220	$170	5
Sacron River	140	130	190	150	6
Calorie River	190	200	230	—	5
Needed	2	5	4	1.5	(million acre feet)

Production Scheduling

The Northern Airplane Company builds commercial airplanes for various airline companies around the world. The last stage in the production process is to produce the jet engines and then to install them (a very fast operation) in the completed airplane frame. The company has been working under some contracts to deliver a considerable number of airplanes in the near future, and the production of the jet engines for these planes must now be scheduled for the next four months.

To meet the contracted dates for delivery, the company must supply engines for installation in the quantities indicated in the second column of Table 15.10. Thus, the cumulative number of engines produced by the end of months 1, 2, 3, and 4 must be at least 10, 25, 50, and 70, respectively.

Table 15.10   Production Scheduling Data for the Northern Airplane Company Problem

| Month | Scheduled Installations | Maximum Production | | Unit Cost of Production ($million) | | Unit Cost of Storage ($thousand) |
		Regular Time	Overtime	Regular Time	Overtime	
1	10	20	10	1.08	1.10	15
2	15	30	15	1.11	1.12	15
3	25	25	10	1.10	1.11	15
4	20	5	10	1.13	1.15	

The facilities that will be available for producing the engines vary according to other production, maintenance, and renovation work scheduled during this period. The resulting monthly differences in the maximum number of engines that can be produced during *regular time* hours (no overtime) are shown in the third column of Table 15.10, and the additional numbers that can be produced during *overtime* hours are shown in the fourth column. The cost of producing each one on either regular time or overtime is given in the fifth and sixth columns.

Because of the variations in production costs, it may well be worthwhile to produce some of the engines a month or more before they are scheduled for installation, and this possibility is being considered. The drawback is that such engines must be stored until the scheduled installation (the airplane frames will not be ready early) at a storage cost of $15,000 per month (including interest on expended capital) for each engine[1], as shown in the rightmost column of Table 15.10.

The production manager wants a schedule developed for the number of engines to be produced in each of the four months so that the total of the production and storage costs will be minimized.

Formulation and Solution

Figure 15.7 shows the formulation of this problem as a variant of a transportation problem. The *sources* of the jet engines are their production on *regular time* (RT) and on *overtime* (OT) in each of the four months. Their *supplies* are obtained from the third and fourth columns of Table 15.10. The *destinations* for these engines are their installation in each of the four months, so their *demands* are given in the second column of Table 15.10.

	A	B	C	D	E	F	G	H	I	J
1	**Northern Airplane Co. Production-Scheduling Problem**									
2										
3		Production Cost		Regular		Storage Cost				
4		($millions)		Time	Overtime	($millions per month)				
5			Month 1	1.08	1.10	0.015				
6			Month 2	1.11	1.12					
7			Month 3	1.10	1.11					
8			Month 4	1.13	1.15					
9										
10										
11		Unit Cost			Month Installed					
12		($millions)		1	2	3	4			
13			1 (RT)	1.08	1.10	1.11	1.13			
14			1 (OT)	1.10	1.12	1.13	1.15			
15			2 (RT)	-	1.11	1.13	1.14			
16		Month	2 (OT)	-	1.12	1.14	1.15			
17		Produced	3 (RT)	-	-	1.10	1.12			
18			3 (OT)	-	-	1.11	1.13			
19			4 (RT)	-	-	-	1.13			
20			4 (OT)	-	-	-	1.15			
21										
22										
23					Month Installed					Maximum
24		Units Produced		1	2	3	4	Produced		Production
25			1 (RT)	10	5	0	5	20	<=	20
26			1 (OT)	0	0	0	0	0	<=	10
27			2 (RT)	0	10	0	0	10	<=	30
28		Month	2 (OT)	0	0	0	0	0	<=	15
29		Produced	3 (RT)	0	0	25	0	25	<=	25
30			3 (OT)	0	0	0	10	10	<=	10
31			4 (RT)	0	0	0	5	5	<=	5
32			4 (OT)	0	0	0	0	0	<=	10
33			Installed	10	15	25	20			
34				=	=	=	=			Total Cost
35		Scheduled Installations		10	15	25	20			($millions)
36										77.4

---

[1] For modeling purposes, it is being assumed that the storage cost is incurred at the end of the month to just those engines that are being held over into the next month. Thus, engines that are produced in a given month for installation in the same month are assumed to incur no storage cost.

(Figure 15.7 continued)

	B	C	D	E	F	G
11	Unit Cost				Month Installed	
12	($millions)		1	2	3	4
13		1 (RT)	=D5	=D5+StorageCost	=D5+2*StorageCost	=D5+3*StorageCost
14		1 (OT)	=E5	=E5+StorageCost	=E5+2*StorageCost	=E5+3*StorageCost
15		2 (RT)	-	=D6	=D6+StorageCost	=D6+2*StorageCost
16	Month	2 (OT)	-	=E6	=E6+StorageCost	=E6+2*StorageCost
17	Produced	3 (RT)	-	-	=D7	=D7+StorageCost
18		3 (OT)	-	-	=E7	=E7+StorageCost
19		4 (RT)	-	-	-	=D8
20		4 (OT)	-	-	-	=E8

Solver Parameters

Set Objective Cell: TotalCost
To: Min
By Changing Variable Cells:
  UnitsProduced
Subject to the Constraints:
  D27:D32 = 0
  E29:E32 = 0
  F31:F32 = 0
  Installed = ScheduledInstallations
  Produced <= MaxProduction
Solver Options:
  Make Variables Nonnegative
  Solving Method: Simplex LP

Range Name	Cells
Installed	D33:G33
MaxProduction	J25:J32
Produced	H25:H32
ProductionCost	D5:E8
ScheduledInstallations	D35:G35
StorageCost	G5
TotalCost	J36
UnitCost	D13:G20
UnitsProduced	D25:G32

	H
24	Produced
25	=SUM(D25:G25)
26	=SUM(D26:G26)
27	=SUM(D27:G27)
28	=SUM(D28:G28)
29	=SUM(D29:G29)
30	=SUM(D30:G30)
31	=SUM(D31:G31)
32	=SUM(D32:G32)

	C	D	E	F	G
33	Installed	=SUM(D25:D32)	=SUM(E25:E32)	=SUM(F25:F32)	=SUM(G25:G32)

	J
34	Total Cost
35	($millions)
36	=SUMPRODUCT(UnitCost,UnitsProduced)

Figure 15.7   A spreadsheet formulation of the Northern Airplane Co. problem as a variant of a transportation problem, including the objective cell TotalCost (J36) and the othr output cells UnitCost (D13:G20), Produced (H25:H32), and Installed (D33:G33), as well as the specifications needed to set up the model. The changing cells UnitsProduced (D25:G32) display the optimal production schedule obtained by Solver.

It is not possible to install an engine in some month prior to its production, so the Solver Parameters box includes constraints that the number installed must be zero in each of these cases. Similarly, dashes are inserted into the UnitCost table for these cases. Otherwise, the unit costs given in this table (in units of $1 million) are obtained by combining the unit cost of production from the fifth or sixth column of Table 15.10 with any storage costs ($0.015 million per unit per month stored). (The equations entered into UnitCost (D13:G20) are shown after the spreadsheet in Figure 15.7.) Since the quantities in MaxProduction (J25:J32) represent the maximum amounts that can be produced, they are preceded by ≤ signs in column I. The corresponding supply constraints, Produced (H25:H32) ≤ MaxProduction (J25:J32), are included in the Solver Parameters box along with the usual demand constraints.

Table 15.11   Optimal Production Schedule for the Northern Airplane Co.

Month	Production	Installations	Stored
1 (RT)	20	10	10
2 (RT)	10	15	5
3 (RT)	25	25	5
3 (OT)	10	0	10
4 (RT)	5	20	0

The changing cells UnitsProduced (D25:G32) show an optimal solution for this problem. Table 15.11 summarizes the key features of this solution. Overtime is used only once (in month 3). Despite the hefty costs incurred by storing engines, extra engines are produced in the first and third months to be stored for installation later. Even month 2 produces enough engines that five will remain in storage for installation in month 3, despite the fact that production costs are higher in month 2 than in month 3. Thus, a human scheduler would have difficulty in finding this schedule. However, Solver has no difficulty in balancing all the factors involved to reduce the total cost to an absolute minimum, which turns out to be $77.4 million (as shown in the objective cell TotalCost [J36]) in this case.

Designing School Attendance Zones

The Middletown School District is opening a third high school and thus needs to redraw the boundaries for the areas of the city that will be assigned to the respective schools.

For preliminary planning, the city has been divided into nine tracts with approximately equal populations. (Subsequent detailed planning will divide the city further into over 100 smaller tracts.) The main body of Table 15.12 shows the approximate distance between each tract and school. The rightmost column gives the number of high school students in each tract next year. (These numbers are expected to grow slowly over the next several years.) The last two rows show the minimum and maximum number of students each school should be assigned.

Table 15.12   Data for the Middletown School District Problem

	Distance (Miles) to School			Number of High
Tract	1	2	3	School Students
1	2.2	1.9	2.5	500
2	1.4	1.3	1.7	400
3	0.5	1.8	1.1	450
4	1.2	0.3	2.0	400
5	0.9	0.7	1.0	500
6	1.1	1.6	0.6	450
7	2.7	0.7	1.5	450
8	1.8	1.2	0.8	400
9	1.5	1.7	0.7	500
Minimum enrollment	1,200	1,100	1,000	
Maximum enrollment	1,800	1,700	1,500	

The school district management has decided that the appropriate objective in setting school attendance zone boundaries is to minimize the *average distance* that students must travel to school. At this preliminary stage, they want to determine how many students from each tract should be assigned to each school to achieve this objective, while also satisfying the enrollment constraints at each school indicated by the bottom two rows of Table 15.12.

Formulation and Solution

Minimizing the average distance that students must travel is equivalent to *minimizing the sum of the distances* that individual students must travel. Therefore, adopting the latter objective, this is just a variant of a transportation problem where the unit costs are distances.

Because each school has both a minimum and maximum enrollment, we proceed just as in the Nifty Co. example (Section 15.3) to provide two rows of data cells below the changing cells that specify these minimum and maximum amounts in the spreadsheet model shown in Figure 15.8. The corresponding constraints are included in the Solver Parameters box along with the usual supply constraints. After solving, the optimal solution is shown in the changing cells NumberOfStudents (C17:E25).

This optimal solution gives the following plan:

Assign tracts 2 and 3 to school 1.

Assign tracts 1, 4, and 7 to school 2.

Assign tracts 6, 8, and 9 to school 3.

Split tract 5, with 350 students assigned to school 1 and 150 students assigned to school 2.

As indicated in the objective cell TotalDistance (H30), the total distance traveled to school by all the students is 3,530 miles (an average of 0.872 mile per student).

CD 15-26

	A	B	C	D	E	F	G	H
1		**Middletown School District Zoning Problem**						
2								
3		**Distance (Miles)**	School 1	School 2	School 3			
4		Tract 1	2.2	1.9	2.5			
5		Tract 2	1.4	1.3	1.7			
6		Tract 3	0.5	1.8	1.1			
7		Tract 4	1.2	0.3	2			
8		Tract 5	0.9	0.7	1			
9		Tract 6	1.1	1.6	0.6			
10		Tract 7	2.7	0.7	1.5			
11		Tract 8	1.8	1.2	0.8			
12		Tract 9	1.5	1.7	0.7			
13								
14								
15		**Number of**				Total		Total
16		**Students**	School 1	School 2	School 3	From Tract		In Tract
17		Tract 1	0	500	0	500	=	500
18		Tract 2	400	0	0	400	=	400
19		Tract 3	450	0	0	450	=	450
20		Tract 4	0	400	0	400	=	400
21		Tract 5	350	150	0	500	=	500
22		Tract 6	0	0	450	450	=	450
23		Tract 7	0	450	0	450	=	450
24		Tract 8	0	0	400	400	=	400
25		Tract 9	0	0	500	500	=	500
26								
27		Min Enrollment	1,200	1,500	1,350			
28			<=	<=	<=			Total Distance
29		Total At School	1,200	1,500	1,350			(miles)
30			<=	<=	<=			3,530
31		Max Enrollment	1,800	1,700	1,500			

Solver Parameters
Set Objective Cell: TotalCost
To: Min
By Changing Variable Cells:
NumberOfStudents
Subject to the Constraints:
TotalAtSchool <= MaxEnrollment
TotalAtSchool >= MinEnrollment
TotalFromTract = TotalInTract
Solver Options:
Make Variables Nonnegative
Solving Method: Simplex LP

	F
15	Total
16	From Tract
17	=SUM(C17:E17)
18	=SUM(C18:E18)
19	=SUM(C19:E19)
20	=SUM(C20:E20)
21	=SUM(C21:E21)
22	=SUM(C22:E22)
23	=SUM(C23:E23)
24	=SUM(C24:E24)
25	=SUM(C25:E25)

Range Name	Cells
MaxEnrollment	C31:E31
Miles	C4:E12
MinEnrollment	C27:E27
NumberOfStudents	C17:E25
TotalAtSchool	C29:E29
TotalDistance	H30
TotalFromTract	F17:F25
TotalInTract	H17:H25

	H
28	Total Distance
29	(miles)
30	=SUMPRODUCT(Miles,NumberOfStudents)

	B	C	D	E
29	Total At School	=SUM(C17:C25)	=SUM(D17:D25)	=SUM(E17:E25)

Figure 15.8 A spreadsheet formulation of the Middletown School District problem as a variant of a transportation problem, including the objective cell TotalDistance (H30) and the other output cells TotalFromTract (F17:F25) and the TotalAtSchool (C29:E29), as well as the specifications needed to set up the model. The changing cells NumberOfStudents (C17:E25) show the optimal zoning plan obtained by Solver.

Meeting Energy Needs Economically

The Energetic Company needs to make plans for the *energy systems* for a new building.

The *energy needs* in the building fall into three categories: (1) electricity, (2) heating water, and (3) heating space in the building. The daily requirements for these three categories (all measured in the same units) are 20 units, 10 units, and 30 units, respectively.

The three possible *sources of energy* to meet these needs are electricity, natural gas, and a solar heating unit that can be installed on the roof. The size of the roof limits the largest possible solar heater to providing 30 units per day. However, there is no limit to the amount of electricity and natural gas available.

Electricity needs can be met only by purchasing electricity. Both other energy needs (water heating and space heating) can be met by any of the three sources of energy or a combination thereof.

The unit costs for meeting these energy needs from these sources of energy are shown in Table 15.13. The objective of management is to minimize the total cost of meeting all the energy needs.

Table 15.13　Cost Data for the Energetic Co. Problem

| | Unit Cost | | |
Energy Need:	Electricity	Water Heating	Space Heating
Source of Energy			
Electricity	$400	$500	$600
Natural gas	—	600	500
Solar heater	—	300	400

Formulation and Solution

Figure 15.9 shows the formulation of this problem as a variant of a transportation problem. The changing cells DailyEnergyUse (D12:F14) show the resulting optimal solution for how many units of each energy source should be used to meet each energy need. The objective cell TotalCost (I18) gives the total cost as $24,000 per day.

CD 15-28

	A	B	C	D	E	F	G	H	I
1	**Energetic Co. Energy-Sourcing Problem**								
2									
3					Energy Need				
4		Unit Cost ($/day)		Electricity	Water Heating	Space Heating			
5		Source	Electricity	400	500	600			
6		of	Natural Gas	-	600	500			
7		Energy	Solar Heater	-	300	400			
8									
9									
10					Energy Need		Total		
11		Daily Energy Use		Electricity	Water Heating	Space Heating	Used		
12		Source	Electricity	20	0	0	20		
13		of	Natural Gas	0	0	10	10		Max Solar
14		Energy	Solar Heater	0	10	20	30	<=	30
15			Total Supplied	20	10	30			
16				=	=	=			Total Cost
17			Demand	20	10	30			($/day)
18									24,000

Solver Parameters

Set Objective Cell: TotalCost
To: Min
By Changing Variable Cells:
   DailyEnergyUse
Subject to the Constraints:
   D13:D14 = 0
   TotalSolar <= MaxSolar
   TotalSupplied = Demand
Solver Options:
   Make Variables Nonnegative
   Solving Method: Simplex LP

Range Name	Cells
DailyEnergyUse	D12:F14
Demand	D17:F17
MaxSolar	I14
TotalCost	I18
TotalSolar	G14
TotalSupplied	D15:F15
TotalUsed	G12:G14
UnitCost	D5:F7

	G
10	Total
11	Used
12	=SUM(D12:F12)
13	=SUM(D13:F13)
14	=SUM(D14:F14)

	C	D	E	F
15	Total Supplied	=SUM(D12:D14)	=SUM(E12:E14)	=SUM(F12:F14)

	I
16	Total Cost
17	($/day)
18	=SUMPRODUCT(UnitCost,DailyEnergyUse)

Figure 15.9   A spreadsheet formulation of the Energetic Co. problem as a variant of a transportation problem, including the objective cell TotalCost (I18) and the other output cells TotalUsed (G12:G14) and TotalSupplied (D15:F15), as well as the specifications needed to set up the model. The changing cells DailyEnergyUse (D12:F14) give the optimal energy-sourcing plan obtained by Solver.

CD 15-29

Choosing a New Site Location

One of the most important decisions that the management of many companies must face is where to locate a major new facility. The facility might be a new factory, a new distribution center, a new administrative center, or some other building. The new facility might be needed because of expansion. In other cases, the company may be abandoning an unsatisfactory location.

There generally are several attractive potential sites from which to choose. Increasingly, in today's global economy, the potential sites may extend across national borders.

There are a number of important factors that go into management's decision. One of them is *shipping costs*. For example, when evaluating a potential site for a new factory, management needs to consider the impact of choosing this site on the cost of shipping goods from *all* the factories (including the new factory at this site) to the distribution centers. By locating the new factory near some distribution centers that are far from all the current factories, the company can obtain low shipping costs for the new factory and, at the same time, substantially reduce the shipping costs from the current factories as well. Management needs to know what the *total* shipping cost would be, following an optimal shipping plan, for each potential site for the new factory.

A similar question may arise regarding the total cost of shipping some raw material from its various sources to all the factories (including the new one) for each potential site for the new factory.

A transportation problem (or a variant) often provides the appropriate way of formulating such questions. Solving this formulation for each potential site then provides key input to management, who must evaluate both this information and other relevant considerations in making its final selection of the site.

The case study presented in the next section illustrates this kind of application.

REVIEW QUESTIONS

1. What are the areas of application illustrated in this section for variants of transportation problems?
2. What is the objective of management for the Metro Water District problem?
3. What are the sources and destinations in the formulation of the Northern Airplane Co. production scheduling problem?
4. What plays the role of unit costs in the Middletown School District problem?
5. What is the objective of management for the Energetic Co. problem?

15.5   A CASE STUDY: THE TEXAGO CORP. SITE SELECTION PROBLEM

The Texago Corporation is a large, fully integrated petroleum company based in the United States. The company produces most of its oil in its own oil fields and then imports the rest of what it needs from the Middle East. An extensive distribution network is used to transport the oil to the company's refineries and then to transport the petroleum products from the refineries to Texago's distribution centers. The locations of these various facilities are given in Table 15.14.

Table 15.14   Location of Texago's Current Facilities

Type of Facility	Locations
Oil fields	1. Several in Texas 2. Several in California 3. Several in Alaska
Refineries	1. Near New Orleans, Lousiana 2. Near Charleston, South Carolina 3. Near Seattle, Washington
Distribution Centers	1. Pittsburgh, Pennsylvania 2. Atlanta, Georgia 3. Kansas City, Missouri 4. San Francisco, California

Texago is continuing to increase its market share for several of its major products. Therefore, management has made the decision to expand its output by building an additional refinery and increasing its imports of crude oil from the Middle East. The crucial remaining decision is where to locate the new refinery.

The addition of the new refinery will have a great impact on the operation of the entire distribution system, including decisions on how much crude oil to transport from each of its sources to each refinery (including the new one) and how much finished product to ship from each refinery to each distribution center. Therefore, the three key factors for management's decision on the location of the new refinery are

1. The cost of transporting the oil from its sources to all the refineries, including the new one.

2. The cost of transporting finished product from all the refineries, including the new one, to the distribution centers.

3. Operating costs for the new refinery, including labor costs, taxes, the cost of needed supplies (other than crude oil), energy costs, the cost of insurance, and so on. (Capital costs are not a factor since they would be essentially the same at any of the potential sites.)

Management has set up a task force to study the issue of where to locate the new refinery. After considerable investigation, the task force has determined that there are three attractive potential sites. These sites and the main advantages of each are spelled out in Table 15.15.

Table 15.15   Potential Sites for Texago's New Refinery and Their Main Advantages

Potential Site	Main Advantages
Near Los Angeles, California	1. Near California oil fields. 2. Ready access from Alaska oil fields. 3. Fairly near San Francisco distribution center.
Near Galveston, Texas	1. Near Texas oil fields. 2. Ready access from Middle East imports. 3. Near corporate headquarters.
Near St. Louis, Missouri	1. Low operating costs. 2. Centrally located for distribution centers. 3. Ready access to crude oil via the Mississippi River.

Gathering the Necessary Data

The task force needs to gather a large amount of data, some of which requires considerable digging, in order to perform the analysis requested by management.

Management wants all the refineries, including the new one, to operate at full capacity. Therefore, the task force begins by determining how much crude oil each refinery would need brought in annually under these conditions. Using units of 1 million barrels, these needed amounts are shown on the left side of Table 15.16. The right side of the table shows the current annual output of crude oil from the various oil fields. These quantities are expected to remain stable for some years to come. Since the refineries need a total of 360 million barrels of crude oil, and the oil fields will produce a total of 240 million barrels, the difference of 120 million barrels will need to be imported from the Middle East.

Table 15.16   Production Data for Texago Corp.

Refinery	Crude Oil Needed Annually (Million Barrels)	Oil Fields	Crude Oil Produced Annually (Million Barrels)
New Orleans	100	Texas	80
Charleston	60	California	60
Seattle	80	Alaska	100
New site	120	Total	240
Total	360	Needed imports = 360 − 240 = 120	

Since the amounts of crude oil produced or purchased will be the same regardless of which location is chosen for the new refinery, the task force concludes that the associated production or purchase costs (exclusive of shipping costs) are not relevant to the site selection decision. On the other hand, the costs for transporting the crude oil from its source to a refinery are very relevant. These costs are shown in Table 15.17 for both the three current refineries and the three potential sites for the new refinery.

Table 15.17 Cost Data for Shipping Crude Oil to a Texago Refinery

	Cost per Unit Shipped to Refinery or Potential Refinery (Millions of Dollars per Million Barrels)					
Source	New Orleans	Charleston	Seattle	Los Angeles	Galveston	St. Louis
Texas	2	4	5	3	1	1
California	5	5	3	1	3	4
Alaska	5	7	3	4	5	7
Middle East	2	3	5	4	3	4

Also very relevant are the costs of shipping the finished product from a refinery to a distribution center. Letting one unit of finished product correspond to a refinery's production from 1 million barrels of crude oil, these costs are given in Table 15.18. The bottom row of the table shows the number of units of finished product needed by each distribution center.

Table 15.18 Cost Data for Shipping Finished Product to a Distribution Center

	Cost per Unit Shipped to Distribution Center (Millions of Dollars)			
Refinery	Pittsburgh	Atlanta	Kansas City	San Francisco
New Orleans	6.5	5.5	6	8
Charleston	7	5	4	7
Seattle	7	8	4	3
Potential Refinery				
Los Angeles	8	6	3	2
Galveston	5	4	3	6
St. Louis	4	3	1	5
Number of units needed	100	80	80	100

The final key body of data involves the *operating costs* for a refinery at each potential site. Estimating these costs requires site visits by several members of the task force to collect detailed information about local labor costs, taxes, and so forth. Comparisons then are made with the operating costs of the current refineries to help refine these data. In addition, the task force gathers information on one-time site costs for land, construction, and other expenses and amortizes these costs on an equivalent uniform annual cost basis. This process leads to the estimates shown in Table 15.19.

Table 15.19   Estimated Operating Costs for a Texago Refinery at Each Potential Site

Site	Annual Operating Cost (Millions of Dollars)
Los Angeles	620
Galveston	570
St. Louis	530

Analysis (Six Applications of a Transportation Problem)

Armed with these data, the task force now needs to develop the following key financial information for management:

1.   Total shipping cost for crude oil with each potential choice of a site for the new refinery.

2.   Total shipping cost for finished product with each potential choice of a site for the new refinery.

For both types of costs, once a site is selected, an optimal shipping plan will be determined and then followed. Therefore, to find either type of cost with a *potential* choice of a site, it is necessary to solve for the optimal shipping plan given that choice and then calculate the corresponding cost.

The task force recognizes that the problem of finding an optimal shipping plan for a given choice of a site is just a transportation problem. In particular, for shipping crude oil, Figure 15.10 shows the spreadsheet model for this transportation problem, where the entries in the data cells come directly from Tables 15.16 and 15.17. The entries for the *New Site* column (cells G5:G8) will come from one of the last three columns of Table 15.17, depending on which potential site currently is being evaluated. At this point, before solving, a trial solution of 0 for each of the shipment quantities has been entered into the changing cells ShipmentQuantity (D13:G16).

These same changing cells in Figures 15.11, 15.12, and 15.13 show the optimal shipping plan for each of the three possible choices of a site. The objective cell TotalCost (J20) gives the resulting total annual shipping cost in millions of dollars. In particular, if Los Angeles were to be chosen as the site for the new refinery (Figure 15.11), the total annual cost of shipping crude oil in the optimal manner would be $880 million. If Galveston were chosen instead (Figure 15.12), this cost would be $920 million, whereas it would be $960 million if St. Louis were chosen (Figure 15.13).

	A	B	C	D	E	F	G	H	I	J
1			**Texago Corp. Site-Selection Problem (Shipping to Refineries)**							
2										
3						Refineries				
4			**Unit Cost ($millions)**	New Orleans	Charleston	Seattle	New Site			
5			Texas	2	4	5				
6		Oil	California	5	5	3				
7		Fields	Alaska	5	7	3				
8			Middle East	2	3	5				
9										
10										
11			**Shipment Quantity**			Refineries				
12			**(millions of barrels)**	New Orleans	Charleston	Seattle	New Site	Total Shipped		Supply
13			Texas	0	0	0	0	0	=	80
14		Oil	California	0	0	0	0	0	=	60
15		Fields	Alaska	0	0	0	0	0	=	100
16			Middle East	0	0	0	0	0	=	120
17			Total Received	0	0	0	0			
18				=	=	=	=			Total Cost
19			Demand	100	60	80	120			($millions)
20										0

Solver Parameters

Set Objective Cell: TotalCost
To: Min
By Changing Variable Cells:
   ShipmentQuantity
Subject to the Constraints:
   TotalReceived = Demand
   TotalShipped = Supply
Solver Options:
   Make Variables Nonnegative
   Solving Method: Simplex LP

Range Name	Cells
Demand	D19:G19
ShipmentQuantity	D13:G16
Supply	J13:J16
TotalCost	J20
TotalReceived	D17:G17
TotalShipped	H13:H16
UnitCost	D5:G8

	H
12	Total Shipped
13	=SUM(D13:G13)
14	=SUM(D14:G14)
15	=SUM(D15:G15)
16	=SUM(D16:G16)

	C	D	E	F	G
17	Total Received	=SUM(D13:D16)	=SUM(E13:E16)	=SUM(F13:F16)	=SUM(G13:G16)

	J
18	Total Cost
19	($millions)
20	=SUMPRODUCT(UnitCost,ShipmentQuantity)

Figure 15.10 The basic spreadsheet formulation for the Texago transportation problem for shipping crude oil from oil fields to the refineries, including the new refinery at a site still to be selected. The objective cell is TotalCost (J20) and the other ouput cells are TotalShipped (H13:H16) and TotalReceived (D17:G17). Before entering the data for a new site and then solving, a trial solution of 0 has been entered into each of the changing cells ShipmentQuantity (D13:G16).

CD 15-35

	A	B	C	D	E	F	G	H	I	J
1			Texago Corp. Site-Selection Problem (Shipping to Refineries, Including Los Angeles)							
2										
3						Refineries				
4			Unit Cost ($millions)	New Orleans	Charleston	Seattle	Los Angeles			
5			Texas	2	4	5	3			
6		Oil	California	5	5	3	1			
7		Fields	Alaska	5	7	3	4			
8			Middle East	2	3	5	4			
9										
10										
11			Shipment Quantity			Refineries				
12			(millions of barrels)	New Orleans	Charleston	Seattle	Los Angeles	Total Shipped		Supply
13			Texas	40	0	0	40	80	=	80
14		Oil	California	0	0	0	60	60	=	60
15		Fields	Alaska	0	0	80	20	100	=	100
16			Middle East	60	60	0	0	120	=	120
17			Total Received	100	60	80	120			
18				=	=	=	=			Total Cost
19			Demand	100	60	80	120			($millions)
20										880

Figure 15.11 The changing cells ShipmentQuantity (D13:G16) give Texago management an optimal plan for shipping crude oil if Los Angeles is selected as the new site for the refinery in column G of Figure 15.10.

	A	B	C	D	E	F	G	H	I	J
1			Texago Corp. Site-Selection Problem (Shipping to Refineries, Including Galveston)							
2										
3						Refineries				
4			Unit Cost ($millions)	New Orleans	Charleston	Seattle	Galveston			
5			Texas	2	4	5	1			
6		Oil	California	5	5	3	3			
7		Fields	Alaska	5	7	3	5			
8			Middle East	2	3	5	3			
9										
10										
11			Shipment Quantity			Refineries				
12			(millions of barrels)	New Orleans	Charleston	Seattle	Galveston	Total Shipped		Supply
13			Texas	20	0	0	60	80	=	80
14		Oil	California	0	0	0	60	60	=	60
15		Fields	Alaska	20	0	80	0	100	=	100
16			Middle East	60	60	0	0	120	=	120
17			Total Received	100	60	80	120			
18				=	=	=	=			Total Cost
19			Demand	100	60	80	120			($millions)
20										920

Figure 15.12 The changing cells ShipmentQuantity (D13:G16) give Texago management an optimal plan for shipping crude oil if Galveston is selected as the new site for a refinery in column G of Figure 15.10.

CD 15-36

	A	B	C	D	E	F	G	H	I	J
1		**Texago Corp. Site-Selection Problem (Shipping to Refineries, Including St. Louis)**								
2										
3						Refineries				
4		Unit Cost ($millions)		New Orleans	Charleston	Seattle	St. Louis			
5			Texas	2	4	5	1			
6		Oil	California	5	5	3	4			
7		Fields	Alaska	5	7	3	7			
8			Middle East	2	3	5	4			
9										
10										
11		Shipment Quantity				Refineries				
12		(millions of barrels)		New Orleans	Charleston	Seattle	St. Louis	Total Shipped		Supply
13			Texas	0	0	0	80	80	=	80
14		Oil	California	0	20	0	40	60	=	60
15		Fields	Alaska	20	0	80	0	100	=	100
16			Middle East	80	40	0	0	120	=	120
17			Total Received	100	60	80	120			
18				=	=	=	=			Total Cost
19			Demand	100	60	80	120			($millions)
20										960

Figure 15.13 The changing cells ShipmentQuantity (D13:G16) give Texago management an optimal plan for shipping crude oil if St. Louis is selected as the new site for a refinery in column G of Figure 15.10.

The analysis of the cost of shipping finished product is similar. Figure 15.14 shows the spreadsheet model for this transportation problem, where rows 5–7 come directly from the first three rows of Table 15.18. The *New Site* row would be filled in from one of the next three rows of Table 15.18, depending on which potential site for the new refinery is currently under evaluation. Since the units for finished product leaving a refinery are equivalent to the units for crude oil coming in, the data in Supply (J13:J16) come from the left side of Table 15.16.

The changing cells ShipmentQuantity (D13:G16) in Figures 15.15, 15.16, and 15.17 show the optimal plan for shipping finished product for each of the sites being considered for the new refinery. The objective cell TotalCost (J20) in Figure 15.15 indicates that the resulting total annual cost for shipping finished product if the new refinery were in Los Angeles is $1.57 billion. Similarly, this total cost would be $1.63 billion if Galveston were the chosen site (Figure 15.16) and $1.43 billion if St. Louis were chosen (Figure 15.17).

	A	B	C	D	E	F	G	H	I	J
1	**Texago Corp. Site-Selection Problem (Shipping to D.C.'s)**									
2										
3					Distribution Center					
4		Unit Cost ($millions)		Pittsburgh	Atlanta	Kansas City	San Francisco			
5			New Orleans	6.5	5.5	6	8			
6		Refineries	Charleston	7	5	4	7			
7			Seattle	7	8	4	3			
8			New Site							
9										
10										
11		Shipment Quantity				Distribution Center				
12		(millions of barrels)		Pittsburgh	Atlanta	Kansas City	San Francisco	Total Shipped		Supply
13			New Orleans	0	0	0	0	0	=	100
14		Refineries	Charleston	0	0	0	0	0	=	60
15			Seattle	0	0	0	0	0	=	80
16			New Site	0	0	0	0	0	=	120
17			Total Received	0	0	0	0			
18				=	=	=	=			Total Cost
19			Demand	100	80	80	100			($millions)
20										0

Solver Parameters

Set Objective Cell: TotalCost
To: Min
By Changing Variable Cells:
    ShipmentQuantity
Subject to the Constraints:
    TotalReceived = Demand
    TotalShipped = Supply
Solver Options:
    Make Variables Nonnegative
    Solving Method: Simplex LP

Range Name	Cells
Demand	D19:G19
ShipmentQuantity	D13:G16
Supply	J13:J16
TotalCost	J20
TotalReceived	D17:G17
TotalShipped	H13:H16
UnitCost	D5:G8

	H
12	Total Shipped
13	=SUM(D13:G13)
14	=SUM(D14:G14)
15	=SUM(D15:G15)
16	=SUM(D16:G16)

	C	D	E	F	G
17	Total Received	=SUM(D13:D16)	=SUM(E13:E16)	=SUM(F13:F16)	=SUM(G13:G16)

	J
18	Total Cost
19	($millions)
20	=SUMPRODUCT(UnitCost,ShipmentQuantity)

Figure 15.14   The basic spreadsheet formulation for the Texago transportation problem for shipping finished product from the refineries (including the new one at a site still to be selected) to the distribution centers. The objective cell is TotalCost (J20) and the other output cells are TotalShipped (H13:H16) and TotalReceived (D17:G17). Before entering the data for a new site and solving, a trial solution of 0 has been entered into each of the changing cells ShipmentQuantity (D13:G16).

	A	B	C	D	E	F	G	H	I	J
1		**Texago Corp. Site-Selection Problem (Shipping to D.C.'s When Choose Los Angeles)**								
2										
3					Distribution Center					
4		Unit Cost ($millions)		Pittsburgh	Atlanta	Kansas City	San Francisco			
5			New Orleans	6.5	5.5	6	8			
6		Refineries	Charleston	7	5	4	7			
7			Seattle	7	8	4	3			
8			Los Angeles	8	6	3	2			
9										
10										
11		Shipment Quantity			Distribution Center					
12		(millions of barrels)		Pittsburgh	Atlanta	Kansas City	San Francisco	Total Shipped		Supply
13			New Orleans	80	20	0	0	100	=	100
14		Refineries	Charleston	0	60	0	0	60	=	60
15			Seattle	20	0	0	60	80	=	80
16			Los Angeles	0	0	80	40	120	=	120
17			Total Received	100	80	80	100			
18				=	=	=	=			
19			Demand	100	80	80	100			Total Cost
20										($millions)
										1,570

Figure 15.15   The changing cells ShipmentQuantity (D13:G16) give Texago management an optimal plan for shipping finished product if Los Angeles is selected as the new site for a refinery in rows 8 and 16 of Figure 15.14.

	A	B	C	D	E	F	G	H	I	J
1		**Texago Corp. Site-Selection Problem (Shipping to D.C.'s When Choose Galveston)**								
2										
3					Distribution Center					
4		Unit Cost ($millions)		Pittsburgh	Atlanta	Kansas City	San Francisco			
5			New Orleans	6.5	5.5	6	8			
6		Refineries	Charleston	7	5	4	7			
7			Seattle	7	8	4	3			
8			Galveston	5	4	3	6			
9										
10										
11		Shipment Quantity			Distribution Center					
12		(millions of barrels)		Pittsburgh	Atlanta	Kansas City	San Francisco	Total Shipped		Supply
13			New Orleans	100	0	0	0	100	=	100
14		Refineries	Charleston	0	60	0	0	60	=	60
15			Seattle	0	0	0	80	80	=	80
16			Galveston	0	20	80	20	120	=	120
17			Total Received	100	80	80	100			
18				=	=	=	=			
19			Demand	100	80	80	100			Total Cost
20										($millions)
										1,630

Figure 15.16   The changing cells ShipmentQuantity (D13:G16) give Texago management an optimal plan for shippig finished product if Galveston is selected as the new site for a refinery in rows 8 and 16 of Figure 15.14.

CD 15-39

	A	B	C	D	E	F	G	H	I	J
1		**Texago Corp. Site-Selection Problem (Shipping to D.C.'s When Choose St. Louis)**								
2										
3					Distribution Center					
4		Unit Cost ($millions)		Pittsburgh	Atlanta	Kansas City	San Francisco			
5			New Orleans	6.5	5.5	6	8			
6		Refineries	Charleston	7	5	4	7			
7			Seattle	7	8	4	3			
8			St. Louis	4	3	1	5			
9										
10										
11		Shipment Quantity			Distribution Center					
12		(millions of barrels)		Pittsburgh	Atlanta	Kansas City	San Francisco	Total Shipped		Supply
13			New Orleans	100	0	0	0	100	=	100
14		Refineries	Charleston	0	60	0	0	60	=	60
15			Seattle	0	0	0	80	80	=	80
16			St. Louis	0	20	80	20	120	=	120
17			Total Received	100	80	80	100			
18				=	=	=	=			Total Cost
19			Demand	100	80	80	100			($millions)
20										1,430

Figure 15.17   The changing cells ShipmentQuantity (D13:G16) give Texago management an optimal plan for shipping product if St. Louis is selected as the new site for a refinery in rows 8 and 16 of Figure 15.14.

For each of the three alternative sites, two separate spreadsheet models have been used for planning the shipping of crude oil and the shipping of finished product. However, another option would have been to combine all this planning into a single spreadsheet model for each site and then to simultaneously optimize the plans for the two types of shipments. This would essentially involve combining Figure 15.11 with Figure 15.15, Figure 15.12 with Figure 15.16, and Figure 15.13 with Figure 15.17, and then using the sum of the shipping costs for the pair of transportation problems as the objective cell to be minimized. This would have the advantage of showing all the shipment planning for a given site on a single spreadsheet. At the end of the chapter, Case 15-1 will continue this Texago case study by considering a situation where this kind of combined spreadsheet model is needed to find the best overall shipping plan for each possible choice of a site.

The Message to Management

The task force now has completed its financial analysis of the three alternative sites for the new refinery. Table 15.20 shows all the major *variable* costs (costs that vary with the decision) on an annual basis that would result from each of the three possible choices for the new site. The second column summarizes what the total annual cost of shipping crude oil to all refineries (including the new one) would be for each alternative (as already given in Figures 15.11, 15.12, and 15.13). The third column repeats the data in Figures 15.15, 15.16, and 15.17 on the total annual cost of shipping finished product from the refineries to the distribution centers. The fourth column shows the estimated operating costs for a refinery at each potential site, as first given in Table 15.19.

Table 15.20   Annual Variable Costs Resulting from the Choice of Each Site for the New Texago Refinery

Site	Total Cost of Shipping Crude Oil	Total Cost of Shipping Finished Product	Operating Cost for New Refinery	Total Variable Cost
Los Angeles	$880 million	$1.57 billion	$620 million	$3.07 billion
Galveston	920 million	1.63 billion	570 million	3.12 billion
St. Louis	960 million	1.43 billion	530 million	2.92 billion

Adding across these three columns gives the total variable cost for each alternative.

> *Conclusion:* From a purely financial viewpoint, St. Louis is the best site for the new refinery. This site would save the company about $200 million annually as compared to the Galveston alternative and about $150 million as compared to the Los Angeles alternative.

However, as with any site selection decision, management must consider a wide variety of factors, including some nonfinancial ones. (For example, remember that one important advantage of the Galveston site is that it is close to corporate headquarters.) Furthermore, if ways can be found to reduce some of the costs in Table 15.20 for either the Los Angeles or Galveston sites, this might change the financial evaluation substantially. Management also must consider whether there are any cost trends or trends in the marketplace that might alter the picture in the future.

After careful consideration, Texago management tentatively chooses the St. Louis site. (This story continues in Case 15-1, where the task force is asked to analyze the option of enlarging the capacity of the new refinery before the final decision is made on its site.)

REVIEW QUESTIONS

1. What are the three key factors for management's decision on the location of the new refinery?
2. Why do shipping costs to and from the *current* refineries need to be considered along with those for the new refinery?
3. Why did the Texago task force find it necessary to solve six transportation problems instead of just one?
4. What else must Texago management consider in addition to the financial analysis based on solving?

15.6 CHARACTERISTICS OF ASSIGNMENT PROBLEMS

We now turn to another special type of linear programming problem (first introduced in Section 3.6) called *assignment problems*. As the name suggests, this kind of problem involves making *assignments*. Frequently,these are assignments of people to jobs. Thus, many applications of the assignment problem involve aiding managers in matching up their personnel with tasks to be performed. Other applications might instead involve assigning machines, vehicles, or plants to tasks.

The Sellmore Company problem presented in Section 3.6 is a prototype example of an assignment problem. For completeness, we begin with this same example.

CD 15-41

An Example: The Sellmore Company Problem

The marketing manager of the Sellmore Company will be holding the company's annual sales conference soon for sales regional managers and personnel. To assist in the administration of the conference, he is hiring four temporary employees (Ann, Ian, Joan, and Sean), where each will handle one of the following four tasks:

1. Word processing of written presentations.

2. Computer graphics for both oral and written presentations.

3. Preparation of conference packets, including copying and organizing written materials.

4. Handling of advance and on-site registrations for the conference.

He now needs to decide which person to assign to each task.

Although each temporary employee has at least the minimal background necessary to perform any of the four tasks, they differ considerably in how efficiently they can handle the different types of work. Table 15.21 shows how many hours each would need for each task. The rightmost column gives the hourly wage based on the background of each employee.

Formulation of a Spreadsheet Model

Figure 15.18 shows a spreadsheet model for this problem. Table 15.21 is entered at the top. Combining these required times and wages gives the cost (cells D15:G18) for each possible assignment of a temporary employee to a task, using equations shown at the bottom of Figure 15.18. This *cost table* is just the way that any assignment problem is displayed. The objective is to determine which assignments should be made to minimize the sum of the associated costs.

Table 15.21   Data for the Sellmore Co. Problem

Temporary Employee	Required Time per Task (Hours)				Hourly Wage
	Word Processing	Graphics	Packets	Registrations	
Ann	35	41	27	40	$14
Ian	47	45	32	51	12
Joan	39	56	36	43	13
Sean	32	51	25	46	15

CD 15-42

	A	B	C	D	E	F	G	H	I	J
1	**Sellmore Co. Assignment Problem**									
2										
3						Task				
4		**Required Time**			Word					Hourly
5		**(Hours)**			Processing	Graphics	Packets	Registrations		Wage
6				Ann	35	41	27	40		$14
7			Assignee	Ian	47	45	32	51		$12
8				Joan	39	56	36	43		$13
9				Sean	32	51	25	46		$15
10										
11										
12						Task				
13					Word					
14		**Cost**			Processing	Graphics	Packets	Registrations		
15				Ann	$490	$574	$378	$560		
16			Assignee	Ian	$564	$540	$384	$612		
17				Joan	$507	$728	$468	$559		
18				Sean	$480	$765	$375	$690		
19										
20										
21						Task				
22					Word				Total	
23		**Assignment**			Processing	Graphics	Packets	Registrations	Assignments	Supply
24				Ann	0	0	1	0	1	=	1
25			Assignee	Ian	0	1	0	0	1	=	1
26				Joan	0	0	0	1	1	=	1
27				Sean	1	0	0	0	1	=	1
28			Total Assigned		1	1	1	1			
29					=	=	=	=			Total Cost
30				Demand	1	1	1	1			$1,957

Solver Parameters

Set Objective Cell: TotalCost
To: Min
By Changing Variable Cells:
    Assignment
Subject to the Constraints:
    TotalAssigned = Demand
    TotalAssignments = Supply
Solver Options:
    Make Variables Nonnegative
    Solving Method: Simplex LP

	H
22	Total
23	Assignments
24	=SUM(D24:G24)
25	=SUM(D25:G25)
26	=SUM(D26:G26)
27	=SUM(D27:G27)

Range Name	Cells
Assignment	D24:G27
Cost	D15:G18
Demand	D30:G30
HourlyWage	I6:I9
RequiredTime	D6:G9
Supply	J24:J27
TotalAssigned	D28:G28
TotalAssignments	H24:H27
TotalCost	J30

	J
29	Total Cost
30	=SUMPRODUCT(Cost,Assignment)

	C	D	E	F	G
28	Total Assigned	=SUM(D24:D27)	=SUM(E24:E27)	=SUM(F24:F27)	=SUM(G24:G27)

Figure 15.18 A spreadsheet formulation of the Sellmore Co. problem as an assignment problem, including the objective cell TotalCost (J30) and the other output cells Cost (D15:G18), TotalAssignments (H24:H27), and Total Assigned (D28:G28), as well as the specifications needed to set up the model. The values of 1 in the changing cells Assignment (D24:G27) show the optimal plan obtained by Solver for assigning the people to the tasks.

The values of 1 in Supply (J24:J27) indicate that each person (assignee) listed in column C must perform exactly one task. The values of 1 in Demand (D30:G30) indicate that each task must be performed by exactly one person. These requirements then are specified in the constraints given in the Solver Parameters box.

Each of the changing cells Assignment (D24:G27) is given a value of 1 when the corresponding assignment is being made, and a value of 0 otherwise. Therefore, the Excel equation for the objective cell, TotalCost = SUMPRODUCT(Cost, Assignment), gives the total cost for the assignments being made. The Solver Parameters box specifies that the objective is to minimize this objective cell.

The changing cells in Figure 15.18 show the optimal solution obtained after running Solver. This solution is

Assign Ann to prepare conference packets.

Assign Ian to do the computer graphics.

Assign Joan to handle registrations.

Assign Sean to do the word processing.

The total cost given in cell J30 is $1,957.

The Model for Assignment Problems

Any assignment problem can be described in the following general terms. Given a set of **tasks** to be performed and a set of **assignees** who are available to perform these tasks, the problem is to determine which assignee should be assigned to each task.

To fit the model for an assignment problem, the following assumptions need to be satisfied:

1. The number of assignees and the number of tasks are the same.

2. Each assignee is to be assigned to exactly *one* task.

3. Each task is to be performed by exactly *one* assignee.

4. There is a cost associated with each combination of an assignee performing a task.

5. The objective is to determine how all the assignments should be made to minimize the total cost.

The first three assumptions are fairly restrictive. Many potential applications do not quite fit these assumptions. However, these *variants* of assignment problems still can be solved by Solver, as we will describe in Section 15.7.

When the assumptions are satisfied, all that needs to be done to formulate a problem as an assignment problem is to (1) identify the assignees and tasks and (2) construct a **cost table** that gives the cost associated with each combination of an assignee performing a task. Figure 15.18 illustrates how to display this formulation on a spreadsheet. The spreadsheet model for any assignment problem will include constraints to enforce assumptions 2 and 3. In Figure 15.18, these constraints are TotalAssignments (H24:H27) = Supply (J24:J27) and TotalAssigned (D28:G28) = Demand (D30:G30), where values of 1 are entered in the data cells Supply (J24:J27) and Demand (D30:G30).

The Network Representation of an Assignment Problem

In addition to a cost table, the *network representation* provides an alternative way of displaying an assignment problem. Figure 15.19 shows the network representation of the Sellmore Co.

assignment problem, where all the assignees are lined up in order on the left and all the tasks are lined up in order on the right. The arrows show the possible assignments, where exactly four arrows are to be chosen—one emanating from each assignee and one leading to each task. The number next to each arrow gives the cost if that particular assignment is chosen.

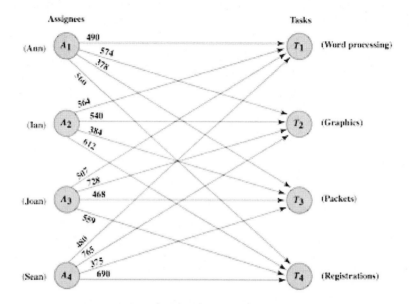

| **Figure 15.19** | The network representation of the Sellmore Co. assignment problem shows all the possible assignments and their costs graphically. |

This network representation provides a way of visualizing an assignment problem graphically. This representation also can be used to clarify the relationship between assignment problems and the other network optimization problems considered in Chapter 6.

The Assignment Problem Is a Special Type of Transportation Problem

Did you happen to notice that the network representation in Figure 15.19 is strikingly similar to the network representation for a transportation problem shown in Figure 15.3? Look and see.

This similarity is no coincidence. The assignment problem is, in fact, just a special type of transportation problem where the *sources* now are *assignees* and the *destinations* now are *tasks*. Furthermore, as illustrated by the Sellmore Co. assignment problem in Figure 15.18, every source has a supply of 1 (since each assignee is to be assigned to exactly one task) and every destination has a demand of 1 (since each task is to be performed by exactly one assignee).

Therefore, all the characteristics of transportation problems described in Section 15.2 also apply to assignment problems.

Solving Assignment Problems

Solver uses the simplex method to solve any kind of linear programming problem, including both transportation problems and assignment problems and their variants. This works fine for problems of the size considered in this book (or even considerably larger).

CD 15-45

However, as discussed in Section 15.2, either the *transportation simplex method* or the *network simplex method* provides a far more efficient way of solving big transportation problems. Consequently, since the assignment problem is a special type of transportation problem, these same algorithms can be used to solve big assignment problems quickly.

Nevertheless, even these special algorithms do not provide the fastest way of solving assignment problems. There are much faster algorithms available that have been designed specifically to solve assignment problems. The most famous of these is called the **Hungarian method.** In practice, one of these special algorithms normally would be used to solve large assignment problems. Although Solver does not have *special-purpose algorithms* such as the Hungarian method for efficiently solving special types of linear programming problems, other linear programming software packages are available that do.

REVIEW QUESTIONS

1. Give a one-sentence description of assignment problems.
2. What assumptions about *assignees* and *tasks* need to hold for a problem to be an assignment problem?
3. What needs to be done to formulate a problem as an assignment problem?
4. What are the sources, destinations, supplies, and demands when an assignment problem is described as a special kind of transportation problem?
5. Name an algorithm that has been designed specifically just to solve assignment problems very quickly.

15.7 MODELING VARIANTS OF ASSIGNMENT PROBLEMS

Variants of assignment problems frequently arise because they have one or more features that do not quite fit all the assumptions enumerated in the preceding section for the model of an assignment problem. The features we will consider are the following:

1. Certain assignees are unable to perform certain tasks.

2. Although each assignee will perform exactly one task, there are more tasks than assignees, so some tasks will not be done.

3. Although each task will be performed by exactly one assignee, there are more assignees than tasks, so some assignees will not perform any task.

4. Each assignee can be assigned to perform more than one task simultaneously.

5. Each task can be performed jointly by more than one assignee.

For each of these features, there is a clever way of reformulating the problem to make it fit the format for an assignment problem, which then enables using an extremely efficient special purpose algorithm (such as the *Hungarian method*). However, this isn't necessary except on problems that are much larger than any considered in this book. Therefore, we instead will formulate a spreadsheet model in the most straightforward way and solve it with Solver.

Three examples are presented below to illustrate the above features. The first example focuses on features 1 and 2. The second combines feature 4 with a variation of feature 3. The third deals with feature 5.

To illuminate the close relationships between transportation problems and assignment problems, the second and third examples are based on earlier examples of variants of transportation problems.

Example 1: Assigning Machines to Locations

The Job Shop Company has purchased three new machines of different types. There are five available locations in the shop where a machine could be installed. Some of these locations are more desirable than others for particular machines because of their proximity to work centers that will have a heavy workflow to and from these machines. (There will be no workflow *between* the new machines.) Therefore, the objective is to assign the new machines to the available locations to minimize the total cost of materials handling. The estimated cost per hour of materials handling involving each of the machines is given in Table 15.22 for the respective locations. Location 2 is not considered suitable for machine 2, so no cost is given for this case.

Table 15.22   Materials-Handling Cost Data for the Job Shop Co. Problem

	Cost per Hour				
Location:	**1**	**2**	**3**	**4**	**5**
Machine					
1	$13	$16	$12	$14	$15
2	15	—	13	20	16
3	4	7	10	6	7

Formulation of a Spreadsheet Model

As it stands, this is almost an assignment problem, since the machines can be viewed as *assignees* to be assigned to locations as the *tasks*. However, it does not quite qualify because assumption 1 for the assignment problem model is violated (we have two more locations than machines), as are assumption 3 (two locations will not be filled by a machine) and assumption 4 (we do not have a cost associated with assigning machine 2 to location 2).

Figure 15.20 shows a spreadsheet model for this variant of an assignment problem. Because location 2 cannot be used for machine 2, the Solver Parameters box includes the constraint that D12 = 0. The usual supply constraints, TotalAssignments (H11:H13) = Supply (J11:J13), ensure that each machine will be assigned to exactly one location. The fact that two locations will not be used is taken into account by using a $\leq$ sign in the demand constraints, TotalAssigned (C14:G14) $\leq$ Demand (C16:G16).

CD 15-47

	A	B	C	D	E	F	G	H	I	J
1		**Job Shop Co. Machine-Location Problem**								
2										
3		Cost ($/hour)	Location 1	Location 2	Location 3	Location 4	Location 5			
4		Machine 1	13	16	12	14	15			
5		Machine 2	15	-	13	20	16			
6		Machine 3	4	7	10	6	7			
7										
8										
9								Total		
10		Assignment	Location 1	Location 2	Location 3	Location 4	Location 5	Assignments		Supply
11		Machine 1	0	0	0	1	0	1	=	1
12		Machine 2	0	0	1	0	0	1	=	1
13		Machine 3	1	0	0	0	0	1	=	1
14		Total Assigned	1	0	1	1	0			
15			<=	<=	<=	<=	<=			Total Cost
16		Demand	1	1	1	1	1			($/hour)
17										31

Solver Parameters

Set Objective Cell: TotalCost
To: Min
By Changing Variable Cells:
   Assignment
Subject to the Constraints:
   D12 = 0
   TotalAssigned <= Demand
   TotalAssignments = Supply
Solver Options:
   Make Variables Nonnegative
   Solving Method: Simplex LP

Range Name	**Cells**
Assignment	C11:G13
Cost	C4:G6
Demand	C16:G16
Supply	J11:J13
TotalAssigned	C14:G14
TotalAssignments	H11:H13
TotalCost	J17

	H
9	Total
10	Assignments
11	=SUM(C11:G11)
12	=SUM(C12:G12)
13	=SUM(C13:G13)

	B	C	D	E	F	G
14	Total Assigned	=SUM(C11:C13)	=SUM(D11:D13)	=SUM(E11:E13)	=SUM(F11:F13)	=SUM(G11:G13)

	J
15	Total Cost
16	($/hour)
17	=SUMPRODUCT(Cost,Assignment)

Figure 15.20   A spreadsheet formulation of the Job Shop Co. problem as a variant of an assignment problem, including the objective cell TotalCost (J17) and the other output cells TotalAssignments (H11:H13) and TotalAssigned (C14:G14), as well as the specifications needed to set up the model. The values of 1 in the changing cells Assignment (C11:G13) show the optimal plan obtained by Solver for assigning the machines to the locations.

The changing cells Assignment (C11:G13) with a value of 1 show the assignments being made in the optimal solution after running Solver. Since none of these cells for locations 2 and 5 have a value of 1, a machine will not be placed in either of these locations. The objective cell TotalCost (J17) indicates that the total cost for this optimal solution is $31 per hour.

Example 2: Assigning Plants to Products

Reconsider Example 1 in Section 15.3, where the Better Products Co. needs to assign three plants to produce four new products. The relevant data are given in Table 15.6.

As described in Section 15.3, management had permitted *product splitting* (where the same product is produced in more than one plant). However, there are some *hidden costs* associated with product splitting that are not reflected in Table 15.6, including extra setup, distribution, and administration costs. Therefore, management now has decided to have the problem analyzed again under the additional restriction that *product splitting is prohibited*.

> New Problem Statement: Given the data in Table 15.6, minimize the total cost of assigning each plant to at least one new product where each product is to be produced in only one plant (no product splitting). Since there are three plants and four new products, two plants will produce one new product and a third plant will produce two. Only plants 1 and 2 have the capacity to produce two.

Formulation of a Spreadsheet Model

Since we want to assign plants to products, the plants can be viewed as *assignees* and the products as the *tasks* to be performed for this variant of an assignment problem. Figure 15.21 shows the resulting spreadsheet model.

CD 15-49

	A	B	C	D	E	F	G	H	I
1		Better Products Co. Production Planning Problem (Revised)							
2									
3		Unit Cost	Product 1	Product 2	Product 3	Product 4			
4		Plant 1	$41	$27	$28	$24			
5		Plant 2	$40	$29	-	$23			
6		Plant 3	$37	$30	$27	$21			
7									
8		Required Production	20	30	30	40			
9									
10									
11		Cost ($/day)	Product 1	Product 2	Product 3	Product 4			
12		Plant 1	$820	$810	$840	$960			
13		Plant 2	$800	$870	-	$920			
14		Plant 3	$740	$900	$810	$840			
15									
16									
17							Total		
18		Assignment	Product 1	Product 2	Product 3	Product 4	Assignments		Supply
19		Plant 1	0	1	1	0	2	<=	2
20		Plant 2	1	0	0	0	1	<=	2
21		Plant 3	0	0	0	1	1	=	1
22		Total Assigned	1	1	1	1			
23			=	=	=	=			Total Cost
24		Demand	1	1	1	1			$3,290

Range Name	Cells
Assignment	C19:F21
Cost	C12:F14
Demand	C24:F24
RequiredProduction	C8:F8
Supply	I19:I21
TotalAssigned	C22:F22
TotalAssignments	G19:G21
TotalCost	I24
UnitCost	C4:F6

	G
17	Total
18	Assignments
19	=SUM(C19:F19)
20	=SUM(C20:F20)
21	=SUM(C21:F21)

	B	C	D	E	F
22	Total Assigned	=SUM(C19:C21)	=SUM(D19:D21)	=SUM(E19:E21)	=SUM(F19:F21)

	I
23	Total Cost
24	=SUMPRODUCT(Cost,Assignment)

Figure 15.21 In contrast to Figure 15.4, product splitting is not allowed, so the Better Products Co. problem becomes a variant of an assignment problem. The objective cell is TotalCost (I24) and the other output cells are Cost (C12:F14), TotalAssignments (G19:G21), and TotalAssigned(C22:F22), where the equations entered into these cells are shown below the spreadsheet. The values of 1 in the changing cells Assignment (C19:F21) display the optimal production plan obtained by Solver.

The data from Table 15.6 are given at the top. However, the unit costs given in cells C4:F6 are not the appropriate costs for the cost table for a variant of an assignment problem. To construct the appropriate cost table, we must determine each cost associated with assigning a plant to *all* the required production of a product. The corresponding unit cost shown in rows 4–6 is the cost of producing only one unit rather than the entire required (daily) production given in row 8. Therefore, we must multiply this unit cost by the required (daily) production to obtain the total (daily) cost of the assignment. For example, consider the assignment of Plant 1 to product 1.

Cost of Plant 1 producing one unit of product 1   = \$41

Required (daily) production of product 1   = 20 units

Total (daily) cost of assigning Plant 1 to product 1   = 20 (\$41)

                                                  = \$820

Cost(C12:F14) gives the total (daily) assignment costs, calculated in this way (see the equations at the bottom of the figure), for each combination of assigning a plant to a product.

Since Plant 2 cannot produce product 3, the Solver Parameters box includes the constraint that E20 = 0. Either Plant 1 or Plant 2 (but not both) needs to be chosen to produce a second product, so these two plants are given a supply of 2 in cells I19:I20. A ≤ sign is then used for the corresponding supply constraints, G19:G20 ≤ I19:I20. However, the supply constraint for Plant 3 and the demand constraints are the usual ones for an assignment problem.

After running Solver, the optimal solution shown in the changing cells Assignment (C19:F21) is obtained, namely, Plant 1 produces products 2 and 3, Plant 2 produces product 1, and Plant 3 produces product 4. The objective cell TotalCost (I24) gives the total daily cost of \$3,290 for this production plan.

It is interesting to compare this solution with the one given in DailyProduction (C11:F13) of Figure 15.4 when product splitting was permitted. Note that the assignments for plants 2 and 3 in Figure 15.4 are quite different than here. The total cost calculated for the production plan shown in that figure is \$3,260 per day, or \$30 per day less than for the plan in Figure 15.21.

However, the formulation of the original problem (product splitting permitted) as a variant of a transportation problem does not take into account *hidden costs* of product splitting (extra setup, distribution, and administration costs), which probably are considerably more than \$30 per day. Therefore, management adopted the production plan based on this new formulation (product splitting prohibited) as a variant of an assignment problem.

Example 3: Designing School Attendance Zones

Now refer back to Section 15.4 for the problem faced by the management of the Middletown School District in designing school attendance zones. Table 15.12 gives the data for the problem and Figure 15.8 shows its formulation as a variant of a transportation problem.

The optimal solution obtained from this formulation has two problems that concern management. One is that this solution splits tract 5 between two schools (schools 1 and 2). Each tract is a cohesive neighborhood that has always stayed together in attending the same school prior to high school. The school district superintendent and the school board are in agreement that it would be much better to continue to keep each neighborhood (including tract 5) together in assigning it to a single school. The second problem with the solution is that it assigns the smallest number of students (1,200) to the school with the largest capacity (school 1, with a capacity of 1,800 students). Although this is marginally acceptable (the school board has chosen 1,200 as the minimum number of students it would allow to be assigned to school 1), a more even allocation of students to the schools would be preferable.

CD 15-51

Therefore, the school district management has decided to prohibit splitting any tract between schools. To provide a relatively even allocation of students to schools, management also will require that exactly three tracts be assigned to each school.

New Problem Statement: Given the data in Table 15.12, minimize the total distance that all students must travel to school when each tract is assigned entirely to one school (no tract splitting) and each school is assigned exactly three tracts.

Formulation of a Spreadsheet Model

Since tracts are being assigned to schools, this problem can be interpreted as a variant of an assignment problem where the tracts are the *assignees* and the schools are the *tasks*. It is only a variant because each school is to be assigned exactly three tracts, whereas assumption 3 for the assignment problem model specifies that each task is to be performed by exactly *one* assignee. Therefore, in the spreadsheet model shown in Figure 15.22, each task (school) is given a demand of 3 rather than 1. Otherwise, the constraints for this model are the same as for an assignment problem.

	A	B	C	D	E	F	G	H	I	J	K
1		**Middletown School District Zoning Problem (Revised)**									
2											
3		Distance				Number of		Cost			
4		(Miles)	School 1	School 2	School 3	Students		(Miles)	School 1	School 2	School 3
5		Tract 1	2.2	1.9	2.5	500		Tract 1	1100	950	1250
6		Tract 2	1.4	1.3	1.7	400		Tract 2	560	520	680
7		Tract 3	0.5	1.8	1.1	450		Tract 3	225	810	495
8		Tract 4	1.2	0.3	2	400		Tract 4	480	120	800
9		Tract 5	0.9	0.7	1	500		Tract 5	450	350	500
10		Tract 6	1.1	1.6	0.6	450		Tract 6	495	720	270
11		Tract 7	2.7	0.7	1.5	450		Tract 7	1215	315	675
12		Tract 8	1.8	1.2	0.8	400		Tract 8	720	480	320
13		Tract 9	1.5	1.7	0.7	500		Tract 9	750	850	350
14											
15											
16						Total					
17		Assignment	School 1	School 2	School 3	Assignments		Supply			
18		Tract 1	0	1	0	1	=	1			
19		Tract 2	1	0	0	1	=	1			
20		Tract 3	1	0	0	1	=	1			
21		Tract 4	0	1	0	1	=	1			
22		Tract 5	1	0	0	1	=	1			
23		Tract 6	0	0	1	1	=	1			
24		Tract 7	0	1	0	1	=	1			
25		Tract 8	0	0	1	1	=	1			
26		Tract 9	0	0	1	1	=	1			
27		Total Assigned	3	3	3						
28			=	=	=			Total Distance			
29		Demand	3	3	3			(Miles)			
30								3560			

Figure 15.22 continued

Solver Parameters
Set Objective Cell: TotalDistance
To: Min
By Changing Variable Cells:
Assignment
Subject to the Constraints:
TotalAssigned = Demand
TotalAssignments = Supply
Solver Options:
Make Variables Nonnegative
Solving Method: Simplex LP

Range Name	Cells
Assignment	C18:E26
Cost	I5:K13
Demand	C29:E29
Distance	C5:E13
NumberOfStudents	F5:F13
Supply	H18:H26
TotalAssigned	C27:E27
TotalAssignments	F18:F26
TotalDistance	H30

	H	I	J	K
3	**Cost**			
4	**(Miles)**	School 1	School 2	School 3
5	Tract 1	=C5*F5	=D5*F5	=E5*F5
6	Tract 2	=C6*F6	=D6*F6	=E6*F6
7	Tract 3	=C7*F7	=D7*F7	=E7*F7
8	Tract 4	=C8*F8	=D8*F8	=E8*F8
9	Tract 5	=C9*F9	=D9*F9	=E9*F9
10	Tract 6	=C10*F10	=D10*F10	=E10*F10
11	Tract 7	=C11*F11	=D11*F11	=E11*F11
12	Tract 8	=C12*F12	=D12*F12	=E12*F12
13	Tract 9	=C13*F13	=D13*F13	=E13*F13

	F
16	Total
17	Assignments
18	=SUM(C18:E18)
19	=SUM(C19:E19)
20	=SUM(C20:E20)
21	=SUM(C21:E21)
22	=SUM(C22:E22)
23	=SUM(C23:E23)
24	=SUM(C24:E24)
25	=SUM(C25:E25)
26	=SUM(C26:E26)

	H
28	Total Distance
29	(Miles)
30	=SUMPRODUCT(Cost,Assignment)

	B	C	D	E
27	Total Assigned	=SUM(C18:C26)	=SUM(D18:D26)	=SUM(E18:E26)

Figure 15.22	In contrast to Figure 15.8, tract splitting is no longer allowed, so the Middletown School District problem becomes a variant of an assignment problem. The objective cell is TotalDistance (H30) and the other output cells are TotalAssignments (F18:26), TotalAssigned (C27: E27), and (in units of miles) Cost (I5:K13), where the equations entered into these cells are shown after the spreadsheet. The values of 1 in the changing cells Assignment (C18:E26) show the optimal zoning plan found by Solver.

The objective for an assignment problem is to minimize the total cost of all the assignments made, but now *cost* is being measured in terms of the total *distance* that students travel. Therefore, the cost of assigning any tract to a particular school is the number of students in that tract *times* the distance to that school per student, where both of these quantities are given in the table called Distance (C5:E13) in Figure 15.22. To illustrate, consider the cost of assigning tract 1 to school 1.

CD 15-53

Distance from tract 1 to school 1   = 2.2 miles

Number of students in tract 1   = 500

Cost of assigning tract 1 to school 1   = 500(2.2 miles)

                                      = 1,100 miles

The table called Cost (I5:K13) shows the costs calculated in this way for all the combinations of tracts and schools, using the equations given for these cells.

The changing cells Assignment (C18:E26) show the optimal assignments of tracts to schools obtained by running Solver. As indicated in the objective cell TotalDistance (H30), the resulting total distance traveled to school by all the students is 3,560 miles. This amounts to an average of 0.879 mile per student.

This plan is very similar to the one obtained in Section 15.4 (see Figure 15.8) when tract splitting was permitted. The only difference is that the earlier plan splits tract 5, with 150 of its 500 students assigned to school 2 rather than to school 1, thereby reducing the distance traveled to school for each of these 150 students from 0.9 mile to 0.7 mile. However, the school district management feels that this small saving in distance traveled does not justify separating these 150 students from their neighbors who had always gone to school with them. Therefore, management adopted the new plan.

As this example and the preceding one illustrate, management often needs to have modifications made in the original model of the problem to better consider managerial concerns.

REVIEW QUESTIONS

1. When formulating a spreadsheet model for a variant of an assignment problem where certain assignees are unable to perform certain tasks, how is this feature formulated in the model?
2. If an assignee will perform more than one task, how is this feature formulated in the spreadsheet model?
3. If a task will be performed jointly by more than one assignee, how is this feature formulated in the spreadsheet model?

15.8 SUMMARY

Transportation problems and assignment problems (and their variants) are special types of linear programming problems that have a variety of important applications.

A transportation problem is concerned (literally or figuratively) with distributing a commodity from its *sources* to some *destinations*. Each source has a fixed supply and each destination has a fixed demand for the commodity. A basic assumption is that the cost of distribution from each source to each destination is directly proportional to the amount distributed. Formulating a transportation problem requires identifying the unit costs of distribution, the supplies, and the demands.

Given a set of *tasks* to be performed and a set of *assignees* who are available to perform the tasks (one assignee per task), an assignment problem deals with the question of which assignee should be assigned to each task so as to minimize the total cost of performing all the tasks. The assignees can be people, machines, vehicles, plants, and so on, so there are many applications. The formulation of the problem requires constructing a *cost table* that gives the cost for each possible assignment of an assignee to a task.

A variety of features that do not quite fit either the transportation problem format or the assignment problem format also can be readily formulated in a spreadsheet model.

The overriding goal of this chapter has been to enable you to recognize when a problem you might face as a future manager can be formulated and analyzed as a transportation or assignment problem, or as a variant of one of these problem types.

Glossary

assignees The entities (people, machines, vehicles, plants, etc.) that are to perform the tasks when formulating a problem as an assignment problem. (Section 15.6)

cost table The table that summarizes the formulation of an assignment problem by giving the cost for each possible assignment of an assignee to a task. (Section 15.6)

demand at a destination The number of units that need to be received by this destination from the sources. (Section 15.2)

destinations The receiving centers for a transportation problem. (Section 15.2)

Hungarian method An algorithm designed specifically to solve assignment problems very efficiently. (Section 15.6)

network simplex method A streamlined version of the simplex method for solving distribution-network problems, including transportation and assignment problems, very efficiently. (Section 15.2)

sources The supply centers for a transportation problem. (Section 15.2)

supply from a source The number of units to be distributed from this source to the destinations. (Section 15.2)

tasks The jobs to be performed by the assignees when formulating a problem as an assignment problem. (Section 15.6)

transportation simplex method A streamlined version of the simplex method for solving transportation problems very efficiently. (Section 15.2)

Learning Aids for This Chapter in Your MS Courseware

Chapter 15 Excel Files:

P & T Case Study	*Energetic Example*
Better Products Example	*Texago Case Study* (6 spreadsheets)
Nifty Example	*Sellmore Example*
Metro Example	*Job Shop Example*
Northern Airplane Example	*Revised Better Products Example*
Middletown Example	*Revised Middletown Example*

An Excel Add-in:

Risk Solver Platform for Education

Problems

We have inserted the symbol E* to the left of each problem (or its parts) where Excel should be used (unless your instructor gives you contrary instructions). An asterisk on the problem number indicates that at least a partial answer is given at the end of the problems.

15.1.   Consider the transportation problem having the following data:

		Unit Cost ($)			
Destination:		1	2	3	Supply
Source					
1		9	6	8	4
2		7	12	10	3
3		6	7	6	2
Demand		4	2	3	

    a. Draw the network representation of this problem.

E*   *b.* Display the problem on a spreadsheet and then use the Excel Solver to obtain an optimal solution.

15.2.   Consider the transportation problem having the following data:

		Unit Cost ($)				
Destination:		1	2	3	4	Supply
Source						
1		3	7	6	4	5
2		2	4	3	2	2
3		4	3	8	5	3
Demand		3	3	2	2	

    a. Draw the network representation of this problem.

E*   *b.* Display the problem on a spreadsheet and then use the Excel Solver to obtain an optimal solution.

15.3. The Cost-Less Corp. supplies its four retail outlets from its four plants. The shipping cost per shipment from each plant to each retail outlet is given below.

	Unit Shipping Cost			
Retail Outlet:	1	2	3	4
Plant				
1	$500	$600	$400	$200
2	200	900	100	300
3	300	400	200	100
4	200	100	300	200

Plants 1, 2, 3, and 4 make 10, 20, 20, and 10 shipments per month, respectively. Retail outlets 1, 2, 3, and 4 need to receive 20, 10, 10, and 20 shipments per month, respectively.

The distribution manager, Randy Smith, now wants to determine the best plan for how many shipments to send from each plant to the respective retail outlets each month. Randy's objective is to minimize the total shipping cost.

a. Formulate this problem as a transportation problem by constructing a table that identifies all the sources, supplies, destinations, demands, and unit costs.

E* b. Display the transportation problem on a spreadsheet and then use the Excel Solver to obtain an optimal solution.

15.4. The Childfair Company has three plants producing child push chairs that are to be shipped to four distribution centers. Plants 1, 2, and 3 produce 12, 17, and 11 shipments per month, respectively. Each distribution center needs to receive 10 shipments per month. The distance from each plant to the respective distribution centers is given below:

	Distance to Distribution Center (Miles)			
	1	2	3	4
Plant				
1	800	1,300	400	700
2	1,100	1,400	600	1,000
3	600	1,200	800	900

The freight cost for each shipment is $100 plus 50 cents/mile.

How much should be shipped from each plant to each of the distribution centers to minimize the total shipping cost?

a. Formulate this problem as a transportation problem by constructing a table that identifies all the sources, supplies, destinations, demands, and unit costs.

E* b. Display the transportation problem on a spreadsheet and then use the Excel Solver to obtain an optimal solution.

E* 15.5.* Tom would like 3 pints of home brew today and an additional 4 pints of home brew tomorrow. Dick is willing to sell a maximum of 5 pints total at a price of $3.00/pint today and $2.70/pint tomorrow. Harry is willing to sell a maximum of 4 pints total at a price of $2.90/pint today and $2.80/pint tomorrow.

Tom wishes to know what his purchases should be to minimize his cost while satisfying his thirst requirements. Formulate and solve a spreadsheet model for this problem.

E* 15.6. The Versatech Corporation has decided to produce three new products. Five branch plants now have excess product capacity. The unit manufacturing cost of the first product would be $31, $29, $32, $28, and $29 in plants 1, 2, 3, 4, and 5, respectively. The unit manufacturing cost of the second product would be $45, $41, $46, $42, and $43 in plants 1, 2, 3, 4, and 5, respectively. The unit manufacturing cost of the third product would be $38, $35, and $40 in plants 1, 2, and 3, respectively, whereas plants 4 and 5 do not have the capability for producing this product. Sales forecasts indicate that 600, 1,000, and 800 units of products 1, 2, and 3, respectively, should be produced per day. Plants 1, 2, 3, 4, and 5 have the capacity to produce 400, 600, 400, 600, and 1,000 units daily, respectively, regardless of the product or combinations of products involved. Assume that any plant having the capability and capacity to produce them can produce any combination of the products in any quantity.

Management wishes to know how to allocate the new products to the plants to minimize total manufacturing cost. Formulate and solve a spreadsheet model for this problem.

E* 15.7. Suppose that England, France, and Spain produce all the wheat, barley, and oats in the world. The world demand for wheat requires 125 million acres of land devoted to wheat production. Similarly, 60 million acres of land are required for barley and 75 million acres of land are required for oats. The total amount of land available for these purposes in England, France, and Spain is 70 million acres, 110 million acres, and 80 million acres, respectively. The number of hours of labor needed in England, France, and Spain, respectively, to produce an acre of wheat is 18, 13, and 16; to produce an acre of barley is 15, 12, and 12; and to produce an acre of oats is 12, 10, and 16. The labor cost per hour in England, France, and Spain, respectively, for producing wheat is $9.00, $7.20, and $9.90; for producing barley is $8.10, $9.00, and $8.40; and for producing oats is $6.90, $7.50, and $6.30. The problem is to allocate land use in each country so as to meet the world food requirements and minimize the total labor cost. Formulate and solve a spreadsheet model for this problem.

E* 15.8. A contractor, Susan Meyer, has to haul gravel to three building sites. She can purchase as much as 18 tons at a gravel pit in the north of the city and 14 tons at one in the south. She needs 10, 5, and 10 tons at sites 1, 2, and 3, respectively. The purchase price per ton at each gravel pit and the hauling cost per ton are given in the following table.

Pit	Hauling Cost per Ton at Site			Price per Ton
	1	2	3	
North	$30	$60	$50	$100
South	60	30	40	120

Susan wishes to determine how much to haul from each pit to each site to minimize the total cost for purchasing and hauling gravel. Formulate and solve a spreadsheet model for this problem.

E* 15.9.   Reconsider the P & T Co. case study presented in Sections 15.1 and 15.2. Refer to the spreadsheet in Figure 15.2, which shows the formulation as a transportation problem and displays an optimal solution. You now learn that one or more of the unit costs in the data cells UnitCost (D5:G7) may change slightly before shipments begin.

Use Solver to generate the sensitivity report for this problem. Use this report to determine the allowable range for each of the unit costs. What do these allowable ranges tell P & T management?

E* 15.10.   Reconsider the Metro Water District problem presented in Section 15.4. Refer to the spreadsheet in Figure 15.6, which shows the formulation as a variant of a transportation problem and displays an optimal solution.

The numbers given in the data cells are only estimates that may be somewhat inaccurate, so management now wishes to do some what-if analysis. Use Solver to generate the sensitivity report. Then use this report to address the following questions. (In each case, assume that the indicated change is the only change in the model.)

a.   Would the optimal solution in Figure 15.6 remain optimal if the cost per acre foot of shipping Calorie River water to San Go were actually $200 rather than $230?

b.   Would this solution remain optimal if the cost per acre foot of shipping Sacron River water to Los Devils were actually $160 rather than $130?

c.   Must this solution remain optimal if the costs considered in parts *a* and *b* were simultaneously changed from their original values to $215 and $145, respectively?

d.   Suppose that the supply from the Sacron River and the demand at Hollyglass are decreased simultaneously by the same amount. Must the shadow prices for evaluating these changes remain valid if the decrease were 0.5 million acre feet?

E* 15.11.   Reconsider the Metro Water District problem presented in Section 15.4, including the data given in Table 15.9.

The numbers in this table for the amount of water needed by the respective cities actually represent the absolute minimum that each city must have. Each city would like to have as much as 2 million additional acre feet beyond this minimum amount.

Since the amount of water available exceeds the sum of these minimum amounts by 3.5 million acre feet, Metro management has decided to distribute this additional water to the cities as well. The decisions on how much additional water the respective cities will receive beyond meeting their minimum needs will be based on minimizing Metro's total cost. Management wants to know which plan for distributing water from the rivers to the cities will achieve this objective.

Formulate and solve a spreadsheet model for this problem.

E* 15.12. The Onenote Co. produces a single product at three plants for four customers. The three plants will produce 60, 80, and 40 units, respectively, during the next week. The firm has made a commitment to sell 40 units to customer 1, 60 units to customer 2, and at least 20 units to customer 3. Both customers 3 and 4 also want to buy as many of the remaining units as possible. The net profit associated with shipping a unit from plant i for sale to customer j is given by the following table:

	Customer			
	1	2	3	4
Plant				
1	$800	$700	$500	$200
2	500	200	100	300
3	600	400	300	500

Management wishes to know how many units to sell to customers 3 and 4 and how many units to ship from each of the plants to each of the customers to maximize profit. Formulate and solve a spreadsheet model for this problem.

E* 15.13. The Move-It Company has two plants building forklift trucks that then are shipped to three distribution centers. The production costs are the same at the two plants, and the cost of shipping each truck is shown below for each combination of plant and distribution center:

	Distribution Center		
	1	2	3
Plant			
A	$800	$700	$400
B	600	800	500

A total of 60 forklift trucks are produced and shipped per week. Each plant can produce and ship any amount up to a maximum of 50 trucks per week, so there is considerable flexibility on how to divide the total production between the two plants so as to reduce shipping costs. However, each distribution center must receive exactly 20 trucks per week.

Management's objective is to determine how many forklift trucks should be produced at each plant, and then what the overall shipping pattern should be to minimize total shipping cost. Formulate and solve a spreadsheet model for this problem.

E* 15.14. Redo Problem 15.13 when any distribution center may receive any quantity between 10 and 30 forklift trucks per week in order to further reduce total shipping cost, provided only that the total shipped to all three distribution centers must still equal 60 trucks per week.

E* 15.15. The Build-Em-Fast Company has agreed to supply its best customer with three widgits during *each* of the next three weeks, even though producing them will require some overtime work. The relevant production data are as follows:

| | Maximum Production | | |
Week	Regular Time	Overtime	Production Cost per Unit, Regular Time
1	2	2	$300
2	3	2	500
3	1	2	400

The cost per unit produced with overtime for each week is $100 more than for regular time. The cost of storage is $50 per unit for each week it is stored. There is already an inventory of two widgets on hand currently, but the company does not want to retain any widgets in inventory after the three weeks.

Management wants to know how many units should be produced in each week to minimize the total cost of meeting the delivery schedule. Formulate and solve a spreadsheet model for this problem.

E* 15.16. The MJK Manufacturing Company must produce two products in sufficient quantity to meet contracted sales in each of the next three months. The two products share the same production facilities, and each unit of both products requires the same amount of production capacity. The available production and storage facilities are changing month by month, so the production capacities, unit production costs, and unit storage costs vary by month. Therefore, it may be worthwhile to overproduce one or both products in some months and store them until needed.

For each of the three months, the initialed columns of the following table give the maximum number of units of the two products combined that can be produced on regular time (RT) and on overtime (OT). For each of the two products, the subsequent columns give (1) the number of units needed for the contracted sales, (2) the cost (in thousands of dollars) per unit produced on regular time, (3) the cost (in thousands of dollars) per unit produced on overtime, and (4) the cost (in thousands of dollars) of storing each extra unit that is held over into the next month. In each case, the numbers for the two products are separated by a slash /, with the number for product 1 on the left and the number for product 2 on the right.

| | | | | Product 1/Product 2 | | |
| | Maximum Combined Production | | | Unit Cost of Production ($1,000s) | | Unit Cost of Storage ($1,000s) |
Month	RT	OT	Sales	RT	OT	
1	10	3	5/3	15/16	18/20	1/2
2	8	2	3/5	17/15	20/18	2/1
3	10	3	4/4	19/17	22/22	

The production manager wants a schedule developed for the number of units of each of the two products to be produced on regular time and, if regular time production capacity is used up, on overtime in each of the three months. The objective is to minimize the total of the production and storage costs while meeting the contracted sales for each month. There is no initial inventory, and no final inventory is desired after the three months.

Formulate and solve a spreadsheet model for this problem.

15.17. Consider the transportation problem having the following data:

		Unit Cost ($)			
Destination:	1	2	3	4	Supply
Source					
1	7	4	1	4	1
2	4	6	7	2	1
3	8	5	4	6	1
4	6	7	6	3	1
Demand	1	1	1	1	

a. What property ensures that this problem has feasible solutions?

b. What property ensures that this problem has an optimal solution with values of 0 or 1 for all the shipment amounts?

c. Explain how this problem can be interpreted to be an assignment problem.

d. Draw the network representation of this assignment problem.

E*   e. Display the problem on a spreadsheet and then use the Excel Solver to obtain an optimal solution.

15.18. Consider the assignment problem having the following cost table:

	Job		
	1	2	3
Person			
A	$5	$7	$4
B	3	6	5
C	2	3	4

The optimal solution is A-3, B-1, C-2, with a total cost of $10.

a. Draw the network representation of this problem.

E*   b. Formulate this problem on a spreadsheet and then use the Excel Solver to obtain the optimal solution identified above.

15.19.* Consider the assignment problem having the following cost table:

Assignee	Task 1	Task 2	Task 3	Task 4
A	$8	$6	$5	$7
B	6	5	3	4
C	7	8	4	6
D	6	7	5	6

   a. Draw the network representation of this assignment problem.

E*   b. Formulate this problem on a spreadsheet and then use the Excel Solver to obtain an optimal solution.

15.20. Four cargo ships will be used for shipping goods from one port to four other ports (labeled 1, 2, 3, 4). Any ship can be used for making any one of these four trips. However, because of differences in the ships and cargoes, the total cost of loading, transporting, and unloading the goods for the different ship–port combinations varies considerably, as shown in the following table:

Ship	Port 1	Port 2	Port 3	Port 4
1	$500	$400	$600	$700
2	600	600	700	500
3	700	500	700	600
4	500	400	600	600

   The objective is to assign the four ships to four different ports in such a way as to m total cost for all four shipments.

   a. Describe how this problem fits into the format for an assignment problem.

E*   b. Formulate and solve this problem on a spreadsheet.

E* 15.21. Reconsider Problem 15.6. Suppose that the sales forecasts have been revised downward to 240, 400, and 320 units per day of products 1, 2, and 3, respectively. Thus, each plant now has the capacity to produce all that is required of any one product. Therefore, management has decided that each new product should be assigned to only one plant and that no plant should be assigned more than one product (so that three plants are each to be assigned one product, and two plants are to be assigned none). The objective is to make these assignments so as to minimize the *total* cost of producing these amounts of the three products. Formulate and solve a spreadsheet model for this problem.

15.22.* The coach of an age group swim team needs to assign swimmers to a 200-yard medley relay team to send to the Junior Olympics. Since most of his best swimmers are very fast in more than one stroke, it is not clear which swimmer should be assigned to each of the four strokes. The five fastest swimmers and the best times (in seconds) they have achieved in each of the strokes (for 50 yards) are

Stroke	Carl	Chris	David	Tony	Ken
Backstroke	37.7	32.9	33.8	37.0	35.4
Breaststroke	43.4	33.1	42.2	34.7	41.8
Butterfly	33.3	28.5	38.9	30.4	33.6
Freestyle	29.2	26.4	29.6	28.5	31.1

The coach wishes to determine how to assign four swimmers to the four different strokes to minimize the sum of the corresponding best times.

   a. Describe how this problem fits into the format for a variant of an assignment problem even though it does not involve costs. What plays the role of costs?

E*   b. Formulate and solve this problem on a spreadsheet.

E* 15.23. Reconsider Problem 15.8. Now suppose that trucks (and their drivers) need to be hired to do the hauling, where each truck can only be used once to haul gravel from a single pit to a single site. Enough trucks are available to haul all the gravel that can be purchased at each site. Each truck can haul five tons, and the cost per truck is five times the hauling cost per ton given earlier. Only full trucks are to supply each site.

Formulate and solve a spreadsheet model for this problem.

E* 15.24. Reconsider Problem 15.13. Now distribution centers 1, 2, and 3 must receive exactly 10, 20, and 30 units per week, respectively. For administrative convenience, management has decided that each distribution center will be supplied totally by a single plant, so that one plant will supply one distribution center and the other plant will supply the other two distribution centers. The choice of these assignments of plants to distribution centers is to be made solely on the basis of minimizing total shipping cost.

Formulate and solve a spreadsheet model for this problem.

Partial Answers to Selected Problems

15.5.   3 pints from Harry today, 4 pints from Dick tomorrow. Total cost = $19.50.

15.19. b. A–2, B–4, C–3, D–1. Total cost = $20.

15.22. b. David–backstroke, Tony–breaststroke, Chris–butterfly, Carl–freestyle. Total time = 126.20 seconds.

CD 15-65

Case 15-1 Continuation of the Texago Case Study

Reconsider the case study presented in Section 15.5 involving the Texago Corp. site selection problem.

Texago management has tentatively chosen St. Louis as the site of the new refinery. However, management now is addressing the question of what the capacity of the new refinery should be.

While analyzing the site selection problem, the task force was told to assume that the new refinery would have the capacity to process 120 million barrels of crude oil per year. As indicated in Table 15.16, this then would increase the total capacity of all the corporation's refineries from 240 million barrels to 360 million barrels. According to marketing forecasts, Texago will be able to sell all its finished product once this new capacity becomes available, but no more. Therefore, the choice of 120 million barrels as the capacity of the new refinery would enable all the corporation's refineries to operate at full capacity while also fully meeting the forecasted demand for Texago's products.

However, to prepare for possible future increases in demand beyond the current forecasts, management now wants to also consider the option of enlarging the plans for the new refinery so that it would have the capacity to process 150 million barrels of crude oil annually. Although this would force the corporation's refineries collectively to operate below full capacity by 30 million barrels for a while, the extra capacity then would be available later if Texago were to continue to increase its market share. This might be well worthwhile since the capital and operating costs incurred by enlarging the plans for the new refinery would be far less (perhaps 40 percent less) than constructing and operating another refinery later to process only 30 million barrels of crude oil per year. Furthermore, management feels that this extra capacity might be needed within a few years.

The extra capital costs needed to increase the capacity of the new refinery by 30 million barrels is estimated to be $1.2 billion. The cost of carrying this extra capital would be about $100 million per year, depending on future interest rates. If some of this extra capacity were used at the new refinery, the total operating cost for the refinery would be somewhat larger than the amount shown in Table 15.19, but decreasing the production rate by the same amount at another refinery would decrease its total operating cost by a comparable amount. Since the operating cost per million barrels of crude oil processed is roughly the same at all the refineries, including the new one, the total operating cost for processing 360 million barrels should not be substantially affected by the allocation of this work to the refineries. However, management feels that having some flexibility for where to allocate this work might permit a substantial reduction in the cost of shipping crude oil and finished product. Since Table 15.20 indicates that the total annual shipping cost for crude oil and finished product would be $2.92 billion with St. Louis as the site for the refinery, management hopes that substantial reductions can be achieved in this way.

Figures 15.13 and 15.17 show the optimal shipping plans for crude oil and finished product, respectively, when the new refinery is in St. Louis and has a capacity of processing 120 million barrels of crude oil per year. Management now is asking the task force to analyze the situation under the option of increasing this capacity to 150 million barrels. In particular, management wants the following questions addressed. Under the new option, how should the shipping plan for crude oil in Figure 15.13 change and how much reduction in the total shipping cost would be achieved? How should the shipping plan for finished product in Figure 15.17 change and how much reduction in the total shipping cost would be achieved? Finally, assuming that the differences in operating costs shown in Table 15.19 would continue to apply under the new option, would the financial comparison of the three sites given in Table 15.20 be altered substantially if this option were to be adopted?

As the head of the task force, you have decided to lead the way in executing the following steps with the new option.

CD 15-66

a. Formulate and solve a spreadsheet model to find an optimal plan for shipping 360 million barrels of crude oil per year from the oil fields to the refineries, including the new one in St. Louis, where the amount of crude oil each refinery will receive (up to its capacity) is based on minimizing the total annual cost for these shipments. (**Hint:** You can save some time in this and subsequent parts by using the live spreadsheets for the Texago case study in this chapter's Excel files as a starting point.) Compare the resulting total annual cost for these shipments with the results obtained in Figure 15.13 under the original assumption of a smaller refinery in St. Louis.

b. Assume that the plan found in part *a* (including its specification of how much crude oil each refinery will receive) will be used. On this basis, formulate and solve a spreadsheet model to find an optimal plan for shipping finished product from the refineries to the distribution centers. Compare the resulting total annual cost for these shipments with the results obtained in Figure 15.17. Also calculate the total annual cost of shipping both crude oil and finished product under this plan and compare it with the corresponding total of $2.92 billion obtained from Table 15.20.

c. You realize that the cost of shipping final product tends to be somewhat larger than the cost of shipping crude oil. Therefore, rather than having the decisions regarding the amount of crude oil each refinery will receive and process be dictated by minimizing the total annual cost of shipping crude oil (as in parts *a* and *b*), you decide to check what would happen if these decisions were based on minimizing the total annual cost of shipping final product instead. Formulate and solve a spreadsheet model to find an optimal plan for shipping final product from the refineries (including the new one in St. Louis) to the distribution centers, where the allocation of the 360 million barrels of crude oil per year to the refineries is based on minimizing the total annual cost for these shipments. Compare the resulting total annual cost for these shipments with the results obtained in part *b* and in Figure 15.17.

d. Assume that the plan found in part *c* (including its specification regarding how much crude oil each refinery will receive and process) will be used. On this basis, formulate and solve a spreadsheet model to find an optimal plan for shipping crude oil from the oil fields to the refineries. Compare the resulting total annual cost for these shipments with the results obtained in part *a* and in Figure 15.13. Also calculate the total annual cost of shipping both crude oil and finished product under this plan and compare it with the corresponding total obtained in part *b* and in Table 15.20.

e. You realize that, so far, you have been *suboptimizing* the overall problem by optimizing only one part of the problem at a time, so now it is time to get down to serious business. Formulate a single spreadsheet model that simultaneously considers the shipping of 360 million barrels of crude oil per year from the oil fields to the refineries (including the new one in St. Louis) and the shipping of final product from the refineries to the distribution centers. Use the objective of minimizing the grand total of all these shipping costs. Since the refineries collectively have a capacity of processing 390 million barrels of crude oil per year, the decisions regarding the amount of crude oil each refinery will receive and process (up to each refinery's capacity) also are to be based on this same objective. Solve the model and compare the resulting total of all the shipping costs with the corresponding total calculated in parts *b* and *d* and in Table 15.20.

CD 15-67

f. Repeat part *e* if the new refinery (with a capacity of processing 150 million barrels of crude oil per year) were to be placed in Los Angeles instead of St. Louis. Then repeat it again if Galveston were to be selected as the site instead of St. Louis. Using the operating costs given in Table 15.19 for the three sites, construct a table like Table 15.20 to show the new financial comparison between the sites. (Although the operating costs will be larger than given in Table 15.19 if the new refinery processes more than 120 million barrels of crude oil per year, management has instructed the task force to assume that the differences in operating costs shown in Table 15.19 would continue to apply, so the differences in the total variable costs in the table being constructed would still be valid.)

g. You now are ready to submit all your results (including your spreadsheets) to management. Write an accompanying memorandum that presents your recommendations.

CD 16-1

CHAPTER 16
PERT/CPM MODELS FOR PROJECT MANAGEMENT

Learning objectives

After completing this chapter, you should be able to

1. Describe the kind of help that PERT/CPM can provide a project manager.
2. Identify the types of information needed to construct a project network for PERT/CPM.
3. Use this information to construct a project network for a particular project.
4. Use a project network to develop a complete schedule, including both the earliest and latest times when each activity should start and finish.
5. Identify the critical bottleneck activities where any delays must be avoided to prevent delaying project completion.
6. Find an approximate probability of completing a project by the deadline.
7. Find the least expensive way of expediting a project to meet a target completion date.
8. Use a systematic procedure to help plan, schedule, and control project costs.
9. Provide an evaluation of PERT/CPM from a managerial perspective.
10. Identify some kinds of extensions to PERT/CPM that now are becoming available.

One of the most challenging jobs that any manager can take on is the management of a large scale project that requires coordinating numerous activities throughout the organization. A myriad of details must be considered in planning how to coordinate all these activities, in developing a realistic schedule, and then in monitoring the progress of the project.

Fortunately, two closely related management science techniques, PERT (*program evaluation and review technique*) and CPM (*critical path method*), are available to assist the project manager in carrying out these responsibilities. These techniques make heavy use of *networks* (as introduced in Chapter 6) to help plan and display the coordination of all the activities. They also normally use a *software package* to deal with all the data needed to develop schedule information and then to monitor the progress of the project. *Project management software* now is widely available for these purposes.

PERT and CPM have been widely used for a variety of projects, including the following types:

1. Construction of a new plant.
2. Research and development of a new product.
3. NASA space exploration projects.
4. Movie productions.
5. Building of a ship.
6. Government-sponsored projects for developing a new weapons system.
7. Relocation of a major facility.
8. Maintenance of a nuclear reactor.
9. Installation of a management information system.
10. Conducting of an advertising campaign.

PERT and CPM were independently developed in the late 1950s. Ever since, they have been among the most widely used management science techniques.

The original versions of PERT and CPM had some important differences, as we will point out later in the chapter. However, they also had a great deal in common, and the two techniques have gradually merged further over the years. In fact, today's software packages often include all the important options from both original versions.

Consequently, practitioners now commonly use the two names interchangeably, or combine them into the single acronym PERT/CPM as we often will do. We will make the distinction between them only when we are describing an option that was unique to one of the original versions.

The next section introduces a case study that will carry through the chapter to illustrate the various options for analyzing projects provided by PERT/CPM.

16.1   A CASE STUDY: THE RELIABLE CONSTRUCTION CO. PROJECT

The Reliable Construction Company has just made the winning bid of $5.4 million to construct a new plant for a major manufacturer. The manufacturer needs the plant to go into operation within a year. Therefore, the contract includes the following provisions:

- A *penalty* of $300,000 if Reliable has not completed construction by the deadline 47 weeks from now.

- To provide additional incentive for speedy construction, a *bonus* of $150,000 to be paid to Reliable if the plant is completed within 40 weeks.

Reliable is assigning its best construction manager, David Perty, to this project to help ensure that it stays on schedule. Mr. Perty has earned the confidence of management through many years of exemplary performance with the company. He began as a carpenter fresh out of community college and soon became the youngest foreman in the company, so he knows the construction business from the ground up. While a foreman, he went back to college part time at night to earn his business degree. It was an arduous schedule that stretched out over five years, but he found that he enjoyed his business major and was good at it. His favorite course was a graduate-level elective in project management, and it was there that he thoroughly learned the techniques of PERT/CPM. Immediately after earning his business degree with honors, Mr. Perty was promoted to construction manager. He has been serving the company in this capacity now for 14 years, and rumors have it that he may be next in line to move into top management in a year when the retirement of the company president will cause some shuffling of the top positions. Although Mr. Perty would welcome this opportunity, he does not feel any hurry to move up. Despite its many stresses, he thoroughly enjoys the challenges of being a construction manager, including the opportunities to apply the latest project management techniques.

Mr. Perty is very pleased to receive this latest assignment as the project manager for such an important project. He looks forward to the challenge of bringing the project in on schedule, and perhaps earning a promotion in the process. However, since he is doubtful that it will be feasible to finish within 40 weeks without incurring excessive costs, he has decided to focus his initial planning on meeting the deadline of 47 weeks.

He will need to arrange for a number of crews to perform the various construction activities at different times. Table 16.1 shows his list of the various activities. The third column provides important additional information for coordinating the scheduling of the crews.

> For any given activity, its **immediate predecessors** (as given in the third column of Table 16.1) are those activities that must be completed by no later than the start time of the given activity. (Similarly, the given activity is called an **immediate successor** of each of its immediate predecessors.)

Table 16.1   Activity List for the Reliable Construction Co. Project

Activity	Activity Description	Immediate Predecessors	Estimated Duration
A	Excavate	—	2 weeks
B	Lay the foundation	A	4 weeks
C	Put up the rough wall	B	10 weeks
D	Put up the roof	C	6 weeks
E	Install the exterior plumbing	C	4 weeks
F	Install the interior plumbing	E	5 weeks
G	Put up the exterior siding	D	7 weeks
H	Do the exterior painting	E, G	9 weeks
I	Do the electrical work	C	7 weeks
J	Put up the wallboard	F, I	8 weeks
K	Install the flooring	J	4 weeks
L	Do the interior painting	J	5 weeks
M	Install the exterior fixtures	H	2 weeks
N	Install the interior fixtures	K, L	6 weeks

For example, the top entries in this column indicate that

1. Excavation does not need to wait for any other activities.

2. Excavation must be completed before starting to lay the foundation.

3. The foundation must be completely laid before starting to put up the rough wall, and so on.

When a given activity has *more than one* immediate predecessor, all must be finished before the activity can begin.

In order to schedule the activities, Mr. Perty consults with each of the crew foremen to develop an estimate of how long each activity should take when it is done in the normal way. These estimates are given in the rightmost column of Table 16.1.

Adding up these times gives a grand total of 79 weeks, which is far beyond the deadline for the project. Fortunately, some of the activities can be done in parallel, which substantially reduces the project completion time.

Given all the information in Table 16.1, Mr. Perty now wants to develop answers to the following questions.

1. How can the project be displayed graphically to better visualize the flow of the activities? (Section 16.2)

2. What is the total time required to complete the project if no delays occur? (Section 16.3)

3. When do the individual activities need to start and finish (at the latest) to meet this project completion time? (Section 16.3)

4. When can the individual activities start and finish (at the earliest) if no delays occur? (Section 16.3)

5. Which are the critical bottleneck activities where any delays must be avoided to prevent delaying project completion? (Section 16.3)

6. For the other activities, how much delay can be tolerated without delaying project completion? (Section 16.3)

7. Given the uncertainties in accurately estimating activity durations, what is the probability of completing the project by the deadline (47 weeks)? (Section 16.4)

8. If extra money is spent to expedite the project, what is the least expensive way of attempting to meet the target completion time (40 weeks)? (Section 16.5)

9. How should ongoing costs be monitored to try to keep the project within budget? (Section 16.6)

Being a regular user of PERT/CPM, Mr. Perty knows that this technique will provide invaluable help in answering these questions (as you will see in the sections indicated in parentheses above).

REVIEW QUESTIONS

1. What are the financial terms in the contract that the Reliable Construction Co. has just won?
2. What is the deadline that Mr. Perty is focusing on meeting?
3. What is meant by an immediate predecessor of an activity? An immediate successor?
4. What are the three types of information that Mr. Perty gathered regarding the project?

16.2   USING A NETWORK TO VISUALLY DISPLAY A PROJECT

Chapter 6 describes how valuable *networks* can be to represent and help analyze many kinds of problems. In much the same way, networks play a key role in dealing with projects. They enable showing the relationships between the activities and placing everything into perspective. They then are used to help analyze the project and answer the kinds of questions raised at the end of the preceding section.

Project Networks

A network used to represent a project is called a project network. A project network consists of a number of nodes (typically shown as small circles or rectangles) and a number of arcs (shown as arrows) that lead from some node to another. (If you have not previously studied Chapter 6, where nodes and arcs are discussed extensively, just think of them as the names given to the small circles or rectangles and to the arrows in the network.)

As Table 16.1 indicates, there are three types of information needed to describe a project.

CD 16-5

1. Activity information: Break down the project into its individual activities (at the desired level of detail).

2. Precedence relationships: Identify the immediate predecessor(s) for each activity.

3. Time information: Estimate the duration of each activity.

The project network needs to convey all this information. There are two alternative types of project networks available for doing this.

One type is the activity-on-arc (AOA) project network, where each activity is represented by an *arc*. A node is used to separate an activity (an outgoing arc) from each of its immediate predecessors (an incoming arc). The sequencing of the arcs thereby shows the precedence relationships between the activities.

The second type is the activity-on-node (AON) project network, where each activity is represented by a *node*. The arcs then are used just to show the precedence relationships between the activities. In particular, the node for each activity with immediate predecessors has an arc coming in from each of these predecessors.

The original versions of PERT and CPM used AOA project networks, so this was the conventional type for some years. However, AON project networks have some important advantages over AOA project networks for conveying exactly the same information.

1. AON project networks are considerably easier to construct than AOA project networks.

2. AON project networks are easier to understand than AOA project networks for inexperienced users, including many managers.

3. AON project networks are easier to revise than AOA project networks when there are changes in the project.

For these reasons, AON project networks have become increasingly popular with practitioners. It appears somewhat likely that they will become the conventional type to use. Therefore, we now will focus solely on AON project networks.

Figure 16.1 shows the project network for Reliable's project[1] Referring also to the third column of Table 16.1, note how there is an arc leading to each activity from each of its immediate predecessors. Because activity A has no immediate predecessors, there is an arc leading from the start node to this activity. Similarly, since activities M and N have no immediate successors, arcs lead from these activities to the finish node. Therefore, the project network nicely displays at a glance all the precedence relationships between all the activities (plus the start and finish of the project). Based on the rightmost column of Table 16.1, the number next to the node for each activity then records the estimated duration (in weeks) of that activity.

---

[1] Although project networks often are drawn from left to right, we go from top to bottom to better fit on the printed page.

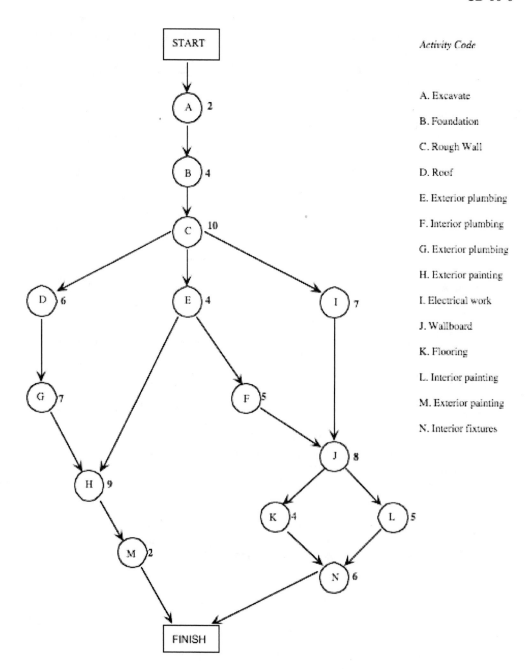

Activity Code

A. Excavate

B. Foundation

C. Rough Wall

D. Roof

E. Exterior plumbing

F. Interior plumbing

G. Exterior plumbing

H. Exterior painting

I. Electrical work

J. Wallboard

K. Flooring

L. Interior painting

M. Exterior painting

N. Interior fixtures

Figure 16.1 The project network for the Reliable Construction Co. project.

CD 16-7

REVIEW QUESTIONS

1. What three types of information does a project network need to convey?
2. What is the difference between an activity-on-arc (AOA) project network and an activity-onnode (AON) project network? Which type is being used here?

16.3 SCHEDULING A PROJECT WITH PERT/CPM

At the end of Section 16.1, we mentioned that Mr. Perty, the project manager for the Reliable Construction Co. project, wants to answer a series of questions and so will use PERT/CPM as the best method for obtaining answers. His first question has been answered in the preceding section. Here are the five questions that will be answered in this section.

> **Question 2**: What is the total time required to complete the project if no delays occur?

> **Question 3**: When do the individual activities need to start and finish (at the latest) to meet this project completion time?

> **Question 4**: When can the individual activities start and finish (at the earliest) if no delays occur?

> **Question 5**: Which are the critical bottleneck activities where any delays must be avoided to prevent delaying project completion?

> **Question 6**: For the other activities, how much delay can be tolerated without delaying project completion?

The project network in Figure 16.1 enables answering all these questions by providing two crucial pieces of information, namely, the *order* in which certain activities must be performed and the (estimated) *duration* of each activity. We begin by focusing on Questions 2 and 5.

The Critical Path

How long should the project take? We noted earlier that summing the durations of all the activities gives a grand total of 79 weeks. However, this isn't the answer to the question because some of the activities can be performed (roughly) simultaneously. What is relevant instead is the *length* of each *path* through the network.

> A **path** through a project network is one of the routes following the arrows (arcs) from the start node to the finish node. The **length of a path** is the *sum* of the (estimated) *durations* of the activities on the path.

The six paths through the project network in Figure 16.1 are given in Table 16.2, along with the calculations of the lengths of these paths. The path lengths range from 31 weeks up to 44 weeks for the longest path (the fourth one in the table).

Table 16.2   The Paths and Path Lengths Through Reliable's Project Network

Path	Length (weeks)
START →A→B→C→D→G→H→M→FINISH	2 + 4 + 10 + 6 + 7 + 9 + 2 = 40 weeks
START →A→B→C→E→H→M→FINISH	2 + 4 + 10 + 4 + 9 + 2 = 31 weeks
START →A→B→C→E→F→J→K→N→FINISH	2 + 4 + 10 + 4 + 5 + 8 + 4 + 6 = 43 weeks
START →A→B→C→E→F→J→L→N→FINISH	2 + 4 + 10 + 4 + 5 + 8 + 5 + 6 = 44 weeks
START →A→B→C→I→J→K→N→FINISH	2 + 4 + 10 + 7 + 8 + 4 + 6 = 41 weeks
START →A→B→C→I→J→L→N→FINISH	2 + 4 + 10 + 7 + 8 + 5 + 6 = 42 weeks

So given these path lengths, what do you think should be the (estimated) *project duration* (the total time required for the project)? Let us reason it out.

Since the activities on any given path must be done one after another with no overlap, the project duration cannot be *shorter* than the path length. However, the project duration can be *longer* because some activity on the path with multiple immediate predecessors might have to wait longer for an immediate predecessor *not* on the path to finish than for the one on the path. For example, consider the second path in Table 16.2 and focus on activity H. This activity has two immediate predecessors, one (activity G) *not* on the path and one (activity E) that is. After activity C finishes, only 4 more weeks are required for activity E but 13 weeks will be needed for activity D and then activity G to finish. Therefore, the project duration must be considerably longer than the length of the second path in the table.

However, the project duration will not be longer than one particular path. This is the *longest path* through the project network. The activities on this path can be performed sequentially without interruption. (Otherwise, this would not be the longest path.) Therefore, the time required to reach the finish node equals the length of this path. Furthermore, all the shorter paths will reach the finish node no later than this.

Here is the key conclusion.

> The (estimated) *project duration* equals the *length of the longest path* through the project network. This longest path is called the **critical path**. (If more than one path tie for the longest, they all are critical paths.)

Thus, for the Reliable Construction Co. project, we have

Critical path: Start→A→B→C→E→F→J→L→N→Finish

(Estimated) project duration = 44 weeks

We now have answered Mr. Perty's Questions 2 and 5 given at the beginning of the section. If no delays occur, the total time required to complete the project should be about 44 weeks. Furthermore, the activities on this critical path are the critical bottleneck activities where any delays in their completion must be avoided to prevent delaying project completion. This is valuable information for Mr. Perty since he now knows that he should focus most of his attention on keeping these particular activities on schedule in striving to keep the overall project on schedule. Furthermore, if he decides to reduce the duration of the project (remember that bonus for completion within 40 weeks), these are the main activities where changes should be made to reduce their durations.

For small project networks like Figure 16.1, finding all the paths and determining the longest path is a convenient way to identify the critical path. However, this is not an efficient procedure for larger projects. PERT/CPM uses a considerably more efficient procedure instead.

CD 16-9

Not only is this PERT/CPM procedure very efficient for larger projects, it also provides much more information than is available from finding all the paths. In particular, it answers *all five* of Mr. Perty's questions listed at the beginning of the section rather than just two. These answers provide the key information needed to schedule all the activities and then to evaluate the consequences should any activities slip behind schedule.

The components of this procedure are described in the remainder of this section.

Scheduling Individual Activities

The PERT/CPM scheduling procedure begins by addressing Question 4: When can the individual activities start and finish (at the earliest) if no delays occur? Having no delays means that (1) the *actual* duration of each activity turns out to be the same as its *estimated* duration and (2) each activity begins as soon as all its immediate predecessors are finished. The starting and finishing times of each activity if no delays occur anywhere in the project are called the **earliest start time** and the **earliest finish time** of the activity. These times are represented by the symbols

ES = Earliest start time for a particular activity

EF = Earliest finish time for a particular activity

where

$EF = ES$ + (estimated) duration of the activity

Rather than assigning calendar dates to these times, we will use the convention of counting the number of time periods (weeks for Reliable's project) from when the project started. Thus,

Starting time for project = 0

Since activity A starts Reliable's project, we have

Activity A: ES = 0

EF = 0 + duration (2 weeks)

= 2

where the duration (in weeks) of activity A is given in Figure 16.1 as the boldfaced number next to this activity. Activity B can start as soon as activity A finishes, so

Activity B: ES = EF for activity A

= 2

EF = 2 + duration (4 weeks)

= 6

This calculation of ES for activity B illustrates our first rule for obtaining ES.

If an activity has only a *single* immediate predecessor, then

ES for the activity = EF for the immediate predecessor

This rule (plus the calculation of each EF) immediately gives ES and EF for activity C, then for activities D, E, I, and then for activities G, F as well. Figure 16.2 shows ES and EF for each of these activities to the right of its node. For example,

CD 16-10

Activity G: ES = EF for activity D

= 22

EF = 22 + duration (7 weeks)

= 29

which means that this activity (putting up the exterior siding) should start 22 weeks and finish 29 weeks after the start of the project.

Now consider activity H, which has *two* immediate predecessors, activities G and E. Activity H must wait to start until *both* activities G and E are finished, which gives the following calculation.

Immediate predecessors of activity H:

Activity G has EF = 29

Activity E has EF = 20

Larger EF = 29

Therefore,

ES for activity H = Larger EF above

= 29

This calculation illustrates the general rule for obtaining the earliest start time for any activity.

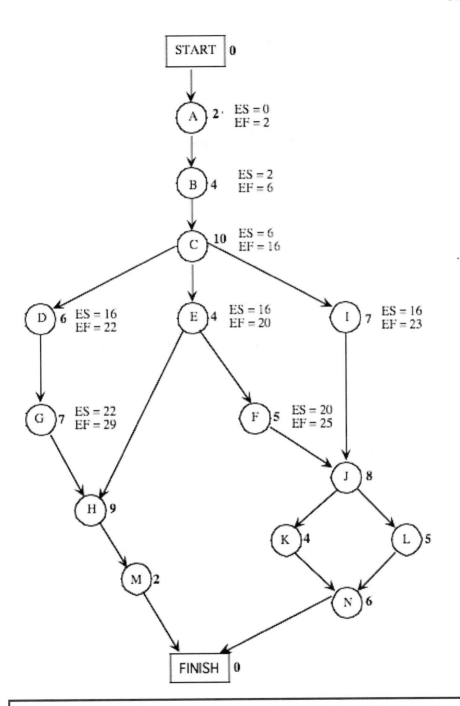

Figure 16.2   Earliest start time (ES) and earliest finish time (EF) values for the initial activities in Figure 16.1 that have only a single immediate predecessor.

Earliest Start Time Rule

The earliest start time of an activity is equal to the *largest* of the earliest finish times of its immediate predecessors. In symbols,

$$ES = \text{Largest EF of the immediate predecessors}$$

When the activity has only a single immediate predecessor, this rule becomes the same as the first rule given earlier. However, it also allows any larger number of immediate predecessors, as well. Applying this rule to the rest of the activities in Figure 16.2 (and calculating each EF from ES) yields the complete set of ES and EF values given in Figure 16.3.

Note that Figure 16.3 also includes ES and EF values for the start and finish nodes. The reason is that these nodes are conventionally treated as *dummy activities* that require no time. For the start node, ES = 0 = EF automatically. For the finish node, the earliest start time rule is used to calculate ES in the usual way, as illustrated next.

Immediate predecessors of the finish node:

$$\text{Activity M has EF} = 40$$
$$\text{Activity N has EF} = 44$$
$$\text{Larger EF} = 44$$

Therefore,

$$\text{ES for the finish node} = \text{Larger EF above}$$
$$= 44$$
$$\text{EF for the finish node} = 44 + 0 = 44$$

This last calculation indicates that the project should be completed in 44 weeks if everything stays on schedule according to the start and finish times for each activity given in Figure 16.3. (This answers Question 2.) Mr. Perty now can use this schedule to inform the crew responsible for each activity as to when it should plan to start and finish its work.

Here is a summary of the overall procedure for obtaining such a schedule for any project.

Procedure for Obtaining Earliest Times for All Activities

1. For each activity that starts the project (including the start node), set its earliest start time as ES = 0.

2. For each activity whose ES value has just been obtained, calculate its earliest finish time as EF = ES + (estimated) duration of the activity

3. For each new activity whose immediate predecessors now have EF values, obtain its ES byapplying the *earliest start time rule*. Then apply step 2 to calculate its EF.

4. Repeat step 3 over and over again until ES and EF have been obtained for *all* activities (including the finish node).

This process of starting with the initial activities and working *forward* in time toward the final activities is referred to as making a **forward pass** through the network.

Keep in mind that the schedule obtained from this procedure assumes that the *actual* duration of each activity will turn out to be the same as its *estimated* duration. What happens if some activity takes longer than expected? Would this delay project completion? Perhaps, but not necessarily. It depends on which activity and the length of the delay.

The next part of the procedure focuses on determining how much later than indicated in Figure 16.3 an activity can start or finish without delaying project completion.

CD 16-13

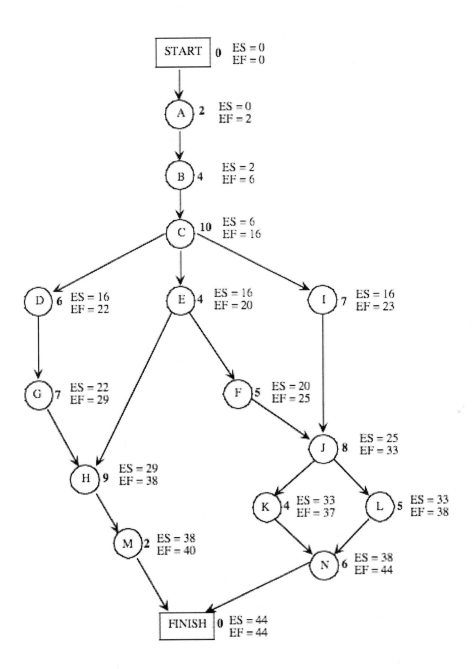

Figure 16.3   Earliest start time (ES) and earliest finish time (EF) values for all the activities (plus the start and finish modes) of the Reliable Construction Co. project.

CD 16-14

Later Schedules That Avoid Delaying Project Completion

Having found *earliest* start and finish times for each activity, we next want to answer Question 3 by finding the *latest* start and finish times that will still enable completing the project in 44 weeks.

> The **latest start time for an activity** is the latest possible time that it can start without delaying the completion of the project (so the finish node still is reached at its earliest finish time), assuming no subsequent delays in the project. The latest finish time has the corresponding definition with respect to finishing the activity.

In symbols,

> **LS** = Latest start time for a particular activity

> **LF** = Latest finish time for a particular activity

where

> LS = LF - (estimated) duration of the activity

To find LF, we have the following rule.

Latest Finish Time Rule

> The latest finish time of an activity is equal to the *smallest* of the latest start times of its immediate successors. In symbols,

> LF = Smallest LS of the immediate successors

Since an activity's immediate successors cannot start until the activity finishes, this rule is saying that the activity must finish in time to enable *all* its immediate successors to begin by their latest start times.

For example, consider activity M in Figure 16.1. Its only immediate successor is the finish node. This node must be reached by time 44 to complete the project within 44 weeks, so we begin by assigning values to this node as follows.

> Finish node: LF = its EF = 44

> LS = 44 - 0 = 44

Now we can apply the latest finish time rule to activity M.

> Activity M: LF = LS for the finish node

> = 44

> LS = 44 - duration (2 weeks)

> = 42

(Since activity M is one of the activities that together complete the project, we also could have automatically set its LF equal to the earliest finish time of the finish node without applying the latest finish time rule.)

Since activity M is the only immediate successor of activity H, we now can apply the latest finish time rule to the latter activity.

CD 16-15

$$\text{Activity H: } LF = LS \text{ for activity M}$$

$$= 42$$

$$LS = 42 - \text{duration (9 weeks)}$$

$$= 33$$

Note that the procedure being illustrated above is to start with the final activities and work *backward* in time toward the initial activities. Thus, in contrast to the *forward pass* used to find earliest start and finish times, we now are making a **backward pass** through the network, as summarized below.

Procedure for Obtaining Latest Times for All Activities

1. For each of the activities that together complete the project (including the finish node), set its latest finish time (LF) equal to the earliest finish time of the finish node.

2. For each activity whose LF value has just been obtained, calculate its latest start time as

   $$LS = LF - \text{(estimated) duration of the activity}$$

3. For each new activity whose immediate successors now have LS values, obtain its LF by applying the *latest finish time rule*. Then apply step 2 to calculate its LS.

4. Repeat step 3 over and over again until LF and LS have been obtained for *all* activities (including the start node).

Figure 16.4 shows the results of applying this procedure to its conclusion. For example, consider activity C, which has three immediate successors.

Immediate successors of activity C:

$$\text{Activity D has LS } = 20$$

$$\text{Activity E has LS } = 16$$

$$\text{Activity I has LS } = 18$$

$$\text{Smallest LS } = 16$$

Therefore,

$$\text{LF for activity C } = \text{Smallest LS above}$$

$$= 16$$

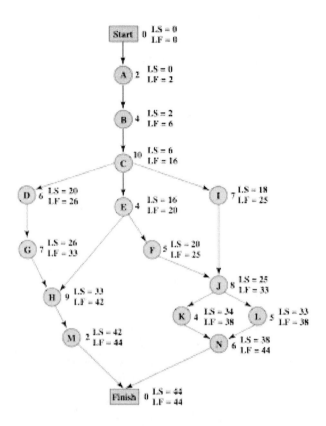

Figure 16.4   Latest start time (LS) amd latest finish time (LF) for the activities (plus the start and finish nodes) of the Reliable Construction Co. project.

Mr. Perty now knows that the schedule given in Figure 16.4 represents his "last chance schedule." Even if an activity starts and finishes as late as indicated in the figure, he still will be able to avoid delaying project completion beyond 44 weeks as long as there is no subsequent slippage in the schedule. However, to allow for unexpected delays, he would prefer to stick instead to the *earliest time schedule* given in Figure 16.3 whenever possible in order to provide some slack in parts of the schedule.

If the start and finish times in Figure16.4 for a particular activity are later than the corresponding earliest times in Figure 16.3, then this activity has some slack in the schedule. The last part of the PERT/CPM procedure for scheduling a project is to identify this slack and then to use this information to find the *critical path*. (This will answer both Questions 5 and 6.)

Identifying Slack in the Schedule

To identify slack, it is convenient to combine the latest times in Figure 16.4 and the earliest times in Figure 16.3 into a single figure. Using activity M as an example, this is done by displaying the information for each activity as follows.

CD 16-17

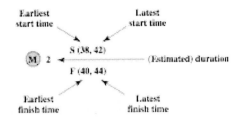

(Note that the S or F in front of each parenthesis will remind you of whether these are start times or finish times.) Figure 16.5 displays this information for the entire project.

This figure makes it easy to see how much slack each activity has.

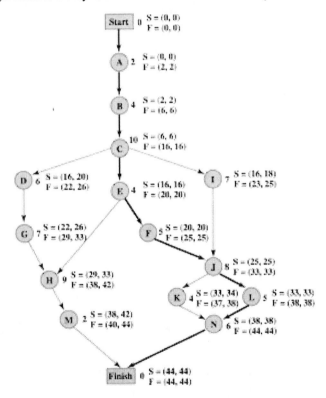

Figure 16.5	The complete project network showing ES and LS (in the upper parentheses next to the node) and EF and LF (in the lower parentheses next to the node) for each activity of the Reliable Construction Co. project. The darker arrows show the critical path through the project network.

CD 16-18

The **slack for an activity** is the difference between its latest finish time and its earliest finish time. In symbols,

$$Slack = LF - EF$$

(Since LF - EF = LS - ES, either difference actually can be used to calculate slack.)

For example,

$$Slack\ for\ activity\ M = 44 - 40 = 4$$

This indicates that activity M can be delayed up to 4 weeks beyond the earliest time schedule without delaying the completion of the project at 44 weeks. This makes sense since the project is finished as soon as both activities M and N are completed and the earliest finish time for activity N (44) is 4 weeks later than for activity M (40). As long as activity N stays on schedule, the project still will finish at 44 weeks if any delays in starting activity M (perhaps due to preceding activities taking longer than expected) and in performing activity M do not cumulate more than 4 weeks.

Table 16.3 shows the slack for each of the activities. Note that some of the activities have *zero slack,* indicating that any delays in these activities will delay project completion. This is how PERT/CPM identifies the critical path(s).

Each activity with *zero slack* is on a *critical path* through the project network such that any delay along this path will delay project completion.

Thus, the critical path is

$$Start \rightarrow A \rightarrow B \rightarrow C \rightarrow E \rightarrow F \rightarrow J \rightarrow L \rightarrow N \rightarrow Finish$$

just as we found by a different method at the beginning of the section. This path is highlighted in Figure 16.5 by the darker arrows. It is the activities on this path that Mr. Perty must monitor with special care to keep the project on schedule.

Table 16.3   Slack for Reliable's Activities

Activity	Slack (LF — EF)	On Critical Path?
A	0	Yes
B	0	Yes
C	0	Yes
D	4	No
E	0	Yes
F	0	Yes
G	4	No
H	4	No
I	2	No
J	0	Yes
K	1	No
L	0	Yes
M	4	No
N	0	Yes

CD 16-19

Review

Now let us review Mr. Perty's questions at the beginning of the section and see how all of them have been answered by the PERT/CPM scheduling procedure.

Question 2: What is the total time required to complete the project if no delays occur? This is the earliest finish time at the finish node (EF = 44 weeks), as given at the bottom of Figures 16.3 and 16.5.

Question 3: When do the individual activities need to start and finish (at the latest) to meet this project completion time? These times are the latest start times (LS) and latest finish times (LF) given in Figures 16.4 and 16.5. These times provide a "last chance schedule" to complete the project in 44 weeks if no further delays occur.

Question 4: When can the individual activities start and finish (at the earliest) if no delays occur? These times are the earliest start times (ES) and earliest finish times (EF) given in Figures 16.3 and 16.5. These times usually are used to establish the initial schedule for the project. (Subsequent delays may force later adjustments in the schedule.)

Question 5: Which are the critical bottleneck activities where any delays must be avoided to prevent delaying project completion? These are the activities on the critical path shown by the darker arrows in Figure 16.5. Mr. Perty needs to focus most of his attention on keeping these particular activities on schedule in striving to keep the overall project on schedule.

Question 6: For the other activities, how much delay can be tolerated without delaying project completion? These tolerable delays are the positive slacks given in the middle column of Table 16.3.

Using a Computer to Answer These Questions

If you prefer to use a spreadsheet to do the work involved in answering these questions, Figure 16.6 shows how this can be done. The top half gives the answers. To obtain these answers, you need to enter the appropriate equations into the various cells (as shown in the bottom half of the figure) by applying the logic described in this section. The column E equations are directly based on the *earliest start time rule*. Column F uses the formula that EF = ES + Duration of the activity, where the duration of all the activities is given by Time (D4:D17). Similarly, column G uses the formula that LS = LF - Duration of the activity. Column H directly applies the *latest finish time rule*. Column I uses the formula that Slack = LF - EF. Column J answers *Yes* if Slack = 0 and *No* otherwise.

It may take longer to set up the spreadsheet and enter all the equations than to mentally perform all the calculations directly on the project network. However, if you don't trust your arithmetic, Excel can be relied on to do that part of the job correctly. The spreadsheet also displays the results in a nice format.

	A	B	C	D	E	F	G	H	I	J
1		**Reliable Construction Co. Project Scheduling Problem**								
2										
3		**Activity**	**Description**	**Time**	**ES**	**EF**	**LS**	**LF**	**Slack**	**Critical?**
4		A	Excavate	2	0	2	0	2	0	Yes
5		B	Foundation	4	2	6	2	6	0	Yes
6		C	Rough Wall	10	6	16	6	16	0	Yes
7		D	Roof	6	16	22	20	26	4	No
8		E	Exterior Plumbing	4	16	20	16	20	0	Yes
9		F	Interior Plumbing	5	20	25	20	25	0	Yes
10		G	Exterior Siding	7	22	29	26	33	4	No
11		H	Exterior Painting	9	29	38	33	42	4	No
12		I	Electrical Work	7	16	23	18	25	2	No
13		J	Wallboard	8	25	33	25	33	0	Yes
14		K	Flooring	4	33	37	34	38	1	No
15		L	Interior Painting	5	33	38	33	38	0	Yes
16		M	Exterior Fixtures	2	38	40	42	44	4	No
17		N	Interior Fixtures	6	38	44	38	44	0	Yes
18										
19					**Project Duration**		44			

	E	F	G	H	I	J
3	**ES**	**EF**	**LS**	**LF**	**Slack**	**Critical?**
4	0	=ES+Time	=LF-Time	=MIN(G5)	=LF-EF	=IF(Slack=0,"Yes","No")
5	=MAX(F4)	=ES+Time	=LF-Time	=MIN(G6)	=LF-EF	=IF(Slack=0,"Yes","No")
6	=MAX(F5)	=ES+Time	=LF-Time	=MIN(G7,G8,G12)	=LF-EF	=IF(Slack=0,"Yes","No")
7	=MAX(F6)	=ES+Time	=LF-Time	=MIN(G10)	=LF-EF	=IF(Slack=0,"Yes","No")
8	=MAX(F6)	=ES+Time	=LF-Time	=MIN(G9,G11)	=LF-EF	=IF(Slack=0,"Yes","No")
9	=MAX(F8)	=ES+Time	=LF-Time	=MIN(G13)	=LF-EF	=IF(Slack=0,"Yes","No")
10	=MAX(F7)	=ES+Time	=LF-Time	=MIN(G11)	=LF-EF	=IF(Slack=0,"Yes","No")
11	=MAX(F8,F10)	=ES+Time	=LF-Time	=MIN(G16)	=LF-EF	=IF(Slack=0,"Yes","No")
12	=MAX(F6)	=ES+Time	=LF-Time	=MIN(G13)	=LF-EF	=IF(Slack=0,"Yes","No")
13	=MAX(F9,F12)	=ES+Time	=LF-Time	=MIN(G14,G15)	=LF-EF	=IF(Slack=0,"Yes","No")
14	=MAX(F13)	=ES+Time	=LF-Time	=MIN(G17)	=LF-EF	=IF(Slack=0,"Yes","No")
15	=MAX(F13)	=ES+Time	=LF-Time	=MIN(G17)	=LF-EF	=IF(Slack=0,"Yes","No")
16	=MAX(F11)	=ES+Time	=LF-Time	=ProjectDuration	=LF-EF	=IF(Slack=0,"Yes","No")
17	=MAX(F14,F15)	=ES+Time	=LF-Time	=ProjectDuration	=LF-EF	=IF(Slack=0,"Yes","No")
18						
19	**Project Duration**	=MAX(EF)				

Range Name	Cells
Activity	B4:B17
Critical?	J4:J17
Description	C4:C17
EF	F4:F17
ES	E4:E17
LF	H4:H17
LS	G4:G17
ProjectDuration	F19
Slack	I4:I17
Time	D4:D17

Figure 16.6   The equations in the bottom half show how to develop the schedule for the Reliable Construction Co. project on a spreadsheet.

REVIEW QUESTIONS
1. What is meant by the following terms: (*a*) a path through the project network; (*b*) the length of a path; and (*c*) a critical path?
2. What needs to happen in order to meet a schedule based on earliest start times and earliest finish times?
3. What does the earliest start time rule say?
4. What is a forward pass through the project network?
5. Why is a schedule based on latest start times and latest finish times a "last chance schedule"?
6. What does the latest finish time rule say?
7. How does a backward pass through the project network differ from a forward pass?
8. What is the significance of a critical path for the project manager?
9. What are two methods of finding a critical path through the project network?

16.4 DEALING WITH UNCERTAIN ACTIVITY DURATIONS

Now we come to the next of Mr. Perty's questions posed at the end of Section 16.1.

> **Question 7**: Given the uncertainties in accurately estimating activity durations, what is the probability of completing the project by the deadline (47 weeks)?

Recall that Reliable will incur a large penalty ($300,000) if this deadline is missed. Therefore, Mr. Perty needs to know the probability of meeting the deadline. If this probability is not very high, he will need to consider taking costly measures (using overtime, etc.) to shorten the duration of some of the activities.

It is somewhat reassuring that the PERT/CPM scheduling procedure in the preceding section obtained an estimate of 44 weeks for the project duration. However, Mr. Perty understands very well that this estimate is based on the assumption that the *actual* duration of each activity will turn out to be the same as its *estimated* duration for at least the activities on the critical path. Since the company does not have much prior experience with this kind of project, there is considerable uncertainty about how much time actually will be needed for each activity. In reality, the duration of each activity is a *random variable* having some probability distribution.

The original version of PERT took this uncertainty into account by using three different types of estimates of the duration of an activity to obtain basic information about its probability distribution, as described below.

The PERT Three-Estimate Approach
Applying the PERT three-estimate approach, the three estimates to be obtained for each activity are

> **Most likely estimate** (*m*) = Estimate of the most likely value of the duration

> **Optimistic estimate** (*o*) = Estimate of the duration under the most favorable conditions

> **Pessimistic estimate** (*p*) = Estimate of the duration under the most unfavorable conditions

The intended location of these three estimates with respect to the probability distribution is shown in Figure 16.7.

CD 16-22

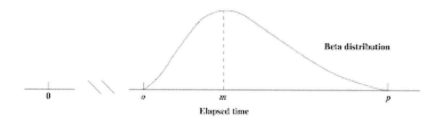

| Figure 16.7 | Model of the probability distribution of the duration of an activity for the PERT three-estimate approach: m = most likely estimate, o = optimistic estimate, and p = pessimistic estimate. |

Thus, the optimistic and pessimistic estimates are meant to lie at the extremes of what is possible, whereas the most likely estimate provides the highest point of the probability distribution. PERT also assumes that the *form* of the probability distribution is a *beta distribution* (which has a shape like that in the figure) in order to calculate the *mean* and *variance* of the probability distribution. As Figure 16.7 illustrates, a beta distribution provides a reasonable shape for a distribution of activity times, including having two endpoints (o and p) and a single highest point (m) that correspond to the definitions of the three time estimates.

Let

μ = Mean of the probability distribution in Figure 16.7

σ^2 = Variance of the probability distribution in Figure 16.7

Thus, if the activity were to be performed numerous times and the duration recorded each time, μ would be essentially the *average* of these durations and σ^2 would be a measure of the *variability* of these durations. If $\sigma^2 = 0$, then all the durations would be exactly the same (no variability), whereas a large value of σ^2 indicates a lot of variability in the durations. The *standard deviation* (the square root of σ^2) also helps to measure the variability. Many of the durations would be spread out over the interval between ($\mu - \sigma$) and ($\mu + \sigma$), but some would be further from μ than this. However, for most probability distributions such as the beta distribution, essentially all the durations would lie inside the interval between ($\mu - 3\sigma$) and ($\mu + 3\sigma$). (For example, for a normal distribution, 99.73 percent of the distribution lies inside this interval.) In other words, the spread between the smallest and largest durations (essentially $p - o$) would be roughly 6σ. Therefore, an approximate formula for σ^2 is

$$\sigma^2 = \left(\frac{p-o}{6} \right)^2$$

Similarly, an approximate formula for μ is

$$\mu = \frac{o + 4m + p}{6}$$

Intuitively, this formula is placing most of the weight on the *most likely estimate* and then small equal weights on the other two estimates.

We should mention here that these formulas for estimating μ and σ^2 have become somewhat controversial in recent years. As discussed further in Section 16.7, some research studies have questioned the accuracy of these estimates and suggested alternative estimation procedures. However, for the time being, these formulas continue to be part of the standard PERT procedure.

Mr. Perty now has contacted the foreman of each crew that will be responsible for one of the activities to request that these three estimates be made of the duration of the activity. The responses are shown in the first four columns of Table 16.4.

Table 16.4   Expected Value and Variance of the Duration of Each Activity for Reliable's Project

Activity	Optimistic Estimate, o	Most Likely Estimate, m	Pessimistic Estimate, p	Mean, $\mu = \dfrac{o + 4m + p}{6}$	Variance, $\sigma^2 = \left(\dfrac{p - o}{6}\right)^2$
A	1	2	3	2	$\frac{1}{9}$
B	2	$3\frac{1}{2}$	8	4	1
C	6	9	18	10	4
D	4	$5\frac{1}{2}$	10	6	1
E	1	$4\frac{1}{2}$	5	4	$\frac{4}{9}$
F	4	4	10	5	1
G	5	$6\frac{1}{2}$	11	7	1
H	5	8	17	9	4
I	3	$7\frac{1}{2}$	9	7	1
J	3	9	9	8	1
K	4	4	4	4	0
L	1	$5\frac{1}{2}$	7	5	1
M	1	2	3	2	$\frac{1}{9}$
N	5	$5\frac{1}{2}$	9	6	$\frac{4}{9}$

For example, the three estimates for activity C are

Activity C: $o = 6$ $m = 9$ $p = 18$

Therefore, applying the above formulas, the mean and variance of the duration of this activity are approximately

$$\mu = \frac{6 + 4(9) + 18}{6} = 10$$

$$\sigma^2 = \left(\frac{18 - 6}{6}\right)^2 = 4$$

Note that the value of the mean (μ) is not the same as the most likely estimate (m). This is not unusual (the possibility of *much* higher durations here pushes the mean up), but μ generally is at least fairly close to m.

The last two columns of Table 16.4 show the approximate mean and variance of the duration of each activity, calculated in this same way. In this example, all the means happen to be the same as the estimated duration obtained in Table 16.1 of Section 16.1. Therefore, if all the activity durations were to equal their means, the duration of the project still would be 44 weeks, or 3 weeks before the deadline. (See Figure 16.5 for the critical path requiring 44 weeks.)

However, this piece of information is not very reassuring to Mr. Perty. He knows that the durations fluctuate around their means. Consequently, it is inevitable that the duration of some activities will be larger than the mean, perhaps even nearly as large as the pessimistic estimate, which could greatly delay the project.

To check the *worst case scenario,* Mr. Perty reexamines the project network with the duration of each activity set equal to the *pessimistic estimate* (as given in the fourth column of Table 16.4). Table 16.5 shows the six paths through this network (as given previously in Table 16.2) and the length of each path using the pessimistic estimates. The fourth path, which was the critical path in Figure 16.5, now has increased its length from 44 weeks to 69 weeks. However, the length of the first path, which originally was 40 weeks (as given in Table 16.2), now has increased all the way up to 70 weeks. Since this is the longest path, it is the critical path with pessimistic estimates, which would give a project duration of 70 weeks.

Table 16.5   The Paths and Path Lengths through Reliable's Project Network When the Duration of Each Activity Equals Its Pessimistic Estimate

Path	Length (weeks)
Start→A→B→C→D→G→H→M→Finish	3 + 8 + 18 + 10 + 11 + 17 + 3 = 70
Start→A→B→C→E→H→M→Finish	3 + 8 + 18 + 5 + 17 + 3 = 54
Start→A→B→C→E→F→J→K→N→Finish	3 + 8 + 18 + 5 + 10 + 9 + 4 + 9 = 66
Start→A→B→C→E→F→J→L→N→Finish	3 + 8 + 18 + 5 + 10 + 9 + 7 + 9 = 69
Start→A→B→C→I→J→K→N→Finish	3 + 8 + 18 + 9 + 9 + 4 + 9 = 60
Start→A→B→C→I→J→L→N→Finish	3 + 8 + 18 + 9 + 9 + 7 + 9 = 63

Given this dire (albeit unlikely) worst case scenario, Mr. Perty realizes that it is far from certain that the deadline of 47 weeks will be met. But what is the probability of doing so?

PERT/CPM makes three *simplifying approximations* to help calculate this probability.

Three Simplifying Approximations

To calculate the probability that *project duration* will be no more than 47 weeks, it is necessary to obtain the following information about the probability distribution of project duration.

Probability Distribution of Project Duration

1. What is the *mean* (denoted by μ_p) of this distribution?

2. What is the *variance* (denoted by σ_p^2) of this distribution?

3. What is the *form* of this distribution?

Recall that project duration equals the *length* (total elapsed time) of the *longest path* through the project network. However, just about any of the six paths listed in Table 16.5 can turn out to be the longest path (and so the critical path), depending on what the duration of each activity turns out to be between its optimistic and pessimistic estimates. Since dealing with all these paths would be complicated, PERT/CPM focuses on just the following path.

> The **mean critical path** is the path through the project network that would be the critical path if the duration of each activity were to equal its *mean.*

To find Reliable's mean critical path, note again that the mean durations listed in the fifth column of Table 16.4 happen to equal the estimated durations given in the rightmost column of Table 16.1 for every activity. Therefore, in this case, the critical path based on mean durations is the same as the one based on estimated durations that was found in the preceding section. Thus, the mean critical path is

$$\text{Start} \rightarrow A \rightarrow B \rightarrow C \rightarrow E \rightarrow F \rightarrow J \rightarrow L \rightarrow N \rightarrow \text{Finish}$$

as highlighted in Figure 16.5.

> **Simplifying Approximation 1**: Assume that the *mean critical path* will turn out to be the longest path through the project network. This is only a rough approximation since the assumption occasionally does not hold in the usual case where some of the activity durations do not equal their means. Fortunately, when the assumption does not hold, the true longest path commonly is not much longer than the mean critical path (as illustrated in Table 16.5).

Although this approximation will enable us to calculate μ_p, we need one more approximation to obtain σ_p^2.

> **Simplifying Approximation 2**: Assume that the durations of the activities on the mean critical path are *statistically independent*. Thus, the three estimates of the duration of an activity would never change after learning the durations of some of the other activities. This assumption should hold if the activities are performed truly independently of each other. However, the assumption becomes only a rough approximation if the circumstances that cause the duration of one activity to deviate from its mean also tend to cause similar deviations for some other activities.

We now have a simple method for computing μ_p and σ_p^2.

> **Calculation of μ_p and σ_p^2**: Because of simplifying approximation 1, the *mean* of the probability distribution of project duration is approximately

$$\mu_p = \text{Sum of the } \textit{means} \text{ of the durations for the activities on the mean critical path}$$

Because of both simplifying approximations 1 and 2, the *variance* of the probability distribution

of project duration is approximately

$$\sigma_p^2 = \text{Sum of the } \textit{variances} \text{ of the durations for the activities on the mean critical path}$$

Since the means and variances of the durations for all the activities of Reliable's project already are given in Table 16.4, we only need to record these values for the activities on the mean critical path, as shown in Table 16.6. Summing the second column and then summing the third column give

$$\mu_p = 44 \qquad \sigma_p^2 = 9$$

Table 16.6   Calculation of μ_p and σ_p^2 for Reliable's Project

Activities on Mean Critical Path	Mean	Variance
A	2	¼
B	4	1
C	10	4
E	4	¼
F	5	1
J	8	1
L	5	1
N	6	¼
Project duration	$\mu_p = 44$	$\sigma_p^2 = 9$

Now we just need an approximation for the *form* of the probability distribution of project duration.

> **Simplifying Approximation 3**: Assume that the form of the probability distribution of project duration is the *normal distribution,* which has the bell shape illustrated in Figure 16.8. By using simplifying approximations 1 and 2, there is some statistical theory (one version of the central limit theorem) that justifies this assumption as being a reasonable approximation if the number of activities on the mean critical path is not too small (say, at least five). The approximation becomes better as this number of activities increases.

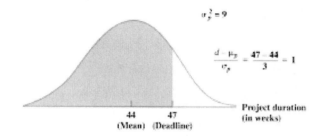

$$\sigma_p^2 = 9$$

$$\frac{d - \mu_p}{\sigma_p} = \frac{47 - 44}{3} = 1$$

Project duration (in weeks)

44   47
(Mean) (Deadline)

> **Figure 16.8**   The three simplifying approximations lead to the probability distribution of the duration of Reliable' project being approximated by the normal distribution shown here. The shaded area is the portion of the distribution that meets the deadline of 47 weeks.

Now we are ready to determine (approximately) the probability of completing Reliable's project within 47 weeks.

Approximating the Probability of Meeting the Deadline

Let

d = Deadline for the project

= 47 weeks

$P(T \le d)$ = Probability that the project duration (T) does not exceed the deadline (given the three simplifying approximations)

To find $P(T \le d)$, first calculate the *standard deviation* of project duration as

$$\sigma_p = \sqrt{\sigma_p^2} = \sqrt{9} = 3$$

and then compute

$$\frac{d - \mu_p}{\sigma_p} = \frac{47 - 44}{3} = 1$$

= Number of standard deviations by which d exceeds μ_p.

Finally, use this latter number to read off the corresponding value of $P(T \le d)$ in Table 16.7, so

$$P(T = d) = 0.84$$

(This table is an abbreviation of the table for the normal distribution given in Appendix 16.1 at the end of this chapter.)

Table 16.7 Approximate Probability of Meeting a Project Deadline

$\dfrac{d - \mu_p}{\sigma_p}$	$P(T \le d)$	$\dfrac{d - \mu_p}{\sigma_p}$	$P(T \le d)$
−3.0	0.0014	0	0.50
−2.5	0.0062	0.25	0.60
−2.0	0.023	0.5	0.69
−1.75	0.040	0.75	0.77
−1.5	0.067	1.0	0.84
−1.25	0.11	1.25	0.89
−1.0	0.16	1.5	0.933
−0.75	0.23	1.75	0.960
−0.5	0.31	2.0	0.977
−0.25	0.40	2.5	0.9938
0	0.50	3.0	0.9986

Warning: This $P(T \le d)$ is only a rough approximation of the true probability of meeting the project deadline. Furthermore, because of simplifying approximation 1, it usually overstates the true probability somewhat. Therefore, the project manager should view $P(T \le d)$ as only providing rough guidance on the best odds of meeting the deadline without taking new costly measures to try to reduce the duration of some activities.

Because this $P(T \le d)$ is only a rough approximation of the true probability of meeting the project deadline, another prominent management science technique (computer simulation) often is used to obtain a better approximation. Section 13.3 describes how this is done for this same example.

To assist you in carrying out the PERT/CPM procedure for calculating $P (T \leq d)$, we have provided an Excel template (labeled PERT) in this chapter's Excel files in your MS Courseware. Figure 16.9 illustrates the use of this template for Reliable's project. The data for the problem are entered in the cells shaded light blue in the spreadsheet. After entering data, the results immediately appear in the other sections. In particular, by entering the three time estimates for each activity, the spreadsheet will automatically calculate the corresponding estimates for the mean and variance in columns G and H. Next, by specifying the mean critical path (by entering * in column F for each activity on the mean critical path) and the deadline (in cell K12), the spreadsheet automatically calculates the mean and variance of the length of the mean critical path (in cells K7:K8) along with the probability that the project will be completed by the deadline (in cell K10). (If you are not sure which path is the mean critical path, the mean length of *any* path can be checked by entering a * for each activity on that path in column F. After checking every candidate, the path with the longest mean length in cell K7 then is the mean critical path.)

Realizing that $P (T \leq d) = 0.84$ is probably an optimistic approximation, Mr. Perty is somewhat concerned that he may have perhaps only a 60 to 80 percent chance of meeting the deadline with the current plan. Therefore, rather than taking the significant chance of the company incurring the late penalty of $300,000, he decides to investigate what it would cost to reduce the project duration down to about 40 weeks. If the *time–cost trade-off* for doing this is favorable, the company might then be able to earn the bonus of $150,000 for finishing within 40 weeks.

You will see this story unfold in the next section.

REVIEW QUESTIONS

1. What are the names of the three estimates in the PERT three-estimate approach?
2. Where are these three estimates meant to be located in the probability distribution of the duration of an activity?
3. What simplifying approximation is made about which path will be the longest path through the project network?
4. What simplifying approximation is made about the relationship between the durations of different activities?
5. What is the formula for the mean (μ_p) of the probability distribution of project duration?
6. What is the formula for the variance (σ_p^2) of the probability distribution of project duration?
7. What simplifying approximation is made about the form of the probability distribution of project duration?
8. The approximation obtained for the probability of meeting the project deadline is likely to be on which side (higher or lower) of the true probability?

CD 16-29

	A	B	C	D	E	F	G	H	I	J	K
1		**Template for PERT Three-Estimate Approach**									
2											
3				Time Estimates		On Mean					
4		Activity	o	m	p	Critical Path	μ	σ^2		Mean Critical	
5		A	1	2	3	*	2	0.1111		Mean Critical	
6		B	2	3.5	8	*	4	1		Path	
7		C	6	9	18	*	10	4		$\mu =$	44
8		D	4	5.5	10		6	1		$\sigma^2 =$	9
9		E	1	4.5	5	*	4	0.4444			
10		F	4	4	10	*	5	1		P(T<=d) =	0.8413
11		G	5	6.5	11		7	1		where	
12		H	5	8	17		9	4		d =	47
13		I	3	7.5	9		7	1			
14		J	3	9	9	*	8	1			
15		K	4	4	4		4	0			
16		L	1	5.5	7	*	5	1			
17		M	1	2	3		2	0.1111			
18		N	5	5.5	9	*	6	0.4444			

	J	K
5		Mean Critical
6		Path
7	$\mu =$	=SUMIF(OnMeanCriticalPath,"*",ActivityMean)
8	$\sigma^2 =$	=SUMIF(OnMeanCriticalPath,"*",ActivityVariance)
9		
10	P(T<=d) =	=NORMDIST(d,CriticalPathMean,SQRT(CriticalPathVariance),1)
11	where	
12	d =	47

	G	H
4	μ	σ^2
5	=IF(o="","",(o+4*m+p)/6)	=IF(o="","",((p-o)/6)^2)
6	=IF(o="","",(o+4*m+p)/6)	=IF(o="","",((p-o)/6)^2)
7	=IF(o="","",(o+4*m+p)/6)	=IF(o="","",((p-o)/6)^2)
8	=IF(o="","",(o+4*m+p)/6)	=IF(o="","",((p-o)/6)^2)
9	:	:
10	:	:

Range Name	Cells
Activity	B5:B18
ActivityMean	G5:G18
ActivityVariance	H5:H18
CompletionProbability	K10
CriticalPathMean	K7
CriticalPathVariance	K8
d	K12
m	D5:D18
o	C5:C18
OnMeanCriticalPath	F5:F18
p	E5:E18

Figure 16.9   This Excel template in your MS Courseware enables efficient application of the PERT three-estimate approach, as illustrated here for Reliable's project.

16.5   CONSIDERING TIME–COST TRADE-OFFS

Mr. Perty now wants to investigate how much extra it would cost to reduce the expected project duration down to 40 weeks (the deadline for the company earning a bonus of $150,000 for early completion). Therefore, he is ready to address the next of his questions posed at the end of Section 16.1.

Question 8: If extra money is spent to expedite the project, what is the least expensive way of attempting to meet the target completion time (40 weeks)?

Mr. Perty remembers that CPM provides an excellent procedure for using *linear programming* to investigate such *time–cost trade-offs,* so he will use this approach again to address this question.

We begin with some background.

Time–Cost Trade-Offs for Individual Activities

The first key concept for this approach is that of *crashing.*

> **Crashing an activity** refers to taking special costly measures to reduce the duration of an activity below its normal value. These special measures might include using overtime, hiring additional temporary help, using special time-saving materials, obtaining special equipment, and so forth. **Crashing the project** refers to crashing a number of activities to reduce the duration of the project below its normal value.

The **CPM method of time–cost trade-offs** is concerned with determining how much (if any) to crash each of the activities to reduce the anticipated duration of the project down to a desired value.

The data necessary for determining how much to crash a particular activity are given by the *time–cost graph* for the activity. Figure 16.10 shows a typical time–cost graph. Note the two key points on this graph labeled *normal* and *crash.*

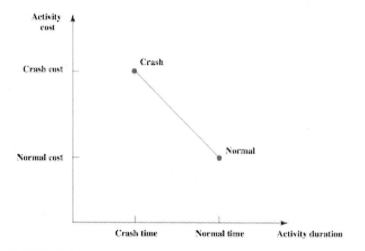

Figure 16.10　A typical time-cost graph for an activity.

> The **normal point** on the time–cost graph shows the time (duration) and cost of the activity when it is performed in the normal way. The crash point shows the time and cost when the activity is *fully crashed;* that is, it is fully expedited with no cost spared to reduce its duration as much as possible.

For most applications, it is assumed that *partially crashing* the activity at any level will give a combination of time and cost that will lie somewhere on the line segment between these two

CD 16-31

points. (For example, this assumption says that *half* of a full crash will give a point on this line segment that is midway between the normal and crash points.) This simplifying approximation reduces the necessary data gathering to estimating the time and cost for just two situations: *normal conditions* (to obtain the normal point) and a *full crash* (to obtain the crash point).

Using this approach, Mr. Perty has his staff and crew foremen working on developing these data for each of the activities of Reliable's project. For example, the foreman of the crew responsible for putting up the wallboard indicates that adding two temporary employees and using overtime would enable him to reduce the duration of this activity from eight weeks to six weeks, which is the minimum possible. Mr. Perty's staff then estimates the cost of fully crashing the activity in this way as compared to following the normal eight-week schedule, as shown below.

Activity J (Put up the wallboard)

Normal point: Time = 8 weeks, Cost = $430,000

Crash point: Time = 6 weeks, Cost = $490,000

Maximum reduction in time = 8 − 6 = 2 weeks

$$\text{Crash cost per week saved} = \frac{\$490,000 - 430,000}{2}$$

$$= \$30,000$$

Table 16.8 gives the corresponding data obtained for all the activities.

Table 16.8   Time-Cost Trade-Off Data for the Activities of Reliable's Project

Activity	Time (weeks) Normal	Time (weeks) Crash	Cost Normal	Cost Crash	Maximum Reduction in Time (weeks)	Crash Cost per Week Saved
A	2	1	$180,000	$ 280,000	1	$100,000
B	4	2	320,000	420,000	2	50,000
C	10	7	620,000	860,000	3	80,000
D	6	4	260,000	340,000	2	40,000
E	4	3	410,000	570,000	1	160,000
F	5	3	180,000	260,000	2	40,000
G	7	4	900,000	1,020,000	3	40,000
H	9	6	200,000	380,000	3	60,000
I	7	5	210,000	270,000	2	30,000
J	8	6	430,000	490,000	2	30,000
K	4	3	160,000	200,000	1	40,000
L	5	3	250,000	350,000	2	50,000
M	2	1	100,000	200,000	1	100,000
N	6	3	330,000	510,000	3	60,000

Which Activities Should be Crashed?

Summing the *normal cost* and *crash cost* columns of Table 16.8 gives

Sum of normal costs   = $4.55 mission

Some of crash costs   = $6.15 million

Recal that the company will be paid $5.4 million for doing this project. (This figure excludes the $150,000 bonus for finishing within 40 weeks and the $300,000 penalty for not finishing within 47 weeks.) This payment needs to cover some *overhead costs* in addition to the costs of the activities listed in the table, as well as provide a reasonable profit to the company. When developing the (winning) bid of $5.4 million, Reliable's management felt that this amount would provide a reasonable profit as long as the total cost of the activities could be held fairly close to the normal level of about $4.55 million. Mr. Perty understands very well that it is now his responsibility to keep the project as close to both budget and schedule as possible.

As found previously in Figure 16.5, if all the activities are performed in the normal way, the anticipated duration of the project would be 44 weeks (if delays can be avoided). If *all* the activities were to be *fully crashed* instead, then a similar calculation would find that this duration would be reduced to only 28 weeks. But look at the prohibitive cost ($6.15 million) of doing this! Fully crashing all activities clearly is not an option that can be considered.

However, Mr. Perty still wants to investigate the possibility of partially or fully crashing just a few activities to reduce the anticipated duration of the project down to 40 weeks.

> **The problem**: What is the least expensive way of crashing some activities to reduce project duration to the specified level (40 weeks)?

One way of solving this problem is marginal cost analysis, which uses the last column of Table 16.8 (along with Figure 16.5 in Section 16.3) to determine the least expensive way to reduce project duration one week at a time. The easiest way to conduct this kind of analysis is to set up a table like Table 16.9 that lists all the paths through the project network and the current length of each of these paths. To get started, this information can be copied directly from Table 16.2.

Since the fourth path listed in Table 16.9 has the longest length (44 weeks), the only way to reduce project duration by a week is to reduce the duration of the activities on this particular path by a week. Comparing the crash cost per week saved given in the last column of Table 16.8 for these activities, the smallest cost is $30,000 for activity J. (Note that activity I with this same cost is not on this path.) Therefore, the first change is to crash activity J enough to reduce its duration by a week.

This change results in reducing the length of each path that includes activity J (the third, fourth, fifth, and sixth paths in Table 16.9) by a week, as shown in the second row of Table 16.10. Because the fourth path still is the longest (43 weeks), the same process is repeated to find the least expensive activity to shorten on this path. This again is activity J, since the next-to-last column in Table 16.8 indicates that a maximum reduction of two weeks is allowed for this activity. This second reduction of a week for activity J leads to the third row of Table 16.10.

Table 16.9   The Initial Table for Starting Marginal Cost Analysis of Reliable's Project

Activity to Crash	Crash Cost	Length of Path					
		ABCDGHM	ABCEHM	ABCEFJKN	ABCEFJLN	ABCIJKN	ABCIJLN
		40	31	43	44	41	42

Table 16.10   The Final Table for Performing Marginal Cost Analysis on Reliable's Project

Activity to Crash	Crash Cost	Length of Path					
		ABCDGHM	ABCEHM	ABCEFJKN	ABCEFJLN	ABCIJKN	ABCIJLN
		40	31	43	44	41	42
J	$30,000	40	31	42	43	40	41
J	30,000	40	31	41	42	39	40
F	40,000	40	31	40	41	39	40
F	40,000	40	31	39	40	39	40

At this point, the fourth path still is the longest (42 weeks), but activity J cannot be shortened any further. Among the other activities on this path, activity F now is the least expensive to shorten ($40,000 per week) according to the last column of Table 16.8. Therefore, this activity is shortened by a week to obtain the fourth row of Table 16.10, and then (because a maximum reduction of two weeks is allowed) is shortened by another week to obtain the last row of this table.

The longest path (a tie between the first, fourth, and sixth paths) now has the desired length of 40 weeks, so we don't need to do any more crashing. (If we did need to go further, the next step would require looking at the activities on all three paths to find the least expensive way of shortening all three paths by a week.) The total cost of crashing activities J and F to get down to this project duration of 40 weeks is calculated by adding the costs in the second column of Table 16.10—a total of $140,000. Figure 16.11 shows the resulting project network.   Since $140,000 is slightly less than the bonus of $150,000 for finishing within 40 weeks, it might appear that Mr. Perty should proceed with this solution. However, he actually concludes that he probably should not crash the project at all, as we will discuss at the end of the section. (Meanwhile, be mulling over why his conclusion makes sense because of the preceding section on dealing with uncertain activity durations.)

Figure 16.11 shows that reducing the durations of activities F and J to their crash times has led to now having *three* critical paths through the network. The reason is that, as we found earlier from the last row of Table 16.10, the three paths tie for being the longest, each with a length of 40 weeks.

With larger networks, marginal cost analysis can become quite unwieldy. A more efficient procedure would be desirable for large projects. For these reasons, the standard CPM procedure is to apply *linear programming* instead (commonly with a customized software package).

For these reasons, the standard CPM procedure is to apply *linear programming* instead (commonly with a customized software package).

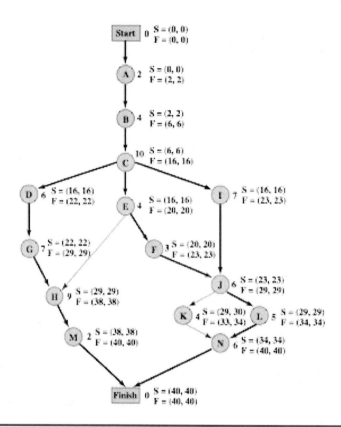

Figure 16.11   The project network if activities J and F are fully crashed (with all other activities normal) for Reliable's project. The darker arrows show the various critical paths through the project network.

Using Linear Programming to Make Crashing Decisions

The problem of finding the least expensive way of crashing activities can be rephrased in a form more familiar to linear programming as follows.

> **Restatement of the problem**: Consider the total cost of the project, including the extra cost of crashing activities. The problem then is to minimize this total cost, subject to the constraint that project duration must be less than or equal to the time desired by the project manager.

The decisions to be made are the following:

1. The start time of each activity.

2. The reduction in the duration of each activity due to crashing.

3. The finish time of the project (must not exceed 40 weeks).

Figure 16.12 shows how this problem can be formulated as a linear programming model on a spreadsheet. The decisions to be made are shown in the changing cells, StartTime (I6:I19), TimeReduction (J6:J19), and ProjectFinishTime (I22). Columns B to H correspond to the columns in Table 16.8. As the equations in the bottom half of the figure indicate, columns G and H are calculated in a straightforward way. The equations for column K express the fact that the finish time for each activity is its start time *plus* its normal time *minus* its time reduction due to crashing. The equation entered into the objective cell TotalCost (I24) adds all the normal costs plus the extra costs due to crashing to obtain the total cost.

	A	B	C	D	E	F	G	H	I	J	K
1		**Reliable Construction Co. Project Scheduling Problem with Time-Cost Trade-offs**									
2											
3							Maximum	Crash Cost			
4			Time		Cost		Time	per Week	Start	Time	Finish
5		Activity	Normal	Crash	Normal	Crash	Reduction	saved	Time	Reduction	Time
6		A	2	1	$180,000	$280,000	1	$100,000	0	0	2
7		B	4	2	$320,000	$420,000	2	$50,000	2	0	6
8		C	10	7	$620,000	$860,000	3	$80,000	6	0	16
9		D	6	4	$260,000	$340,000	2	$40,000	16	0	22
10		E	4	3	$410,000	$570,000	1	$160,000	16	0	20
11		F	5	3	$180,000	$260,000	2	$40,000	20	2	23
12		G	7	4	$900,000	$1,020,000	3	$40,000	22	0	29
13		H	9	6	$200,000	$380,000	3	$60,000	29	0	38
14		I	7	5	$210,000	$270,000	2	$30,000	16	0	23
15		J	8	6	$430,000	$490,000	2	$30,000	23	2	29
16		K	4	3	$160,000	$200,000	1	$40,000	30	0	34
17		L	5	3	$250,000	$350,000	2	$50,000	29	0	34
18		M	2	1	$100,000	$200,000	1	$100,000	38	0	40
19		N	6	3	$330,000	$510,000	3	$60,000	34	0	40
20											
21											Max Time
22								Project Finish Time	40	<=	40
23											
24								Total Cost	$4,690,000		

Figure 16.12 continued

Solver Parameters

Set Objective Cell: TotalCost
To: Min
By Changing Variable Cells:
    StartTime, TimeReduction, ProjectFinishTime
Subject to the Constraints:

BStart >= AFinish	CStart >= BFinish
DStart >= CFinish	EStart >= CFinish
FStart >= EFinish	GStart >=DFinish
HStart >= EFinish	HStart >= GFinish
IStart >= CFinish	JStart >= FFinish
JStart >= IFinish	KStart >= JFinish
LStart >= JFinish	MStart >= HFinish
NStart >= KFinish	NStart >= LFinish

    ProjectFinishTime <= MaxTime
    ProjectFinishTime >= MFinish
    ProjectFinishTime >= NFinish
    TimeReduction <= MaxTimeReduction
Solver Options:
    Make Variables Nonnegative
    Solving Method: Simplex LP

Range Name	Cells
AFinish	K6
AStart	I6
BFinish	K7
BStart	I7
CFinish	K8
CrashCost	F6:F19
CrashCostPerWeekSaved	H6:H19
CrashTime	D6:D19
CStart	I8
DFinish	K9
DStart	I9
EFinish	K10
EStart	I10
FFinish	K11
FinishTime	K6:K19
FStart	I11
GFinish	K12
GStart	I12
HFinish	K13
HStart	I13
IFinish	K14
IStart	I14
JFinish	K15
JStart	I15
KFinish	K16
KStart	I16
LFinish	K17
LStart	I17
MaxTime	K22
MaxTimeReduction	G6:G19
MFinish	K18
MStart	I18
NFinish	K19
NormalCost	E6:E19
NormalTime	C6:C19
NStart	I19
ProjectFinishTime	I22
StartTime	I6:I19
TimeReduction	J6:J19
TotalCost	I24

	K
4	Finish
5	Time
6	=StartTime+NormalTime-TimeReduction
7	=StartTime+NormalTime-TimeReduction
8	=StartTime+NormalTime-TimeReduction
9	=StartTime+NormalTime-TimeReduction
10	:
11	:

	G	H
3	Maximum	Crash Cost
4	Time	per Week
5	Reduction	saved
6	=NormalTime-CrashTime	=(CrashCost-NormalCost)/MaxTimeReduction
7	=NormalTime-CrashTime	=(CrashCost-NormalCost)/MaxTimeReduction
8	=NormalTime-CrashTime	=(CrashCost-NormalCost)/MaxTimeReduction
9	=NormalTime-CrashTime	=(CrashCost-NormalCost)/MaxTimeReduction
10	:	:
11	:	:

Figure 16.12   The spreadsheet displays the application of the CPM method of time-cost trade-offs to Reliable's project, where columns I and J show the optimal solution obtained by using Solver with the entries shown in the Solver Parameters dialog box.

The last set of constraints in the Solver Parameters box, TimeReduction (J6:J19) ≤ Max-TimeReduction (G6:G19), specifies that the time reduction for each activity cannot exceed its maximum time reduction given in column G. The two preceding constraints, ProjectFinishTime (I22) ≥ MFinish (K18) and ProjectFinishTime (I22) ≥ NFinish (K19), indicate that the project cannot finish until each of the two immediate predecessors (activities M and N) finish. The constraint that ProjectFinishTime (I22) ≤ MaxTime (K22) is a key one that specifies that the project must finish within 40 weeks.

The constraints involving StartTime (I6:I19) all are *start-time constraints* that specify that an activity cannot start until each of its immediate predecessors have finished. For example, the first constraint shown, BStart (I7) ≥ AFinish (K6), says that activity B cannot start until activity A (its immediate predecessor) finishes. When an activity has more than one immediate predecessor, there is one such constraint for each of them. To illustrate, activity H has both activities E and G as immediate predecessors. Consequently, activity H has two start-time constraints, HSTART (I13) ≥ EFINISH (K10) and HSTART (I13) ≥ GFINISH (K12).

You may have noticed that the ≥ form of the *start-time constraints* allows a delay in starting an activity after all its immediate predecessors have finished. Although such a delay is feasible in the model, it cannot be optimal for any activity on a critical path since this needless delay would increase the total cost (by necessitating additional crashing to meet the project duration constraint). Therefore, an optimal solution for the model will not have any such delays, except possibly for activities not on a critical path.

Columns I and J in Figure 16.12 show the optimal solution obtained running Solver. (Note that this solution involves one delay—activity K starts at 30 even though its only immediate predecessor, activity J, finishes at 29—but this doesn't matter since activity K is not on a critical path.) This solution corresponds to the one displayed in Figure 16.11 that was obtained by marginal cost analysis.

Mr. Perty's Conclusions

Mr. Perty always keeps a sharp eye on the bottom line. Therefore, when his staff brings him the above plan for crashing the project to try to reduce its duration from about 44 weeks to about 40 weeks, he first looks at the estimated total cost of $4.69 million. Since the estimated total cost without any crashing is $4.55 million, the additional cost from the crashing would be about $140,000. This is $10,000 less than the bonus of $150,000 that the company would earn by finishing within 40 weeks.

However, Mr. Perty knows from long experience what we discussed in the preceding section, namely, that there is considerable uncertainty about how much time actually will be needed for each activity and so for the overall project. Recall that the PERT three-estimate approach led to having a *probability distribution* for project duration. Without crashing, this probability distribution has a *mean* of 44 weeks but such a large *variance* that there is even a substantial probability (roughly 0.2) of not even finishing within 47 weeks (which would trigger a penalty of $300,000). With the new crashing plan reducing the mean to 40 weeks, there is as much chance that the actual project duration will turn out to exceed 40 weeks as being within 40 weeks. Why spend an extra $140,000 to obtain a 50 percent chance of earning the bonus of $150,000?

> **Conclusion 1**: The plan for crashing the project only provides a 50 percent chance of actually finishing the project within 40 weeks, so the extra cost of the plan ($140,000) is not justified. Therefore, Mr. Perty rejects any crashing at this stage.

Mr. Perty does note that the two activities that had been proposed for crashing (F and J) come about halfway through the project. Therefore, if the project is well ahead of schedule before reaching activity F, then implementing the crashing plan almost certainly would enable finishing the project within 40 weeks. Furthermore, Mr. Perty knows that it would be good for the company's reputation (as well as a feather in his own cap) to finish this early.

> **Conclusion 2**: The extra cost of the crashing plan can be justified if it almost certainly would earn the bonus of $150,000 for finishing the project within 40 weeks. Therefore, Mr. Perty will hold the plan in reserve to be implemented if the project is running well ahead of schedule before reaching activity F.

Mr. Perty is more concerned about the possibility that the project will run so far behind schedule that the penalty of $300,000 will be incurred for not finishing within 47 weeks. If this becomes likely without crashing, Mr. Perty sees that it probably can be avoided by crashing activity J (at a cost of $30,000 per week saved) and, if necessary, crashing activity F as well (at a cost of $40,000 per week saved). This will hold true as long as these activities remain on the critical path (as is likely) after the delays have occurred.

> **Conclusion 3**: The extra cost of part or all of the crashing plan can be easily justified if it likely would make the difference in avoiding the penalty of $300,000 for not finishing the project within 47 weeks. Therefore, Mr. Perty will hold the crashing plan in reserve to be partially or wholly implemented if the project is running far behind schedule before reaching activity F or activity J.

In addition to carefully monitoring the schedule as the project evolves (and making a later decision about any crashing), Mr. Perty will be closely watching the costs to try to keep the project within budget. The next section describes how he plans to do this.

REVIEW QUESTIONS

1. What are some ways of crashing an activity?
2. What are the two key points in a time–cost graph for an activity? What do these points show?
3. Does crashing an activity always reduce the duration of the project? Why?
4. What are the costs being examined when performing marginal cost analysis on a project?
5. What are the decisions to be made when using linear programming to make crashing decisions?
6. In the linear programming formulation, describe in words what each starting time constraint is saying.
7. Why did Mr. Perty decide to reject the proposed plan for crashing the project even though the extra cost of the plan is less than the bonus for early completion of the project?

16.6 SCHEDULING AND CONTROLLING PROJECT COSTS

Any good project manager like Mr. Perty carefully plans and monitors both the *time* and *cost* aspects of the project. Both schedule and budget are important.

Sections 16.3 and 16.4 have described how PERT/CPM deals with the *time* aspect in developing a schedule and taking uncertainties in activity or project durations into account. Section 16.5 then placed an equal emphasis on time and cost by describing the CPM method of time–cost trade-offs.

Mr. Perty now is ready to turn his focus to *costs* by addressing the last of his questions posed at the end of Section 16.1.

> **Question 9**: How should ongoing costs be monitored to try to keep the project within budget?

Mr. Perty recalls that the PERT/CPM technique known as PERT/Cost is specifically designed for this purpose.

PERT/Cost is a systematic procedure (normally computerized) to help the project manager plan, schedule, and control project costs.

The PERT/Cost procedure begins with the hard work of developing an estimate of the cost of each activity when it is performed in the planned way (including any crashing). At this stage, Mr. Perty does not plan on any crashing, so the estimated costs of the activities in Reliable's project are given in the normal cost column of Table 16.8 in the preceding section. These costs then are displayed in the *project budget* shown in Table 16.11. This table also includes the estimated duration of each activity (as already given in Table 16.1, Figures 16.1–16.6, and the normal time column of Table 16.8). Dividing the cost of each activity by its duration gives the amount in the rightmost column of Table 16.11.

> **Assumption: A** common assumption when using PERT/Cost is that the costs of performing an activity are incurred at a constant rate throughout its duration. Mr. Perty is making this assumption, so the estimated cost during each week of an activity's duration is given by the rightmost column of Table 16.11.

Table 16.11   The Project Budget for Reliable's Project

Activity	Estimated Duration (weeks)	Estimated Cost	Cost per Week of Its Duration
A	2	$180,000	$ 90,000
B	4	320,000	80,000
C	10	620,000	62,000
D	6	260,000	43,333
E	4	410,000	102,500
F	5	180,000	36,000
G	7	900,000	128,571
H	9	200,000	22,222
I	7	210,000	30,000
J	8	430,000	53,750
K	4	160,000	40,000
L	5	250,000	50,000
M	2	100,000	50,000
N	6	330,000	55,000

When applying PERT/Cost to larger projects with numerous activities, it is common to combine each group of related activities into a "work package." Both the project budget and the schedule of project costs (described below) then are developed in terms of these work packages rather than the individual activities. Mr. Perty has chosen not to do this since his project has only 14 activities.

Scheduling Project Costs

Mr. Perty needs to know how much money is required to cover project expenses week by week. PERT/Cost provides this information by using the rightmost column of Table 16.11 to develop a weekly schedule of expenses when the individual activities begin at their earliest start times. Then, to indicate how much flexibility is available for delaying expenses, PERT/Cost does the same thing when the individual activities begin at their latest start times instead.

To do this, this chapter's Excel files in your MS Courseware include an Excel template (labeled PERT Cost) for generating a project's schedule of costs for up to 45 time periods. Figure 16.13 shows this Excel template (including the equations entered into its output cells) for the beginning of Reliable's project, based on earliest start times (column E) as first obtained in Figure 16.3, where Columns B, C, and D come directly from Table 16.11. Figure 16.14 jumps ahead to show this same template for weeks 17 to 25. Since activities D, E, and I all have earliest start times of 16 (16 weeks after the commencement of the project), they all start in week 17, while activities F and G commence later during the period shown. Columns W through AE give the weekly cost (in dollars) of each of these activities, as obtained from column F (see Figure 16.13), for the duration of the activity (given by column C). Row 21 shows the sum of the weekly activity costs for each week.

	A	B	C	D	E	F	G	H	I	J
1		**Template for PERT/Cost**								
2										
3			Estimated							
4			Duration	Estimated	Start	Cost Per Week	Week	Week	Week	Week
5		Activity	(weeks)	Cost	Time	of Its Duration	1	2	3	4
6		A	2	$180,000	0	$90,000	$90,000	$90,000	$0	$0
7		B	4	$320,000	2	$80,000	$0	$0	$80,000	$80,000
8		C	10	$620,000	6	$62,000	$0	$0	$0	$0
9		D	6	$260,000	16	$43,333	$0	$0	$0	$0
10		E	4	$410,000	16	$102,500	$0	$0	$0	$0
11		F	5	$180,000	20	$36,000	$0	$0	$0	$0
12		G	7	$900,000	22	$128,571	$0	$0	$0	$0
13		H	9	$200,000	29	$22,222	$0	$0	$0	$0
14		I	7	$210,000	16	$30,000	$0	$0	$0	$0
15		J	8	$430,000	25	$53,750	$0	$0	$0	$0
16		K	4	$160,000	33	$40,000	$0	$0	$0	$0
17		L	5	$250,000	33	$50,000	$0	$0	$0	$0
18		M	2	$100,000	38	$50,000	$0	$0	$0	$0
19		N	6	$330,000	38	$55,000	$0	$0	$0	$0
20										
21						Weekly Project Cost	$90,000	$90,000	$80,000	$80,000
22						Cumulative Project Cost	$90,000	$180,000	$260,000	$340,000

	F	G	H
4	Cost Per Week	Week	Week
5	of Its Duration	1	2
6	=EstimatedCost/EstimatedDuration	=IF(AND(Week>StartTime,Week<=StartTime+EstimatedDuration),CostPerWeek,0)	...
7	=EstimatedCost/EstimatedDuration	=IF(AND(Week>StartTime,Week<=StartTime+EstimatedDuration),CostPerWeek,0)	...
8	=EstimatedCost/EstimatedDuration	=IF(AND(Week>StartTime,Week<=StartTime+EstimatedDuration),CostPerWeek,0)	...
9	=EstimatedCost/EstimatedDuration	:	
10	=EstimatedCost/EstimatedDuration	:	

	F	G	H	I	J
21	Weekly Project Cost	=SUM(G6:G19)	=SUM(H6:H19)	=SUM(I6:I19)	...
22	Cumulative Project Cost	=G21	=G22+H21	=H22+I21	...

Range Name	Cells
Activity	B6:B19
CostPerWeek	F6:F19
CumulativeProjectCost	G22:AY22
EstimatedCost	D6:D19
EstimatedDuration	C6:C19
StartTime	E6:E19
Week	G5:AY5
WeeklyProjectCost	G21:AY21

Figure 16.13 This Excel template in your MS Courseware enables efficient application of the PERT/Cost procedure, as illustrated here for the beginning of Reliable's project when using earliest start times.

CD 16-41

Row 22 of this template gives the total project cost from week 1 on up to the indicated week. For example, consider week 17. Prior to week 17, activities A, B, and C all have been completed but no other activities have begun, so the total cost for the first 16 weeks (from the third column of Table 16.11) are $180,000 + $320,000 + $620,000 = $1,120,000. Adding the weekly project cost for week 17 then gives $1,120,000 + $175,833 = $1,295,833.

Thus, Figure 16.14 (and its extension to earlier and later weeks) shows Mr. Perty just how much money he will need to cover each week's expenses, as well as the cumulative amount, assuming the project can stick to the earliest start time schedule.

Next, PERT/Cost uses the same procedure to develop the corresponding information when each activity begins at its *latest* start times instead. These latest start times were first obtained in Figure 16.4 and are repeated here in column E of Figure 16.15. The rest of this figure then is generated in the same way as for Figure 16.14. For example, since activity D has a latest start time of 20 (versus an earliest start time of 16), its weekly cost of $43,333 now begins in week 21 rather than week 17. Similarly, activity G has a latest start time of 26, so it has no entries for the weeks considered in this figure.

	Activity	Start Time	Cost Per Week of Its Duration	Week 17	Week 18	Week 19	Week 20	Week 21	Week 22	Week 23	Week 24	Week 25
		Reliable's Early Start Schedule of Costs										
	A	0	$90,000	$0	$0	$0	$0	$0	$0	$0	$0	$0
	B	2	$80,000	$0	$0	$0	$0	$0	$0	$0	$0	$0
	C	6	$62,000	$0	$0	$0	$0	$0	$0	$0	$0	$0
	D	16	$43,333	$43,333	$43,333	$43,333	$43,333	$43,333	$43,333	$0	$0	$0
	E	16	$102,500	$102,500	$102,500	$102,500	$102,500	$0	$0	$0	$0	$0
	F	20	$36,000	$0	$0	$0	$0	$36,000	$36,000	$36,000	$36,000	$36,000
	G	22	$128,571	$0	$0	$0	$0	$0	$0	$128,571	$128,571	$128,571
	H	29	$22,222	$0	$0	$0	$0	$0	$0	$0	$0	$0
	I	16	$30,000	$30,000	$30,000	$30,000	$30,000	$30,000	$30,000	$30,000	$0	$0
	J	25	$53,750	$0	$0	$0	$0	$0	$0	$0	$0	$0
	K	33	$40,000	$0	$0	$0	$0	$0	$0	$0	$0	$0
	L	33	$50,000	$0	$0	$0	$0	$0	$0	$0	$0	$0
	M	38	$50,000	$0	$0	$0	$0	$0	$0	$0	$0	$0
	N	38	$55,000	$0	$0	$0	$0	$0	$0	$0	$0	$0
			Weekly Project Cost	$175,833	$175,833	$175,833	$175,833	$109,333	$109,333	$194,571	$164,571	$164,571
			Cumulative Project Cost	$1,295,833	$1,471,667	$1,647,500	$1,823,333	$1,932,667	$2,042,000	$2,236,571	$2,401,143	$2,565,714

Figure 16.14 This spreadsheet extends the template in Figure 16.13 to weeks 17 to 25.

Figure 16.15 (and its extension to earlier and later weeks) tells Mr. Perty what his weekly andcumulative expenses would be if he were to postpone each activity as long as possible without delaying project completion (assuming no unexpected delays occur). Comparing row 22 of Figures 16.14 and 16.15 indicates that fairly substantial *temporary* savings can be achieved by such postponements, which is very helpful if the company is incurring cash shortages. (However, such postponements would only be used reluctantly since they would remove any latitude for avoiding a delay in the completion of the project if any activities were to incur unexpected delays.)

	Activity	Start Time	Cost Per Week of Its Duration	Week 16	Week 17	Week 18	Week 19	Week 20	Week 21	Week 22	Week 23	Week 24	Week 25
1	Reliable's Late Start Schedule of Costs												
6	A	0	$90,000	$0	$0	$0	$0	$0	$0	$0	$0	$0	$0
7	B	2	$80,000	$0	$0	$0	$0	$0	$0	$0	$0	$0	$0
8	C	6	$62,000	$62,000	$0	$0	$0	$0	$0	$0	$0	$0	$0
9	D	20	$43,333	$0	$0	$0	$0	$0	$43,333	$43,333	$43,333	$43,333	$43,333
10	E	16	$102,500	$0	$102,500	$102,500	$102,500	$102,500	$0	$0	$0	$0	$0
11	F	20	$36,000	$0	$0	$0	$0	$0	$36,000	$36,000	$36,000	$36,000	$36,000
12	G	26	$128,571	$0	$0	$0	$0	$0	$0	$0	$0	$0	$0
13	H	33	$22,222	$0	$0	$0	$0	$0	$0	$0	$0	$0	$0
14	I	18	$30,000	$0	$0	$0	$30,000	$30,000	$30,000	$30,000	$30,000	$30,000	$30,000
15	J	25	$53,750	$0	$0	$0	$0	$0	$0	$0	$0	$0	$0
16	K	34	$40,000	$0	$0	$0	$0	$0	$0	$0	$0	$0	$0
17	L	33	$50,000	$0	$0	$0	$0	$0	$0	$0	$0	$0	$0
18	M	42	$50,000	$0	$0	$0	$0	$0	$0	$0	$0	$0	$0
19	N	38	$55,000	$0	$0	$0	$0	$0	$0	$0	$0	$0	$0
21			Weekly Project Cost	$62,000	$102,500	$102,500	$132,500	$132,500	$109,333	$109,333	$109,333	$109,333	$109,333
22			Cumulative Project Cost	$1,120,000	$1,222,500	$1,325,000	$1,457,500	$1,590,000	$1,699,333	$1,808,667	$1,918,000	$2,027,333	$2,136,667

Figure 16.15   The application of the PERT/Cost procedure to weeks 17 to 25 of Reliable's project when using latest start times.

To better visualize the comparison between row 22 of Figures 16.14 and 16.15, it is helpful to graph these two rows together over all 44 weeks of the project, as shown in Figure 16.16. Since the earliest start times and latest start times are the same for the first three activities (A, B, C), which encompass the first 16 weeks, the cumulative project cost is the same for the two kinds of start times over this period. After week 16, we obtain two distinct cost curves by plotting the values in row 22 of Figures 16.14 and 16.15 (and their extensions to later weeks). Since sticking to either earliest start times or latest start times leads to project completion at the end of 44 weeks, the two cost curves come together again at that point with a total project cost of $4.55 million. The dots on either curve are the points at which the weekly project costs change.

Naturally, the start times and activity costs that led to Figure 16.16 are only estimates of what actually will transpire. However, the figure provides a *best forecast* of cumulative project costs week by week when following a work schedule based on either earliest or latest start times. If either of these work schedules is selected, this best forecast then becomes a *budget* to be followed as closely as possible. A budget in the shaded area between the two cost curves also can be obtained by selecting a work schedule that calls for beginning each activity somewhere between its earliest and latest start times. The only *feasible* budgets for scheduling project completion at the end of week 44 (without any crashing) lie in this shaded area or on one of the two cost curves.

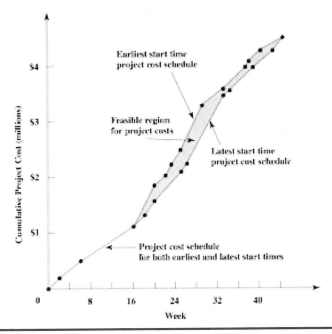

Figure 16.16 The schedule of cumulative project costs when all activities begin at their earliest start times (the top curve) or at their latest start times (the bottom cost curve).

Reliable Construction Co. has adequate funds to cover expenses until payments are received. Therefore, Mr. Perty has selected a work schedule based on earliest start times to provide the best chance for prompt completion. (He is still nervous about the significant probability of incurring the penalty of \$300,000 for not finishing within 47 weeks.) Consequently, his budget is provided by the top cost curve in Figure 16.16.

Controlling Project Costs

Once the project is under way, Mr. Perty will need to monitor actual costs carefully and take corrective action as needed to avoid serious cost overruns. One important way of monitoring costs is to compare actual costs to date with his budget provided by the top curve in Figure 16.16.

However, since deviations from the planned work schedule may occur, this method of monitoring costs is not adequate by itself. For example, suppose that individual activities have been costing more than budgeted, but delays have prevented some activities from beginning when scheduled. These delays might cause the total cost to date to be less than the budgeted cumulative project cost, thereby giving the illusion that project costs are well under control. Furthermore, regardless of whether the cost performance of the project as a whole seems satisfactory, Mr. Perty needs information about the cost performance of individual activities to identify trouble spots where corrective action is needed.

Therefore, PERT/Cost periodically generates a report that focuses on the cost performance of the individual activities. To illustrate, Table 16.12 shows the report that Mr. Perty received after the completion of week 22 (halfway through the project schedule). The first column lists the activities that have at least begun by this time. The next column gives the budgeted total cost of each activity (as given previously in the third column of Table 16.11). The third column indicates what percentage of the activity now has been completed. Multiplying the second and third columns then gives the fourth column, which thereby represents the budgeted value of the work completed on the activity.

Table 16.12   PERT/Cost Report after Week 22 of Reliable's Project

Activity	Budgeted Cost	Percent Completed	Value Completed	Actual Cost to Date	Cost Overrun to Date
A	$ 180,000	100%	$ 180,000	$ 200,000	$20,000
B	320,000	100	320,000	330,000	10,000
C	620,000	100	620,000	600,000	−20,000
D	260,000	75	195,000	200,000	5,000
E	410,000	100	410,000	400,000	−10,000
F	180,000	25	45,000	60,000	15,000
I	210,000	50	105,000	130,000	25,000
Total	$2,180,000		$1,875,000	$1,920,000	$45,000

The fourth column is the one that Mr. Perty wants to compare to the *actual cost* to date given in the fifth column. Subtracting the fourth column from the fifth gives the *cost overrun* to date of each activity, as shown in the rightmost column. (A negative number in the cost overrun column indicates a cost underrun.)

Mr. Perty pays special attention in the report to the activities that are not yet completed, since these are the ones that he can still affect. (He used earlier reports to monitor activities A, B, C, and E while they were under way, which led to meeting the total budget for these four activities.) Activity D is barely over budget (less than 3 percent), but Mr. Perty is very concerned about the large cost overruns to date for activities F and I. Therefore, he next will investigate these two activities and work with the foremen involved to improve their cost performances.

Note in the bottom row of Table 16.12 that the cumulative project cost after week 22 is $1.92 million. This is considerably less than Mr. Perty's *budgeted* cumulative project cost of $2.042 million given in cell AB22 of Figure 16.14. Without any further information, this comparison would suggest an excellent cost performance for the project so far. However, the real reason for being under budget is that the current activities all are behind schedule and so have not yet incurred some expenses that had been scheduled to occur earlier. Fortunately, the PERT/Cost report provides valuable additional information that paints a truer picture of cost performance to date. By focusing on individual activities rather than the overall project, the report identifies the current trouble spots (activities F and I) that require Mr. Perty's immediate attention. Thus, the report enables him to take corrective action while there is still time to reverse these cost overruns.

CD 16-45

Review QUESTIONS

1. What is the purpose of PERT/Cost?
2. How does the PERT/Cost procedure begin?
3. What assumption is commonly made about how the cost of performing an activity is spread over the duration of the activity?
4. What is a work package?
5. Which two work schedules does PERT/Cost use as a basis for developing cost schedules?
6. What two types of information about project cost are provided for each time period by a PERT/Cost schedule of costs?
7. What information does a PERT/Cost report provide about the cost performance of each activity?
8. Why is a PERT/Cost report needed when the project manager already can evaluate the cost performance of the overall project by comparing the actual cost to date with the budgeted cumulative cost?

16.7   AN EVALUATION OF PERT/CPM FROM A MANAGERIAL PERSPECTIVE

PERT/CPM has stood the test of time. Despite being more than 50 years old, it continues to be one of the most widely used techniques of management science. It is a standard tool of project managers.

The Value of PERT/CPM

Much of the value of PERT/CPM derives from the basic framework it provides for planning a project. Recall its planning steps: (1) identify the activities that are needed to carry out the project; (2) estimate how much time will be needed for each activity; (3) determine the activities that must immediately precede each activity; and (4) develop the project network that visually displays the relationships between the activities. The discipline of going through these steps forces the needed planning to be done.

The scheduling information generated by PERT/CPM also is vital to the project manager. When can each activity begin if there are no delays? How much delay in an activity can be tolerated without delaying project completion? What is the critical path of activities where no delay can be tolerated? What is the effect of uncertainty in activity times? What is the probability of meeting the project deadline under the current plan? PERT/CPM provides the answers.

PERT/CPM also assists the project manager in other ways. Schedule and budget are key concerns. The CPM method of time–cost trade-offs enables investigating ways of reducing the duration of the project at an additional cost. PERT/Cost provides a systematic procedure for planning, scheduling, and controlling project costs.

In many ways, PERT/CPM exemplifies the application of management science at its finest. Its modeling approach focuses on the key features of the problem (activities, precedence relationships, time, and cost) without getting mired down in unimportant details. The resulting model (a project network and an optional linear programming formulation) are easy to understand and apply. It addresses the issues that are important to management (planning, scheduling, dealing with uncertainty, making time–cost trade-offs, and controlling costs). It assists the project manager in dealing with these issues in useful ways and in a timely manner.

Using the Computer

PERT/CPM continues to evolve to meet new needs. At its inception over 50 years ago, it was largely executed manually. The project network sometimes was spread out over the walls of the project manager. Recording changes in the plan became a major task. Communicating changes to crew foremen and subcontractors was cumbersome. The computer has changed all of that.

For many years now, PERT/CPM has become highly computerized. There has been a remarkable growth in the number and power of software packages for PERT/CPM that run on personal computers or workstations. *Project management software* now is a standard tool for project managers. This has enabled applications to numerous projects that each involve many millions of dollars and perhaps even thousands of activities. Possible revisions in the project plan now can be investigated almost instantaneously. Actual changes and the resulting updates in the schedule, and so forth, are recorded virtually effortlessly. Communications to all parties involved through computer networks and telecommunication systems also have become quick and easy.

Nevertheless, PERT/CPM still is not a panacea. It has certain major deficiencies for some applications. We briefly describe each of these deficiencies below along with how it is being addressed through research on improvements or extensions to PERT/CPM.

Approximating the Means and Variances of Activity Durations

The PERT three-estimate approach described in Section 16.4 provides a straightforward procedure for approximating the mean and variance of the probability distribution of the duration of each activity. Recall that this approach involved obtaining a most likely estimate, an optimistic estimate, and a pessimistic estimate of the duration. Given these three estimates, simple formulas were given for approximating the mean and variance. The means and variances for the various activities then were used to estimate the probability of completing the project by a specified time.

Unfortunately, considerable subsequent research has shown that this approach tends to provide a pretty rough approximation of the mean and variance. Part of the difficulty lies in aiming the optimistic and pessimistic estimates at the *end points* of the probability distribution. These end points correspond to very rare events (the best and worst that could ever occur) that typically are outside the estimator's realm of experience. The accuracy and reliability of such estimates are not as good as for points that are not at the extremes of the probability distribution. For example, research has demonstrated that much better estimates can be obtained by aiming them at the 10 percent and 90 percent points of the probability distribution. The optimistic and pessimistic estimates then would be described in terms of having 1 chance in 10 of doing better or 1 chance in 10 of doing worse. The middle estimate also can be improved by aiming it at the 50 percent point (the median value) of the probability distribution.

Revising the definitions of the three estimates along these lines leads to considerably more complicated formulas for the mean and variance of the duration of an activity. However, this is no problem since the analysis is computerized anyway. The important consideration is that much better approximations of the mean and variance are obtained in this way.[2]

Approximating the Probability of Meeting the Deadline

Of all the assumptions and simplifying approximations made by PERT/CPM, one is particularly controversial. This is simplifying approximation 1 in Section 16.4, which assumes that the *mean critical path* will turn out to be the longest path through the project network. This approximation

---

[2] For further information, see, for example, D.L. Keefer and W.A. Verdini, "Better Estimation of PERT Activity Time Parameters," *Management Science* 39 (September 1993), pp. 1086-91. Also see A.H-L Laue, H-S. Lau, and Y. Zhang, "A Simple and Logical Alternative for Making PERT Time Estimates," *IIE Transactions* 28 (March 1996). pp. 183-92.

greatly simplifies the calculation of the approximate probability of completing the project by a specified deadline. Unfortunately, in reality, there usually is a significant chance, and sometimes a very substantial chance, that some other path or paths will turn out to be longer than the mean critical path. Consequently, the calculated probability of meeting the deadline usually overstates the true probability somewhat. PERT/CPM provides no information on the likely size of the error. (Research has found that the error often is modest, but can be very large.) Thus, the project manager who relies on the calculated probability can be badly misled.

Considerable research has been conducted to develop more accurate (albeit more complicated) analytical approximations of this probability. Of special interest are methods that provide both upper and lower bounds on the probability.[3]

Another alternative is to use the technique of computer simulation described in Chapters 12 and 13 to approximate this probability. This appears to be the most commonly used method in practice (when any is used) to improve upon the PERT/CPM approximation. We describe in Section 13.3 how this would be done for the Reliable Construction Co. project.

Dealing with Overlapping Activities

Another key assumption of PERT/CPM is that an activity cannot begin until all its immediate predecessors are completely finished. Although this may appear to be a perfectly reasonable assumption, it too is sometimes only a rough approximation of reality.

For example, in the Reliable Construction Co. project, consider activity H (do the exterior painting) and its immediate predecessor, activity G (put up the exterior siding). Naturally, this painting cannot begin until the exterior siding is there on which to paint. However, it certainly is possible to begin painting on one wall while the exterior siding still is being put up to form the other walls. Thus, activity H actually can begin before activity G is completely finished. Although careful coordination is needed, this possibility to overlap activities can significantly reduce project duration below that predicted by PERT/CPM.

The **precedence diagramming method (PDM)** has been developed as an extension of PERT/CPM to deal with such overlapping activities.[4] PDM provides four options for the relationship between an activity and any one of its immediate predecessors.

Option 1: The activity cannot begin until the immediate predecessor has been in progress a certain amount of time.

Option 2: The activity cannot finish until a certain amount of time after the immediate predecessor has finished.

Option 3: The activity cannot finish until a certain amount of time after the immediate predecessor has started.

Option 4: The activity cannot begin until a certain amount of time after the immediate predecessor has finished. (Rather than overlapping the activities, note that this option creates a lag between them such as, for example, waiting for the paint to dry before beginning the activity that follows painting.)

---

[3] See, for example, J. Kamburowski, "Bounding the Distribution of Project Duration in PERT Networks," *Operations Research Letters* 12 (July 1992), pp. 17-22. Also see T. Ida, "Computing Bounds on Project Duration Distributions for Stochastic PERT Networks," *Naval Research Logistics* 47 (October 2000), pp. 559-80.

[4] For an an introduction to PDM, see pp. 136–44 in A. B. Badiru and P. S. Pulat, *Comprehensive Project Management:* Integrating Optimization Models, Management Principles, and Computers (Englewood Cliffs, NJ: Prentice-Hall, 1995).

CD 16-48

Alternatively, the *certain amount of time* mentioned in each option also can be expressed as a certain percentage of the work content of the immediate predecessor.

After incorporating these options, PDM can be used much like PERT/CPM to determine earliest start times, latest start times, and the critical path and to investigate time–cost tradeoffs, and so on.

Although it adds considerable flexibility to PERT/CPM, PDM is neither as well known nor as widely used as PERT/CPM. This should gradually change.

Incorporating the Allocation of Resources to Activities

PERT/CPM assumes that each activity has available all the resources (money, personnel, equipment, etc.) needed to perform the activity in the normal way (or on a crashed basis). In actuality, many projects have only limited resources for which the activities must compete. A major challenge in planning the project then is to determine how the resources should be allocated to the activities.

Once the resources have been allocated, PERT/CPM can be applied in the usual way. However, it would be far better to combine the allocation of the resources with the kind of planning and scheduling done by PERT/CPM so as to strive simultaneously toward a desired objective. For example, a common objective is to allocate the resources so as to minimize the duration of the project.

Much research has been conducted (and is continuing) to develop the methodology for simultaneously allocating resources and scheduling the activities of a project. This subject is beyond the scope of this book, but considerable reading is available elsewhere.[5]

The Future

Despite its deficiencies, PERT/CPM undoubtedly will continue to be widely used for the foreseeable future. It provides the project manager with most of what he or she wants: structure, scheduling information, tools for controlling schedule (latest start times, slacks, the critical path, etc.) and controlling costs (PERT/Cost), as well as the flexibility to investigate time–cost trade-offs.

Even though some of the approximations involved with the PERT three-estimate approach are questionable, these inaccuracies ultimately may not be too important. Just the process of developing estimates of the duration of activities encourages effective interaction between the project manager and subordinates that leads to setting mutual goals for start times, activity durations, project duration, and so forth. Striving together toward these goals may make them self-fulfilling prophecies despite inaccuracies in the underlying mathematics that led to these goals.

Similarly, possibilities for a modest amount of overlapping of activities need not invalidate a schedule generated by PERT/CPM, despite its assumption that no overlapping can occur. Actually having a small amount of overlapping may just provide the slack needed to compensate for the "unexpected" delays that inevitably seem to slip into a schedule. Even when needing to allocate resources to activities, just using common sense in this allocation and then applying PERT/CPM should be quite satisfactory for some projects.

---

[5] See, for example, ibid., pp. 162–209. Also see L. Özdamar and G. Ulusay, "A Survey on the Resource-Constrained Project Scheduling Problem," *IIE Transactions* 27 (October 1995), pp. 574–86, as well as S. S. Erenguc, T. Ahn, and D. G. Conway, "The Resource Constrained Project Scheduling Problem with Multiple Crashable Modes: An Exact Solution Method," *Naval Research Logistics* 48 (March 2001), pp. 107–27.

CD 16-49

Nevertheless, it is unfortunate that the kinds of improvements and extensions to PERT/CPM described in this section have not been incorporated much into practice to date. Old comfortable methods that have proven their value are not readily discarded, and it takes awhile to learn about and gain confidence in new better methods. However, we anticipate that these improvements and extensions gradually will come into more widespread use as they prove their value as well. We also expect that the extensive research on techniques for project management and scheduling (much of it in Europe) will continue and will lead to further improvements in the future.

REVIEW QUESTIONS

1. What are some important managerial issues in managing a project that PERT/CPM addresses?
2. What have been some benefits from changing from the original manual execution of PERT/CPM to its computer implementation in more recent years?
3. In the PERT three-estimate approach, what has research shown regarding how the accuracy of the optimistic and pessimistic estimates is affected by the choice of the points at which these estimates are aimed in the probability distribution of the duration of the activity involved?
4. What is an alternative technique for improving the PERT/CPM approximation of the probability that the project will meet its deadline?
5. What is the name of a method for extending PERT/CPM to permit activities and their immediate predecessors to overlap?
6. What does PERT/CPM assume about the availability of the resources needed to perform each activity in the normal way?
7. Beyond the estimates themselves, what is an additional benefit of conducting the process of developing estimates of the duration of activities?
8. Considering that PERT/CPM has become such a well-established management science technique, are new improvements and extensions still being developed?

16.8 SUMMARY

Ever since their inception in the late 1950s, PERT (program evaluation and review technique) and CPM (critical path method) have been used extensively to assist project managers in planning, scheduling, and controlling their projects. Over time, these two techniques gradually have merged, so PERT/CPM today refers to the combined version that includes all the various options of either of the original techniques.

The application of PERT/CPM begins by breaking the project down into its individual activities, identifying the immediate predecessors of each activity, and estimating the duration of each activity. The next step is to construct a project network to visually display all this information. The type of network that is becoming increasingly popular for this purpose is the activity-on-node (AON) project network, where each activity is represented by a node.

PERT/CPM then generates scheduling information for the project manager, including the earliest start time, the latest start time, and the slack for each activity. It also identifies the critical path of activities such that any delay along this path will delay project completion. Since the critical path is the longest path through the project network, its length determines the duration of the project, assuming all activities remain on schedule.

However, it is difficult for all activities to remain on schedule because there frequently is considerable uncertainty about what the duration of an activity will turn out to be. The PERT three-estimate approach addresses this situation by obtaining three different kinds of estimates (most likely, optimistic, and pessimistic) for the duration of each activity. This information is used to approximate the mean and variance of the probability distribution of this duration. It then is possible to approximate the probability that the project will be completed by the deadline.

The CPM method of time–cost trade-offs enables the project manager to investigate the effect on total cost of changing the estimated duration of the project to various alternative values. The data needed for this activity are the time and cost for each activity when it is done in the normal way and then when it is fully crashed (expedited). Either marginal cost analysis or linear programming can be used to determine how much (if any) to crash each activity to minimize the total cost of meeting any specified deadline for the project.

The PERT/CPM technique called PERT/Cost provides the project manager with a systematic procedure for planning, scheduling, and controlling project costs. It generates a complete schedule for what the project costs should be in each time period when activities begin at either their earliest start times or latest start times. It also generates periodic reports that evaluate the cost performance of the individual activities, including identifying those where cost overruns are occurring.

PERT/CPM does have some important deficiencies. These include questionable approximations made when estimating the mean and variance of activity durations as well as when estimating the probability that the project will be completed by the deadline. Another deficiency is that it does not allow an activity to begin until all its immediate predecessors are completely finished, even though some overlap is sometimes possible. In addition, PERT/CPM does not address the important issue of how to allocate limited resources to the various activities.

Nevertheless, PERT/CPM has stood the test of time in providing project managers with most of the help they want. Furthermore, much progress is being made in developing improvements and extensions to PERT/CPM (such as the precedence diagramming method for dealing with overlapping activities) that address these deficiencies.

CD 16-51

Appendix 16.1
Table for the Normal Distribution

The table in this appendix can be used to find any desired probabilities from a normal distribution. To do this, you need to identify the values of the following parameters of the distribution.

μ = Mean of the distribution

σ = Standard deviation of the distribution.

FINDING PROBABILITIES WHEN $\mu = 0$ AND $\sigma = 1$

When $\mu = 0$ and $\sigma = 1$, probabilities can be read immediately from the table. In particular, for any specific value of $z \geq 0$, suppose you want to know the probability that the value of a random observation from the distribution will be less than or equal to z. The table gives this probability

$$F(z) = \text{Prob } \{\text{Value} \leq z\}$$

by reading the number in the table that corresponds to the value of z. For example, if $z = 1.25$, look in the 1.2 row and the 0.5 column to read the probability .8944. Thus,

$$F(1.25) = \text{Prob } \{\text{Value} \leq 1.25\} = 0.8944$$

Because the normal curve is symmetrical about the mean and the total area under the curve is 1, the probabilities for other ranges of values also can be obtained easily. For example,

$$\text{Prob } \{\text{Value} > 1.25\} = 1 - F(1.25) = 1 - 0.8944 = 0.1056$$

$$\text{Prob } \{\text{Value} < -1.25\} = \text{Prob } \{\text{Value} > 1.25\} = 0.1056$$

$$\text{Prob } \{-1.25 \leq \text{Value} \leq 1.25\} = \text{Prob } \{\text{Value} \leq 1.25\} - \text{Prob } \{\text{Value} < -1.25\}$$
$$= 0.8944 - 0.1056 = 0.7888$$

FINDING PROBABILITIES FOR OTHER VALUES OF μ AND σ

When you don't have both $\mu = 0$ and $\sigma = 1$, one quick calculation is needed before using the table. In particular, for a specific value of x, suppose you want to know the probability that the value of a random observation from the distribution will be less than or equal to x. The first step is to calculate

$$z = \frac{x - \mu}{\sigma}$$

Then the desired probability is

$$\text{Prob } \{\text{Value} \leq x\} = F(z)$$

where F{z} is read from the table in the usual way.

To illustrate, suppose that $\mu = 10$, $\sigma = 4$, and $x = 15$. Since

$$z = \frac{15 - 10}{4} = 1.25$$

the desired probability is

$$\text{Prob } \{\text{Value} \leq 15\} = F(1.25) = 0.8944$$

Similarly,

$$\text{Prob } \{\text{Value} > 15\} = 1 - F(1.25) = 1 - 0.8944 = 0.1056$$

If $x = 5$ instead, then

$$z = \frac{5 - 10}{4} = -1.25$$

so the corresponding probability is

$$\begin{aligned} P \{\text{Value} \leq 5\} &= F(-1.25) = 1 - F(1.25) \\ &= 1 - 0.8944 = 0.1056 \end{aligned}$$

Therefore,

$$\begin{aligned} \text{Prob } \{5 \leq \text{Value} \leq 15\} &= \text{Prob } \{\text{Value} \leq 15\} - \text{Prob } \{\text{Value} < 5\} \\ &= 0.8944 - 0.1056 = 0.7888 \end{aligned}$$

Probabilities for various other ranges of values can be obtained in the same way.

CD 16-53

Table for the Normal Distribution

Areas under the standardized normal curve, from $-\infty$ to $+z$

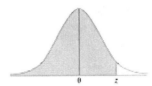

z	.00	.01	.02	.03	.04	.05	.06	.07	.08	.09
.0	.5000	.5040	.5080	.5120	.5160	.5199	.5239	.5279	.5319	.5359
.1	.5398	.5438	.5478	.5517	.5557	.5596	.5636	.5675	.5714	.5753
.2	.5793	.5832	.5871	.5910	.5948	.5987	.6026	.6064	.6103	.6141
.3	.6179	.6217	.6255	.6293	.6331	.6368	.6406	.6443	.6480	.6517
.4	.6554	.6591	.6628	.6664	.6700	.6736	.6772	.6808	.6844	.6879
.5	.6915	.6950	.6985	.7019	.7054	.7088	.7123	.7157	.7190	.7224
.6	.7257	.7291	.7324	.7357	.7389	.7422	.7454	.7486	.7517	.7549
.7	.7580	.7611	.7642	.7673	.7703	.7734	.7764	.7794	.7823	.7852
.8	.7881	.7910	.7939	.7967	.7995	.8023	.8051	.8078	.8106	.8133
.9	.8159	.8186	.8212	.8238	.8264	.8289	.8315	.8340	.8365	.8389
1.0	.8413	.8438	.8461	.8485	.8508	.8531	.8554	.8577	.8599	.8621
1.1	.8643	.8665	.8686	.8708	.8729	.8749	.8770	.8790	.8810	.8830
1.2	.8849	.8869	.8888	.8907	.8925	.8944	.8962	.8980	.8997	.9015
1.3	.9032	.9049	.9066	.9082	.9099	.9115	.9131	.9147	.9162	.9177
1.4	.9192	.9207	.9222	.9236	.9251	.9265	.9279	.9292	.9306	.9319
1.5	.9332	.9345	.9357	.9370	.9382	.9394	.9406	.9418	.9429	.9441
1.6	.9452	.9463	.9474	.9484	.9495	.9505	.9515	.9525	.9535	.9545
1.7	.9554	.9564	.9573	.9582	.9591	.9599	.9608	.9616	.9625	.9633
1.8	.9641	.9649	.9656	.9664	.9671	.9678	.9686	.9693	.9699	.9706
1.9	.9713	.9719	.9726	.9732	.9738	.9744	.9750	.9756	.9761	.9767
2.0	.9772	.9778	.9783	.9788	.9793	.9798	.9803	.9808	.9812	.9817
2.1	.9821	.9826	.9830	.9834	.9838	.9842	.9846	.9850	.9854	.9857
2.2	.9861	.9864	.9868	.9871	.9875	.9878	.9881	.9884	.9887	.9890
2.3	.9893	.9896	.9898	.9901	.9904	.9906	.9909	.9911	.9913	.9916
2.4	.9918	.9920	.9922	.9925	.9927	.9929	.9931	.9932	.9934	.9936
2.5	.9938	.9940	.9941	.9943	.9945	.9946	.9948	.9949	.9951	.9952
2.6	.9953	.9955	.9956	.9957	.9959	.9960	.9961	.9962	.9963	.9964
2.7	.9965	.9966	.9967	.9968	.9969	.9970	.9971	.9972	.9973	.9974
2.8	.9974	.9975	.9976	.9977	.9977	.9978	.9979	.9979	.9980	.9981
2.9	.9981	.9982	.9982	.9983	.9984	.9984	.9985	.9985	.9986	.9986
3.0	.9987	.9987	.9987	.9988	.9988	.9989	.9989	.9989	.9990	.9990
3.1	.9990	.9991	.9991	.9991	.9991	.9992	.9992	.9992	.9993	.9993
3.2	.9993	.9993	.9994	.9994	.9994	.9994	.9994	.9995	.9995	.9995
3.3	.9995	.9995	.9995	.9996	.9996	.9996	.9996	.9996	.9996	.9997
3.4	.9997	.9997	.9997	.9997	.9997	.9997	.9997	.9997	.9997	.9998

CD 16-54

Glossary

activity A distinct task that needs to be performed as part of a project. (Section 16.1)

activity-on-arc (AOA) project network A project network where each activity is represented by an arc (arrow). (Section 16.2)

activity-on-node (AON) project network A project network where each activity is represented by a node (small circle or rectangle) and the arcs (arrows) show the precedence relationships between the activities. (Section 16.2)

arc An arrow in the project network. (Section 16.2)

backward pass The process of moving backward through the project network to determine the latest finish time and latest start time of each activity. (Section 16.3)

CPM An acronym for critical path method, a technique for assisting project managers with carrying out their responsibilities. (Introduction),

CPM method of time–cost trade-offs A method of investigating the trade-off between the total cost of a project and its duration when various levels of crashing are used to reduce the duration. (Section 16.5)

crash point The point on the time–cost graph for an activity that shows the time (duration) and cost when the activity is fully crashed; that is, it is fully expedited with no cost spared to reduce its duration as much as possible. (Section 16.5)

crashing an activity Taking special costly measures to reduce the duration of an activity below its normal value. (Section 16.5)

critical path The longest path through the project network, so the activities on this path are the critical bottleneck activities where any delays in their completion must be avoided to prevent delaying project completion. (Section 16.3)

earliest finish time for an activity The time at which this activity will finish if there are no delays anywhere in the project. (Section 16.3)

earliest start time for an activity The time at which this activity will begin if there are no delays anywhere in the project. (Section 16.3)

EF Abbreviation for the earliest finish time of an activity. (Section 16.3)

ES Abbreviation for the earliest start time of an activity. (Section 16.3)

finish node The node (small rectangle) in the project network that represents the finish of the project. (Section 16.2)

forward pass The process of moving forward through the project network to determine the earliest start time and earliest finish time of each activity. (Section 16.3)

immediate predecessor The immediate predecessors of a given activity are those activities that must be completed by no later than the start time of the given activity. (Section 16.1)

immediate successor Given the immediate predecessors of an activity, this activity then becomes the immediate successor of each of these immediate predecessors. (Section 16.1)

latest finish time for an activity The latest possible time that this activity can finish without delaying project completion (assuming no subsequent delays in the project). (Section 16.3)

latest start time for an activity The latest possible time that this activity can start without delaying project completion (assuming no subsequent delays in the project). (Section 16.3)

length of a path The sum of the (estimated) durations of the activities on the path. (Section 16.3)

LF Abbreviation for the latest finish time of an activity. (Section 16.3)

LS Abbreviation for the latest start time of an activity. (Section 16.3)

marginal cost analysis A method of using the marginal cost of crashing individual activities on the current critical path to determine the least expensive way of reducing project duration to a desired level. (Section 16.5)

mean critical path The path through the project network that would be the critical path if the duration of each activity were to equal its mean. (Section 16.4)

most likely estimate An estimate of the most likely value of the duration of an activity. (Section 16.4)

node A small circle or rectangle that serves as a junction point in the project network. (Section 16.2)

normal point The point on the time–cost graph for an activity that shows the time (duration) and cost of the activity when it is performed in the normal way. (Section 16.5)

optimistic estimate An estimate of the duration of an activity under the most favorable conditions. (Section 16.4)

path A path through a project network is one of the routes following the arrows (arcs) from the start node to the finish node. (Section 16.3)

PERT An acronym for program evaluation and review technique, a technique for assisting project managers with carrying out their responsibilities. (Introduction)

PERT/Cost A systematic procedure (normally computerized) to help the project manager plan, schedule, and control project costs. (Section 16.6)

PERT/CPM The merger of the two techniques originally known as PERT and CPM. (Introduction),

PERT three-estimate approach An approach to dealing with uncertainties in activity times by obtaining three different kinds of estimates (most likely, optimistic, and pessimistic) for the duration of each activity. (Section 16.4)

pessimistic estimate An estimate of the duration of an activity under the most unfavorable conditions. (Section 16.4)

precedence diagramming method (PDM) An extension of PERT/CPM that deals with overlapping activities. (Section 16.7)

project network A network used to visually display a project. (Section 16.2)

slack for an activity The amount of time that this activity can be delayed without delaying project completion (assuming no subsequent delays in the project); it is calculated as the difference between the latest finish time and the earliest finish time for the activity. (Section 16.3)

start node The node (small rectangle) in the project network that represents the start of the project. (Section 16.2)

Learning Aids for This Chapter in Your MS Courseware

Chapter 16 Excel Files:

Reliable Example (Project Schedule)

Template for PERT Three-Estimate Approach (labeled PERT)

Reliable Example (CPM Method of Time–Cost Trade-Offs)

Template for PERT/Cost (labeled PERT Cost)

Reliable's ES Schedule of Costs

Reliable's LS Schedule of Costs

An Excel Add-in:

Risk Solver Platform for Education

Problems

To the left of the problems (or their parts), we have inserted an E whenever Excel can be helpful. An asterisk on this symbol indicates that it definitely should be used (unless your instructor gives you contrary instructions). An asterisk on the problem number indicates that at least a partial answer is given at the end of the problems.

16.1. Christine Phillips is in charge of planning and coordinating next spring's sales management training program for her company. Christine has listed the following activity information for this project:

Activity	Activity Description	Immediate Predecessors	Estimated Duration (Weeks)
A	Select location	—	2
B	Obtain speakers	—	3
C	Make speaker travel plans	A, B	2
D	Prepare and mail brochure	A, B	2
E	Take reservations	D	3

    a. Construct the project network for this project.

    b. Find all the paths and path lengths through this project network. Which of these paths is a critical path?

    c. Find the earliest times, latest times, and slack for each activity. Use this information to determine which of the paths is a critical path.

    d. It is now one week later, and Christine is ahead of schedule. She has already selected a location for the sales meeting, and all the other activities are right on schedule. Will this shorten the length of the project? Why or why not?

16.2.* Reconsider Problem 16.1. Christine has done more detailed planning for this project and so now has the following expanded activity list:

Activity	Activity Description	Immediate Predecessors	Estimated Duration (weeks)
A	Select location	—	2
B	Obtain keynote speaker	—	1
C	Obtain other speakers	B	2
D	Make speaker travel plans for keynote speaker	A, B	2
E	Make travel plans for other speakers	A, C	3
F	Make food arrangements	A	2
G	Negotiate hotel rates	A	1
H	Prepare brochure	C, G	1
I	Mail brochure	H	1
J	Take reservations	I	3
K	Prepare handouts	C, F	4

Follow the instructions for Problem 8.1 with this expanded activity list.

16.3. Consider a project with the following activity list.

Activity	Immediate Predecessors	Estimated Duration (months)
A	—	1
B	A	2
C	B	4
D	B	3
E	B	2
F	C	3
G	D, E	5
H	F	1
I	G, H	4
J	I	2
K	I	3
L	J	3
M	K	5
N	L	4

a. Construct the project network for this project.

b. Find the earliest start time and earliest finish time for each activity.

c. Find the latest start time and latest finish time for each activity.

d. Find the slack for each activity. Which of the paths is a critical path?

16.4.   You and several friends are about to prepare a lasagna dinner. The tasks to be performed, their immediate predecessors, and their estimated durations are as follows:

Task	Task Description	Tasks That Must Precede	Time (minutes)
A	Buy the mozzarella cheese*	—	30
B	Slice the mozzarella	A	5
C	Beat 2 eggs	—	2
D	Mix eggs and ricotta cheese	C	3
E	Cut up onions and mushrooms	—	7
F	Cook the tomato sauce	E	25
G	Boil large quantity of water	—	15
H	Boil the lasagna noodles	G	10
I	Drain the lasagna noodles	H	2
J	Assemble all the ingredients	I, F, D, B	10
K	Preheat the oven	—	15
L	Bake the lasagna	J, K	30

*There is none in the refrigerator.

a.   Construct the project network.

b.   Find all the paths and path lengths through this project network. Which of these paths is a critical path?

c.   Find the earliest start time and earliest finish time for each activity.

d.   Find the latest start time and latest finish time for each activity.

e.   Find the slack for each activity. Which of the paths is a critical path?

f.   Because of a phone call, you were interrupted for 6 minutes when you should have been cutting the onions and mushrooms. By how much will the dinner be delayed? If you use your food processor, which reduces the cutting time from 7 to 2 minutes, will the dinner still be delayed?

CD 16-59

16.5.* Ken Johnston, the data processing manager for Stanley Morgan Bank, is planning a project to install a new management information system. He now is ready to start the project and wishes to finish in 20 weeks. After identifying the 14 separate activities needed to carry out this project, as well as their precedence relationships and estimated durations (in weeks), Ken has constructed the following project network:

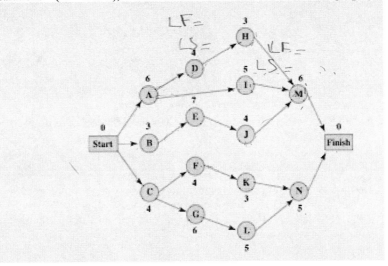

a. Find all the paths and path lengths through this project network. Which of these paths is a critical path?

b. Find the earliest times, latest times, and slack for each activity. Will Ken be able to meet his deadline if no delays occur?

c. Use the information from part b to determine which of the paths is a critical path. What does this tell Ken about which activities he should focus most of his attention on for staying on schedule?

d. Use the information from part b to determine what the duration of the project would be if the only delay is that activity I takes 2 extra weeks. What if the only delay is that activity H takes 2 extra weeks? What if the only delay is that activity J takes 2 extra weeks?

16.6.   You are given the following information about a project consisting of six activities:

Activity	Immediate Predecessors	Estimated Duration (months)
A	—	5
B	—	1
C	B	2
D	A, C	4
E	A	6
F	D, E	3

a.   Construct the project network for this project.

b.   Find the earliest times, latest times, and slack for each activity. Which of the paths is a critical path?

c.   If all other activities take the estimated amount of time, what is the maximum duration of activity D without delaying the completion of the project?

16.7.   Reconsider the Reliable Construction Co. case study introduced in Section 16.1, including the complete project network obtained in Figure 16.5 at the end of Section 16.3. Note that the estimated durations of the activities in this figure turn out to be the same as the mean durations given in Table 16.4 (Section 16.4) when using the PERT three-estimate approach.

Now suppose that the *pessimistic* estimates in Table 16.4 are used instead to provide the estimated durations in Figure 16.5. Find the new earliest times, latest times, and slacks for all the activities in this project network. Also identify the critical path and the total estimated duration of the project. (Table 16.5 provides some clues.)

16.8.* Follow the instructions for Problem 16.7 except use the *optimistic* estimates in Table 16.4 instead.

16.9.   Follow the instructions for Problem 16.7 except use the *crash times* given in Table 16.8 (Section 16.5) instead.

16.10.* Using the PERT three-estimate approach, the three estimates for one of the activities of a project are as follows: optimistic estimate = 30 days, most likely estimate = 36 days, pessimistic estimate = 48 days. What are the resulting estimates of the mean and variance of the duration of the activity?

16.11. Alfred Lowenstein is the president of the Research Division for Better Health, Inc., a major pharmaceutical company. His most important project coming up is the development of a new drug to combat AIDS. He has identified 10 groups in his division that will need to carry out different phases of this research-and-development project. Referring to the work to be done by the respective groups as activities A, B, . . ., J, the precedence relationships for when these groups need to do their work are shown in the following project network.

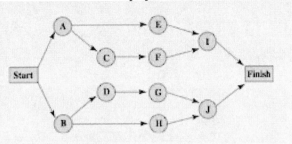

To beat the competition, Better Health's CEO has informed Alfred that he wants the drug ready within 22 months if possible.

Alfred knows very well that there is considerable uncertainty about how long each group will need to do its work. Using the PERT three-estimate approach, the manager of each group has provided a most likely estimate, an optimistic estimate, and a pessimistic estimate of the duration of that group's activity. Using PERT formulas, these estimates now have been converted into estimates of the mean and variance of the probability distribution of the duration of each group's activity, as given in the following table (after rounding to the nearest integer).

Activity	Duration (months)	
	Estimated Mean	Estimated Variance
A	4	5
B	6	10
C	4	8
D	3	6
E	8	12
F	4	6
G	3	5
H	7	14
I	5	8
J	5	7

a. Find the mean critical path for this project.

b. Use this mean critical path and Table 16.7 to find the approximate probability that the project will be completed within 22 months.

c. Now consider the other three paths through this project network. For each of these paths, use Table 16.7 to find the approximate probability that the path will be completed within 22 months.

d. What should Alfred tell his CEO about the likelihood that the drug will be ready within 22 months?

E* 16.12. Reconsider Problem 16.11. For each of the 10 activities, here are the three estimates that led to the estimates of the mean and variance of the duration of the activity (rounded to the nearest integer) given in the table for Problem 16.11.

	Time Required (Months)		
Activity	Optimistic Estimate	Most Likely Estimate	Pessimistic Estimate
A	1.5	2	15
B	2	3.5	21
C	1	1.5	18
D	0.5	1	15
E	3	5	24
F	1	2	16
G	0.5	1	14
H	2.5	3.5	25
I	1	3	18
J	2	3	18

(Note how the great uncertainty in the duration of these research activities causes each pessimistic estimate to be several times larger than either the optimistic estimate or the most likely estimate.)

Now use the Excel template in your MS Courseware (as depicted in Figure 16.9) to help you carry out the instructions for Problem 16.11. In particular, enter the three estimates for each activity and the template immediately will display the estimates of the means and variances of the activity durations. After indicating each path of interest, the template also will display the approximate probability that the path will be completed within 22 months.

16.13. Bill Fredlund, president of Lincoln Log Construction, is considering placing a bid on a building project. Bill has determined that five tasks would need to be performed to carry out the project. Using the PERT three-estimate approach, Bill has obtained the estimates in the table below for how long these tasks will take. Also shown are the precedence relationships   for   these   tasks.

Task	Time Required (Weeks)			Immediate Predecessors
	Optimistic Estimate	Most Likely Estimate	Pessimistic Estimate	
A	3	4	5	—
B	2	2	2	A
C	3	5	6	B
D	1	3	5	A
E	2	3	5	B, D

There is a penalty of $500,000 if the project is not completed in 11 weeks. Therefore, Bill is very interested in how likely it is that his company could finish the project in time.

a. Construct the project network for this project.

E b. Find the estimate of the mean and variance of the duration of each activity.

E c. Find the mean critical path.

E d. Find the approximate probability of completing the project within 11 weeks.

e. Bill has concluded that the bid he would need to make to have a realistic chance of winning the contract would earn Lincoln Log Construction a profit of about $250,000 if the project is completed within 11 weeks. However, because of the penalty for missing this deadline, his company would lose about $250,000 if the project takes more than 11 weeks. Therefore, he wants to place the bid only if he has at least a 50 percent chance of meeting the deadline. How would you advise him?

16.14.* Sharon Lowe, vice president for marketing for the Electronic Toys Company, is about to begin a project to design an advertising campaign for a new line of toys. She wants the project completed within 57 days in time to launch the advertising campaign at the beginning of the Christmas season. Sharon has identified the six activities (labeled A, B, . . . F) needed to execute this project. Considering the order in which these activities need to occur,   she   also   has   constructed   the   following   project   network.

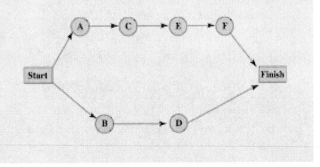

CD 16-64

Using the PERT three-estimate approach, Sharon has obtained the following estimates of the duration of each activity.

Activity	Time Required (days)		
	Optimistic Estimate	Most Likely Estimate	Pessimistic Estimate
A	12	12	12
B	15	21	39
C	12	15	18
D	18	27	36
E	12	18	24
F	2	5	14

E *a.* Find the estimate of the mean and variance of the duration of each activity.

   b. Find the mean critical path.

E *c.* Use the mean critical path to find the approximate probability that the advertising campaign will be ready to launch within 57 days.

E *d.* Now consider the other path through the project network. Find the approximate probability that this path will be completed within 57 days.

   e. Since these paths do not overlap, a better estimate of the probability that the project will finish within 57 days can be obtained as follows. The project will finish within 57 days if both paths are completed within 57 days. Therefore, the approximate probability that the project will finish within 57 days is the product of the probabilities found in parts c and d. Perform this calculation. What does this answer say about the accuracy of the standard procedure used in part *c*?

16.15. The Lockhead Aircraft Co. is ready to begin a project to develop a new fighter airplane for the U.S. Air Force. The company's contract with the Department of Defense calls for project completion within 100 weeks, with penalties imposed for late delivery.

The project involves 10 activities (labeled A, B, . . ., J), where their precedence relationships are shown in the following project network.

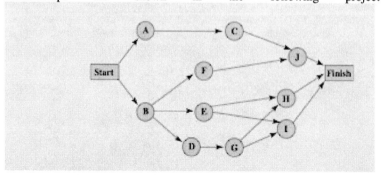

Using the PERT three-estimate approach, the usual three estimates of the duration of each activity have been obtained as given below.

CD 16-65

Activity	Time Required (Weeks)		
	Optimistic Estimate	Most Likely Estimate	Pessimistic Estimate
A	28	32	36
B	22	28	32
C	26	36	46
D	14	16	18
E	32	32	32
F	40	52	74
G	12	16	24
H	16	20	26
I	26	34	42
J	12	16	30

E   *a.*   Find the estimate of the mean and variance of the duration of each activity.

      b.   Find the mean critical path.

E   *c.*   Find the approximate probability that the project will finish within 100 weeks.

      d.   Is the approximate probability obtained in part *c* likely to be higher or lower than the true value?

16.16.   Label each of the following statements about the PERT three-estimate approach as true or false, and then justify your answer by referring to specific statements (with page citations) in the chapter.

      a.   Activity durations are assumed to be no larger than the optimistic estimate and no smaller than the pessimistic estimate.

      b.   Activity durations are assumed to have a normal distribution.

      c.   The mean critical path is assumed to always require the minimum elapsed time of any path through the project network.

16.17. The Tinker Construction Company is ready to begin a project that must be completed in 12 months. This project has four activities (A, B, C, D) with the project network shown below.

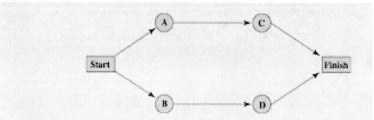

The project manager, Sean Murphy, has concluded that he cannot meet the deadline by performing all these activities in the normal way. Therefore, Sean has decided to use the CPM method of time–cost trade-offs to determine the most economical way of crashing the project to meet the deadline. He has gathered the following data for the four activities.

Activity	Normal Time (Months)	Crash Time (Months)	Normal Cost	Crash Cost
A	8	5	$25,000	$40,000
B	9	7	20,000	30,000
C	6	4	16,000	24,000
D	7	4	27,000	45,000

Use marginal cost analysis to solve the problem.

16.18. Reconsider the Tinker Construction Co. problem presented in Problem 16.17. While in college, Sean Murphy took a management science course that devoted a month to linear programming, so Sean has decided to use linear programming to analyze this problem.

   a. Consider the upper path through the project network. Formulate a two-variable linear programming model (in algebraic form) for the problem of how to minimize the cost of performing this sequence of activities within 12 months. Use the graphical method to solve this model.

   b. Repeat part a for the lower path through the project network.

   c. Combine the models in parts a and b into a single complete linear programming model (in algebraic form) for the problem of how to minimize the cost of completing the project *within 12 months. What must an optimal solution for this model be?*

   E* d. Formulate and solve a spreadsheet model in the format of Figure 16.14 for this problem.

   E* e. Check the effect of changing the deadline by re-solving this model with a deadline of 11 months and then with a deadline of 13 months.

16.19. Reconsider the Electronic Toys Co. problem presented in Problem 16.14. Sharon Lowe is concerned that there is a significant chance that the vitally important deadline of 57 days will not be met. Therefore, to make it virtually certain that the deadline will be met, she has decided to crash the project, using the CPM method of time–cost trade-offs to determine how to do this in the most economical way.

Sharon now has gathered the data needed to apply this method, as given below.

CD 16-67

Activity	Normal Time (Days)	Crash Time (Days)	Normal Cost	Crash Cost
A	12	9	$210,000	$270,000
B	23	18	410,000	460,000
C	15	12	290,000	320,000
D	27	21	440,000	500,000
E	18	14	350,000	410,000
F	6	4	160,000	210,000

The normal times are the estimates of the means obtained from the original data in Problem 16.14. The mean critical path gives an estimate that the project will finish in 51 days. However, Sharon knows from the earlier analysis that some of the pessimistic estimates are far larger than the means, so the project duration might be considerably longer than 51 days. Therefore, to better ensure that the project will finish within 57 days, she has decided to require that the estimated project duration based on means (as used throughout the CPM analysis) must not exceed 47 days.

a. Consider the lower path through the project network. Use marginal cost analysis to determine the most economical way of reducing the length of this path to 47 days.

b. Repeat part a for the upper path through the project network. What is the total crashing cost for the optimal way of decreasing estimated project duration to 47 days?

E* c. Formulate and solve a spreadsheet model that fits linear programming for this problem.

16.20.* Good Homes Construction Company is about to begin the construction of a large new home. The company's president, Michael Dean, is currently planning the schedule for this project. Michael has identified the five major activities (labeled A, B, . . ., E) that will need to be performed according to the following project network.

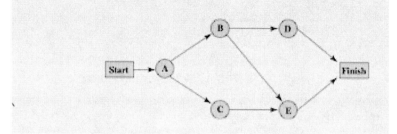

He also has gathered the following data about the normal point and crash point for each of these activities.

Activity	Normal Time (Weeks)	Crash Time (Weeks)	Normal Cost	Crash Cost
A	3	2	$54,000	$60,000
B	4	3	62,000	65,000
C	5	2	66,000	70,000
D	3	1	40,000	43,000
E	4	2	75,000	80,000

These costs reflect the company's direct costs for the material, equipment, and direct labor required to perform the activities. In addition, the company incurs indirect project costs such as supervision and other customary overhead costs, interest charges for capital tied up, and so forth. Michael estimates that these indirect costs run $5,000 per week. He wants to minimize the overall cost of the project. Therefore, to save some of these indirect costs, Michael concludes that he should shorten the project by doing some crashing to the extent that the crashing cost for each additional week saved is less than $5,000.

a. To prepare for analyzing the effect of crashing, find the earliest times, latest times, and slack for each activity when they are done in the normal way. Also identify the corresponding critical path(s) and project duration.

b. Use marginal cost analysis to determine which activities should be crashed and by how much to minimize the overall cost of the project. Under this plan, what is the duration and cost of each activity? How much money is saved by doing this crashing?

E* c. Now formulate a spreadsheet model that fits linear programming and repeatedly solve it to do part b by shortening the deadline one week at a time from the project duration found in part a.

E* 16.21.* 21st Century Studios is about to begin the production of its most important (and most expensive) movie of the year. The movie's producer, Dusty Hoffmer, has decided to use PERT/CPM to help plan and control this key project. He has identified the eight major activities (labeled A, B, . . ., H) required to produce the movie. Their precedence relationships are shown in the project network below.

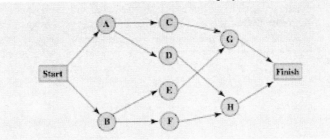

Dusty now has learned that another studio also will be coming out with a blockbuster movie during the middle of the upcoming summer, just when his movie was to be released. This would be very unfortunate timing. Therefore, he and the top management of 21st Century Studios have concluded that they must accelerate production of their movie and bring it out at the beginning of the summer (15 weeks from now) to establish it as *the* movie of the year. Although this will require substantially increasing an already huge budget, management feels that this will pay off in much larger box office earnings both nationally and internationally.

Dusty now wants to determine the least costly way of meeting the new deadline 15 weeks hence. Using the CPM method of time–cost trade-offs, he has obtained the following data.

Activity	Normal Time (weeks)	Crash Time (weeks)	Normal Cost (millions)	Crash Cost (millions)
A	5	3	$20	$30
B	3	2	10	20
C	4	2	16	24
D	6	3	25	43
E	5	4	22	30
F	7	4	30	48
G	9	5	25	45
H	8	6	30	44

Formulate and solve a spreadsheet model that fits linear programming for this problem.

E* 16.22. Reconsider the Lockhead Aircraft Co. problem presented in Problem 16.15 regarding a project to develop a new fighter airplane for the U.S. Air Force. Management is extremely concerned that current plans for this project have a substantial likelihood (roughly a probability of 0.5) of missing the deadline imposed in the Department of Defense contract to finish within 100 weeks. The company has a bad record of missing deadlines, and management is worried that doing so again would jeopardize obtaining future contracts for defense work. Furthermore, management would like to avoid the hefty penalties for missing the deadline in the current contract. Therefore, the decision has been made to crash the project using the CPM method of time–cost trade-offs to determine how to do this in the most economical way. The data needed to apply this method   is   given   below.

Activity	Normal Time (Weeks)	Crash Time (Weeks)	Normal Cost (Millions)	Crash Cost (Millions)
A	32	28	$160	$180
B	28	25	125	146
C	36	31	170	210
D	16	13	60	72
E	32	27	135	160
F	54	47	215	257
G	17	15	90	96
H	20	17	120	132
I	34	30	190	226
J	18	16	80	84

These normal times are the rounded estimates of the means obtained from the original data in Problem 16.15. The corresponding mean critical path provides an estimate that the project will finish in 100 weeks. However, management understands well that the high variability of activity durations means that the actual duration of the project may be much longer. Therefore, the decision is made to require that the estimated project duration based on means (as used throughout the CPM analysis) must not exceed 92 weeks.

Formulate and solve a spreadsheet model that fits linear programming for this problem.

16.23. Reconsider Problem 16.20 involving the Good Homes Construction Co. project to construct a large new home. Michael Dean now has generated the plan for how to crash this project (as given as an answer in the back of the book). Since this plan causes all three paths through the project network to be critical paths, the earliest start time for each activity also is its latest start time.

Michael has decided to use PERT/Cost to schedule and control project costs.

a. Find the earliest start time for each activity and the earliest finish time for the completion of the project.

b. Construct a table like Table 16.11 to show the budget for this project.

c. Construct a table like Figure 16.14 (by hand) to show the schedule of costs based on earliest times for each of the eight weeks of the project.

E* d. Now use the corresponding Excel template in your MS Courseware to do parts b and c on a single spreadsheet.

e. After four weeks, activity A has been completed (with an actual cost of $65,000) and activity B has just now been completed (with an actual cost of $55,000), but activity C is just 33 percent completed (with an actual cost to date of $44,000). Construct a PERT/Cost report after week 4. Where should Michael concentrate his efforts to improve cost performances?

16.24.* The P-H Microchip Co. needs to undertake a major maintenance and renovation program to overhaul and modernize its facilities for wafer fabrication. This project involves six activities (labeled A, B, . . ., F), with the precedence relationships shown in the following network.

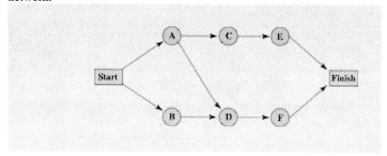

The estimated durations and costs of these activities are shown next.

Activity	Estimated Duration (Weeks)	Estimated Cost
A	6	$420,000
B	2	180,000
C	4	540,000
D	5	360,000
E	7	590,000
F	9	630,000

    a. Find the earliest times, latest times, and slack for each activity. What is the earliest finish time for the completion of the project?

E* *b.* Use the Excel template for PERT/Cost in your MS Courseware to display the budget and schedule of costs based on earliest start times for this project on a single spreadsheet.

E* *c.* Repeat part *b* except based on latest start times.

    d. Use these spreadsheets to draw a figure like Figure 16.16 to show the schedule of cumulative project costs when all activities begin at their earliest start times or at their latest start times.

    e. After four weeks, activity B has been completed (with an actual cost of $200,000), activity A is 50 percent completed (with an actual cost to date of $200,000), and activity D is 50 percent completed (with an actual cost to date of $210,000). Construct a PERT/Cost report after week 4. Where should the project manager focus her attention to improve cost performance?

16.25. Reconsider Problem 16.5 involving a project at Stanley Morgan Bank to install a new management information system. Ken Johnston already has obtained the earliest times, latest times, and slack for each activity. He now is getting ready to use PERT/Cost to schedule and control the costs for this project. The estimated durations and costs of the

CD 16-73

various   activities   are   given   in   the   following   table.

Activity	Estimated Duration (Weeks)	Estimated Cost
A	6	$180,000
B	3	75,000
C	4	120,000
D	4	140,000
E	7	175,000
F	4	80,000
G	6	210,000
H	3	45,000
I	5	125,000
J	4	100,000
K	3	60,000
L	5	50,000
M	6	90,000
N	5	150,000

E* *a.* Use the Excel template for PERT/Cost in your MS Courseware to display the budget and schedule of costs based on earliest start times for this project on a single spreadsheet.

E* *b.* Repeat part *a* except based on latest start times.

c. Use these spreadsheets to draw a figure like Figure 16.16 to show the schedule of cumulative project costs when all activities begin at their earliest start times or at their latest start times.

d. After eight weeks, activities A, B, and C have been completed with actual costs of $190,000, $70,000, and $150,000, respectively. Activities D, E, F, G, and I are under way, with the percent completed being 40 percent, 50 percent, 60 percent, 25 percent, and 20 percent, respectively. Their actual costs to date are $70,000, $100,000, $45,000, $50,000, and $35,000, respectively. Construct a PERT/Cost report after week 8. Which activities should Ken Johnston investigate to try to improve their cost performances?

CD 16-74

PARTIAL ANSWERS TO SELECTED PROBLEMS

16.2.   *c.* AFK, AGHIJ, BCHIJ.

16.5.   *c.* BEJM, CGLN.

16.8.   ABCEFJKN. Total duration = 26 weeks.

16.10. $\mu = 37$, $\sigma^2 = 9$.

16.14. *b.* ACEF. Length = 51 days.

      c. 0.9772

      d. 0.9192

16.20. *b.* Crash B 1 week, C 2 weeks, D 1 week, and E 2 weeks. $7834 is saved.

16.21. Crash A 2 weeks, B 1 week, G 1 week, and H 1 week. Total Cost = $217.

16.24. *d.*

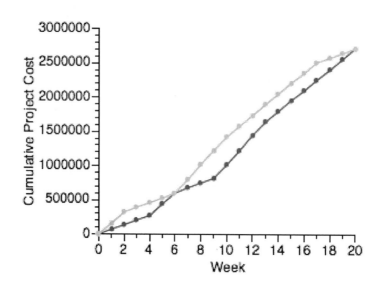

e. The project manager should focus attention on activity D since it is not yet finished and is running over budget.

Case 16-1   Steps to Success

Janet Richards fixes her eyes on those of her partner Gilbert Baker and says firmly, "Alright. Let's do it."

And with those words, InterCat, a firm founded by Janet and Gilbert that specializes in the design and maintenance of Internet catalogues for small consumer businesses, will be going public. InterCat employs 30 individuals, with the majority of them computer programmers. Many of the employees have followed the high-technology market very closely and have decided that since high-technology firms are more understood and valued in the United States than in other countries, InterCat should issue its stock only in the United States. Five million shares of InterCat stock will comprise this new issue.

The task the company has ahead of itself is certainly daunting. Janet and Gilbert know that many steps have to be completed in the process of making an initial public offering. They also know that they need to complete the process within 28 weeks because they need the new capital fairly soon to ensure that InterCat has the resources to capture valuable new business from its competitors and continue growing. They also value a speedy initial public offering because they believe that the window of opportunity for obtaining a good stock price is presently wide open—the public is wild about shopping on the Internet, and few companies offering Web page design services have gone public.

Because the 28-week deadline is breathing down their necks, Janet and Gilbert decide to map the steps in the process of making an initial public offering. They list each major activity that needs to be completed, the activities that directly precede each activity, the time needed to complete each activity, and the cost of each activity. This list is shown below.

CD 16-76

Activity	Immediate Predecessors	Time (Weeks)	Cost
Evaluate the prestige of each potential underwriter.		3	$ 8,000
Select a syndicate of underwriters.	Evaluate the prestige of each potential underwriter.	1.5	4,500
Negotiate the commitment of each member of the syndicate.	Select a syndicate of underwriters.	2	9,000
Negotiate the spread* for each member of the syndicate.	Select a syndicate of underwriters.	3	12,000
Prepare the registration statement, including the proposed financing and information about the firm's history, existing business, and plans for the future.	Negotiate both the commitment and spread for each member of the syndicate.	5	50,000
Submit the registration statement to the Securities and Exchange Commission (SEC).	Prepare the registration statement.	1	1,000
Make presentations to institutional investors and develop the interest of potential buyers.	Submit the registration statement to the SEC.	6	25,000
Distribute the preliminary prospectus, affectionately termed the red herring.	Submit the registration statement to the SEC.	3	15,000
Calculate the issue price.	Submit the registration statement to the SEC.	5	12,000
Receive deficiency memorandum from the SEC.	Submit the registration statement to the SEC.	3	0
Amend the registration statement and resubmit it to the SEC.	Receive deficiency memorandum from the SEC.	1	6,000
Receive registration confirmation from the SEC.	Amend the registration statement and resubmit it to the SEC.	2	0
Confirm that the new issue complies with the "blue sky" laws of each state.	Make presentations to institutional investors and develop the interest of potential buyers. Distribute the preliminary prospectus, affectionately termed the red herring. Calculate the issue price. Receive registration confirmation from the SEC.	1	5,000
Appoint a registrar.	Receive registration confirmation from the SEC.	3	12,000
Appoint a transfer agent.	Receive registration confirmation from the SEC.	3.5	13,000
Issue final prospectus that includes the final offer price and any amendments to all purchasers offered securities through the mail.	Confirm that the new issue complies with the "blue sky" laws of each state. Appoint a registrar and transfer agent	4.5	40,000
Phone interested buyers.	Confirm that the new issue complies with the "blue sky" laws of each state. Appoint a registrar and transfer agent.	4	9,000

* The spread is the payment an underwriter receives for services.

Janet and Gilbert present the list of steps to the employees of InterCat. The head of the finance department, Leslie Grey, is fresh out of business school. She remembers the various project management tools she has learned in business school and suggests that Janet and Gilbert use PERT/CPM analysis to understand where their priorities should lie.

a. Draw the project network for completing the initial public offering of InterCat stock. How long is the initial public offering process? What are the critical steps in the process?

b. How would the change in the following activities affect the time to complete the initial public offering? Please evaluate each change independently.

i. Some members of the syndicate are playing hardball. Therefore, the time it takes to negotiate the commitment of each member of the syndicate increases from two to three weeks.

ii. The underwriters are truly math geniuses. Therefore, the time it takes to calculate the issue price decreases to four weeks.

iii. Whoa! The SEC found many deficiencies in the initial registration statement. The underwriters must therefore spend 2.5 weeks amending the statement and resubmitting it to the SEC.

CD 16-77

iv. The new issue does not comply with the "blue sky" laws of a handful of states. The time it takes to edit the issue for each state to ensure compliance increases to four weeks.

c. Janet and Gilbert hear through the grapevine that their most fierce competitor, Soft Sales, is also planning to go public. They fear that if InterCat does not complete its initial public offering before Soft Sales, the price investors are willing to pay for InterCat stock will drop since investors will perceive Soft Sales to be a stronger, more organized company. Janet and Gilbert therefore decide that they want to complete the process of issuing new stock within 22 weeks. They think such a goal is possible if they throw more resources—workers and money—into some activities. They list the activities that can be shortened, the time the activity will take when it is fully shortened, and the cost of shortening the activity this much. They also conclude that partially shortening each activity listed below is possible and will give a time reduction and cost proportional to the amounts when fully shortened.

Activity	Time (Weeks)	Cost
Evaluate the prestige of each potential underwriter.	1.5	$14,000
Select a syndicate of underwriters.	0.5	8,000
Prepare the registration statement, including the proposed financing and information about the firm's history, existing business, and plans for the future.	4	95,000
Make presentations to institutional investors and develop the interest of potential buyers.	4	60,000
Distribute the preliminary prospectus, affectionately termed the red herring.	2	22,000
Calculate the issue price.	3.5	31,000
Amend the registration statement and resubmit it to the SEC.	0.5	9,000
Confirm that the new issue complies with the "blue sky" laws of each state.	0.5	8,300
Appoint a registrar.	1.5	19,000
Appoint a transfer agent.	1.5	21,000
Issue final prospectus that includes the final offer price and any amendments to all purchasers offered securities through the mail.	2	99,000
Phone interested buyers.	1.5	20,000

How can InterCat meet the new deadline set by Janet and Gilbert at minimum cost?

d. Janet and Gilbert learn that the investment bankers are two-timing scoundrels! They are also serving as lead underwriters for the Soft Sales new issue! To keep the deal with InterCat, the bankers agree to let Janet and Gilbert in on a little secret. Soft Sales has been forced to delay its public issue because the company's records are disorganized and incomplete. Given this new information, Janet and Gilbert decide that they can be more lenient on the initial public offering timeframe. They want to complete the process of issuing new stock within 24 weeks instead of 22 weeks. Assume that the cost and time to complete the appointment of the registrar and transfer agent are the same as in part c. How can InterCat meet this new deadline set by Janet and Gilbert at minimum cost?

CD 16-78

Case 16-2 "School's Out Forever . . ."

Alice Cooper

Brent Bonnin begins his senior year of college filled with excitement and a twinge of fear. The excitement stems from his anticipation of being done with it all—professors, exams, problem sets, grades, group meetings, all-nighters . . . The list could go on and on. The fear stems from the fact that he is graduating in December and has only four months to find a job.

Brent is a little unsure about how he should approach the job search. During his sophomore and junior years, he had certainly heard seniors talking about their strategies for finding the perfect job, and he knows that he should first visit the Campus Career Planning Center to devise a search plan.

On September 1, the first day of school, he walks through the doors of the Campus Career PlanningCenter and meets Elizabeth Merryweather, a recent graduate overflowing with energy and comforting smiles. Brent explains to Elizabeth that since he is graduating in December and plans to begin work in January, he wants to leave all of November and December open for interviews. Such a plan means that by October 31 he has to have all his preliminary materials, such as cover letters and résumés, submitted to the companies where he wants to work.

Elizabeth recognizes that Brent has to follow a very tight schedule, if he wants to meet his goal within the next 60 days. She suggests that the two of them sit down together and decide the major milestones that need to be completed in the job search process. Elizabeth and Brent list the 19 major milestones. For each of the 19 milestones, they identify the other milestones that must be accomplished directly before Brent can begin this next milestone. They also estimate the time needed to complete each milestone. The list is shown below.

Milestone	Milestones Directly Preceding Each Milestone	Time to Complete Each Milestone
A. Complete and submit an online registration form to the career center.	None.	2 days (This figure includes the time needed for the career center to process the registration form.)
B. Attend the career center orientation to learn about the resources available at the center and the campus recruiting process.	None.	5 days (This figure includes the time Brent must wait before the career center hosts an orientation.)
C. Write an initial résumé that includes all academic and career experiences.	None.	7 days
D. Search the Internet to find job opportunities available outside of campus recruiting.	None.	10 days
E. Attend the company presentations hosted during the fall to understand the cultures of companies and to meet with company representatives.	None.	25 days
F. Review the industry resources available at the career center to understand the career and growth opportunities available in each industry. Take a career test to understand the career that provides the best fit with your skills and interests. Contact alumni listed in the career center directories to discuss the nature of a variety of jobs.	Complete and submit an online registration form to the career center. Attend the career center orientation.	7 days

(continued)

CD 16-79

Milestone	Milestones Directly Preceding Each Milestone	Time to Complete Each Milestone
G. Attend a mock interview hosted by the career center to practice interviewing and to learn effective interviewing styles.	Complete and submit an online registration form to the career center. Attend the career center orientation. Write the initial résumé.	4 days (This figure includes the time that elapses between the day that Brent signs up for the interview and the day that the interview takes place.)
H. Submit the initial résumé to the career center for review.	Complete and submit an online registration form to the career center. Attend the career center orientation. Write the initial résumé.	2 days (This figure includes the time the career center needs to review the résumé.)
I. Meet with a résumé expert to discuss improvements to the initial résumé.	Submit the initial résumé to the career center for review.	1 day
J. Revise the initial résumé	Meet with a résumé expert to discuss improvements.	4 days
K. Attend the career fair to gather company literature, speak to company representatives, and submit résumés	Revise the initial résumé.	1 day
L. Search campus job listings to identify the potential jobs that fit your qualifications and interests.	Review the industry resources, take the career test, and contact alumni.	5 days
M. Decide which jobs you will pursue given the job opportunities you found on the Internet, at the career fair, and through the campus job listings.	Search the Internet. Search the campus job listings. Attend the career fair.	3 days
N. Bid to obtain job interviews with companies that recruit through the campus career center and have open interview schedules.*	Decide which jobs you will pursue.	3 days
O. Write cover letters to seek jobs with companies that either do not recruit through the campus career center or recruit through the campus career center but have closed interview schedules.** Tailor each cover letter to the culture of each company.	Decide which jobs you will pursue. Attend company presentations.	10 days
P. Submit the cover letters to the career center for review.	Write the cover letters.	4 days (This figure includes the time the career center needs to review the cover letters.)
Q. Revise the cover letters.	Submit the cover letters to the career center for review.	4 days
R. For the companies that are not recruiting through the campus career center, mail the cover letter and résumé to the company's recruiting department.	Revise the cover letters.	6 days (This figure includes the time needed to print and package the application materials and the time needed for the materials to reach the companies.)
S. For the companies that recruit through the campus career center but that hold closed interview schedules, drop the cover letter and résumé at the career center.	Revise the cover letters.	2 days (This figure includes the time needed to print and package the application materials.)

*An open interview schedule occurs when the company does not select the candidates that it wants to interview. Any candidate may interview, but since the company has only a limited number of interview slots, interested candidates must bid points (out of their total allocation of points) for the interviews. The candidates with the highest bids win the interview slots.
**Closed interview schedules occur when a company requires candidates to submit their cover letters, résumés, and test scores so that the company is able to select the candidates it wants to interview.

CD 16-80

In the evening after his meeting with Elizabeth, Brent meets with his buddies at the college coffee house to chat about their summer endeavors. Brent also tells his friends about the meeting he had earlier with Elizabeth. He describes the long to-do list he and Elizabeth developed and says that he is really worried about keeping track of all the major milestones and getting his job search organized. One of his friends reminds him of the cool management science class they all took together in the first semester of Brent's junior year and how they had learned about some techniques to organize large projects. Brent remembers this class fondly since he was able to use a number of the methods he studied in that class in his last summer job.

a. Draw the project network for completing all milestones before the interview process. If everything stays on schedule, how long will it take Brent until he can start with the interviews? What are the critical steps in the process?

b. Brent realizes that there is a lot of uncertainty in the times it will take him to complete some of the milestones. He expects to get really busy during his senior year, in particular since he is taking a demanding course load. Also, students sometimes have to wait quite a while before they get appointments with the counselors at the career center. In addition to the list estimating the most likely times that he and Elizabeth wrote down, he makes a list of optimistic and pessimistic estimates of how long the various milestones might take.

Milestone	Optimistic Estimate (Days)	Pessimistic Estimate (Days)
A	1	4
B	3	10
C	5	14
D	7	12
E	20	30
F	5	12
G	3	8
H	1	6
I	1	1
J	3	6
K	1	1
L	3	10
M	2	4
N	2	8
O	3	12
P	2	7
Q	3	9
R	4	10
S	1	3

How long will it take Brent to get everything done under the worst-case scenario? How long will it take if all his optimistic estimates are correct?

c. Determine the mean critical path for Brent's job search process. What is the variance of the project duration?

d. Give a rough estimate of the probability that Brent will be done within 60 days.

CD 16-81

e. Brent realizes that he has made a serious mistake in his calculations so far. He cannot schedule the career fair to fit his schedule. Brent read in the campus newspaper that the fair has been set 24 days from today on September 25th. Draw a revised project network that takes into account this complicating fact.

f. What is the mean critical path for the new network? What is the probability that Brent will complete his project within 60 days?

CHAPTER 17
GOAL PROGRAMMING

Learning objectives

After completing this chapter, you should be able to

1. Identify the kinds of managerial problems that goal programming can address.
2. Describe how a goal programming model differs from other kinds of management science models.
3. Discuss the differences between the weighted goal programming approach and the preemptive goal programming approach.
4. Determine which of these approaches seems more appropriate for a given situation.
5. Formulate and apply a weighted goal programming model from a description of the problem.
6. Formulate and apply a preemptive goal programming model from a description of the problem.

In Chapters 2–8, you have seen various kinds of management science models that can address a wide variety of managerial problems. However, all these models share one common characteristic. They all have a single objective function that expresses the overall measure of performance for the problem. For example, the objective might be to maximize total profit.

Unfortunately, it is not always possible to encapsulate management's objectives into one overall measure of performance in this way. The objectives might be so disparate that there is no common basis for measuring progress toward these objectives. In this kind of situation, management might instead set numeric goals for the various objectives and then seek a solution that makes as much progress as possible toward all these goals. This is the kind of problem that goal programming addresses.

The chapter begins with a case study that demonstrates how this kind of situation can arise. You will see three members of top management championing three very different goals for a project. The CEO agrees that all three goals are important and then mediates to assess their relative importance. You also will see how the head of the Management Science Department works with top management to elicit the kind of input needed to apply goal programming.

Goal programming provides two alternative ways of formulating problems with multiple goals. One, called *weighted goal programming*, assigns weights to the goals that measure their relative importance and then seeks a solution that minimizes the weighted sum of the deviations from the goals. This approach is described in Section 17.2 in the context of the case study. The second approach, called *preemptive goal programming*, requires deciding on the order of importance of the goals. It then focuses on one goal at a time in this order. This approach is described in Section 17.3. The dialogue for the case study in Section 17.1 also introduces both approaches, including when each one is more appropriate and how management should provide the needed input, in a practical setting.

17.1 A CASE STUDY: THE DEWRIGHT CO. GOAL-PROGRAMMING PROBLEM

"What's the matter, honey? A rough day at the office?"

"Well, it really wasn't all that bad," Kathleen responds to her husband Scott. "Mainly just frustrating. Ever since I got this job as head of Dewright's Management Science Department, I have emphasized making sure that everything we do is responding to management's needs.

CD 17-2

Understand what management's objectives are for the decisions they need to make based on our studies. Then address those objectives rather than what we think the goals should be. I preach that all the time."

"So what happened?"

"Well, we've just been handed an extremely important new project, a really juicy management science study. So I made the rounds today interviewing the key people in top management to clarify just what they wanted to get out of our study. What is the basic objective for the decisions they need to make? Usually this goes pretty smoothly, with a lot of consensus about what the overriding objective should be. But not today. First I was told that we should focus on such and such as the main goal of the study. Then the next person I interviewed said no, the key goal was something completely different. Then the next guy had an entirely new slant on it. I've never seen so much disagreement. Each one was only protecting his or her own interests instead of looking at the big picture of what is best for the company as a whole. So now we're stymied. I've already selected the members of the team to work on this study. But we can't really get started until we receive much clearer direction from management. And, of course, management needs the study completed quickly. One jokester said they would like our report the day before yesterday. I laughed politely, but I felt like kicking him. Don't they realize that our output from the study can only be as good as their input!?! And that we can only act as quickly as they give us the direction we need!"

"Wow, no wonder you're frustrated," Scott responds. "It sounds like management really dropped the ball on this one."

"Yes, they did. It was clear that they hadn't talked to each other about this issue, even though they knew I would be interviewing all of them about this today. It's management's responsibility to thrash this out and come to a common understanding of what they want out of a management science study, and then give us clear direction. They really didn't do their job this time!"

"So what's the next step?"

"I've already called our CEO late this afternoon. Direction needs to come from the top. Actually, Gary was pretty sympathetic. He even volunteered that he thought his people had let me down this time."

"So did he give you the direction you need?" Scott asks Kathleen.

"No, I really wasn't asking for that at this point. He wasn't involved with requesting this management science study, so I was hitting him cold. But he understood right away what had gone wrong. Even before I could suggest it, he said that the managers involved with this project should be brought together in a meeting to thrash out what the main goals should be. He even said he would chair the meeting himself. He also wants me and key members of my team there. He says it is very important that we have a clear understanding of management's thinking on this issue. And I certainly agreed."

"Great! So it sounds to me like all you have to do is attend the meeting and listen carefully. Let them do their homework and then come to a meeting of the minds. Press them if necessary to get the clarity you need. Then you'll be off and running."

Background

The Dewright Company is one of the largest producers of power tools in the United States. The company has had its ups and downs but has managed to maintain its position as one of the market leaders for over 20 years. This is largely due to superior products produced by a skilled and loyal work force, many of whom have been with the company for most of its existence. One of management's priorities has been to maintain a relatively stable employment level to retain the high morale and loyalty of this work force.

The company has just gone through one of its leaner years. Sales were down slightly from the preceding year and earnings dipped as well (much to the discontent of the company's stockholders). One consequence is that the company now has less capital available than usual with which to invest in new product development. Management also is concerned that some downsizing may be needed if sales don't improve soon.

Fortunately, help is on the way. The company is preparing to replace its current product line with the next generation of products—specifically, three exciting new power tools with the latest state-of-the-art features, so they are expected to sell well for at least a year or two. Because of the limited amount of capital available, management needs to make some difficult choices about how much to invest in each of these products. Another concern is the effect of these decisions on the company's ability to maintain a relatively stable employment level. A competitor is known to be developing similar new products, so decisions must be made quickly.

These kinds of considerations recently led the company's president, Tasha Johnson, to call Kathleen Donaldson, head of the Management Science Department, to request an urgent management science study to analyze what the product mix should be. Tasha asked Kathleen to come see her for a briefing on management's objectives in making the product-mix decisions. Tasha also suggested that Kathleen talk with Vijay Shah (vice president for manufacturing) and Hien Nguyen (the chief financial officer).

Kathleen has just completed these interviews, with the unsatisfactory results reported to her husband.

Gary Lang, the company's CEO, now has arranged for the meeting to bring these parties together with Kathleen and key members of her team.

The Management Science Team Meets with Top Management

After some pleasantries, the meeting gets under way.

Gary Lang (CEO): I've called this meeting to clarify what we want to accomplish when we introduce these three new products. What are our main goals? I have some thoughts on that. But first I want to hear your thinking. Then we can work this out together. Once this is settled, planning can get under way to accomplish what we want accomplished. As you know, Tasha has asked Kathleen to personally head a management science team from her department to analyze how we can best meet our goals. Before the team can do that, they need some clear direction from us on just what our goals and priorities are. Kathleen, is that a fair summary of what you want to get out of this meeting?

Kathleen Donaldson (head of Management Science Department): Yes, it is, Gary. Thank you.

Gary: OK. Let's make the rounds then and get your thinking. Tasha, let's start with you.

Tasha Johnson (president): Well, as usual, I think we need to focus on the bottom line. If we do that, everything else will fall into place. After the year we just went through, we've got to get our earnings up. That's certainly the message our board of directors has been giving us. You'll recall the plan I presented at the last board meeting. To get our earnings headed up where we want them, we need to generate a total profit of at least $125 million from these three products until they're replaced by the next generation of products. And I think that's doable. I've already told Kathleen that I would like her team to find the mix of the three products that would maximize our profit. And to make sure that it is at least $125 million, as I promised the board of directors. I think that should be our main focus.

Gary: Thank you, Tasha. It's certainly true that the board has been pressing us to substantially improve earnings. And they were encouraged by your plan to generate profits of at least $125 million from these products. Vijay, what is your take on this issue of where our focus should be?

Vijay Shah (vice president for manufacturing): Well, I'm certainly not going to argue against making profits. But there are different ways of accomplishing that. By and large, we've been a very profitable company for over 20 years. And despite our occasional off years like last year, I think we will continue to be a very successful company as long as we don't forget what got us here. Our number one asset is our work force. They're the best in the business and we all know it. Besides our strong leadership at the top, they're our main reason for success. If we simply go scrambling after big profits in the short run to satisfy the board of directors for a little while, I think that's going to mean some downsizing. That would ruin morale! And cause all kinds of disruption. I know a lot of companies have been doing it, often to their regret, but it would be a huge mistake in our case. Let's not kill the goose that's been laying our golden eggs. We have great morale and an exceptionally efficient work force largely because we've kept them together all these years. We're going to have larger profits in the long run if we maintain a stable employment level and continue developing new products to keep them fully utilized. I told Kathleen that I thought her team should develop a plan for the current new products that would maintain our present employment level, and then profits would take care of themselves.

Tasha: But in this global economy, the companies that are surviving are those that downsize quickly when they need to in order to stay competitive.

Vijay: That would be shortsighted, especially in our situation.

Gary: Vijay, I do agree that we have a terrific work force and we should try to maintain it if possible. It is my hope that these three new products will enable us to do just that. We currently have 4,000 employees. We might even be able to increase that if everything falls into place. When you talk about the disadvantages of changing the employment level, how would you feel about an increase rather than a decrease?

Vijay: An increase wouldn't be so bad. But it still would cause some problems, especially since the increase probably would be temporary as these products wind down. First, we would incur the expense and disruption of training these inexperienced workers. Then we would turn around and need to lay them off because we have so little attrition here. Any layoffs are not good for morale. I think we're better off sticking pretty close to the 4,000 employees.

Gary: OK. Thanks, Vijay. Now I'm anxious to hear from Hien, especially after our financial downturn this past year.

Hien Nguyen (chief financial officer): Yes. You know well that we're not in a good financial situation. We seldom have been as strapped for capital as we are right now.

Gary: Unfortunately, we're going to need a lot of capital to launch these new products properly. And it is very important to the future of this company to have a good launch. I'm going to need to depend on you to work your usual magic to come up with at least the minimum amounts necessary to invest in the production facilities, marketing campaigns, and so forth, that we need for these products. How much do you think we can do?

Hien: I've been looking into that pretty carefully. I think we can scrape together something close to $55 million. However, I wouldn't advise trying to go beyond that. If we get that overextended, I fear that our corporate bonds will be downgraded into the junk bond category. And then we would be paying through the nose in high interest rates for all our debt. So when Kathleen saw me recently, I advised her to stick with plans that would hold the capital investment down to no more than $55 million.

Gary: I hear you. OK, here is my conclusion so far. I think all three of you have raised very valid concerns. You each have enunciated a goal: Achieve a total profit from these products of at least $125 million, maintain the current employment level of 4,000 employees, and hold the capital investment down to no more than $55 million. These all are legitimate goals. I seriously doubt that we can fully achieve all of them. However, rather than selecting just one of them, I think we need to try to come as close to meeting all three goals simultaneously as we can.

Kathleen: I have a question.

Gary: Shoot.

Kathleen: Do you see any way of combining all three goals into a single overriding objective—one objective that would encompass all three?

Gary: Such as?

Kathleen: Well, perhaps maximizing *long-run* profit. The problems associated with either changing the employment level or overextending our capital outlays affect our profit in the long run. Can we measure these effects on long-run profits and combine them with the direct profit from the new products?

Gary: Hmmm. An interesting idea. But no, I don't think so. You're really comparing apples and oranges. There are too many intangibles involved in the impact of missing either the second or third goal. I don't see how you can develop any reasonable estimate of the long-run profit that would result from all this.

Kathleen: Yes, that was my reaction too. But yours is the one that counts. So it sounds like we should consider all three goals as separate goals, but then analyze them simultaneously.

Gary: Yes, I think so. Do you have a good way of doing this?

Kathleen: Well, I can think of two possibilities. But we need further guidance from all of you to determine the approach we should use.

Gary: Go ahead.

Kathleen: One possibility is to use a linear programming approach. You'll recall that we've conducted several linear programming studies for you recently.

Gary: Yes.

Kathleen: This would involve maximizing the total profit from the new products, subject to constraints that the second and third goals are met. But this would mean requiring that the second and third goals are completely satisfied. Would that requirement seem reasonable to you?

Tasha: No, no, no! I think the first goal is the most important. We should make sure we meet it even if that means missing the second and third goals somewhat.

Vijay: But we also should permit missing the first goal somewhat to avoid missing the other goals by a large amount.

Gary: Well, there you have it. I agree that we shouldn't require any of the goals to be completely satisfied if they can't all be satisfied simultaneously.

Kathleen: OK, fine. So formulating a linear programming model would not be appropriate to meet your needs. But now it sounds to me like the second approach would be perfect for you.

Gary: What's that?

Kathleen: It's a management science technique called **goal programming.** It is designed to find the best way of striving toward several goals.

Gary: Yes, that sounds like just the ticket. So now you have what you need from us to start your study?

Kathleen: Not quite. I need to ask your indulgence for a few minutes to elicit a little more input—information we need to be able to use goal programming.

Gary: This is important. We'll take as long as you need.

Kathleen: Thank you. What we need is your collective assessment of the relative importance of these three goals.

Gary: I would like to take a crack at that. I've been thinking hard about this during our discussion here. I must say that Tasha, Vijay, and Hien all have made strong cases. I think all three goals are important. However, I don't think we have any choice but to put top priority on achieving our profit goal. That is the engine that drives everything else. And our board of directors has made it very clear that this needs to be our top priority. But I also resonate with what Vijay had to say about our work force being our number one asset. However, I would divide his goal of maintaining a stable employment level into two parts—avoiding a *decrease* in the employment level and avoiding an *increase* in the employment level. I think the negative impact of laying off some of our loyal long-time employees would be much more serious than that of hiring new people and perhaps laying them off in a year or two. Therefore, I would place a pretty strong second priority on avoiding layoffs, but not on avoiding new hiring. Then sorry, Hien, but I think we can only give third priority to the goal of holding our capital investment under $55 million. We mustn't ignore your very legitimate concerns. However, we are in a hole that we need to dig out of, even if that means stretching our finances more than we normally would be willing to do. Then finally, I would put fourth priority on the second part of Vijay's goal— avoiding an increase in our employment level since it might need to be temporary. What do the rest of you think? Does this seem reasonable?

Tasha: Definitely.

Vijay: I can live with it.

Hien: You're the one that needs to set priorities. But we do need to be cautious about getting overextended financially.

Gary: I hear you. OK, Kathleen, what additional input do you need from us?

Kathleen: I need your advice on the following issue. Goal programming is a flexible technique that provides two different approaches to analyzing managerial problems. Which approach is appropriate for any particular problem depends on management's assessment of how big the differences are in the importance of the goals. Are all the goals quite important with only modest differences in their importance? Or are there really big differences in their importance? In the first case, the approach is to literally consider all the goals simultaneously while recognizing the modest differences in their importance. We call this approach **weighted goal programming** because it places weights on the goals to reflect their relative importance. In the second case, because of the really big differences in the importance of the goals, the approach is to begin by focusing solely on the most important goal and going as far as possible toward achieving that goal. Then it turns to the second most important goal, and then to the third one, and so forth. This approach is called **preemptive goal programming** because its focus on each goal in turn is preempting any consideration yet of less important goals. My group would be comfortable with using either approach. However, the decision on which one to use really needs to depend on your input. How big do you think the differences are in the importance of the goals? Which approach seems more appropriate for this situation?

Gary: I could see us going in either direction. It seems to me that there are clear differences in the importance of the goals. However, they all are quite important. I wouldn't say that there are very big differences in their importance. So my inclination would be to go with that first approach you mentioned.

Kathleen: Yes, the weighted goal programming approach. Since you say you could see us going in either direction, this apparently is not a clear-cut situation. Therefore, I think what we'll do is begin with the weighted goal programming approach, but then double-check our conclusions by applying the preemptive goal programming approach as well. We'll include all our results in our report and then the four of you can put your heads together to make the decision on what the product mix should be for the three new products.

Gary: I like it. Full steam ahead. Are you all set now? Does this give you everything you need?

Kathleen: Nearly. This has been extremely helpful. However, we still need your input on one more thing in order to implement the weighted preemptive programming approach. Let me explain a little more about how this approach works. It assigns penalties to not achieving goals. The more you miss a goal, the larger the penalty. The top priority goals get the largest penalties for missing them and the lowest priority goals get the smallest penalties. Then goal programming finds the set of decisions—in this case the production rates for the three products—that minimizes the total number of penalty points incurred by missing goals.

Gary: Sounds like a good approach.

Kathleen: Yes. But what this means is that we need to assign penalty weights that measure the relative seriousness of missing the respective goals. Now we could try to assign the penalty weights based on the discussion here and the priorities you have set. But that really isn't our place. These penalty weights need to reflect *your* assessment, not ours, of the relative seriousness of missing these goals.

Gary: I agree. How do we go about that?

Kathleen: Well, the first step is that we assign any old number as the penalty weight for missing one of the goals, just to establish a standard of comparison. Then you would scale this penalty weight up or down for each of the other goals, depending on whether you think the seriousness of missing that goal is larger or smaller than for missing the first goal. OK, since our top priority is the goal of achieving a total profit from these new products of at least $125 million, let's assign a penalty weight of 5 for each $1 million you undershoot this goal. In other words, if the estimated total profit resulting from the selected profit mix is $124 million, 5 penalty points would be assessed. If the estimated total profit is $115 million, undershooting the goal by $10 million, then 50 penalty points would be assessed. Ten times five is 50.

Gary: I get it.

Kathleen: OK. With this penalty weight of 5 as a standard of comparison, now we're ready for the hard questions. Going down your priorities, what should the penalty weight be for each 100 employees we *undershoot* the goal of maintaining the current employment level at 4,000 employees? For each $1 million we miss the goal of holding the capital investment down to no more than $55 million? For each 100 employees we *overshoot* the goal of sticking with 4,000 employees?

Gary: Hmmm. Good questions. Hmmm. Well, I think I would go 5, 4, 3, 2. Five for the first goal, and then 4, 3, 2 for your three questions.

Kathleen: Great. Understood. That gives us exactly what we need. We can launch into our study immediately now.

Gary: Very good. You understand that we'll need your report quite soon.

Kathleen: Yes, I think we can finish in a month. I'll tell you what our biggest job is going to be. Gathering data. We're going to need to get good data on the effect of each product's production rate toward meeting each of the three goals. How much profit will each product generate? How much employment level? How much capital investment is needed? We'll have to get a lot of help from various staff people.

Gary: I'll see to it that everybody makes this their top priority.

Kathleen: Then we can do it. I don't think any of us will see much of our families for the next month, but I'll make sure that we get it done in time.

Gary: Good for you, Kathleen. Thank you so much. And let us know whenever you need more input or help from any of us.

Kathleen: I will. Thank you.

The meeting concludes, except for a somewhat heated private conversation between Tasha and Vijay.

The Conclusions from This Meeting

To summarize, here are the key conclusions from this meeting.

The management science team led by Kathleen Donaldson will conduct a study to be completed within the next month. The study will focus on determining the mix of the company's three new products that would best meet management's goals. The specific decisions to be made are the production rates for the three products.

In addressing these decisions, management wants primary consideration given to three factors: total profit, stability in the work force, and the level of capital investment needed to launch these products. In particular, management has established the following goals.

Goal 1: Achieve a total profit (net present value) from these products of at least $125 million.

Goal 2: Maintain the current employment level of 4,000 employees.

Goal 3: Hold the capital investment down to no more than $55 million.

However, management realizes that it probably will not be possible to attain all these goals simultaneously, and so they evaluated the relative importance of the goals. All are important, but by small margins their order of importance is

> **Order of Importance:** Goal 1, part of Goal 2 (avoid decreasing the employment level),
> Goal 3, and the other part of Goal 2 (avoid increasing the employment level).

To further quantify this ordering, **penalty weights** were assigned to indicate the relative seriousness of missing these goals. Discussions between management and Kathleen led to the choice of the penalty weights shown in Table 17.1.

Table 17.1   Penalty Weights That Measure the Relative Seriousness of Missing the Goals for the Dewright Co. Problem

Goal	Factor	Penalty Weight for Missing Goal
1	Total profit	5 (per $1 million under the goal)
2	Employment level	4 (per 100 employees under the goal) 2 (per 100 employees over the goal)
3	Capital investment	3 (per $1 million over the goal)

Relevant Data

What the total profit, employment level, and capital investment level will be depends on the *production rates* (number of units produced per day) of the three products. Each product's contribution to each of these three quantities is *proportional* to the rate of production of the product. Therefore, for each of the three products, the management science team focuses on estimating the contribution to each of these quantities *per unit* rate of production of the product. Much of these data are not readily available, so the team has to do considerable digging with much help from knowledgeable staff. Based on the limited information it can uncover, the team then makes the best estimates that it can of each product's contribution to each of the three quantities.

These estimated contributions per unit rate of production are shown in Table 17.2, where the contributions are in the units indicated (in parentheses) in the first column. Thus, for example, producing one unit per day of product 1 would contribute $12 million toward total profit, 500 employees to the employment level, and $5 million to the capital investment level.

Table 17.2   Contributions to the Goals per Unit Rate of Production of Each Product for the Dewright Co. Problem

	Unit Contribution of Product			
Factor	1	2	3	Goal
Total profit (millions of dollars)	12	9	15	≥ 125
Employment level (hundreds of employees)	5	3	4	$= 40$
Capital investment (millions of dollars)	5	7	8	≤ 55

The story of how the team uses these data to complete its study continues in the next section, after we introduce the general subject of goal programming.

REVIEW QUESTIONS

1. What is the problem that Dewright's management science team has been asked to address?
2. What are the three goals that management has established for addressing this problem?
3. What is to be minimized when using a weighted goal-programming approach?

17.2 WEIGHTED GOAL PROGRAMMING

One common characteristic of all the different kinds of management science models introduced in Chapters 2–8 (including linear programming, integer programming, and nonlinear programming) is that they have a single objective function. This implies that all the managerial objectives for the problem being studied can be encompassed within a single overriding objective, such as maximizing total profit or minimizing total cost. However, this is not always possible, as you have just seen in the Dewright case study.

When managing a for-profit organization, the managerial objectives might well include some of the following:

1. Maintain stable profits.

2. Increase market share.

3. Diversify the product line.

4. Maintain stable prices.

5. Improve worker morale.

6. Maintain family control of the business.

7. Increase company prestige.

These objectives are so different in nature that it really is not realistic to combine them into a single overriding objective. Instead, analysis of the problem of concern requires individual consideration of the separate objectives.

Weighted goal programming provides a way of striving toward several such objectives simultaneously. The basic approach is to establish a specific numeric goal for each of the objectives and then to seek a solution that balances how close this solution comes to each of these goals. Penalty weights are assigned to the objectives to measure the relative seriousness of missing their numeric goals. An objective function is formulated for each of the objectives. The overall objective is to minimize the weighted sum of deviations of these objective functions from their respective goals. Assuming that all the individual objective functions and the constraints of the problem fit the format for linear programming, the overall problem then can be formulated as a linear programming problem.

Now let us see how Dewright's management science team does this for the case study introduced in the preceding section.

Formulation of a Weighted Goal-Programming Model for the Dewright Co. Problem

The decisions that need to be made for the Dewright Co. problem are the production rates for the three new products that will be introduced soon. Therefore, the decision variables are

P_1 = Number of units of product 1 to produce per day

P_2 = Number of units of product 2 to produce per day

P_3 = Number of units of product 3 to produce per day

Using the unit contributions given in Table 17.2, the three goals can be expressed in terms of these decision variables as

Goal 1: $12P_1 + 9P_2 + 15P_3 \geq 125$ (Total profit goal)

Goal 2: $5P_1 + 3P_2 + 4P_3 = 40$ (Employment level goal)

Goal 3: $5P_1 + 7P_2 + 8P_3 \leq 55$ (Capital investment goal)

CD 17-11

These mathematical expressions for the goals look like linear programming constraints. However, they cannot be used as constraints in a mathematical model because constraints definitely must be satisfied whereas Dewright management already has concluded that it probably will not be possible to attain all these goals simultaneously. For a goal-programming model, the overall objective instead is to come as close as possible to satisfying all these goals simultaneously.

More precisely, using the penalty weights given in Table 17.1, let

W = Weighted sum of deviations from the goals

= Number of penalty points incurred by missing the goals

For each goal that is missed, the number of penalty points incurred is the penalty weight *times* the deviation from the goal. Therefore, the overall objective then is to choose the values of P_1, P_2, and P_3 so as to

Minimize W = 5 (amount under goal 1) + 2 (amount over goal 2) + 4 (amount under goal 2) + 3 (amount over goal 3)

where no penalty points are incurred for being over goal 1 (exceeding the target for total profit is fine) or for being under goal 3 (underexpending the capital investment budget is satisfactory).

Figure 17.1 shows one way of formulating the spreadsheet model for this problem. Three of the changing cells UnitsProduced (C12:E12) display the values of the decision variables (P_1, P_2, and P_3). Given these values, the equations entered into LevelAchieved (F6:F8) provide the levels achieved toward meeting the goals expressed in columns B, G, and H.

The most subtle part of this formulation involves columns, J, K, M, and O. Deviations (J6:K8) are additional changing cells that display the decisions on the amounts over and amounts under the respective goals. WeightedSumOfDeviations (M13) is the objective cell giving the value of W, where the Solver Parameters box specifies that the objective is to minimize this value. Using the expression for W given earlier, the equation entered into this objective cell is the SUMPRODUCT of the data cells PenaltyWeights (J13:K15) and the changing cells Deviations (J6:K8).

The Solver options selected at the bottom of Figure 17.1 specify that this model now has been formulated in a way that fits linear programming (which enables solving the model) and that all the changing cells need to be nonnegative. There are no constraints involving the output cells LevelAchieved (F6:F8) since these cell values are not required to fully satisfy the goals specified in columns B, G, and H. However, the output cells Balance (M6:M8) do need to satisfy the constraints specified by the Solver Parameters box, Balance (M6:M8) = Goal (H6:H8).

	A	B	C	D	E	F	G	H	I	J	K	L	M	N	O
1		**Dewright Co. Goal Programming (Weighted)**													
2															
3							**Goals**			**Deviations**			**Constraints**		
4			Contribution per Unit Produced			Level				Amount	Amount		Balance		
5			Product 1	Product 2	Product 3	Achieved		Goal		Over	Under		(Level - Over + Under)		Goal
6		Goal 1 (Profit)	12	9	15	125	>=	125		0	0		125	=	125
7		Goal 2 (Employment)	5	3	4	48.333333	=	40		8.333333	0		40	=	40
8		Goal 3 (Investment)	5	7	8	55	<=	55		0	0		55	=	55
9															
10															
11			Product 1	Product 2	Product 3			**Penalty**		Over	Under		Weighted Sum		
12		**Units Produced**	8.3333333	0	1.6666667			**Weights**		Goal	Goal		of Deviations		
13								Profit			5		16.66666667		
14								Employment		2	4				
15								Investment		3					

Solver Parameters
Set Objective Cell: WeightedSumOfDeviations
To: Min
By Changing Variable Cells:
UnitsProduced, Deviations
Subject to the Constraints:
Balance = Goal
Solver Options:
Make Variables Nonnegative
Solving Method: Simplex LP

Range Name	Cells
AmountOver	J6:J8
AmountUnder	K6:K8
Balance	M6:M8
Deviations	J6:K8
Goal	H6:H8
LevelAchieved	F6:F8
PenaltyWeights	J13:K15
UnitsProduced	C12:E12
WeightedSumOfDeviations	M13

	F
4	Level
5	Achieved
6	=SUMPRODUCT(C6:E6,UnitsProduced)
7	=SUMPRODUCT(C7:E7,UnitsProduced)
8	=SUMPRODUCT(C8:E8,UnitsProduced)

	M	N	O
4	Balance		
5	(Level - Over + Under)		Goal
6	=LevelAchieved-AmountOver+AmountUnder	=	=Goal
7	=LevelAchieved-AmountOver+AmountUnder	=	=Goal
8	=LevelAchieved-AmountOver+AmountUnder	=	=Goal

	M
11	Weighted Sum
12	of Deviations
13	=SUMPRODUCT(PenaltyWeights,Deviations)

Figure 17.1   A spreadsheet model for the Dewright Co. weighted goal-programming problem formulated as a linear programming problem, where the changing cells UnitsProduced (C12:E12) show the optimal production rates and the changing cells Deviations (J6:K8) show the optimal amounts over and under the goals. The objective cell WeightedSumOfDeviations (M13) gives the resulting weighted sum of deviations from the goals.

These constraints play the key role of ensuring that the changing cells Deviations (J6:K8) will equal the amounts by which LevelAchieved (F6:F8) deviate from the goals. To see why, note that the equations entered into Balance (M6:M8) are

Balance (M6:M8) = LevelAchieved (F6:F8) -AmountOver (J6:J8)

+AmountUnder (K6:K8)

Therefore, the constraints that Balance (M6:M8) = Goal (H6:H8) require that

Goal (H6:H8) = LevelAchieved (F6:F8) -AmountOver (J6:J8) +AmountUnder (K6:K8)

To minimize the objective cell, the smallest nonnegative values of AmountOver (J6:J8) and AmountUnder (K6:K8) that satisfy these equations will need to be chosen. Consequently, in any row where LevelAchieved deviates from Goal, either AmountOver or AmountUnder will equal this deviation (which one depends on whether it is a positive or negative deviation) and the other one will have a value of 0.

Running Solver yields the optimal solution for all the changing cells shown in Figure 17.1. Since the units being used in the spreadsheet are those given in the first column of Table 17.2, this solution thereby provides the following:

Production rate for product 1 = 8 1/3 units per day

Production rate for product 2 = 0

Production rate for product 3 = 1 2/3 units per day

Total profit = $125 million

Employment level = 4,833 employees

Capital investment = $55 million

The only deviation from management's goals is the one considered least serious (exceeding the employment level goal of 4,000 employees).

REVIEW QUESTIONS

1. What is the one common characteristic of the management science models introduced in previous chapters that is *not* possessed by goal-programming problems?
2. What is the basic approach of goal programming?
3. What is represented by the objective function in a goal-programming model?
4. What is shown by the changing cells (other than those displaying the values of the decision variables for the original problem) in the spreadsheet model for a goal-programming problem?
5. To enable solving a goal-programming problem, it can be formulated to fit what kind of spreadsheet model?

17.3   PREEMPTIVE GOAL PROGRAMMING

Goal programming provides two distinct approaches for dealing with managerial problems where multiple goals need to be considered. The approach described in the preceding section, weighted goal programming, is designed for problems where all the goals are quite important with only modest differences in importance that can be measured by assigning weights to these goals. We now turn to the other approach, preemptive goal programming.

This second approach is used when there are such major differences in the importance of the goals that it is not feasible to assign meaningful weights to these goals to measure their relative importance. Therefore, the goals are instead listed in the order of their importance. Preemptive goal programming then begins by focusing solely on meeting the most important goal as closely as possible, and next doing the same for the second most important goal, and so on through the rest of the goals in order. Thus, while this approach is focusing on one of the goals, it is preempting any consideration yet of less important goals.

One advantage of this approach is that it is less difficult for management to assess the order of importance of its goals than to assign weights to the goals to measure their relative importance. It is not easy to get a handle on what the penalty weights should be for deviations from the goals when these goals are as disparate as those for the Dewright Co. problem. Assessing the order of importance is a much more concrete task. Another advantage is that the process of focusing on one goal at a time in the order of its importance is intuitive and readily understood. Management has more confidence in the output of a model when it has confidence in both the validity of its input and the process involved in obtaining the output.

There are situations where the features of both approaches perhaps should be combined to analyze the problem. This occurs when the goals can be divided into groups where the goals within each group are of comparable importance but there are great differences between the groups in their level of importance. In this kind of situation, weighted goal programming can be used within each group in turn while preemptive goal programming is being applied to deal with each group in order of importance. However, we will not delve further into this more advanced subject.

The spreadsheet models employed by weighted goal programming and preemptive goal programming for the same problem are quite similar. The major difference is in their objective cells. Rather than using the weighted sum of deviations from the goals as the objective cell to be minimized, preemptive goal programming begins by minimizing only the deviation from the most important goal. When this is completed, the second step is to add a constraint that the minimal deviation achieved must continue to be met while switching to minimizing the deviation from the second most important goal. Next, a second constraint is added that the minimal deviation achieved for this second most important goal must continue to be met while switching to minimizing the deviation from the third most important goal. This process continues until all the goals have been considered.

Now let us continue the Dewright Co. case study to see how this approach is applied in that context.

The Application of Preemptive Goal Programming to the Dewright Co. Problem

Dewright's Management Science Department already has applied a weighted goal-programming model to the problem described in Section 17.1 and obtained the results shown in Figure 17.1. However, recall that when the head of this department (Kathleen Donaldson) and key members of her team met with top management to discuss this problem, it was agreed that the preemptive goal-programming approach would be applied as well.

During this meeting, the company's CEO (Gary Lang) had clearly identified the order of importance of the goals, as summarized below.

Priority 1: Strive to achieve a total profit (net present value) from the three new products of at least $125 million (Goal 1).

Priority 2: Strive to avoid decreasing the employment level below 4,000 employees (the under part of Goal 2).

Priority 3: Strive to hold the capital investment down to no more than $55 million (Goal 3).

Priority 4: Strive to avoid increasing the employment level above 4,000 employees (the over part of Goal 2).

Thus, this is the order in which Kathleen and her team will address the four goals.

Figure 17.2 shows the spreadsheet model for focusing on the Priority 1 goal. This model is identical to the weighted goal-programming model in Figure 17.1 except for deleting Penalty-Weights (J13:K15) and changing the objective cell. Because the objective at this point is to minimize the amount under Goal 1 (a profit of at least $125 million), the objective cell now is Under- Goal1 (K6). This again is a linear programming model and so is easily solved.

The changing cells in Figure 17.2 show the solution obtained after running Solver. This actually is only one of numerous optimal solutions that will yield a value of 0 for the objective cell, so the next steps will focus on identifying which of these solutions will do the best job in striving toward the lower priority goals as well.

CD 17-15

The second step is to focus on the Priority 2 goal of minimizing UnderGoal2 (K7). However, this cell already has a value of 0 in Figure 17.2, so this goal already is fully achieved along with the Priority 1 goal by the solution shown in this figure (and many other solutions).

Thus, we can immediately go on to the third step of focusing on the Priority 3 goal (do not exceed a capital investment of $55 million). Figure 17.3 shows the revised spreadsheet model for this step. The objective cell now is OverGoal3 (J8). The other key revision is the addition of the constraints, UnderGoal1 (K6) = 0 and UnderGoal2 (K7) = 0, in the Solver Parameters box (and also displayed in cells J11:K12). The changing cells in this figure show the optimal solution obtained after running Solver. Once again, a value of 0 has been obtained in the new objective cell.

The fourth and final goal is to focus on the Priority 4 goal of minimizing OverGoal2 (J7), as shown in Figure 17.4. The constraint, OverGoal3 (J8) = 0, now has been added to the constraints that were introduced at the preceding step, UnderGoal1 (K6) = 0 and UnderGoal2 (K7) = 0. Running Solver provides the optimal solution displayed in the changing cells along with a value of 8.3333 in the objective cell.

Note that this solution is the same as the one in Figure 17.3. Thus, the revised model in Figure 17.4 did not succeed in making any more progress in striving toward the Priority 4 goal. However, this solution has fully achieved the top three priority goals, so this is an excellent outcome.

Also note that the solution in Figures 17.3 and 17.4 is identical to the one in Figure 17.1 that was obtained by using weighted goal programming. This provides additional assurance that this is the solution that best meets management's needs.

	A	B	C	D	E	F	G	H	I	J	K	L	M	N	O
1		Dewright Co. Goal Programming (Preemptive Priority 1: Minimize Under Goal 1)													
2															
3							Goals			Deviations			Constraints		
4			Contribution per Unit Produced			Level			Amount	Amount		Balance		
5			Product 1	Product 2	Product 3	Achieved		Goal	Over	Under		(Level - Over + Under)		Goal
6		Goal 1 (Profit)	12	9	15	125	>=	125	0	0		125	=	125
7		Goal 2 (Employment)	5	3	4	40	=	40	0	0		40	=	40
8		Goal 3 (Investment)	5	7	8	61.481	<=	55	6.481	0		55	=	55
9														
10										Minimize (Under Goal 1)				
11			Product 1	Product 2	Product 3									
12		Units Produced	3.7037	0	5.3704									

Solver Parameters

Set Objective Cell: UnderGoal1
To: Min
By Changing Variable Cells:
    UnitsProduced, Deviations
Subject to the Constraints:
    Balance = Goal
Solver Options:
    Make Variables Nonnegative
    Solving Method: Simplex LP

Range Name	Cells
AmountOver	J6:J8
AmountUnder	K6:K8
Balance	M6:M8
Deviations	J6:K8
Goal	H6:H8
LevelAchieved	F6:F8
OverGoal1	J6
OverGoal2	J7
OverGoal3	J8
UnderGoal1	K6
UnderGoal2	K7
UnderGoal3	K8
UnitsProduced	C12:E12

	F
4	Level
5	Achieved
6	=SUMPRODUCT(C6:E6,UnitsProduced)
7	=SUMPRODUCT(C7:E7,UnitsProduced)
8	=SUMPRODUCT(C8:E8,UnitsProduced)

	M	N	O
4	Balance		
5	(Level - Over + Under)		Goal
6	=LevelAchieved-AmountOver+AmountUnder	=	=Goal
7	=LevelAchieved-AmountOver+AmountUnder	=	=Goal
8	=LevelAchieved-AmountOver+AmountUnder	=	=Goal

Figure 17.2   A spreadsheet model formulated as a linear programming model for the first step of the Dewright Co. preemptive goal-programming problem. Since Priority 1 is to minimize the deviation under Goal 1, the objective cell is UnderGoal1 (K6) for this step. The changing cells UnitsProduced (C12:E12) show the resulting production rates and the other changing cells Deviations (J6:K8) show the resulting amounts over and under the goals after running Solver. Since Priority 2 is to minimize UnderGoal2 (K7), which already has a value of 0, the procedure next will bypass step 2 and go directly to step 3.

CD 17-17

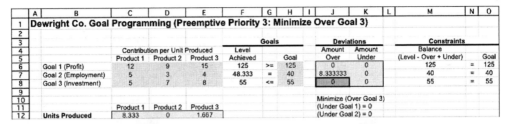

	A	B	C	D	E	F	G	H	I	J	K	L	M	N	O
1		**Dewright Co. Goal Programming (Preemptive Priority 3: Minimize Over Goal 3)**													
2															
3							**Goals**			**Deviations**			**Constraints**		
4				Contribution per Unit Produced		Level			Amount	Amount		Balance		
5			Product 1	Product 2	Product 3	Achieved		Goal	Over	Under		(Level - Over + Under)		Goal
6		Goal 1 (Profit)	12	9	15	125	>=	125	0	0		125	=	125
7		Goal 2 (Employment)	5	3	4	48.333	=	40	8.333333	0		40	=	40
8		Goal 3 (Investment)	5	7	8	55	<=	55	0	0		55	=	55
9														
10									Minimize (Over Goal 3)					
11			Product 1	Product 2	Product 3				(Under Goal 1) = 0					
12		**Units Produced**	8.333	0	1.667				(Under Goal 2) = 0					

Solver Parameters

Set Objective Cell: OverGoal3
To: Min
By Changing Variable Cells:
    UnitsProduced, Deviations
Subject to the Constraints:
    Balance = Goal
    UnderGoal1 = 0
    UnderGoal2 = 0
Solver Options:
    Make Variables Nonnegative
    Solving Method: Simplex LP

Range Name	Cells
AmountOver	J6:J8
AmountUnder	K6:K8
Balance	M6:M8
Deviations	J6:K8
Goal	H6:H8
LevelAchieved	F6:F8
OverGoal1	J6
OverGoal2	J7
OverGoal3	J8
UnderGoal1	K6
UnderGoal2	K7
UnderGoal3	K8
UnitsProduced	C12:E12

	F
4	Level
5	Achieved
6	=SUMPRODUCT(C6:E6,UnitsProduced)
7	=SUMPRODUCT(C7:E7,UnitsProduced)
8	=SUMPRODUCT(C8:E8,UnitsProduced)

	M	N	O
4	Balance		
5	(Level - Over + Under)		Goal
6	=LevelAchieved-AmountOver+AmountUnder	=	=Goal
7	=LevelAchieved-AmountOver+AmountUnder	=	=Goal
8	=LevelAchieved-AmountOver+AmountUnder	=	=Goal

Figure 17.3 The revision of the spreadsheet model in Figure 17.2 needed to perform step 3 of the preemptive goal-programming procedure. Since Priority 3 is to minimize the deviation over Goal 3, the objective cell is OverGoal3 (J8) for this step. Constraints that UnderGoal1 (K6) = 0 and UnderGoal (K7) = 0 also have been added to the model. The changing cells show the results after running Solver.

	A	B	C	D	E	F	G	H	I	J	K	L	M	N	O
1		Dewright Co. Goal Programming (Preemptive Priority 4: Minimize Over Goal 2)													
2															
3								Goals		Deviations			Constraints		
4				Contribution per Unit Produced		Level				Amount	Amount		Balance		
5			Product 1	Product 2	Product 3	Achieved		Goal		Over	Under		(Level - Over + Under)		Goal
6		Goal 1 (Profit)	12	9	15	125	>=	125		0	0		125	=	125
7		Goal 2 (Employment)	5	3	4	48.333	=	40		8.333	0		40	=	40
8		Goal 3 (Investment)	5	7	8	55	<=	55		0	0		55	=	55
9															
10										Minimize (Over Goal 2)					
11			Product 1	Product 2	Product 3					(Under Goal 1) = 0					
12		Units Produced	8.333	0	1.667					(Under Goal 2) = 0					
13										(Over Goal 3) = 0					

Solver Parameters

Set Objective Cell: OverGoal2
To: Min
By Changing Variable Cells:
    UnitsProduced, Deviations
Subject to the Constraints:
    Balance = Goal
    UnderGoal1 = 0
    UnderGoal2 = 0
    OverGoal3 = 0
Solver Options:
    Make Variables Nonnegative
    Solving Method: Simplex LP

Range Name	Cells
AmountOver	J6:J8
AmountUnder	K6:K8
Balance	M6:M8
Deviations	J6:K8
Goal	H6:H8
LevelAchieved	F6:F8
OverGoal1	J6
OverGoal2	J7
OverGoal3	J8
UnderGoal1	K6
UnderGoal2	K7
UnderGoal3	K8
UnitsProduced	C12:E12

	F
4	Level
5	Achieved
6	=SUMPRODUCT(C6:E6,UnitsProduced)
7	=SUMPRODUCT(C7:E7,UnitsProduced)
8	=SUMPRODUCT(C8:E8,UnitsProduced)

	M	N	O
4	Balance		
5	(Level - Over + Under)		Goal
6	=LevelAchieved-AmountOver+AmountUnder	=	=Goal
7	=LevelAchieved-AmountOver+AmountUnder	=	=Goal
8	=LevelAchieved-AmountOver+AmountUnder	=	=Goal

Figure 17.4	The revision of the spreadsheet model in Figure 17.3 needed to perform step 4 of the preemptive goal-programming procedure. Since Priority 4 is to minimize the deviation over Goal 2, the objective cell is OverGoal2 (J7) for this step. One more constraint, OverGoal3 (J8) = 0, also has been added to the model. Since this is the final step, the changing cells show the optimal solution obtained for Dewright's preemptive goal-programming problem by running Solver.

Epilogue to the Dewright Co. Case Study

Exactly one month after their first meeting, Gary Lang called the same group together again to hear the report of the management science team. The night before, Kathleen Donaldson had made sure that all the parties received the team's written report via courier service. Based on both the above analysis and that in the preceding section, the report recommended that the company focus most of its efforts on producing and marketing large quantities of Product 1 (P_1 = 8 1/3), while providing some diversification with a much smaller output of Product 3 (P_3 =1 2/3). Another recommendation was that any production of Product 2 be postponed indefinitely (P_2 = 0), but that further development work be done on this product to see if it could be made sufficiently attractive for release with the next generation of products. The report then highlighted the fact that this plan would enable meeting all of management's more important goals.

Everybody had read the written report with this wonderful news before entering the meeting. This completely changed the mood from the usual one that Kathleen encountered when presenting an oral report and recommendations to Dewright management. Gone were the usual probing and skeptical questioning of the presentation. (In the privacy of her home with her husband Scott, Kathleen referred to these sessions as her inquisitions.) Also missing was the zealous guarding of territory by some Dewright managers that Kathleen had observed in the past. (Kathleen marveled to Scott afterward that she actually spotted Tasha and Vijay smiling at each other for the first time in months.) Vijay did suggest, with nods all around, that some of the new employees be brought in as "temps" (temporary workers) and that the development of the next generation of new products be accelerated a little to try to avoid any future layoffs of permanent employees. Otherwise, the presentation was virtually uninterrupted. Following a quick pro forma vote to approve the plan recommended by the management science team, Gary had champagne brought in. He then offered a toast to the very fine work done by Kathleen and her team.

Thus began a very good year for the Dewright Company. However, some very rocky times—and managerial changes—awaited the company further down the road. Shortly before the downturn, Kathleen left Dewright to head up her own management science consulting firm. Her firm is doing very well.

REVIEW QUESTIONS
1. When should preemptive goal programming be used instead of weighted goal programming?
2. How does the preemptive goal-programming approach differ from the weighted goal programming approach?
3. What is the major difference between the spreadsheet models employed by weighted goal programming and preemptive goal programming for the same problem?
4. After considering the first goal, what additional constraint needs to be added during each step of the preemptive goal-programming approach when attention is turned to the next goal?
5. How many of the top-priority goals for the Dewright Co. problem did preemptive goal programming succeed in fully achieving?

17.4 SUMMARY

Most management science models make the basic assumption that a single objective function is available that encompasses the overriding objective of management for the problem. However, management sometimes will instead have a variety of rather different objectives that require separate consideration. As illustrated by the Dewright Co. case study, *goal programming* provides some ways of striving toward several such objectives simultaneously.

One basic approach, called weighted goal programming, is to establish a specific numeric goal for each of the objectives and then to seek a solution that balances how close it comes to each of these goals. By introducing some new variables (changing cells) that represent the amounts over or under the respective goals, this approach leads to formulating a model where the objective is to minimize the weighted sum of the deviations from the goals.

The other basic approach, called preemptive goal programming, begins by listing the goals in the order of their importance. It then focuses on one goal at a time in this order. While focusing on a particular goal, the model uses the objective of minimizing the deviation from that goal. The model also includes constraints that require that there be no reduction in the progress toward the goals previously considered.

With either approach, the current model often can be formulated to be a linear programming model, in which case it can be solved very readily. Thus, goal programming often provides a practical way of striving toward various managerial goals simultaneously while giving higher priority to the more important goals.

Glossary

goal programming A technique designed to find the best way of striving toward several goals. (Section 17.1)

penalty weights Values assigned to the goals of a weighted goal-programming problem that measure the relative seriousness of missing these goals. (Sections 17.1 and 17.2)

preemptive goal programming A type of goal programming that focuses on one goal at a time in order of importance while preempting any consideration yet of less important goals. (Sections 17.1 and 17.3)

weighted goal programming A type of goal programming that assigns penalty weights to the various goals and then seeks a solution that minimizes the weighted sum of the deviations from the goals. (Sections 17.1 and 17.2)

Learning Aids for This Chapter in Your MS Courseware

Chapter 17 Excel Files:

> *Dewright, Weighted Goal Programming*
>
> *Dewright Preemptive Goal Programming (three spreadsheets)*

An Excel Add-in:

> *Risk Solver Platform for Education*

Problems

To the left of each of the following problems (or their parts), we have inserted an E* whenever Excel should be used (unless your instructor gives you contrary instructions). An asterisk on the problem number indicates that at least a partial answer is given at the end of the problems.

17.1.* One of management's goals in a goal-programming problem is to maintain the company's employment level next year at its current level of 60 full-time equivalents (60 FTEs). Each FTE under this goal is considered three times as serious as each FTE over the goal. Suppose that the *amount over* appears in cell K7 of the spreadsheet model and the *amount under* appears in cell L7. (Both cells are changing cells.) What is the relationship between the coefficients of K7 and L7 in the equation entered into the objective cell?

17.2. Management of the Albert Franko Co. has established goals for the market share it wants each of the company's two new products to capture in their respective markets. Specifically, management wants product 1 to capture at least 15 percent of its market and product 2 to capture at least 10 percent of its market. Three advertising campaigns are being planned to try to achieve these market shares. One is targeted directly on the first product. The second targets the second product. The third is intended to enhance the general reputation of the company and its products. Letting x_1, x_2, and x_3 be the amount of money allocated (in millions of dollars) to these respective campaigns, the resulting market share (expressed as a percentage) for the two products are estimated to be

$$\text{Market share for product } 1 = 0.5x_1 + 0.2x_3$$

$$\text{Market share for product } 2 = 0.3x_2 + 0.2x_3$$

A total of $55 million is available for the three advertising campaigns, but management wants at least $10 million devoted to the third campaign. If both market share goals cannot be achieved, management considers each 1 percent decrease in the market share from the goal to be equally serious for the two products. In this light, management wants to know how to most effectively allocate the available money to the three campaigns.

a. Describe why this problem is a weighted goal-programming problem by giving quantitative expressions for the goals and the overall objective.

E* *b.* Formulate and solve this problem as a linear programming model on a spreadsheet.

c. Interpret this solution to management in its language.

17.3.* The Research and Development Division of the Emax Corporation has developed three new products. A decision now needs to be made on which mix of these products should be produced. Management wants primary consideration given to three factors: total profit, stability in the work force, and achieving an increase in the company's earnings next year from the $75 million achieved this year. In particular, using the units given in the following table, they want to

Maximize $M = P - 6C - 3D$

where

M = Overall measure of performance combining the three factors

P = Total (discounted) profit over the life of the new products

C = Change (in either direction) in the current level of employment

D = Decrease (if any) in next year's earnings from the current year's level

The amount of any increase in earnings does not enter into M, because management is concerned primarily with just achieving some increase to keep the stockholders happy. (It has mixed feelings about a large increase that then would be difficult to surpass in subsequent years.)

The impact of each of the new products (per unit rate of production) on each of these factors is shown in the following table:

	Unit Contribution of Product				
Factor	1	2	3	Goal	(Units)
Total profit	20	15	25	Maximize	(millions of dollars)
Employment level	6	4	5	= 50	(hundreds of employees)
Earnings next year	8	7	5	≥ 75	(millions of dollars)

E* a. Formulate and solve a spreadsheet model for this problem.

b. Interpret this solution to management in its language.

17.4. Reconsider the Dewright Co. case study as presented in Sections 17.1 and 17.2. After further reflection about the optimal solution obtained by using weighted goal programming, management now is asking some what-if questions.

a. Gary Lang wonders what would happen if the penalty weights in the rightmost column of Table 17.1 were to be changed to 7, 4, 1, and 3, respectively. Would you expect the optimal solution to change? Why?

E* b. Tasha Johnson is wondering what would happen if the total profit goal were to be increased to wanting at least $140 million (without any change in the original penalty weights). Solve the revised model with this change.

E* c. Solve the revised model if both Gary's and Tasha's changes are made.

17.5. Montega is a developing country that has 15,000,000 acres of publicly controlled agricultural land in active use. Its government currently is planning a way to divide this land among three basic crops (labeled 1, 2, and 3) next year. A certain percentage of each of these crops is exported to obtain badly needed foreign capital (dollars), and the rest of each of these crops is used to feed the populace. Raising these crops also provides employment for a significant proportion of the population. Therefore, the main factors to be considered in allocating the land to these crops are (1) the amount of foreign capital generated, (2) the number of citizens fed, and (3) the number of citizens employed in raising these crops. The following table shows how much each 1,000 acres of each crop contributes toward these factors, and the last column gives the goal established by the government for each of these factors.

| | Contribution per 1,000 Acres of Crop | | | |
Factor	1	2	3	Goal
Foreign capital	$3,000	$5,000	$4,000	≥ $70 million
Citizens fed	150	75	100	≥ 1,750,000
Citizens employed	10	15	12	= 200,000

In evaluating the relative seriousness of *not* achieving these goals, the government has concluded that the following deviations from the goals should be considered *equally undesirable:*

(1) each $100 under the foreign-capital goal,

(2) each person under the citizens-fed goal, and

(3) each deviation of one (in either direction) from the citizens-employed goal.

a. Describe why this problem is a weighted goal-programming problem by giving quantitative expressions for the goals and the overall objective.

E* *b.* Formulate and solve this problem as a linear programming model on a spreadsheet.

c. Interpret this solution to management in its language.

E* 17.6. Reconsider the scenario described in Problem 17.5. The unemployment rate in Montega is rising and the shortage of foreign capital is becoming a more serious problem. Therefore, the Montega government now has decided that it needs to place higher priority on increasing employment and increasing foreign capital than on its other goals. Specifically, it has established the following order of priorities for its goals.

Priority 1:	Citizens employed	≥ 200,000
Priority 2:	Foreign capital	≥ $70 million
Priority 3:	Citizens fed	≥ 1,750,000
Priority 4:	Citizens employed	≤ 200,000

Use preemptive goal programming to determine how the government should allocate the publicly controlled agricultural land to the three basic crops.

CD 17-24

E* 17.7. The city council of Aberdeen must determine the tax policy for the city for the coming year. Four types of taxes are used to raise money:

- Property tax

- Sales tax (a surcharge on the state sales tax)

- Entertainment tax

- Utility tax (on city-owned utilities)

The city consists of three groups of people: low income, middle income, and high income. The amount of revenue (in thousands of dollars) raised from each group by setting a particular tax at a 1 percent level is given in the following table. (For example, a 3 percent sales tax will raise $1.2 million from low-income people.)

Income Group	Thousands of Dollars Collected per 1% Tax Rate			
	Property Tax	Sales Tax	Entertainment Tax	Utility Tax
Low-income	600	400	50	100
Middle-income	800	350	100	120
High-income	1,200	250	120	80

The city council has decided that the tax policy must satisfy the following restrictions.

- The tax burden on middle-income people cannot exceed $2.5 million.

- The tax burden on high-income people cannot exceed $2.3 million.

- The total revenue raised must exceed the current level of $6 million.

- The sales tax must be between 1 percent and 3 percent.

Given these restrictions, the city council has set the following three goals (listed in order of priority):

- Goal 1: Limit the tax burden on low-income people to no more than $2 million.

- Goal 2: Set the property tax rate at no less than 1 percent.

- If their tax burden becomes too high, 20 percent of the low-income people, 20 percent of the middle-income people, and 40 percent of the high-income people may consider moving. This will start to happen if the total tax burden of this subset of the population exceeds $1.5 million. Goal 3 is thus to limit the total tax burden on this group of people to no more than $1.5 million.

a. Use preemptive goal programming to determine how the various tax rates should be set.

b. Use weighted goal programming to determine how the various tax rates should be set when using the following penalty weights: 1 per $1,000 in excess of goal 1; 90 per 1 percent short of goal 2; and 1 per $1,000 in excess of goal 3.

E* 17.8. Reconsider the scenario described in Problem 17.2. Management of the Albert Franko Co. now has decided that it should give higher priority to the goal of having product 2 capture at least 10 percent of its market than to the goal of having product 1 capture at least 15 percent of its market. Use preemptive goal programming to determine how to most effectively allocate the available money to the three advertising campaigns.

CD 17-25

E* 17.9. Reconsider the Dewright Co. case study introduced in Section 17.1. Vijay Shah (vice president for manufacturing) still feels that the top-priority goal should be retaining the employment level at 4,000 employees (avoiding a deviation in either direction) and that satisfactory profits will then follow. Therefore, he places second priority on the goal of holding the capital investment down to no more than $55 million and places only third priority on the goal of achieving a total profit of at least $125 million. Apply preemptive goal programming to the Dewright problem using this revised order of priorities.

E* 17.10. The admissions committee for the Whartvard Business School will be making its decisions regarding which applicants to admit to its MBA program for the coming year. In addition to considering each applicant on his or her own merit, the committee also needs to take three policy guidelines into account. One guideline is that, although a relatively low GMAT total score should not disqualify an applicant if other factors are very positive, the average GMAT total score for the entire MBA class should be reasonably high. (About 85 percent of all individuals taking the GMAT receive a total score below 650, but Whartvard is such a selective school that it considers anything below 650 to be a low score.) A second guideline is that the number of men and number of women in the MBA class should not be too badly out of balance. The third guideline is that the class should include a substantial number of students who are at least 30 years old, since they bring considerable work experience and maturity into the mix.

The committee now has divided both the male applicants and female applicants into three categories according to whether they have high, medium, or low GMAT total scores. The following table shows the number of applicants whose age is under 30 and at least 30 in each category.

Category	Average GMAT Total Score	Number Whose Age Is under 30	Number Whose Age Is at Least 30
High men	720	120	32
High women	720	28	4
Medium men	670	104	56
Medium women	670	32	32
Low men	620	40	40
Low women	620	32	48

The admissions committee has set four goals for this entering MBA class, in the following order of priority:

Goal 1: The entering class should include at least 240 students.

Goal 2: The entering class should have an average GMAT total score of at least 690.

Goal 3: The entering class should consist of at least 35 percent women.

Goal 4: At least 120 members of the entering class should be at least 30 years old.

Based on past experience, 60 percent of all applicants who are admitted will accept admission.

Use preemptive goal programming to determine approximately how many applicants to admit from each category.

CD 17-26

Partial Answers to Selected Problems

17.1.   The coefficient for L7 is three times as large as the coefficient for K7.

17.3.   *a.* Produce 15 units of product 3.

Case 17-1 A Cure for Cuba

Fulgencio Batista led Cuba with a cold heart and iron fist—greedily stealing from poor citizens, capriciously ruling the Cuban population that looked to him for guidance, and violently murdering the innocent critics of his politics. In 1958, tired of watching his fellow Cubans suffer from corruption and tyranny, Fidel Castro led a guerrilla attack against the Batista regime and wrested power from Batista in January 1959. Cubans, along with members of the international community, believed that political and economic freedom had finally triumphed on the island. The next two years showed, however, that Castro was leading a Communist dictatorship—killing his political opponents and nationalizing all privately held assets. The United States responded to Castro's leadership in 1961 by invoking a trade embargo against Cuba. The embargo forbade any country from selling Cuban products in the United States and forbade businesses from selling American products to Cuba. Cubans did not feel the true impact of the embargo until 1989 when the Soviet economy collapsed. Prior to the disintegration of the Soviet Union, Cuba had received an average of $5 billion in annual economic assistance from the Soviet Union. With the disappearance of the economy that Cuba had almost exclusively depended upon for trade, Cubans had few avenues from which to purchase food, clothes, and medicine. The avenues narrowed even further when the United States passed the Torricelli Act in 1992 that forbade American subsidiaries in third world countries from doing business with Cuba that had been worth a total of $700 million annually.

Since 1989, the Cuban economy has certainly felt the impact from decades of frozen trade. Today poverty ravages the island of Cuba. Families do not have money to purchase bare necessities, such as food, milk, and clothing. Children die from malnutrition or exposure. Disease infects the island because medicine is unavailable. Optical neuritis, tuberculosis, pneumonia, and influenza run rampant among the population.

Few Americans hold sympathy for Cuba, but Robert Baker, director of Helping Hand, leads a handful of tender souls on Capitol Hill who cannot bear to see politics destroy so many human lives. His organization distributes humanitarian aid annually to needy countries around the world. Mr. Baker recognizes the dire situation in Cuba, and he wants to allocate aid to Cuba for the coming year.

Mr. Baker wants to send numerous aid packages to Cuban citizens. Three different types of packages are available. The basic package contains only food, such as grain and powdered milk. Each basic package costs $300, weighs 120 pounds, and aids 30 people. The advanced package contains food and clothing, such as blankets and fabrics. Each advanced package costs $350, weighs 180 pounds, and aids 35 people. The supreme package contains food, clothing, and medicine. Each supreme package costs $720, weighs 220 pounds, and aids 54 people.

Mr. Baker has several goals he wants to achieve when deciding upon the number and types of aid packages to allocate to Cuba. First, he wants to aid at least 20 percent of Cuba's 11 million citizens. Second, because disease runs rampant among the Cuban population, he wants at least 3,000 of the aid packages sent to Cuba to be the supreme packages. Third, because he knows many other nations also require humanitarian aid, he wants to keep the cost of aiding Cuba below $20 million.

Mr. Baker places different levels of importance on his three goals. He believes the most important goal is keeping costs down since low costs mean that his organization is able to aid a larger number of needy nations. He decides to penalize his plan by one point for every $1 million above his $20 million goal. He believes the second most important goal is ensuring that at least 3,000 of the aid packages sent to Cuba are supreme packages since he does not want to see an epidemic develop and completely destroy the Cuban population. He decides to penalize his plan by one point for every 1,000 packages below his goal of 3,000 packages. Finally, he believes the least important goal is reaching at least 20 percent of the population since he would rather give a smaller number of individuals all they need to thrive instead of a larger number of individuals only some of what they need to thrive. He therefore decides to penalize his plan by seven points for every 100,000 people below his 20 percent goal.

Mr. Baker realizes that he has certain limitations on the aid packages that he delivers to Cuba. Each type of package is approximately the same size, and because only a limited number of cargo flights from the United States are allowed into Cuba, he is only able to send a maximum of 40,000 packages. Along with a size limitation, he also encounters a weight restriction. He cannot ship more than six million pounds of cargo. Finally, he has a safety restriction. When sending medicine, he needs to ensure that the Cubans know how to use the medicine properly. Therefore, for every 100 supreme packages, Mr. Baker must send one doctor to Cuba at a cost of $33,000 per doctor.

a. How many basic, advanced, and supreme packages should Mr. Baker send to Cuba?

b. Mr. Baker reevaluates the levels of importance he places on each of the three goals. To sell his efforts to potential donors, he must show that his program is effective. Donors generally judge the effectiveness of a program on the number of people reached by aid packages. Mr. Baker therefore decides that he must put more importance on the goal of reaching at least 20 percent of the population. He decides to penalize his plan by 10 points for every half a percentage point below his 20 percent goal. The penalties for his other two goals remain the same. Under this scenario, how many basic, advanced, and supreme packages should Mr. Baker send to Cuba? How sensitive is the plan to changes in the penalty weights?

c. Mr. Baker realizes that sending more doctors along with the supreme packages will improve the proper use and distribution of the packages' contents, which in turn will increase the effectiveness of the program. He therefore decides to send one doctor with every 75 supreme packages. The penalties for the goals remain the same as in part b. Under this scenario, how many basic, advanced, and supreme packages should Mr. Baker send to Cuba?

d. The aid budget is cut, and Mr. Baker learns that he definitely cannot allocate more than $20 million in aid to Cuba. Due to the budget cut, Mr. Baker decides to stay with his original policy of sending one doctor with every 100 supreme packages. How many basic, advanced, and supreme packages should Mr. Baker send to Cuba, assuming that the penalties for not meeting the other two goals remainthe same as in part a?

e. Now that the aid budget has been cut, Mr. Baker feels that the levels of importance of his three goals differ so much that it is difficult to assign meaningful penalty weights to deviations from these goals. Therefore, he decides that it would be more appropriate to apply a preemptive goal-programming approach (which will ensure that his budget goal is fully met if possible), while retaining his original policy of sending one doctor with every 100 supreme packages. How many basic, advanced, and supreme packages should Mr. Baker send to Cuba according to this approach?

CD 17-28

Case 17-2 Remembering September 11

Adeline Jonasson lost two close friends in the collapse of the World Trade Center on September 11, 2001. Both had been vibrant young women who left grieving husbands and children behind. What terrible losses. Even now, many years later, not a day goes by that she doesn't think of these friends and feel the anger yet again over those senseless deaths. She still feels a real sense of mission to do something about it. What a relief it had been to be offered a top managerial position in the Transportation Security Administration. After being told that the job would involve heading a task force on airport security, Adeline had not hesitated a moment in accepting the position. She had greatly enjoyed her career as a management science consultant in the airline industry. It was very satisfying to help several airline companies save many millions of dollars. However, she now felt a greater calling. She would be able to use her expertise in management science to help save lives. There was no way to bring her friends back, but at least she could do everything possible to prevent this from happening again.

Adeline is indeed in the right spot to carry out her mission. Shortly after the tragic events of September 11, 2001, the United States Congress enacted emergency legislation to give the Department of Transportation primary responsibility for providing security at over 400 major U.S. airports. The Transportation Security Administration was then created within the Department of Transportation to carry out this responsibility. One assignment given to Adeline's task force is to investigate what advanced security technology should be developed and used at airport checkpoints to maximize the effectiveness with which passengers can be screened within budget constraints.

Even prior to 2001, airline passengers had become familiar with the two basic types of systems used to check each passenger at a security checkpoint. One is a portal that can detect concealed weapons as the passenger walks through. The other is a screening system that scans the passenger's carry-on luggage. Various proposals have been made for advanced security technology that would improve these two systems. Adeline's task force now needs to make recommendations on which direction to go for the next generation of these systems.

The task force has been told that the functional requirement for the new portal system is that it must be able to detect even one ounce of explosives and hazardous liquids as well as metallic weapons being concealed by a passenger. The technology needed to do this includes quadrupole resonance (closely related to magnetic resonance technology used by the medical industry) and magnetic sensors. There are various ways to design the portal with this technology that would satisfactorily meet the functional requirement. However, the designs would differ greatly in the frequency with which false alarms would occur as well as in the purchase cost and maintenance cost for the portal. The frequency of false alarms is a key consideration since it substantially affects the efficiency with which the passengers can be processed. Even more importantly, a high frequency of false alarms greatly decreases the alertness of the security personnel for detecting the relatively rare terrorists who are actually concealing destructive devices.

The most basic version of the portal system that satisfactorily meets the functional requirement has an estimated purchase price of $90,000 and, on the average, would incur an annual maintenance cost of $15,000. The drawback of this version is that it would generate a false alarm for approximately 10 percent of the passengers. This false alarm rate can be reduced by using more expensive versions of the system. Each additional $15,000 in the cost of the portal system would lower the false alarm rate 1 percent and also would increase the annual maintenance cost by $1,500. The most expensive version would cost $210,000, so it would have a false alarm rate of only 2 percent of the customers as well as an annual maintenance cost of $27,000.

Regarding the new screening system for carry-on luggage, the functional requirement is that it must clearly reveal suspicious objects as small as the smallest Swiss army knife. The technology needed to do this combines X-ray imaging, a thermal neutron scanner, and computer tomography imaging (which compares the density and other physical properties of any suspicious objects with known high-risk materials). It is estimated that the most basic version that satisfactorily meets this functional requirement would cost $60,000 plus an annual maintenance cost of $9,000. As with the most basic portal system, the drawback of this version is that it doesn't sufficiently discriminate between suspicious objects that actually are destructive devices and those that are harmless. Thus, this version would generate false alarms for approximately 6 percent of the customers. In addition to wasting time and delaying passengers, such a high false alarm rate would make it very difficult for the screening operator to pay sufficient attention when the far more unusual true alarms occur. However, more expensive versions of the screening system would be considerably more discriminating. In particular, each additional $30,000 in the cost of the system would enable a reduction of 1 percent in the false alarm rate, while also increasing the annual maintenance cost by $1,200. Thus, the most expensive version, costing $150,000, would decrease the false alarm rate to 3 percent and incur an annual maintenance cost of $12,600.

The task force has been given two budgetary guidelines.

First budgetary guideline: Plan on a total expenditure of $250,000 for both the portal system and the screening system for carry-on luggage at each security checkpoint.

Second budgetary guideline: Plan on holding down the average total maintenance costs for the two systems at each security checkpoint to no more than $30,000.

These budgetary guidelines prohibit using the most expensive versions of both the portal system and the screening system for carry-on baggage. Therefore, the task force needs to determine which financially feasible combination of versions for the two systems will maximize the effectiveness with which passengers can be screened. Doing this requires first obtaining input from the top management of the Transportation Security Administration regarding what the measure of effectiveness should be and then what management's goals and priorities are for achieving substantial effectiveness and meeting the budgetary guidelines.

Fortunately, Adeline already has had extensive discussions with top management to obtain its guidance on these matters. These discussions led to the adoption of a clear policy that was approved all the way up to the Secretary of Transportation (who also informed the chairpersons of the congressional oversight committees of this action). The policy establishes the following order of priorities.

Priority 1: The functional requirement for each of the two new systems *must* be met. (This is satisfied by all the versions under consideration by the task force.)

Priority 2: The total false alarm rate for both systems should not exceed 0.1 per passenger.

Priority 3: Meet the first budgetary guideline.

Priority 4: Meet the second budgetary guideline.

Now that it has obtained all the needed managerial input, the task force is ready to begin its analysis.

a. Identify the two decisions to be made and define a decision variable for each one.

b. Describe why this problem is a preemptive goal-programming problem by giving quantitative expressions for each of the goals in terms of the decision variables defined in part *a*.

c. Draw a single two-dimensional graph where the two axes correspond to the decision variables defined in part *a*. Consider each of the goals in order of priority and use the quantitative expression obtained in part *b* for this goal to draw a plot on the graph that displays the values of the decision variables that fully satisfy this goal. After completing this for all the goals, use the graph to determine the optimal solution for this preemptive goal-programming problem.

d. Use preemptive goal programming to formulate and solve this problem on a spreadsheet.

CD 17-31

e. If it is possible to fully satisfy all the goals except the lowest priority goal, one can quickly solve a preemptive goal-programming problem by formulating and solving a linear programming model that includes all the goals except the last one as constraints and then uses the objective function to strive toward the lowest priority goal. Formulate and solve such a linear programming model for this problem on a spreadsheet. What would be the interpretation for the preemptive goal-programming problem if this linear programming model had no feasible solutions?

f. Perform some what-if analysis by determining how far the total false alarm rate per passenger can be reduced (perhaps even below the goal) by ignoring the second budgetary guideline but fully meeting the first one.

g. What additional what-if analysis do you feel should be performed in order to provide top management with the information needed to make a sound judgment decision about the best trade-off between (1) the total false alarm rate per passenger, (2) the total expenditure for the two new security systems per security checkpoint, and (3) the total annual maintenance cost for these two systems per security checkpoint?

Appendix **A**

Tips for Using Microsoft Excel for Modeling

Microsoft Excel is a powerful and flexible tool with a myriad of features. It is certainly not necessary to master all the features of Excel in order to successfully build models in spreadsheets. However, there are some features of Excel that are particularly useful for modeling that we will highlight here. This appendix is not designed to be a basic tutorial for Excel. It is designed instead for someone with a working knowledge of Excel (at least at a basic level) who wants to take advantage of some of the more advanced features of Excel that are useful for building models more efficiently.

ANATOMY OF THE MICROSOFT EXCEL WINDOW

When Microsoft Excel is first opened (e.g., by choosing Microsoft Excel from the Start menu), a blank spreadsheet appears in an Excel window. The various components of the Excel window are labeled in Figure A.1.

The Excel file is called a *workbook.* A workbook consists of a number of *worksheets* or *spreadsheets,* identified in the sheet tabs at the bottom of the screen (Sheet1, Sheet2, and Sheet3 in Figure A.1). Only one spreadsheet at a time is shown in the window, with the currently displayed spreadsheet highlighted in the sheet tab (Sheet1 in Figure A.1). To show a different spreadsheet (e.g., Sheet2 or Sheet3), click on the appropriate sheet tab.

Each spreadsheet consists of a huge grid, with many rows and columns. The rows are labeled on the left of the grid by numbers (1, 2, 3, . . .). The columns are labeled on the top of the grid by letters (A, B, C, . . .). Each element of the grid is referred to as a *cell,* and is referred to by its row and column label (e.g., cell C7). The currently selected cell is highlighted by the cell cursor (a dark or colored border). A different cell can be selected either by clicking on it or by moving the cell cursor with the arrow keys.

Only a portion of the spreadsheet is shown at any one time. For example, in Figure A.1 only the first 9 columns and first 17 rows are shown. The scroll bars can be used to show a different portion of the spreadsheet.

WORKING WITH WORKBOOKS

When Microsoft Excel is first opened (e.g., by choosing Microsoft Excel from the Start menu), a new workbook is created and given a default name that is visible in the Title Bar (e.g., Book1 in Figure A.1). To give the workbook a different name, save it under whatever name you desire by choosing Save As under the Office Button.

To open an existing workbook that has been saved previously, choose Open from the Office Button. It is possible to have more than one workbook open at a time within Excel. This may be desirable if you want to copy worksheets from one workbook to another or if you want to see the contents of another workbook while you are working on an existing

FIGURE A.1
The Microsoft Excel
window for Excel 2010.

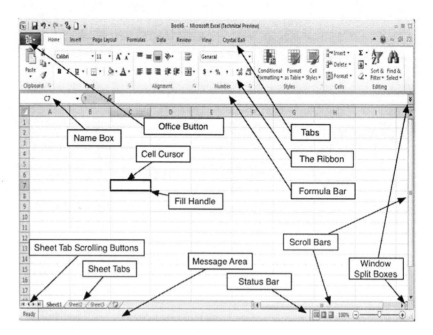

workbook. When multiple workbooks are open, some of the workbooks can become hidden behind another workbook that is being displayed. To bring any workbook to the front, select it under the Switch Windows menu on the View tab. The workbooks also can be arranged on the screen (e.g., one over the other, or one next to the other) by choosing Arrange All on the View tab.

WORKING WITH WORKSHEETS

By default, a new Excel workbook consists of a few worksheets titled Sheet1, Sheet2, Sheet3, and so on. The currently displayed sheet is highlighted in the sheet tabs. To display a different sheet, click on the appropriate tab. If the desired tab is not visible because there are more tabs than can be displayed, the list of tabs can be scrolled using the sheet tab scroll buttons.

The sheets can be given descriptive names by double-clicking on the sheet tab and typing a new name. A new sheet can be added to the workbook by choosing Insert Sheet from the Insert menu of the Cells group on the Home tab. The sheet tabs can be reordered by clicking and dragging a tab to a new location. To make a copy of a sheet, control-click (option-click on a Mac) and drag the tab. If multiple workbooks are open, you can also click (or control-click) and drag a sheet tab to a different workbook to move (or copy) a sheet to a different workbook.

Using Worksheets with Solver

A model must be confined to a single sheet. When using the Excel Solver, all cell references (e.g., the objective cell, changing cells, etc.) must be on the currently displayed sheet. Thus, the different components of the Solver model cannot be spread among different sheets. RSPE's Solver does allow the model on a given sheet to have its components spread across different sheets.

The Solver information is saved with the sheet. When information is entered in Solver (including the objective cell, changing cells, and constraints), all of that information is saved with the sheet when the workbook is saved.

Separate sheets can contain separate models. Separate Solver information (e.g., the objective cell, changing cells, etc.) is kept for each sheet in the workbook. Thus, each sheet in a workbook can contain a separate and independent model. When Solver is run, only the model on the currently displayed sheet is solved.

Copy the whole sheet rather than just the relevant cells to copy models. To copy a model to another workbook or within the current workbook, it is important to control-click and drag the worksheet tab rather than simply selecting the cells containing the model and using copy and paste. Copying the sheet (by control-clicking and dragging the sheet tab) will copy *all* the contents of the sheet (formulas, data, *and* the Solver information). Using copy and paste copies only the formulas and data, but does *not* include the Solver information.

Using Worksheets with RSPE Decision Trees

Separate sheets can contain separate RSPE decision trees. If the currently displayed sheet does not contain an existing RSPE decision tree, then choosing Add Node under the Decision Tree > Node menu on the RSPE ribbon will present the option of adding a new tree to the existing sheet. However, if a decision tree already exists on the sheet, then new nodes and branches can only be added to the existing decision tree. To create a new decision tree, first switch to (or add) a new sheet. A workbook can contain separate decision trees so long as they are on separate sheets.

Using Worksheets with RSPE Simulation Models

The entire workbook is treated as a single simulation model for RSPE. Uncertain variable cells, results cells, and statistic cells can be defined on any or all of the different sheets of the workbook. When a simulation is run, all uncertain variable cells are randomly generated, all results cells are evaluated, and all statistic cells are calculated regardless of whether they are on the currently displayed sheet.

WORKING WITH CELLS

Selecting Cells

To make any changes to a cell or range of cells, such as entering or editing data or changing the formatting, the cell or cells involved first need to be selected. The cell cursor shows the currently selected cell (or range of cells). To select a different single cell, either click on it or use the arrow keys to move the cell cursor to that location. To select an entire row or an entire column, click the row or column heading (i.e., the A, B, C along the top of the spreadsheet, or the 1, 2, 3 along the left of the spreadsheet). To select the entire spreadsheet, click in the blank box at the upper left corner of the worksheet.

There are three ways to select a range of cells within a spreadsheet, which we will illustrate by considering the 3-by-3 range of cells from A1 to C3:

1. Click on one corner of the range (A1) and, without releasing the mouse button, drag to the other corner of the range (C3).
2. Click on one corner of the range (A1) and then hold down the SHIFT key and click on the other corner of the range (C3).
3. Click on one corner of the range (A1), hold down SHIFT or press F8 to turn on the extend mode, use the arrow keys to extend the range to the other corner (C3), and then either release the SHIFT key or press F8 again to turn the extend mode off.

Entering or Editing Data, Text, and Formulas into Cells

There are a number of ways to enter and edit the contents of a cell:

1. **Use the Formula Bar:** The contents of the currently selected cell appear in the formula bar (see Figure A.1). To enter data, text, or a formula into a cell, click on the cell and type or edit the contents in the formula bar. Press Enter when you are done.
2. **Double-click:** Double-clicking on a cell (or pressing F2) will display the contents of the cell and allow typing or editing directly within the cell on the spreadsheet. If the cell

contains a formula, the cells referred to in the formula will be highlighted in different colors on the spreadsheet. The formula can be modified either by clicking and typing within the cell or by dragging the highlighted cell markers to new locations.

3. **Insert Function:** In an empty cell, pressing the *fx* button next to the formula bar will bring up a dialog box showing all of the functions available in Excel sorted by type. After choosing a function from the list, the function is inserted into the cell and all the parameters of the function are shown in a small window.

Moving or Copying Cells

To move a cell or range of cells on the spreadsheet, first select the cell(s). To move the cell(s) a short distance on the spreadsheet (e.g., down a few rows), it is usually most convenient to use the dragging method. Click on an edge of the cell cursor and, without releasing the mouse button, drag the cell(s) to the new location. To move the cell(s) a large distance (e.g., down 100 rows, or to a different worksheet), it is usually more convenient to use Cut and Paste from the Home tab.

Similar methods can be used to make a copy of a cell or range of cells. To copy a cell (or range of cells), press ctrl (option on a Mac) while clicking on the edge of the cell cursor and dragging, or use Copy and Paste from the Home tab.

Filling Cells

When building a spreadsheet, it is common to need a series of numbers or dates in a row or column. For example, Figure A.2 shows a spreadsheet that calculates the projected annual cash flow and taxes due for 2014 through 2018, based upon monthly cash flows. Rather than typing all 12 column labels for the months in cells B2:M2, the fill handle (the small box on the lower-right corner of the cell cursor) can be used to fill in the series. After entering the first couple of elements of the series, for example, Jan in cell B2 and Feb in cell C2, select cells B2:C2 and then click and drag the fill handle to cell M2. The remainder of the series (Mar, Apr, May, etc.) will be filled in automatically. The year labels in cells A3:A7 can be filled in a similar fashion. After entering the first couple of years, 2014 in A3 and 2015 in A4, select cells A3:A4 and then click and drag the fill handle down to A7. On the basis of the data in the cells selected, the fill handle will try to guess the remainder of the series.

The fill handle is also useful for copying similar formulas into adjacent cells in a row or a column. For example, the formula to calculate the annual cash flows in N3:N7 is basically the same formula for every year. After entering the formula for 2014 in cell N3, select cell N3 and then click and drag the fill handle to copy the formula down through cell N7. Similarly, the taxes due formula in cell O3 can be copied down to cells O4:O7. In fact, both the annual

FIGURE A.2

A simple spreadsheet to calculate projected annual cash flow and tax due.

	A	B	C	D	E	F	G	H	I	J	K	L	M	N	O
1						Cash Flow ($000)								Annual	Tax
2		Jan	Feb	Mar	Apr	May	Jun	Jul	Aug	Sep	Oct	Nov	Dec	Cash Flow	Due
3	2014	10	−2	4	5	4	6	8	10	12	3	−4	8	64	16.0
4	2015	15	3	−4	3	10	4	6	10	3	6	−2	12	66	16.5
5	2016	8	4	2	−3	−5	7	4	8	8	11	−3	11	52	13.0
6	2017	7	5	5	3	2	6	10	12	14	8	2	8	82	20.5
7	2018	5	2	2	−4	9	7	12	14	3	−4	6	10	62	15.5
8															
9														Tax Rate	25%

	N	O
1	Annual	Tax
2	Cash Flow	Due
3	=SUM(B3:M3)	=N3*$O$9
4	=SUM(B4:M4)	=N4*$O$9
5	=SUM(B5:M5)	=N5*$O$9
6	=SUM(B6:M6)	=N6*$O$9
7	=SUM(B7:M7)	=N7*$O$9
8		
9	Tax Rate	0.25

cash flow and tax due formulas can be copied at once by selecting both cells N3 and O3 (the range N3:O3) and then dragging the fill handle down to cell O7. This will fill both formulas down into the cells N4:O7.

Relative and Absolute References

When using the fill handle, it is important to understand the difference between relative and absolute references. Consider the formula in cell N3 (=SUM(B3:M3)). The references to cells in the formula (B3:M3) are based upon their relative position to the cell containing the formula. Thus, B3:M3 are treated as the 12 cells immediately to the left. This is known as a **relative reference.** When this formula is copied to new cells using the fill handle, the references are automatically adjusted to refer to the new cell(s) at the same relative location (the 12 cells immediately to the left). For example, the formula in N4 becomes =SUM(B4:M4), the formula in N5 becomes =SUM(B5:M5), and so on.

In contrast, the reference to the tax rate ($O$9) in the formula in cell O3 is called an **absolute reference.** These references do not change when they are filled into other cells. Thus, when the formula in cell O3 is copied into cells O4:O7, the reference still refers to cell O9.

To make an absolute reference, put $ signs in front of the letter and number of the cell reference (e.g., $O$9). Similarly, you can make the column absolute and the row relative (or vice versa) by putting a $ sign in front of only the letter (or number) of the cell reference. After entering a cell reference, repeatedly pressing the F4 key (or command-T on a Mac) will rotate among the four possibilities of relative and absolute references (e.g., O9, $O$9, O$9, $O9).

Using Range Names

A block of related cells can be given a range name. Then, rather than referring to the cells by their cell addresses (e.g., L11:L21 or C3), a more descriptive name can be used (e.g., Total-Profit). To give a cell or range of cells a range name, first select the cell(s). Then click in the Name Box (see Figure A.1) and type a name. For example, for the spreadsheet in Figure A.2 we could define a range name for the tax rate by selecting cell O9 and typing TaxRate into the name box. Spaces are not allowed in range names, so use capital letters or underscore characters to separate words in a name.

Once a range name is defined, rather than typing the cell reference (e.g., O9) when it is used in a formula, the range name can be used instead (e.g., TaxRate). If you click on a cell (or cells) to use it in a formula, the range name is automatically used rather than the cell reference. This can make the formula easier to interpret (e.g., =SUM(B3:M3)*TaxRate, rather than =SUM(B3:M3)*$O$9). When using a range name in a formula, it is treated as an absolute reference. To make a relative reference to a cell that has a range name, type the cell address (e.g., O9) rather than either typing the range name or clicking on the cell (which then automatically uses the range name).

Formatting Cells

To make formatting changes to a cell or range of cells, first select the cell(s). If a range of cells is selected, any formatting changes will apply to every cell in the range. Most common types of formatting of cells, for example, changing the font, making text bold or italic, or changing the borders or shading of a cell, can be done by using the Home tab.

Clicking on the .0 → .00 or .00 → .0 buttons changes the number of decimal places shown in a cell. Note that this only changes how the number is displayed, since Excel always uses the full precision when this cell is used in other formulas.

For more advanced types of formatting, choose Format Cells under the Format menu of the Cells group on the Home tab. A shortcut is to press ctrl-1 on a PC or command-1 on a Mac. This brings up the Format cells dialog box, as shown in Figure A.3. Under the Numbers tab you can choose to display the contents in a cell as a number with any number of decimal places (e.g., 123.4 or 123.486), as currency (e.g., $1,234.10), as a date (e.g., 12/10/2016 or Dec 2016), and so on. The other tabs are used to change the alignment of the text (e.g., left or

FIGURE A.3
The Format Cells
dialog box.

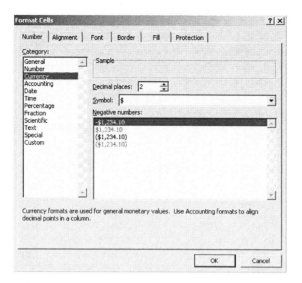

right justified, printed vertically or horizontally, etc.), the font, the borders, the patterns, and the protection.

If a cell displays ####, this means that the column width is not wide enough to show the contents of the cell. To change column widths or row heights, click and drag the vertical or horizontal lines between the column or row labels. Double-clicking on the vertical line between column labels will make the column just wide enough to show the entire contents of every cell in the column.

Appendix **B**

Partial Answers to Selected Problems

CHAPTER 2

2.6. *d.* Fraction of 1st = 0.667, fraction of 2nd = 0.667. Profit = $6,000.

2.13. *b.* $x_1 = 13, x_2 = 5$. Profit = $31.

CHAPTER 3

3.3. *c.* 3.333 of Activity 1, 3.333 of Activity 2. Profit = $166.67.

3.6. *d.* 26 of Product 1, 54.76 of Product 2, 20 of Product 3. Profit = $2,904.76.

3.12. *d.* 1.14 kg of corn, 2.43 kg of alfalfa. Cost = $2.42.

3.17. *b.* Cost = $410,000.

Shipment Quantities	Customer 1	Customer 2	Customer 3
Factory 1	300	0	100
Factory 2	0	200	300

3.19. *c.* $60,000 in Investment A (year 1), $84,000 in Investment A (year 3), $117,600 in Investment D (year 5). Total accumulation in year 6 = $152,880.

3.22. *a.* Profit = $13,330.

Cargo Placement	Front	Center	Back
Cargo 1	0	5	10
Cargo 2	7.333	4.167	0
Cargo 3	0	0	0
Cargo 4	4.667	8.333	0

CHAPTER 4

4.2. *d.* 0 end tables, 40 coffee tables, 30 dining room tables. Profit = $10,600.

4.4. *e.* 19% participation in Project A, 0% participation in Project B, and 100% participation in Project C. Ending Balance = $59.5 million.

4.9. *d.* 4 FT (8AM–4PM), 4 FT (12PM–8PM), 4 FT (4PM–midnight), 2 PT (8AM–12PM), 0 PT (12PM–4PM), 4 PT (4PM–8PM), 2 PT (8PM–midnight). Total cost per day = $1,728.

CHAPTER 5

5.1. *e.* Allowable range for unit profit from producing toys: $2.50 to $5.00.
Allowable range for unit profit from producing subassemblies: −$3.00 to −$1.50.

5.4. *f.* (*Part a*)
Optimal solution does not change (within allowable increase of $10).

(*Part b*)
Optimal solution does change (outside of allowable decrease of $5).

(*Part c*)
By the 100% rule for simultaneous changes in the objective function, the optimal solution may or may not change.

$$C_{8AM}: \quad \$160 \rightarrow \$165 \quad \% \text{ of allowable increase} = 100\left(\frac{165 - 160}{10}\right) = 50\%$$

$$C_{4PM}: \quad \$180 \rightarrow \$170 \quad \% \text{ of allowable decrease} = 100\left(\frac{180 - 170}{5}\right) = \underline{200\%}$$

$$\text{Sum} = 250\%$$

5.11. *a.* Produce 2,000 toys and 1,000 sets of subassemblies. Profit = $3,500.

b. The shadow price for subassembly A is $0.50, which is the maximum premium that the company should be willing to pay.

5.15. *a.* The total expected number of exposures could be increased by 3,000 for each additional $1,000 added to the advertising budget.

b. This remains valid for increases of up to $250,000.

e. By the 100% rule for simultaneous changes in right-hand sides, the shadow prices are still valid. Using units of thousands of dollars,

$$C_A: \quad \$4,000 \rightarrow \$4,100 \quad \% \text{ of allowable increase} = 100\left(\frac{4,100 - 4,000}{250}\right) = 40\%$$

$$C_P: \quad \$1,000 \rightarrow \$1,100 \quad \% \text{ of allowable increase} = 100\left(\frac{1,100 - 1,000}{450}\right) = \underline{22\%}$$

$$\text{Sum} = 62\%$$

CHAPTER 6

6.2. *b.* 0 S1-D1, 10 S1-D2, 30 S1-D3, 30 S2-D1, 30 S2-D2, 0 S2-D3. Total cost = $580.

6.5. *c.* $2,187,000.

6.9. Maximum flow = 15.

6.15. *b.* Replace after year 1. Total cost = $29,000.

CHAPTER 7

7.3. *b.* Marketing and dishwashing by Eve, cooking and laundry by Steven. Total time = 18.4 hours.

7.8. Optimal path = OADT. Total distance = 10 miles.

CHAPTER 8

8.7. *c.* Invest $46,667 in Stock 1 and $3,333 in Stock 2 for $13,000 expected profit.
Invest $33,333 in Stock 1 and $16,667 in Stock 2 for $15,000 expected profit.

8.11. *d.* Dorwyn should produce 1 window and 1 door.

CHAPTER 9

9.4. *a.* Speculative investment.

d. Counter-cyclical investment.

9.7. *b.* A_3

c. A_2

9.12. *a.* A_1

b. $18.

9.16. *c.* EVPI = $3,000. The credit-rating organization should not be used.

9.21. *c.* Choose to build computers (expected payoff is $27 million).

f. They should build when $p \leq 0.722$ and sell when $p > 0.722$.

9.22. *a.* EVPI = $7.5 million.

c. P(Sell 10,000 | Predict Sell 10,000) = 0.667.
P(Sell 100,000 | Predict Sell 100,000) = 0.667.

9.23. *a.* The optimal policy is to do no market research and build the computers.

9.26. *c.* $800,000.

f, g. Leland University should hire William. If he predicts a winning season, then they should hold the campaign. If he predicts a losing season, then they should not hold the campaign.

9.30. *a.* Choose to introduce the new product (expected payoff is $12.5 million).

b. $7.5 million.

c. The optimal policy is not to test but to introduce the new product.

g. Both charts indicate that the expected profit is sensitive to both parameters, but is somewhat more sensitive to changes in the profit if successful than to changes in the loss if unsuccessful.

9.35. *a.* Choose not to buy insurance (expected payoff is $249,840).

b. Choose to buy insurance (expected utility is 499.82).

CHAPTER 10

10.1. *a.* 39.

b. 26.

c. 36.

10.3. MAD = 15.

10.9. 2,091.

10.13. When $\alpha = 0.1$, forecast = 2,072.

10.17. 552.

10.19. *b.* MAD = 5.18.

c. MAD = 3.

d. MAD = 3.93.

10.29. 62 percent.

10.35. *b.* $y = 410 + 17.6x$.

d. 604.

CHAPTER 11

11.3.   *a.* True.

    b. False.

    c. True.

11.8.   *a.* $L = 2$

    b. $L_q = 0.375$

    c. $W = 30$ minutes, $W_q = 5.625$ minutes.

11.12. *a.* 96.9% of the time.

11.15. *b.* $L = 0.333$

    g. Two members.

11.18. L_q is unchanged and W_q is reduced by half.

11.23. *a.* $L = 3$

    d. TC (status quo) = \$85/hour.

      TC (proposal) = \$73/hour.

11.28. *a.* 0.211 hours.

    c. Approximately 3.43 minutes.

11.31. *c.* 0.4.

    d. 7.2 hours.

11.35. Jim should operate 4 cash registers. Expected cost per hour = \$80.59.

CHAPTER 12

12.1.   *b.* Let the numbers 0.0000 to 0.5999 correspond to strikes and the numbers 0.6000 to 0.9999 correspond to balls. The random observations for pitches are 0.3039 = strike, 0.7914 = ball, 0.8543 = ball, 0.6902 = ball, 0.3004 = strike, 0.0383 = strike.

12.5.   *a.* Here is a sample replication.

Summary of Results:

Win? (1 = Yes, 0 = No)	0
Number of Tosses =	3

Simulated Tosses

Toss	Die 1	Die 2	Sum
1	4	2	6
2	3	2	5
3	6	1	7
4	5	2	7
5	4	4	8
6	1	4	5
7	2	6	8

Results

Win?	Lose?	Continue?
0	0	Yes
0	0	Yes
0	1	No
NA	NA	No
NA	NA	No
NA	NA	No
NA	NA	No

12.10. *a.* Let the numbers 0.0000 to 0.3999 correspond to a minor repair and 0.4000 to 0.9999 correspond to a major repair. The average repair time is then $(1.224 + 0.950 + 1.610)/3 = 1.26$ hours.

12.17. *b.* The average waiting time should be approximately 1 day.

    c. The average waiting time should be approximately 0.33 days.

CHAPTER 13

13.3.   *a.* Min Extreme distribution (Mode = 170.3, Scale = 50.9, Shift = 320.0).

13.7.   *a.* The mean project completion time should be approximately 33 months.

    c. Activities B and J have the greatest impact on the variability in the project completion time.

13.15. *a.* Mean profit should be around \$107, with about a 96.5% chance of making at least \$0.

Index